POWER SYSTEM PROTECTION

1 Principles and Components

Edited by
The Electricity Council

PETER PEREGRINUS LTD.

Published by: Peter Peregrinus Ltd., Stevenage, UK, and New York

British Library Cataloguing in Publication Data

Power system protection — 2nd ed.
  Vol. 1
  1. Electric power distribution — Safety appliances
  I. Electricity Council
  621.319   TK3091

ISBN: 0-906048-47-8

Printed in England by A.Wheaton & Co., Ltd., Exeter

Contents

Foreword   xi

Chapter authors   xiii

Editorial panel   xiii

Protection symbols used in circuit diagrams   xiv

1   Role of protection *M.Kaufmann and G.S.H.Jarrett*   1

1.1   **Introduction**   1
     1.1.1   General considerations   1
     1.1.2   Role of protection in a power station   2

1.2   **System and substation layout**   3
     1.2.1   System layout   3
     1.2.2   Substation layout (electrical)   4
     1.2.3   Current transformer location   7

1.3   **System earthing**   7
     1.3.1   Neutral-earthing methods   7
     1.3.2   Special cases of resistance earthing   10

1.4   **Faults**   10
     1.4.1   Faults and other abnormalities   10
     1.4.2   Nature and causes of faults   11
     1.4.3   Fault statistics   12

1.5   **Basic terms used in protection**   15

1.6   **Necessity for back-up protection**   16

1.7   **Economic considerations**   18
     1.7.1   General   18
     1.7.2   Distribution systems   19
     1.7.3   Transmission systems   19

1.8   **Bibliography**   20

2   **Protection principles and components** *H.S.Petch and J.Rushton*   21

2.1   **Fundamental principles**   21
        2.1.1   Methods of discrimination   21
        2.1.2   Derivation of relaying quantities   30
        2.1.3   Combined overcurrent and earth fault relays   33
        2.1.4   Derivation of a representative single-phase quantity from a
                three-phase system   33

2.2   **Components of protection**   37
        2.2.1   Relays   37
        2.2.2   Current transformers   37
        2.2.3   Voltage transforming devices   38
        2.2.4   Capacitor dividers   39
        2.2.5   H.F. capacitor couplers   39
        2.2.6   Line traps   40
        2.2.7   Circuit-breakers   41
        2.2.8   Tripping and other auxiliary supplies   42
        2.2.9   Fuses, small wiring, terminals and test links   44
        2.2.10 Pilot circuits   47

2.3   **Consideration of the protection problem**   48

2.4   **Bibliography**   52

3   **Fault calculations** *J.H.Naylor*   53

3.1   **Introduction**   53
        3.1.1   Purpose of fault calculation   53
        3.1.2   Types of fault   54
        3.1.3   Factors affecting fault severity   58
        3.1.4   Methods of fault calculation   59

3.2   **Basic principles of network analysis**   60
        3.2.1   Fundamental network laws   60
        3.2.2   Mesh-current analysis   65
        3.2.3   Nodal-voltage analysis   66
        3.2.4   Application of mesh-current and nodal-voltage analysis   68
        3.2.5   Network theorems and reduction formulas   69

3.3   **Calculations of balanced fault conditions**   77
        3.3.1   Single-phase representation   77
        3.3.2   Use of a common voltage base   81
        3.3.3   Representation of nominal-ratio transformer circuits   87
        3.3.4   Representation of off-nominal-ratio transformer circuits   94
        3.3.5   Transformer phase-shifts   95
        3.3.6   Representation of synchronous machines   98
        3.3.7   Use of per-unit and per-cent values   104
        3.3.8   Fault-calculation procedure   108
        3.3.9   Example 1   110
        3.3.10 Example 2   115

3.4	**Calculation of unbalanced fault conditions**		126
	3.4.1	Symmetrical components	126
	3.4.2	Phase-sequence networks and impedances	129
	3.4.3	Phase-sequence equivalent circuits	134
	3.4.4	Analysis of short-circuit conditions	153
	3.4.5	Effect of fault impedance	168
	3.4.6	Analysis of open-circuit conditions	173
	3.4.7	Transformer phase-shifts	178
	3.4.8	Fault-calculation procedure	182
	3.4.9	Example 3	182
	3.4.10	Example 4	186
	3.4.11	Example 5	189
	3.4.12	Example 6	198
3.5	**Calculation of simultaneous fault conditions**		202
	3.5.1	Sequence networks	202
	3.5.2	Cross-country earth-fault	204
	3.5.3	Sequence network interconnections	206
	3.5.4	Example 7	210
	3.5.5	Example 8	213
3.6	**Practical network analysis**		217
	3.6.1	Network analysers	217
		3.6.1.1 A.C.analyser	220
		3.6.1.2 D.C. analyser	221
	3.6.2	Digital-computer analysis	221
	3.6.3	Transient analysis	222
3.7	**Winding faults**		223
	3.7.1	General considerations	223
	3.7.2	Generator-winding faults	223
	3.7.3	Transformer-winding faults	228
3.8	**Appendixes**		230
	3.8.1	Representation of off-nominal-ratio transformers	230
	3.8.2	Effects of overhead-line asymmetry	242
3.9	**Bibliography**		245
4	**Protective transformers** *N.Ashton and E.J.Mellor*		247
4.1	**General**		247
	4.1.1	Introduction	247
	4.1.2	Basic transformer principles	247
4.2	**Steady-state theory of current transformers**		248
	4.2.1	Equivalent circuit, vector diagram, errors	248
	4.2.2	Influence of the core, magnetic materials, and magnetisation curves	250
	4.2.3	Single-turn primary current transformers	253
	4.2.4	Flux leakage	253
	4.2.5	Balancing windings and eddy-current shielding	255
	4.2.6	Open-circuit secondary voltage	258

| | 4.2.7 | Secondary currents, borders and connecting lead resistance | 258 |
| | 4.2.8 | Test windings | 259 |

4.3 **Current transformers for protection** 259
	4.3.1	Saturation of the core and ratio on overcurrents. BS 3938	259
	4.3.2	Trip-coil operation	260
	4.3.3	Overcurrent-relay operation	260
	4.3.4	Earth-fault relays with inverse-time characteristics	261
	4.3.5	Relay settings and primary operating currents	261
	4.3.6	Current transformers for balanced differential protective schemes	262
	4.3.7	Simple transient-state theory	264

4.4 **Construction of current transformers** 267
	4.4.1	Basic types	267
	4.4.2	Forms of cores	269
	4.4.3	Windings and insulation	270
	4.4.4	High-voltage current transformers	272

4.5 **Testing of current transformers** 274
	4.5.1	Error measurements	274
	4.5.2	Turns ratio tests	276
	4.5.3	Exciting current	276
	4.5.4	Current transformers for balanced differential protective schemes	277
	4.5.5	Polarity	277
	4.5.6	Insulation tests	277

4.6 **Voltage-transformer theory** 278
	4.6.1	Electromagnetic-type voltage transformers	278
	4.6.2	Capacitor-type voltage transformers	279
	4.6.3	Burdens and lead resistances	283

4.7 **Voltage transformers for protection** 285
| | 4.7.1 | Electromagnetic type, categories, residual voltages | 285 |
| | 4.7.2 | Capacitor type | 287 |

4.8 **Construction of voltage transformers** 293
	4.8.1	Electromagnetic type	293
	4.8.2	Cascade type	300
	4.8.3	Capacitor type	302
	4.8.4	Capacitor divider voltage sensor	302
	4.8.5	Voltage transformers for SF_6 metalclad switchgear	303

4.9 **Fusing and protection of voltage transformers** 304

4.10 **Testing of voltage transformers** 304
	4.10.1	Error measurements	304
	4.10.2	Core losses	305
	4.10.3	Insulation tests	305
	4.10.4	Polarity	305

4.11 **Bibliography** 306

5	**Fuses** *H.W. Turner and C. Turner*	307
5.1	**Introduction**	307
	5.1.1 Definition of a fuse	307
	5.1.2 Definition of a fuselink	307
	5.1.3 Categories of fuse	307
5.2	**Fuse design**	311
	5.2.1 Powder-filled cartridge fuse	311
	5.2.1.1 High-voltage powder-filled fuses	313
	5.2.2 Miniature fuselink	314
	5.2.3 Semi-enclosed fuse	315
	5.2.4 Expulsion fuse	316
	5.2.5 Other fuse developments	316
5.3	**Mechanism of fuse operation**	318
	5.3.1 Operation on small overcurrents	318
	5.3.2 Operation on large overcurrents	319
	5.3.3 Operation on intermediate overcurrents	320
	5.3.4 Operation on pulsed loading	322
	5.3.5 Fulgarite (roping)	322
	5.3.6 Typical oscillograms	323
5.4	**Peak arc voltage**	323
5.5	**Time/current characteristic and factors affecting it**	326
	5.5.1 Definitions related to the operation of fuses at the small overcurrent region of the time/current characteristic and the assignment of current rating	330
5.6	**Discrimination**	331
	5.6.1 Discrimination between fuselinks	331
	5.6.2 Discrimination between h.v. and l.v. fuses and circuit-breaking devices	333
5.7	**Testing of fuses**	334
	5.7.1 Fuse testing on a.c.	334
	5.7.1.1 Breaking capacity	334
	5.7.1.2 Other parameters tested	336
5.8	**Bibliography**	336
6	**Relays** *J.W.Hodgkiss*	339
6.1	**Introduction**	339
6.2	**Principal types of relays**	341
	6.2.1 Attracted-armature relays	341
	6.2.2 Moving-coil relays	351
	6.2.3 Induction relays	357
	6.2.4 Thermal relays	372
	6.2.5 Motor-operated relays	378
	6.2.6 Gas- and oil-operated relays (Buchholz relays)	378

6.3	**Auxiliary d.c. relays**	380
	6.3.1 Operating-voltage limits	380
	6.3.2 Discharge of wiring capacitance	382
	6.3.3 Tripping relays	383
	6.3.4 Time-lag relays	384
	6.3.5 Repeat contactors	386
	6.3.6 Trip-circuit supervision	389
	6.3.7 Alarm relays	390
6.4	**General design considerations**	394
	6.4.1 Coil ratings	394
	6.4.2 Auxiliary supplies	394
	6.4.3 Relay setting adjustment	395
	6.4.4 Contacts	395
	6.4.5 Flag indicators	397
	6.4.6 Resetting	397
6.5	**Static relays**	398
	6.5.1 Basic circuits employed	398
	6.5.1.1 Timers	399
	6.5.1.2 Level detectors	400
	6.5.1.3 Polarity detectors	401
	6.5.1.4 Phase comparators	403
	6.5.1.5 Integrators	408
	6.5.2 Components	408
	6.5.2.1 Resistors	408
	6.5.2.2 Capacitors	409
	6.5.2.3 Diodes	409
	6.5.2.4 Connectors	409
	6.5.3 Transient overvoltages and interference	409
	6.5.3.1 Sources of transients	410
	6.5.3.2 Standard tests	411
	6.5.3.3 Protection against transients	411
	6.5.4 Power supplies for static relays	412
	6.5.5 Output and indicating circuits	415
6.6	**Relay cases**	417
6.7	**Maintenance**	419
6.8	**Application and characteristics**	422
	6.8.1 Instantaneous current- and voltage-operated relays	422
	6.8.2 Double-quantity measurement	423
	6.8.3 Presentation of characteristics	424
	6.8.4 Complex input comparators	425
	6.8.5 Distance relays	428
	6.8.6 Rectifier bridge comparators	430
	6.8.7 Phase-comparison bridge	431
	6.8.8 Range curves	437
	6.8.9 Differential relays	440
	6.8.10 Polar curves	440
	6.8.11 Negative-sequence protection	443

6.9		Testing of relays and protection schemes	444
	6.9.1	Test at manufacturing works	444
	6.9.2	Testing at site	444
6.10		Future trends in relay design	446
6.11		Bibliography	446
7		Protection signalling *P.C.Colbrook*	448
7.1		Introduction	448
7.2		Communication media	449
	7.2.1	Power-line carrier	449
		7.2.1.1 General	449
		7.2.1.2 Coupling equipment	450
		7.2.1.3 Design principles of coupling equipment	456
		7.2.1.4 Coupling bands	466
		7.2.1.5 Protection and earthing of coupling equipment	466
		7.2.1.6 Attenuation	469
		7.2.1.7 Application to feed circuits	476
		7.2.1.8 Application to circuits containing cable sections	476
	7.2.2	Private pilots	476
		7.2.2.1 Underground pilot cables	476
		7.2.2.2 Overhead pilots	480
	7.2.3	Rented pilot circuits	481
		7.2.3.1 General	481
		7.2.3.2 Types of Post Office rented pilot circuit	481
		7.2.3.3 Pilot-circuit characteristics	483
	7.2.4	Radio links	484
		7.2.4.1 General	484
		7.2.4.2 Microwave radio links	485
	7.2.5	Optical-fibre links	487
7.3		Fundamental signalling problem	488
	7.3.1	Effects of noise	488
	7.3.2	Characteristics of electrical noise	489
	7.3.3	Equipment design principles	490
7.4		Performance requirements of signalling facilities and equipment	494
	7.4.1	Operating times	494
		7.4.1.1 General	494
		7.4.1.2 Equipment operating time classification	495
	7.4.2	Reliability of operation	495
	7.4.3	Security against maloperation	496
	7.4.4	Pulse distortion	497
	7.4.5	Power supplies	497
	7.4.6	Other performance requirements	498
7.5		Methods of signalling	498
	7.5.1	D.C. intertripping	498
	7.5.2	Low-frequency a.c. intertripping over private pilots	505
	7.5.3	Voice-frequency signalling equipment	505

		7.5.3.1	General	505
		7.5.3.2	V.F. protection signalling equipment	506
		7.5.3.3	V.F. intertripping equipment	507
	7.5.4		Power-line-carrier signalling equipment	513
		7.5.4.1	Keyed carrier equipment	513
		7.5.4.2	Carrier frequency-shift equipment	513
		7.5.4.3	Single-sideband power-line-carrier communication equipment	516

7.6   **Bibliography**   516

Index   518

Foreword

The three volumes which make up this publication owe their origin to a correspondence tuition course launched in the Electricity Supply Industry in Britain in 1966, written by expert engineers in the Electricity Boards and with electrical manufacturers, and administered by the Education and Training Branch of the Electricity Council. The correspondence course continues to be provided to meet the needs of staff in the Electricity Supply Industry.

It became apparent soon after its inception, however, that the work met a widespread need in Britain and overseas as a standard text on a speciaised subject. Accordingly, the first edition of Power System Protection was published in book form in 1969, and has since come to be recognised as a comprehensive and valuable guide to concepts, practices and equipment in this important field of engineering. Because the books are designed not only to provide a grounding in theory but to cover the range of applications, it was recognised that changes in protection technology required a process of up-dating, and this second edition therefore presents a revision of the original material to take account of recent developments in the field.

The three revised volumes comprise 18 chapters, each with bibliography. The aim remains that of providing sufficient knowledge of protection for those concerned with design, planning, construction and operation to understand the function of protection in those fields, and to meet the basic needs of the engineer intending to specialise in the subject.

In the use of symbols, abbreviations and diagram conventions, the aim has been to comply with British Standards.

The Electricity Council wishes to acknowledge the work of both the original authors, and those new contributors who have undertaken the revision work in preparation for this new edition. They are referred to at the head of the appropriate chapter. The Council also acknowledges the valuable assistance of the CEGB's Transmission and Technical Services Division Drawing Office at Guildford and its staff in preparing the diagrams; and the help of the following in permitting reproduction of illustrations and other relevant material:

Allen West & Co. Limited, ASEA, Brown Boveri Company Limited, BICC Limited, Electrical Apparatus Company, ERA Technology Limited, GEC Measurements Limited, GEC Switchgear Limited, GEC Transformers Limited, Price and Belsham Limited, Reyrolle Protection Limited.

Extracts from certain British Standards are reproduced by permission of the British Standards Institution, from whom copies of the complete standards may be obtained.

A particular indebtedness is acknowledged to the Chairman and members of the Editorial Panel, who directed and co-ordinated the work of revision for publication.

Chapter authors

N. Ashton	C.Eng., F.I.E.E., A.R.T.C.(S) (deceased)
K.A.J. Coates	C.Eng., M.I.E.E.
P.C. Colbrook	B.Sc.Tech., A.M.C.S.T., C.Eng., M.I.E.E.
L. Csuros	Dipl. Eng., C.Eng., F.I.E.E.
P.M. Dolby	C.Eng., M.I.E.E.
L.C.W. Frerk	C.Eng., B.Sc.(Eng.), M.I.E.E., F.I.Nuc.E.
F.W. Hamilton	B.Eng., C.Eng., F.I.E.E., (deceased)
J. Harris	C.Eng., M.I.E.E.
D. Hay	B.Sc., C.Eng., M.I.E.E.
J.W. Hodgkiss	M.Sc.Tech., C.Eng., M.I.E.E.
L. Jackson	B.Sc., Ph.D., C.Eng., F.I.E.E.
G.S.H. Jarrett	Wh.Sc., B.Sc.(Eng.), C.Eng., F.I.E.E.
M. Kaufmann	C.Eng., F.I.E.E., (deceased)
E.J. Mellor	T.D.
K.G. Mewes	Dip.E.E., C.Eng., M.I.E.E.
J.H. Naylor	B.Sc.(Eng.), C.Eng., F.I.E.E., A.M.C.T., D.I.C.
H.S Petch	B.Sc.(Eng.), M.I.E.E., M. Amer.I.E.E. (deceased)
J. Rushton	Ph.D., F.M.C.S.T., C.Eng., F.I.E.E.
E.C. Smith	A.M.C.T., C.Eng., F.I.E.E.
C. Turner	D.Sc., F.Inst.P.
H.W. Turner	B.Sc., F.Inst.P.
J.C. Whittaker	B.Sc.(Eng.), C.Eng., F.I.E.E.

Editorial Panel

J.H. Naylor	B.Sc.(Eng.), C.Eng., F.I.E.E., A.M.C.T., D.I.C. (Chairman)
G.S.H. Jarrett	Wh. Sc., B.Sc.(Eng.), C.Eng., F.I.E.E.
J. Rushton	Ph.D., F.M.C.S.T., C.Eng., F.I.E.E.
P.M. Dolby	C.Eng., M.I.E.E.
J. Harris	C.Eng., M.I.E.E.
W. Looney	T.Eng.(CEI)., M.I.E.E.T.E.

Protection symbols used in circuit diagrams

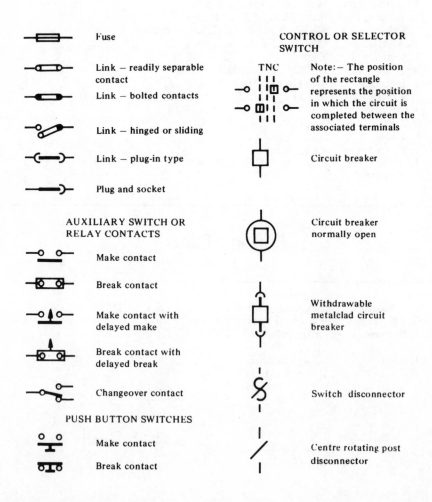

Fuse	CONTROL OR SELECTOR SWITCH
Link — readily separable contact	TNC
Link — bolted contacts	Note:— The position of the rectangle represents the position in which the circuit is completed between the associated terminals
Link — hinged or sliding	
Link — plug-in type	Circuit breaker
Plug and socket	
AUXILIARY SWITCH OR RELAY CONTACTS	Circuit breaker normally open
Make contact	
Break contact	
Make contact with delayed make	Withdrawable metalclad circuit breaker
Break contact with delayed break	
Changeover contact	Switch disconnector
PUSH BUTTON SWITCHES	
Make contact	Centre rotating post disconnector
Break contact	

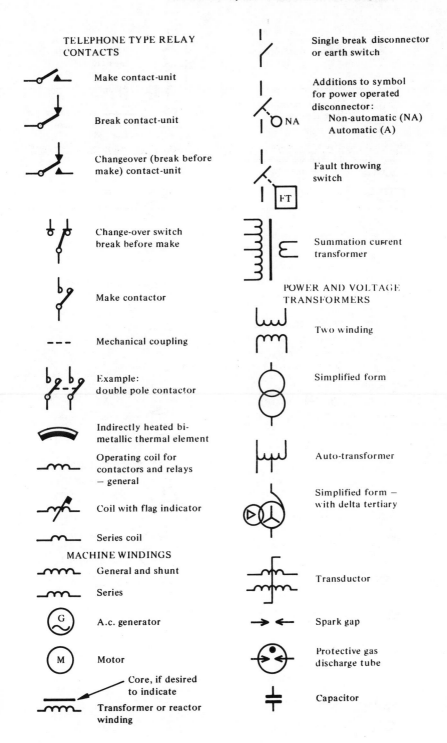

TELEPHONE TYPE RELAY
CONTACTS

Make contact-unit

Break contact-unit

Changeover (break before
make) contact-unit

Change-over switch
break before make

Make contactor

- - - Mechanical coupling

Example:
double pole contactor

Indirectly heated bi-
metallic thermal element

Operating coil for
contactors and relays
– general

Coil with flag indicator

Series coil

MACHINE WINDINGS

General and shunt

Series

G A.c. generator

M Motor

Core, if desired
to indicate

Transformer or reactor
winding

Single break disconnector
or earth switch

Additions to symbol
for power operated
disconnector:
        Non-automatic (NA)
        Automatic (A)

Fault throwing
switch

Summation current
transformer

POWER AND VOLTAGE
TRANSFORMERS

Two winding

Simplified form

Auto-transformer

Simplified form –
with delta tertiary

Transductor

Spark gap

Protective gas
discharge tube

Capacitor

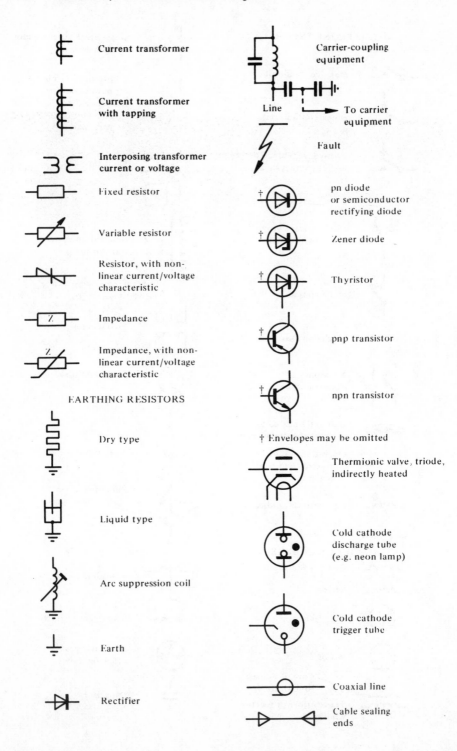

Current transformer

Current transformer
with tapping

Interposing transformer
current or voltage

Fixed resistor

Variable resistor

Resistor, with non-
linear current/voltage
characteristic

Impedance

Impedance, with non-
linear current/voltage
characteristic

EARTHING RESISTORS

Dry type

Liquid type

Arc suppression coil

Earth

Rectifier

Carrier-coupling
equipment

Line

To carrier
equipment

Fault

pn diode
or semiconductor
rectifying diode

Zener diode

Thyristor

pnp transistor

npn transistor

† Envelopes may be omitted

Thermionic valve, triode,
indirectly heated

Cold cathode
discharge tube
(e.g. neon lamp)

Cold cathode
trigger tube

Coaxial line

Cable sealing
ends

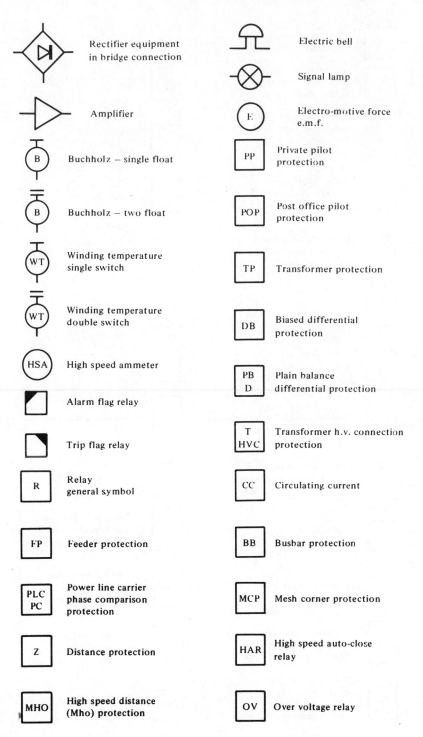

Rectifier equipment in bridge connection	Electric bell
Amplifier	Signal lamp
Buchholz – single float	Electro-motive force e.m.f.
Buchholz – two float	Private pilot protection
Winding temperature single switch	Post office pilot protection
Winding temperature double switch	Transformer protection
High speed ammeter	Biased differential protection
Alarm flag relay	Plain balance differential protection
Trip flag relay	Transformer h.v. connection protection
Relay general symbol	Circulating current
Feeder protection	Busbar protection
Power line carrier phase comparison protection	Mesh corner protection
Distance protection	High speed auto-close relay
High speed distance (Mho) protection	Over voltage relay

X	High speed distance (reactance) protection	RP	Reverse power relay
3OC I	3-pole overcurrent relay (inverse definite minimum time)	E RES	Restricted earth-fault relay
2OC I EI	2-pole overcurrent and single pole earth-fault relay (inverse definite minimum time)	T	Tripping relay
OC I	1-pole overcurrent relay (inverse definite minimum time)	INT	Intertrip relay
EI	Earth-fault relay (inverse definite minimum time)	INT S	Intertrip relay (send)
3OC 2S I	3-pole two stage overcurrent relay (inverse definite minimum time)	INT R	Intertrip relay (receive)
3OC DI	3-pole directional overcurrent relay (inverse definite minimum time)	TD	Definite time relay
3OC	3-pole overcurrent relay (instantaneous)	NEG PH SEQ	Negative phase sequence
3OC XI	3-pole overcurrent relay (extremely inverse definite minimum time)	LE	Lost excitation
E	Earth-fault relay (instantaneous)	3OC VC I	3-pole voltage controlled overcurrent relay (inverse definite minimum time)
3OC HS	3-pole high set overcurrent relay	3OC INT I	3-pole overcurrent, interlocked relay (inverse definite minimum time)
E SB LTI	Standby earth-fault relay (long time inverse definite minimum time)	BF C CK	Breaker fail current check
E2S SB LTI	Two stage standby earth-fault relay (long time inverse definite minimum time)	LVC	L.V. connection protection

Chapter 1

Role of protection

by M.Kaufmann, revised by G.S.H.Jarrett

1.1 Introduction

1.1.1 General considerations

The history of electrical-power technology throughout the world is one of steady and, in recent years, rapid progress, which has made it possible to design and construct economic and reliable power systems capable of satisfying the continuing growth in the demand for electrical energy. In this, power system protection and control play a significant part, and progress in design and development in these fields has necessarily had to keep pace with advances in the design of primary plant, such as generators, transformers, switchgear, overhead lines and underground cables. Indeed, progress in the fields of protection and control is a vital prerequisite for the efficient operation and continuing development of power supply systems as a whole.

This work, in three volumes, deals with all the relevant aspects of protection in current British practice for generation, transmission and distribution systems. The subject matter has been divided into a number of discrete chapters covering, as completely as is necessary for the purpose of the work, general principles, design and performance and, by no means of least importance, application.

The purpose of the present chapter is to provide the background knowledge necessary to a proper understanding of the aims and the role of protection in a power system.

The word 'protection' is used here to describe the whole concept of protecting a power system. The term 'protective gear' (or 'protective equipment') is widely used in that sense: but here that term will be used in the narrower sense of the actual components used in achieving the desired protection.

The function of protective equipment is not the preventive one its name would imply, in that it takes action only after a fault has occurred: it is the ambulance at the foot of the cliff rather than the fence at the top. Exceptions to this are the Buchholz protector, a gas-operated device which is capable of detecting the gas accumulation produced by an incipient fault in a power transformer, and the surge arrester which is designed to prevent a dangerous rise of potential, usually between earth and the conductor or terminal to which it is connected. As commonly used, 'protective gear' refers to relay systems and does not embrace the surge arrester, the arc suppression coil and similar preventive devices.

1.1.2 Role of protection in a power station

We begin with this so that the subject can be seen in its proper perspective. It is fair to say that without discriminative protection it would be impossible to operate a modern power system. The protection is needed to remove as speedily as possible any element of the power system in which a fault has developed. So long as the fault remains connected, the whole system may be in jeopardy from three main effects of the fault, namely:

(*a*) it is likely to cause the individual generators in a power station, or groups of generators in different stations, to lose synchronism and fall out of step with consequent splitting of the system;

(*b*) a risk of damage to the affected plant; and

(*c*) a risk of damage to healthy plant.

There is another effect, not necessarily dangerous to the system, but important from the consumers' viewpoint, namely, a risk of synchronous motors in large industrial premises falling out of step and tripping out, with the serious consequences that entails loss of production and interruption of vital processes.

It is the function of the protective equipment, in association with the circuit breakers, to avert these effects. This is wholly true of large h.v. networks, or transmission systems. In the lower-voltage distribution systems, the primary function of protection is to maintain continuity of supply. This, in effect, is achieved incidentally in transmission systems if the protection operates correctly to avert the effects mentioned above; indeed it must be so, because the ultimate aim is to provide 100 per cent continuity of supply.

Obviously this aim cannot be achieved by the protection alone. In addition the power system and the distribution networks must be so designed that there are duplicate or multiple outlets from power sources to load centres (adequate generation may be taken for granted), and at least two sources of supply (feeders) to each distributing station. There are certain conventional ways of ensuring alternative supplies, as we shall see, but if full advantage is to be taken of their provision (always a costly matter) the protection must be highly *selective* in its functioning. For this it must possess the quality known as *discrimination*, by virtue of which it is able to select and to disconnect only the faulty element in the power system, leaving all others in normal operation so far as that may be possible. With a few exceptions the detection and tripping of a faulty circuit is a very simple matter; the art and skill lie in selecting the faulty one, bearing in mind that many circuits – generators, transformers, feeders – are usually affected, and in much the same way by a given fault. This accounts for the multiplicity of relay types and systems in use. Other chapters will explain their intricacies.

1.2   System and substation layout

1.2.1 System layout

Turning now to the matter of system layout, with particular reference to the implications it has for protection, power systems, and especially distribution systems, can in general be arranged as:
(*a*)   radial feeders
(*b*)   parallel feeders

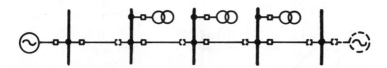

Fig. 1.2.1A   *Radial system*

(*c*)   ring systems
(*d*)   combinations of (*a*), (*b*) and (*c*).
Arrangement (*a*) does not satisfy the requirements of a duplicate supply, unless there is a source of generation at each end (Fig. 1.2.1A): nevertheless, discriminative protection is needed to limit the extent of the dislocation of supply. Arrangement

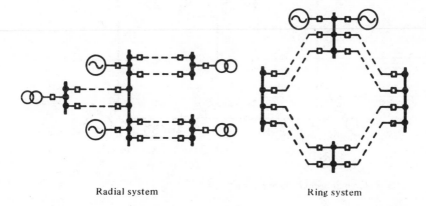

Radial system   Ring system

Fig. 1.2.1B   *Typical applications of parallel feeders*

(*b*), two applications of which are shown in Fig. 1.2.1B, provides a satisfactory duplicate supply. Arrangement (*c*) is, in effect, a logical extension of the idea of two parallel feeders. In its simplest form (Fig. 1.2.1C) it provides a duplicate supply to every substation, provided that the ring is closed. When the ring is open the system reverts to one of two radial feeders.

In the more complex form of Fig. 1.2.1D with interconnecting (tie) lines and multiple power sources – a form suited to a transmission system – more sophisticated forms of protection are needed than would be acceptable for the simple ring system if the aims of the protection, as already defined, are to be fulfilled. In this form can be discerned also combinations of (*a*), (*b*) and (*c*).

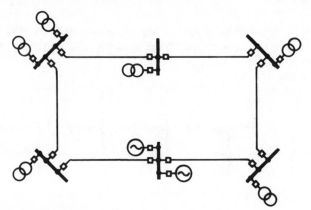

Fig. 1.2.1C   *Ring main system*

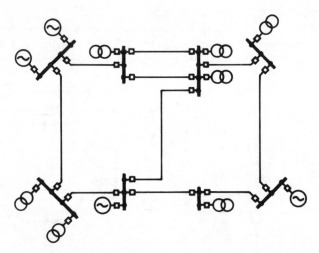

Fig. 1.2.1D   *Interconnected power system*

1.2.2   Substation layout (electrical)

This topic is relevant to the subject inasmuch as the electrical connections of a substation can affect the protection, albeit in minor and rather subtle ways.

Substations, with which can be grouped switching stations, are points in a power system where transmission lines or distribution feeders are marshalled for purposes of controlling load flow and general switching for maintenance purposes, and to which supplies are taken from generating stations and transformed in voltage, if necessary, for distribution.

Although substations differ greatly in size, construction, cost and complexity according to voltage, location and function, the feature they all have in common is the marshalling of all the associated circuits, through circuit-breakers, or switches, on to busbars (see Fig. 1.2.2A). Herein lies one of the ways in which protection is affected.

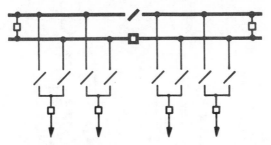

Fig. 1.2.2A   *Typical busbar-type substation*

The busbars are, next to the generators, the most important part of a system. Like other elements, they have some degree of fault liability and must be protected. Their protection can be automatically provided by that of the individual circuits assembled at the substation. This occurs in the mesh-type substation (Fig. 1.2.2B). In this there are no busbars in the conventional sense, but the circuit breakers and

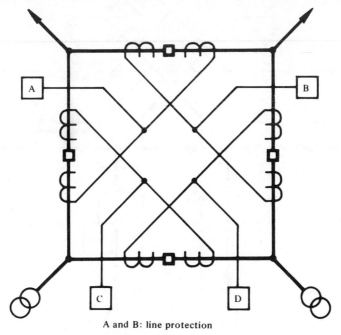

A and B: line protection

C and D: transformer protection

Fig. 1.2.2B   *Four-switch mesh substation showng positions of c.t.s. for circuit protection*

the connections between them form a 'ring' busbar. Each circuit is tapped off this ring between two circuit breakers. If the current transformers are disposed in or near these circuit breakers on the outside, that is the side of each circuit breaker remote from the tapping, then both circuit breakers, their interconnections and the

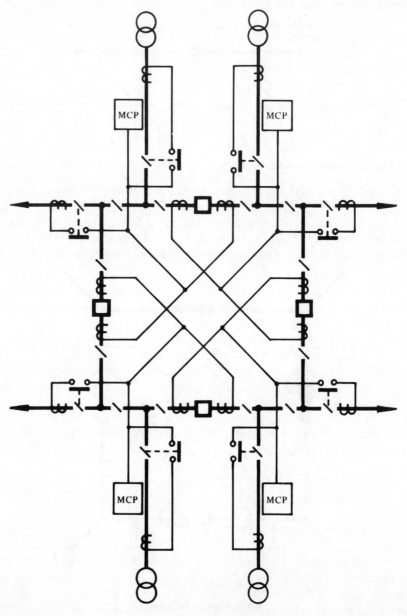

Fig. 1.2.2C   *Four-switch mesh substation showing the arrangement of mesh-corner protection*

tapped circuit are all protected by any protective device connected to those current transformers.

At 275 kV and 400 kV, however, it is now usual for the busbars (mesh-corner connections) of four-switch mesh-type substations to be separately protected, each by a circulating-current differential system of protection, as shown in Fig. 1.2.2C, supplied from current transformers associated with the mesh circuit breakers, the transformer bushings and the outgoing feeder circuits. With this arrangement, the feeder protection is supplied from current transformers in the feeder circuits and the transformer protection (insofar as the h.v. current transformers are concerned) from current transformers in the transformer h.v. bushings.

1.2.3 Current transformer location

In the conventional 'busbar' station (Fig. 1.2.2A) which may be of the metal-clad type or of the 'open-type', indoor or outdoor, the busbars cannot be embraced by the circuit protection. In some types, notably the outdoor open-type substation, there is a choice of current transformer location. If the circuit side of the circuit breaker is chosen, the circuit breaker is left unprotected unless additional protection is provided exclusively for the busbars; if the busbar side is chosen, the circuit breaker is included within the circuit protection. In this latter case, complications enter concerned with the method to be adopted to clear faults that occur between the current transformer and the circuit breaker, which are busbar faults, although not detectable by the busbar protection even if such is provided; it is of course detected by the circuit protection but, although it trips its own circuit breaker the fault remains on its busbar side.

The ideal is to locate current transformers on both sides of the circuit breaker, and to allocate those on the circuit side to the busbar protection and those on the busbar side to the circuit protection. In this way the circuit breaker is in the zone overlapped by both. This ideal is easily attainable in SF_6 and open-type bulk-oil installations. It can be done in airblast and low-oil installations also; but in these cases there are disadvantages in that the cost is much greater and the overlapped zone is much larger. In other types, such as metal-clad, there is usually no alternative to location on the circuit side.

1.3 System earthing

1.3.1 Neutral-earthing methods

It was mentioned earlier that there were a few exceptions to the thesis that fault detection and tripping were intrinsically a simple matter. Fault detection invariably relies on the presence of a significant amount of fault current; and this requirement is usually met as far as faults between phases are concerned and very often faults between one or more phases and earth, also.

The exceptions concern earth-faults alone, the reason being that the value of the earth-fault current is governed by the method adopted of earthing the power-system star (neutral) point.

There are several reasons both technical and economic for 'earthing the neutral' of a power system, apart from satisfying the requirements of the Electricity Regulations.

The economic reason applied only at very high voltages where, by directly (solidly) earthing the neutral point of a transformer, it is permissible to grade the thickness of the winding insulation downwards towards the neutral point. This is almost universal at 100 kV and above.

Among the technical reasons are:

(*a*)   The floating potential on the lower voltage (secondary and tertiary) windings is held to a harmless value.

(*b*)   Arcing faults to earth do not set up dangerously high voltages on the healthy phases.

(*c*)   By controlling the magnitude of the earth-fault current, inductive interference between power and communication circuits can be controlled.

(*d*)   A useful amount of earth-fault current is available (in most cases) to operate normal protection. Even when the ground resistance itself is high, it is still useful to earth the neutral point.

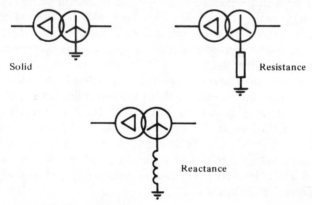

Solid   Resistance

Reactance

Fig. 1.3.1A   *Neutral Earthing methods*

These reasons sufficiently explain the methods commonly used in neutral earthing, shown in Fig. 1.3.1A, which are:

(*a*)   Solid-earthing (already mentioned) in which the only impedance between the neutral and earth is that represented by the earthing conductor itself and the resistance between the earth-plate (or rods) and earth. An internationally accepted definition of a solidly earthed system is 'an effectively-earthed' system which is defined as one 'in which, during a phase-to-earth fault, the voltage-to-earth of any sound phase does not exceed 80 per cent of the voltage between phases of the system.'

(*b*)   Resistance-earthing, in which a resistor is interposed between the star-point and earth. This is also known as 'non-effective' earthing, the converse of effective earthing.

(c) Reactance-earthing (also non-effective), in which a reactor is used instead of a resistor. The reactance (like the resistance of the resistor) is chosen to suit the requirements of the protection, or to control inductive interference, which is the predominant requirement.

(d) Arc-suppression (Petersen) coil earthing, in which a reactor is used but its reactance is adjusted to match, more or less exactly, the value of the capacitance to earth of two phases with the third phase connected solidly to earth. In this way the reactive component of the capacitive current flowing in the connection to earth formed by the fault is neutralized by the coil current, which flows in the same path but is displaced in phase by 180° from the capacitive current (see Fig. 1.3.1B). The coil reactance is adjustable in relatively coarse steps, to allow for variations in system zero-sequence capacitance

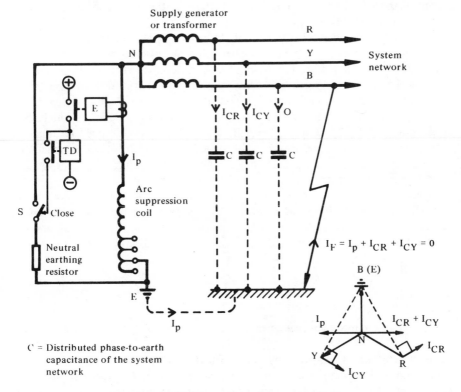

C = Distributed phase-to-earth capacitance of the system network

NOTE: The conditions shown are those existing with the switch 'S' open, I_{CR} and I_{CY} being the total distributed phase-to-earth capacitance currents in phases R and Y respectively. The switch 'S' closes if the earth fault, shown on blue phase, is sustained for longer than the setting of time-lag relay.

Fig. 1.3.1B *Principle of the arc-suppression coil with supplementary earthing resistance*

resulting from the switching out of circuits.

(e)   Earthing through a combination of arc suppression coil and resistor, in which a persistent earth-fault on one phase is 'suppressed' by the coil. As it is not desired that the fault should remain indefinitely on the system, after a delay, adjustable up to 30 s, the coil is automatically shunted by a resistor of low value which permits adequate earth-fault current to flow to operate orthodox discriminative protection. The resistor and its associated circuit-breaker are seen in Fig. 1.3.1B.

1.3.2   Special cases of resistance-earthing

A value commonly used for earthing-resistors is one that limits the earth-fault current, for a fault at full phase-to-neutral voltage, to a value equal to the rated current of the transformer winding whose neutral it earths. This serves the purposes already enumerated, in most cases.

In certain cases, in particular that of the generator star-point in a generator-transformer combined unit, a much higher value of resistance is permissible, and indeed desirable in the interest of avoiding damage to the iron-core of the generator stator in the event of an earth-fault. A typical value of resistor directly connected between the stator star-point and earth is one that limits the current to a maximum of 300 A. However, an alternative method now frequently applied to the larger machines (500 MW and above) is to earth the stator star-point through the primary winding of a single-phase transformer, the secondary winding of which is loaded by a resistor such that the maximum stator earth-fault current is limited to between 10 and 15 amps. Because the generator winding and its associated transformer lower-voltage winding form a separately earthed electrical circuit only magnetically linked with the h.v. system, it can be protected by a sensitive non-discriminative fault detector, provided that precautions are taken to ensure that it does not respond to any third harmonic currents normally present in the neutral earth-connection.

1.4   Faults

1.4.1   Faults and other abnormalities

Power systems are subject to many kinds of faults. The principal types are: three-phase with and without earth connection; phase-to-phase (two-phase); phase-to-earth (single-phase); and double phase-to-earth (phase-phase-earth).

Faults sometimes occur simultaneously at separate points on the system and on different phases (cross-country faults). Sometimes they are accompanied by a broken conductor, or may even take the form of a broken conductor without earth-connection. All of these appertain to lines and feeders, but the principal ones are common to all kinds of plant.

Generators, transformers and motors are subject in addition to short-circuits between turns of the same winding.

With the exception of the three-phase short-circuit with or without earth connection, all of the faults listed represent unbalanced conditions in a three-phase system (with which we are mainly concerned). The accurate electrical analysis of possible fault conditions is vital to the correct design and application of protection and this subject is accordingly treated in some detail in Chapter 3.

1.4.2 Nature and causes of faults

The nature of a fault is simply defined as any abnormal condition which causes a reduction in the basic insulation strength between phase conductors, or between phase conductors and earth or any earthed screens surrounding the conductors. In practice, a reduction is not regarded as a fault until it is detectable; that is, until it results either in an excess current or in a reduction of the impedance between conductors, or between conductors and earth, to a value below that of the lowest load impedance normal to the circuit. Thus a high degree of pollution on an insulator string, although it reduces the insulation strength of the affected phase, does not become a fault until it causes a flashover across the string, which in turn produces excess current or other detectable abnormality: for example, abnormal current in an arc-suppression coil.

Pollution is commonly caused by deposited soot or cement dust in industrial areas, and by salt deposited by wind-borne sea-spray in coastal areas.

Other causes of faults are: on overhead lines—birds, aircraft, lightning, fog, ice and snow loading, punctured or broken insulators, open-circuit conductors, abnormal loading: in machines, cables and transformers—failure of solid insulation because of moisture, mechanical damage, accidental contact with earth or earthed screens, flashover in air caused by overvoltage, abnormal loading.

All incidents arising from these causes are so-called 'primary' or 'system' faults. Another kind of fault is the 'non-system' fault, so called because it defines an operation of protection which results in the tripping of circuit breakers without an accompanying fault on the primary system. Such non-system faults may be the result of defects in the protection, for example incorrect settings, faulty or incorrect connection, or they may result from human error in testing or maintenance work.

For the purposes of statistical analysis, a fault (covering both 'system' and 'non-system' faults) is arbitrarily defined as:

(a)   any abnormal event causing or requiring the automatic tripping of a circuit breaker, or,

(b)   any operation in error of a circuit breaker or isolator.

A system fault, as already indicated, is defined as any fault or system abnormality which involves, or is the result of, failure of primary electrical equipment and which requires the disconnection of the affected equipment from the system by the tripping of the associated circuit breakers. Simultaneous system faults in different protective-gear zones are counted as separate incidents, as are faults resulting from manual or automatic reclosure on to persistent system faults. A non-system fault is formally defined as any incorrect circuit-breaker operation resulting from a cause other than a system-fault condition. This definition excludes, however, incorrect circuit-breaker operations due to incorrect manual operation from a control point. However, the manual operation of a circuit-breaker on receipt of a voltage-transformer Buchholz alarm in order to disconnect the voltage transformer from the system is classed as a fault since such disconnection is obligatory, the fault being classed as a system fault if the alarm is genuine and as a non-system fault if it is not.

1.4.3 Fault statistics

It is an important part of the protection management function that records should be kept of all protection operations, both correct and incorrect, to provide a means of assessing the protection performance achieved on an annual basis, such information being of particular value to those responsible for the design and application of protection. Such assessment requires the adoption of suitable yardsticks by which performance can be measured and compared, the two principal indices, one for system-fault performance and the other for non-system-fault performance, being defined as follows:

discriminative system-fault performance index
$$= 100 \, (A-F)/A\%$$

where A = total number of system faults in year under consideration
    F = number of system faults incorrectly cleared

non-system fault performance index
$$= 100 \, (C-E)/C\%$$

where C = total number of circuit breakers installed on the power system under consideration
    E = number of non-system-fault circuit-breaker operations attributable to protection in the year under consideration

A system fault is counted as correctly cleared if it results in the disconnection of the faulted item of plant or equipment from the system without the tripping of any circuit breakers other than those whose tripping is essential to the clearance of the fault from the system. Thus, the fault clearance is still considered correct if the requisite circuit breakers are tripped by back-up protection and even if the wrong relay or protective system operates to bring about the tripping of the correct circuit breakers. Any incident in which one or more circuit breakers are tripped in addition to those which control the faulted circuit is classed as an incorrect operation; similarly, any incident in which one or more of the circuit breakers required to trip fails to do so is also classed as an incorrect operation.

Table 1.4.3A *System and non-system fault performance indices for the CEGB system over a typical five-year period*

Statistic	Year				
	1	2	3	4	5
Total number of system faults	672	678	505	429	295
Discriminative system-fault performance index	94·2%	96·6%	95·6%	95·9%	92·2%
Total number of circuit breakers installed	10 514	9 784	9 737	9 252	9 252
Non-system fault performance index	98·3%	97·8%	97·6%	98·6%	98·6%

Table 1.4.3A provides system-fault and non-system-fault performance information for five consecutive years of a typical five-year period for the CEGB system, the information relating to the CEGB's 400 kV and 275 kV systems together with some lower voltage circuits operated by the CEGB. It will be noted that the given figures indicate average values of 516 system faults per year, a discriminative system-fault performance index of 95·2% and a non-system-fault performance index of 98·2%. Table 1.4.3B provides an indication of the distribution of system faults over the different types of plant and equipment concerned, again for the five consecutive years of the same five-year period. It will be noted that, on average, over the five-year period, approximately 63% of system faults occurred on overhead-line and cable circuits.

Table 1.4.3B *Distribution of system faults on the CEGB system over a typical five-year period*

Type of plant or equipment concerned	Year				
	1	2	3	4	5
Overhead line and cable circuits	435	460	293	269	174
Transformers and reactors	91	100	102	49	32
Generators and generator transformers	89	75	66	65	51
Busbars and switchgear	50	32	31	33	27
Other plant (motors, compensators, etc.)	7	11	13	13	11

Table 1.4.3C provides an analysis of the causes of failure or maloperation of protection under system and non-system fault conditions, again for the five consecutive years of the same five-year period. The importance of effective maintenance is emphasised in the Table, having regard to the need, within the limitations of resources, to reduce preventable protection failures and maloperations to an absolute minimum. The failures and maloperations which might have been prevented by timely maintenance include those resulting from such causes as loss of calibration or adjustment, corrosion, the presence of foreign particles, the sticking of contacts and insulation failure. No less important than maintenance, however, is the need to ensure correct design, maximum reliability and correct application of protection, and these factors receive particular attention in more detailed analysis of protection performance statistics. Such analysis plays an important role in helping to identify and rectify particular deficiencies and limitations with consequent benefit to the achievement of the desired aim of maximum possible reliability and security of the protection and of the power system which it protects.

Table 1.4.3C   *Causes of failure or maloperation of protection during system and non-system faults on the CEGB system over a typical five-year period*

Cause of failure or maloperation	Year				
	1	2	3	4	5
Failures or maloperations which might have been prevented by maintenance	20	36	16	12	25
Testing	12	10	13	20	6
Incorrect installation	23	25	12	10	7
Physical interference	17	23	23	14	13
Electrical interference	15	11	12	10	15
Mechanical shock or vibration	14	4	4	3	2
Intrinsic design or component fault	19	21	14	10	16
Incorrect setting	9	12	11	15	3
Mechanical failure	6	6	7	2	6
Nature of system fault	11	2	7	6	2
Other causes	40	41	36	28	21
Total	186	191	155	130	116

1.5   Basic terms used in protection

Although the meaning of most of the terms used is self-evident, it will help in understanding the chapters that follow to define some of the more basic ones; some, such as the different classes of fault, have already been defined.

The fundamental quality that all protection must possess is that of *discrimination*, sometimes called selectivity. It is the quality where a relay or protective system is enabled to pick out and cause to be disconnected only the faulty element.

In the wide range of discriminative systems to be dealt with in succeeding chapters some are said to have *absolute discrimination*; these are the *unit systems*. They are able to detect and respond to an abnormal condition occurring only with the zone or the element they are specifically intended to protect.

Others are said to have *dependent* (or *relative*) *discrimination*; these are the *non-unit* systems. Their discrimination is *not* absolute, being dependent on the correlated or co-ordinated responses of a number of (generally) similar systems, all of which respond to a given abnormal condition.

Again discrimination is of two kinds; in one it refers to the ability of a device to discriminate as to the type of fault, so that it responds only to a specific type of fault condition; in the other it refers to the ability of the device to discriminate as to the *location* of the fault. Many discriminative systems of the latter kind incorporate devices of the first-mentioned kind, and this applied both to unit and to non-unit systems.

The term *stability* is often used to describe the quality of a protective system by virtue of which it remains inoperative under specified conditions usually associated with high values of fault current. Strictly speaking, it is a quality that only unit systems can possess because they are required to remain inoperative under all conditions associated with faults *outside* their own zone. Non-unit systems on the other hand can respond to faults anywhere on the power system to which they are applied. Thus they cannot be said to remain *stable* under any fault conditions; they respond positively and are able to discriminate only because their responses are co-ordinated. In short, both kinds of system possess the quality of discrimination, but stability is associated only with unit systems. The same is true of instability. Unit systems, in the main, operate either on the principle of balancing the currents entering and leaving the protected zone, or on that of nullifying the effects of the entering current (or power) by those of the current (or power) leaving the zone. Thus failure to balance or to nullify properly produces *instability* if the fault is outside the protected zone, and *operation* if it is within it.

It is a much easier matter to achieve good balance, and hence stability, under steady state conditions, than it is under transient conditions. In this context a transient condition is roughly the first half-cycle that is 0·01 s for a power system of 50 Hz, from the moment that a detectable fault occurs. It is for this reason that many unit systems incorporate a *bias* feature, which helps to assure stability in the onerous transient period of the fault current duration. Bias makes use of the 'through-current', that is the current flowing into and out of the zone, whether load current or through-fault current, to exert a restraining effect or a counter torque on the moving member of the relay. This is known as *load-bias*. Some systems, notably differential systems for transformer protection, have, in addition to load-bias, a *harmonic-bias* which makes use, for the same purpose, of harmonic currents present in the primary current when a transformer is switched on to the system.

Another property which, along with stability and *operating time*, serves to classify a unit protective system, is *sensitivity*. This refers to the level of fault current at which operation occurs; in other words, it is the fault setting and is usually expressed either in amperes referred to the primary circuit, or as a percentage of the rated current of the current transformers. The term is apt to be confused with a property of the relays used in both unit and non-unit systems. The sensitivity of a relay, as distinct from a system, is expressed as the apparent power in volt-amperes required to cause its operation; thus a 1·0 VA relay is more sensitive than, say, a 3·0 VA relay. To show that the confusion has more than a verbal significance it may be mentioned that the sensitivity of a system is often improved by using a more sensitive relay, that is one with a reduced VA consumption and a given current setting, but it may well be worsened by reducing the current setting and maintaining the VA. In other words the sensitivity of a relay is not reduced by reducing the current netting, but that of a unit system is.

1.6   Necessity for back-up protection

There are two reasons for applying back-up protection to the elements of a power system. One is the obvious one of 'backing-up' the main protection to ensure that in the event of its failure the fault will be cleared with complete discrimination, or at least with the minimum of dislocation of supply or of circuits. The second is to cover those parts of a protected circuit (or element) which are not covered by the main protection by reason of the location of the current or the voltage transformers. To understand this function of back-up protection it is necessary to explain that with every protective installation there is associated a 'protected zone' which is defined, for a unit system, as the zone lying between the two or several sets of current transformers which together with the relays constitute the protective system; and, for a non-unit system, the zone lying between the current transformers and the point or points on the protected circuit beyond which the system is unable to detect the presence of a fault. Figs. 1.6A, 1.6B and 1.6C illustrate this.

Thus faults that occur between the current transformers and circuit breaker, for example, in Fig. 1.6A, are outside the zone of the circuit protection and can be dealt with either by the busbar protection (which is usual in the transmission system, but less so in the distribution systems), or by back-up protection. The latter in performing that function would be acting as 'remote back-up'. This is exemplified in Fig. 1.6B in which the back-up protection at A acts as back-up for a fault at X, or a fault at Y, not cleared for any reason by the circuit breaker at C. A fault between A and B (Fig. 1.6A) not cleared for any reason by the 'main protection' must also be cleared at A (assuming for simplicity a single infeed) by back-up protection. In this instance the latter would be acting as 'local back-up'.

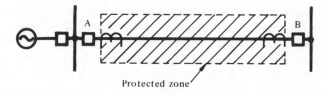

Fig. 1.6A   *Protected zone of a unit system of protection*

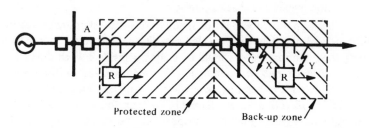

Fig. 1.6B   *Protected and back-up zones of a non-unit system of protection (distance protection)*

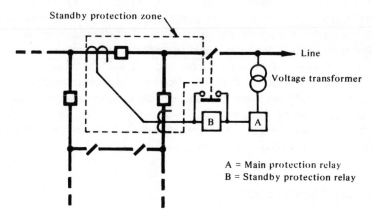

A = Main protection relay
B = Standby protection relay

Fig. 1.6C   *Application of a non-unit system of protection (distance protection with the voltage transformer on the line side of the isolator) and the standby protection zone of the normally shorted standby protection*

These functions of local and remote back-up do not necessarily require protection additional to the main protection. If the latter is of the non-unit type, it possesses an inherent back-up feature. This is true of both graded-time and distance protection, but the 'reach' of the back-up protection is more limited in the latter case. Unit systems, on the other hand, do not possess a back-up feature and must therefore be supplemented by additional protection of a non-unit type. This does not mean that every circuit must necessarily have independent back-up; in distribution systems it may be sufficient to apply it only at strategic points in the system, but in the transmission system it is essential to apply it to all circuit breakers.

As far as possible, back-up protection should be independent of the main protection, with as few common components as possible. In the transmission system only the tripping battery and the voltage transformer are common to both; each has its own set of current transformers, tripping relays and, in some cases, trip coils, with segregated connecting leads and separate fuses for the d.c. circuit. In the distribution systems, the risks attending the use of common components are generally less serious, but it is prudent to segregate the current circuits. Often there are current transformers provided for instrumentation and these can be designed to supply in addition overcurrent back-up relays.

The term 'back-up protection' is not synonymous with 'standby protection'. The latter term is appropriately used to describe protection that is normally out-of-service with the intention that it should be made operational when the main protection has to be taken out of commission for maintenance or for investigation. Standby protection may therefore take the form of fixed equipment allocated to each set of main protection, or there may be only one equipment selectable to any one of several circuits, or it may be transportable and taken to any site where it is needed for the purpose mentioned. It should be noted, however, that such standby protection is now rarely used, it being more appropriate, in general, to ensure that the risks in question are suitably covered by adequate back-up protection.

At the higher transmission voltages of 400 kV and 275 kV, the importance of achieving acceptable main-protection performance and of minimising dependence on slower and possibly less discriminative back-up protection now commonly requires the provision of two sets of main protection, for example on feeder circuits, or the use of some measure of duplication of vital components (e.g. relays, batteries, trip circuits) to achieve the same objective. At such higher transmission voltages it is also now common practice, particularly at 400 kV, to employ circuit-breaker-fail protection designed to ensure satisfactory fault clearance in the event of failure of a circuit breaker to trip in response to a trip signal.

1.7   Economic considerations

1.7.1.   General

The cost of protection can be likened to a premium for insurance against damage to plant, and loss of supply and of consumer goodwill. As in other spheres, there is an economic limit to the amount that can be spent on such insurance, and it is a difficult matter to decide what is the right amount. Up to a point the decision is fairly easy, and that point is reached when the requirements that all faulty equipment must be removed by automatic protection is met. Beyond that point the economic aspect takes in such questions as the speed at which faults shall be cleared, the degree of security inherent in the system itself, the availability of or the relative ease with which auxiliary pilot channels, for example, can be provided, and various imponderables such as the degree of risk that may be taken in leaving out some fault conditions, and the degree of reliability demanded from the protection.

All these considerations are economic, but they have different weightings when applied to distribution and transmission systems. It will be convenient to discuss their implications separately for the two cases.

1.7.2 Distribution systems

In these, the economic factor comes near to overriding the technical mainly on account of the very large number of switching and distribution points, transformers and feeders, as compared with the transmission system, and the reduced importance that this naturally gives to these components. In consequence, the protection may be the barest minimum consistent with safety requirements as laid down in the appropriate statutory regulations.

Speed of fault clearance is not as important a factor as it is in the transmission system where system stability is involved. It has importance, however, in cable systems where the fault current is high, as in cables outgoing from the larger bulk-supply points. Because the cable runs are relatively short, pilot wires are not unduly expensive if laid with the cables and can be considered to enable unit systems to be used when speedy clearance is needed.

Back-up protection can be much simpler and often inherent in the main protection. A high degree of reliability is desirable, but the consequences of a mal-operation or a failure to operate are in general less serious than those of a like kind in transmission systems. Fuses can often be used instead of circuit breakers and protective equipment. Metal-clad construction reduces the risk of interphase faults.

1.7.3 Transmission systems

In this domain, the emphasis must of necessity be on technical rather than economic considerations. The necessity for highly reliable, fully discriminative, high-speed protection is absolute in the context of 275 kV and 400 kV transmission systems. This is not to say that the economic aspect can be ignored; but that it comes second in order of priority.

High-speed clearance and the exigencies of auto-reclosing usually necessitate the use of a unit system which, with the possible exception of those based on the use of rented P.O. pilot circuits, are much more costly than non-unit systems.

Safety requirements are neither more nor less important than they are in distribution systems; but they are more than adequately satisfied as a by-product of the provision of equipment to meet the fundamental need defined above.

This equipment is very comprehensive, even elaborate, but the elaboration is amply justified by the very high capital costs of the elements it protects, and even more by the high costs incurred when, for example, line outages compel the running of low merit generating plant.

The elaboration results from the already stated need, particularly at the higher transmission voltages, to employ appropriate duplication of protective measures, for example by the provision of two sets of fully discriminative protection for feeder circuits, from appropriate use of equipment redundancy in the interests of protection security, as in busbar protection for example, and from the provision of other facilities such as circuit-breaker-fail protection.

Good protection must be based on sound engineering principles, and this implies that the element of risk to security of supply is reduced to the lowest practicable level. The economic factor enters in determining what is practicable, as well as being a factor in all sound engineering.

It has already been said that without discriminative protection it would be impossible to operate a large modern h.v. power system. The need for thoroughly sound, comprehensive and reliable protection is therefore paramount.

1.8   Bibliography

Books

The protective gear handbook by F E Wellman (Pitman)
Protective relays application guide (GEC Measurements, 1975)
Developments in power system protection (IEE Conf. Publ. 125, 1975)

Chapter 2

Protection principles and components

by H.S.Petch, revised by J.Rushton

2.1 Fundamental principles

The essential and discriminative removal of an abnormality from a power system, thereby minimising loss of supply and damage, involves two basic requirements:

(i)   the system must be provided with a sufficient number of circuit-breakers or other correctly-located disconnecting devices adequate for the duty which may be imposed upon them;

(ii)   each of these devices must have controlling means which, being able to recognise abnormal conditions, will cause the appropriate, and only the appropriate, disconnecting devices to function, and thereby remove the abnormal conditions.

The first requirement is the joint province of the System Design Engineer and the Protection Engineer. The second is our sole concern, and this chapter is devoted to a brief review, first of the different ways in which the controlling relays mentioned in paragraph (ii) are enabled to exert their discriminative function; and second, of the principal components that go to make up a discriminative protective system.

The chapter concludes with a review of some of the special problems encountered with high speed protection systems.

Of necessity, most of these topics are dealt with briefly and the chapter provides a general introduction to some of the more advanced aspects of subsequent chapters.

2.1.1 Methods of discrimination

In providing selective fault clearance a protective relay needs to be provided with information to enable it to discriminate between fault conditions within its legitimate zone of operation for which tripping is required, and external faults and healthy load currents for which tripping is not required. This information must, obviously, be derived from the available electrical quantities of current, voltage and the phase angle between them measured at the time of fault. Initially, a basic difference can be recognised between those protective systems which use only local quantities to derive their performance characteristic, and others which take some account of what is happening at both local and remote points of the protected circuit. Generally where only local information is used some element of time delay must be included to provide discrimination between adjacent protection systems whereas, when comparison is made of both local and remote quantities the protection covers one discrete unit of the power system and can provide rapid and wholly discriminative fault clearance. Some basic methods of discrimination may now be considered.

(*a*)   *Discrimination by time:* In this the basic idea is to add time lag features to the controlling relays of a number of circuit-breakers in the power system so that the breaker or breakers nearest to a fault on the system always trips first.

Consider Fig. 2.1.1A, which shows a simple radial line passing through transformer stations A, B, C and D, at each of which the outgoing line has a circuit-breaker. Suppose that the protective systems applied to these breakers are identical, and each is such that it will be tripped if traversed by 2000A. If there is a fault on line section CD, and the fault current exceeds 2000A, the breakers at A, B and C will open and all supply beyond A will be lost.

Suppose instead, that we are able to add time lag features to the protection systems such that after these recognise the existence of a fault the tripping is delayed thus:

D—no added delay
C—0·4 s added delay
B—0·8 s added delay
A—1·2 s added delay.

Again consider the effect of a fault, F, in the line section CD. Now the breaker at C will open after 0·4 s, and will disconnect the fault before the breakers at A and B can trip. Supply is thus maintained to A, B and C. This is known as time discrimination.

It will be noted the 0·4 s steps have been suggested in the time lags. An interval of this order is necessary to give the circuit-breaker and its protective relays time to operate fully before the next breaker with the longer time can receive an impulse to trip.

(*b*)   *Discrimination by current magnitude:* Discrimination can be obtained by recognising the fact that faults in different parts of a power system will cause fault currents of different magnitude on account of the differing impedances between the source and the points of fault. This, in suitable conditions, with the protective relays of the various circuit-breakers set to trip at suitably tapered current values, will ensure that the breakers near to the fault will trip and will leave others traversed by the same fault current undisturbed. Thus,

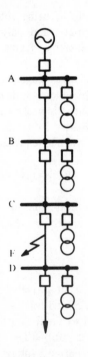

Fig. 2.1.1A *Simple radial system with single infeed at station A and a fault F on feeder CD*

supply will be maintained to those parts of the system which are healthy.

(c) *Discrimination by time and direction:* If the current coil of a wattmeter is carrying the current in a circuit and its voltage coil is across the voltage of that circuit, the instrument will deflect in one or other direction according to the direction of power flow in the circuit. This will provide a discriminative feature if contacts are added to the wattmeter, thereby making it a directional relay; the contacts being used to permit or to inhibit the operation of another relay, which is not inherently directional. This second relay usually operates after a time lag, so that the combination of the directional element and this second relay offers discrimination by time and direction.

Consider Fig. 2.1.1B which shows a normally closed ring main. All the relays shown are non-directional, have the same current setting, and the time lags shown. By trial of the response of the relays to faults in various positions on the ring main it will be found that proper discrimination cannot be obtained, nor can this be improved by varying the time lags from those shown in the figure. Now turn to Fig. 2.1.1C where all the relays operate with the time lags shown, but only with fault power flowing through the relays in the direction shown by the arrows. Trial of the effects of faults anywhere on the ring main show that a fault occurring on any section of ring main will be discriminatively cleared by the relays, and there will be no loss of supply.

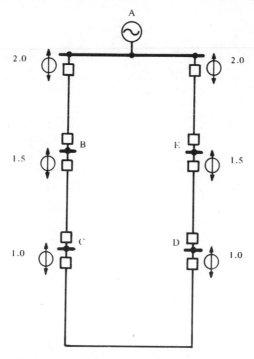

Fig. 2.1.1B *Non-directional time-graded protection applied to a ring main system*

(*d*)   *Discrimination by distance measurement:* The simple methods of discrimination by time and current magnitude so far dealt with have very obvious limitations, in that they are applicable only to very simple systems. In the case of time discrimination it is seen that faults near to the source, which are the more severe, are held on the system for relatively long periods.

These limitations can be reduced if the relays which control circuit-breakers are made such that they will measure the distance from the circuit-breaker location to the fault. If this distance is less than that to the next circuit-breaker out from the source, the fault is within the section controlled by the breaker concerned, and this will trip. If the distance is greater than that to the next breaker out from the source, the fault is beyond the section controlled by the breaker concerned, and it will not trip. Referring again to Fig. 2.1.1A, the breaker at A will trip only for a fault whose measured distance is less than A to B; that at B will trip only for a fault whose distance is less than B to C; and so on. It will be shown later that discrimination by distance need not involve long time delays.

The required measurement of distance is achieved in practice in various ways, which will be dealt with in detail in later chapters, but all these rely on the fact that the length of a circuit for a given conductor diameter and spacing determines its impedance. Therefore the relays measure an impedance directly

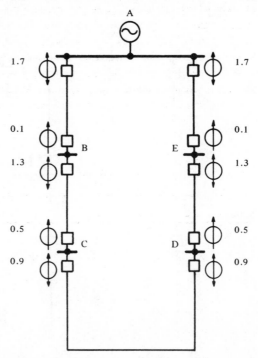

Fig. 2.1.1C   *Combined directional and non-directional time-graded protection applied to a ring main system*

related to that between the circuit-breaker location and the fault, and they do this by measuring simultaneously the current and voltage and phase angle at the circuit-breaker location and suitably combining their effects in relays.

(e) *Time as an addition to current magnitude or distance discrimination:* The addition of time as a factor will often extend the usefulness of current magnitude and distance discrimination. Indeed, such addition may be essential to make a practical scheme out of a theoretical one.

It will be clear that sometimes where discrimination by current magnitude is desired, the power system layout and impedances may not allow simple tapering of the current settings of nominally instantaneous relays. In such cases the ability to add to the current tapering a system of time tapering, as in Section 2.1.1(a), will usually be advantageous and indeed, as will be seen in later chapters, most practical protection schemes of this type are combinations of time and current grading.

The addition of time to distance discrimination is somewhat complex and will be described in Chapter 9, but Fig. 2.1.1D serves to illustrate the principles involved. The system is similar to that of Fig. 2.1.1A, the stations A, B and C and the intervening lines being the same in both drawings. Distance relays, as briefly described in Section 2.1.1.(d) are located at A, B and C and they control the circuit-breakers there. The relay at A is intended to detect faults in the feeder AB and would be set to measure the distance A to B, or more specifically the impedance Z_{AB}. Clearly, the change in impedance seen by the relay at A for a fault either just within the protected circuit at end B or just beyond it is very small, and the relay must therefore have a reach setting which falls short of the remote end if incorrect operation on through faults is to be avoided. Taking account, also, of practical accuracy limits in the relay the zone of instantaneous response (known as first zone, Z_1) is set to 80–85% of Z_{AB}.

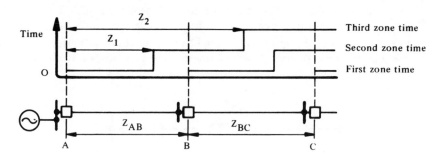

Z_{AB}, Z_{BC} – feeder impedances
Z_1, Z_2 – zone 1 and zone 2 reach of distance protection

Fig. 2.1.1D *Time/distance characteristic of three-zone distance-protection scheme*

If a fault should occur beyond Z_1 up to the circuit-breaker at B, a second time lag step (about 0·4 sec) in the relay at A will then operate, thus clearing the fault after a short time lag.

The distance relays at B and C have similar time lag 'second zones' and Fig. 2.1.1D suggests even a third zone, the reasons for which will be discussed in Chapter 9. This combination of distance relay with time features has the added advantage that it provides a second, or back-up, chance of clearing faults.

It is to be noted that this back-up feature achieved by combined distance/time discrimination does not require to have the long time lags of simple time discrimination.

(f)   *Current balance methods:* A practical power system is invariably more complex than those so far considered. This is because security of supply and the need for interconnection of generating sources results in a multi-mode network with fault infeeds at many points.

As a consequence, time graded methods have great difficulty in providing either adequate discrimination or, equally important, a sufficently fast operating speed to ensure system stability.

Satisfactory discrimination can be provided by a protection system which makes a comparison between currents at each end of the protected circuit and the simplest and most widely used form in that of current balance protection.

This is illustrated in its basic form in Fig. 2.1.1E which shows current transformers at both ends of the protected circuit connected so that for through load or through fault conditions current circulates between the interconnected CTs. The relay is normally connected across equipotential points and therefore does not operate. For an internal fault the balance is disturbed and the out of balance current will operate the relay to trip the associated circuit breaker. The circuit illustrated in Fig. 2.1.1E could represent one phase of a three-phase generator and protection of a three-phase generator requires three such systems. The principle can readily be extended to the protection of a multi-ended circuit (e.g. busbar protection), for which case current transformers at each circuit end are paralleled on to the differential current relay.

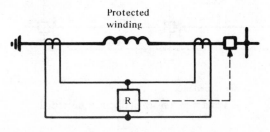

Fig. 2.1.1E   *Current-balance system using circulating current principle*

Circulating balance methods of this kind are widely used for apparatus protection where current transformers are within the same substation area and interconnecting leads between CTs are short. This is not the case for feeder circuits and the current balance principle requires some modification to permit comparison of lower power levels over the interconnecting pilot wire circuit.

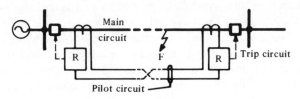

Fig. 2.1.1F   *Principle of opposed voltage feeder protection*

(g)   *Opposed voltage protection:* Fig. 2.1.1F shows a protective scheme for a single feeder. This, like the scheme of Fig. 2.1.1E, relies on the fact that, provided there is no fault on the feeder, the currents entering and leaving it must be equal in phase and magnitude. Balance is therefore between circuit ends, and to accomplish this, an auxiliary circuit is required, connected as shown. In the case illustrated the current transformers are of a special type, designed to produce a secondary voltage linearly proportional to the primary current. With no fault on the feeder these secondary voltages will be equal and opposite, so that no current flows in the relays, which are in series with the pilot circuit.

A fault at F will disturb the balance between ends, the current transformer secondary voltages will no longer balance, and current will flow in the relays, which, on closing their contacts, will trip the circuit-breakers at the two ends.

Under through fault conditions, a current-balance system applied to a line may be regarded in another way. Consider Fig. 2.1.1F again, and particularly the conditions at one end of the line when through fault current is traversing it. The current transformer and relay at this end may be said to be 'aware' that fault current is entering the line, but the relay may be regarded as 'deciding' not to cause tripping because it is also 'aware' (over the auxiliary pilot channel) that exactly similar fault current is leaving the other end of the line.

This perhaps rather fanciful approach illustrates very well the essentials of a unit protection system, which can be stated thus:

(i)   there must be fault-sensing means at each end of the protected circuit;

(ii)   there must be means of communication between the ends so that the fault-sensing means at each end is simultaneously acquainted with conditions at the other end (or ends), so that its tripping function can be exercised or not as appropriate.

(*h*)   *Phase-comparison method:* In situations where the means of communication between circuit ends is unable to provide a linear transmission of current amplitude information, a comparison between relative phase angles is often possible. The most widely used protection of this kind is the phase-comparison carrier current protection system in which alternate half cycles of current at each end of the protected circuit are modulated with a carrier signal and transmitted over the power line, for comparison against the locally derived signal. The comparator will have an angular setting, i.e. it will operate when the phase angle between the two currents exceeds a predetermined value.

Normally, the phase angle between the currents at the two ends for the through load or through fault condition will be such that the comparator is inoperative (i.e. the phase displacement is $0°$) whereas for an internal fault this angular displacement will approach $180°$.

Practical schemes use highly complex electronic circuitry as will be seen in Chapter 10.

(*i*)   *Distance protection with signalling channel:* The basic form of three zone distance protection described in Section 3 has the disadvantage of low speed (Zone 2) fault clearance for faults within the last 20% of the protected feeder. Where high speed fault clearance is necessary over the whole feeder this delayed tripping can be eliminated by the use of an instruction signal.

The most obvious way in which an instruction signal may be used is to initiate it from Zone 1 (which trips its local circuit breaker directly) at either end and to arrange that, on receipt of a signal at the remote end, the circuit breaker is tripped. This is known as direct intertripping.

An alternative approach, shown in Fig. 2.1.1.G(*a*) is to make the tripping conditional.

In this case operation of Zone 1 at the circuit end nearest to the fault sends an 'acceleration' signal to the remote end which in effect, short circuits the time lag associated with an independent Zone 2 (or Zone 3) relay. Tripping is thus dependent upon two criteria:

(i)   receipt of a signal from the remote end of the circuit to advise that tripping has taken place there.

(ii)   operation of an independent Zone 2 (or Zone 3) at the local end to confirm that a fault still persists on the protected line.

If this method is inverted we have the arrangement shown in Fig. 2.1.1.G(*b*) where the distance relay now has an instantaneous zone (Z_2) which extends beyond the protected feeder and the signal transmitted at the remote end is used to block its tripping circuit under through fault conditions.

Blocking signals are not transmitted continuously but are controlled by a high speed starting relay (H.S.S.) which has a longer reach and is faster in operation then the directional distance relay (Z_2). With some schemes the high speed block initiation relay may be directional and operate only for faults outside the protected feeder (i.e. it has a reversed reach). For external faults (say beyond Station B)

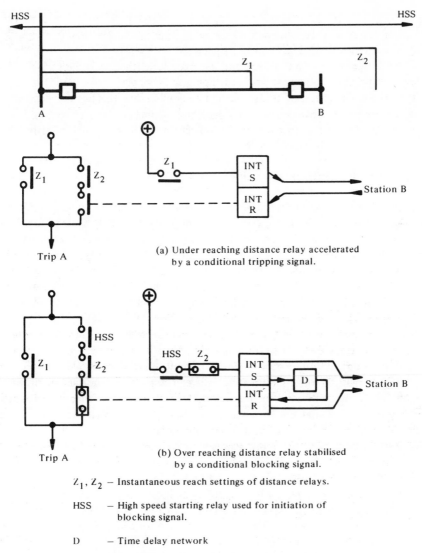

(a) Under reaching distance relay accelerated
by a conditional tripping signal.

(b) Over reaching distance relay stabilised
by a conditional blocking signal.

Z_1, Z_2 — Instantaneous reach settings of distance relays.

HSS — High speed starting relay used for initiation of
blocking signal.

D — Time delay network

Fig. 2.1.1G *Showing two methods of using a communication
channel to accelerate distance protection*

then, at end A, relays H.S.S. and Z_2 will operate while, at end B, only relay H.S.S.
operates.

Tripping at end A is prevented by relay R which is operated, via the signalling
channel from relay S at end B. End B does not wish to trip because Z_2 is not
operated (the fault is 'behind' the relay). Clearly, tripping via relay Z_2 must be
delayed sufficiently to ensure that the blocking signal is received and that relay R
has operated.

To ensure stability for power reversals following through fault clearance, network D in Fig. 2.1.1G(*b*) delays operation of relay R from the local end. A similar result may be obtained by increasing the time delay directly in the Z_2 relay. For internal faults H.S.S. and Z_2 operate at both ends.

For a single infeed fault H.S.S. and Z_2 operate at the infeeding end. Neither relay operates at the other end so that tripping can take place.

Practical schemes are, of course, far more complex than this but the elementary principle described above shows how a signalling channel can be used to modify the basic performance of a distance protection scheme so that it provides high speed fault clearance over the whole feeder.

2.1.2   Derivation of relaying quantities

The foregoing methods of discrimination by location of fault are equally applicable to single-phase and polyphase systems. The majority of supply systems are three phase, and the star points of such systems are nearly always connected to earth for reasons given in Chapter 1. Statistics show that the majority of system faults originate as faults between one phase and earth, possibly developing later into faults involving one or both of the other phases. If a fault can be dealt with quickly, whilst still in the single phase to earth stage, damage may in many cases be limited, and the system little disturbed.

There are cases where the system parameters are such that the currents produced by fault conditions differ little in magnitude from load currents, so that normal current-magnitude discrimination becomes difficult or even impossible to apply.

Clearly a method of discriminating between a fault and normal or overload conditions is a necessity, and such a method is available if use is made by suitable circuitry of the fact that the currents in a three phase system can be resolved into their positive, negative and zero sequence components.

(*a*)   *Zero-phase sequence systems:* Faults involving earth give rise to zero-sequence currents which can be used as a basis for discrimination.

The value of discriminative methods which isolate the zero-sequence component usually resides in their ability to ignore load currents and phase-to-phase short circuits, thus permitting the use of earth-fault relay settings lower than load current values. This is often essential for discrimination, or even for adequate protection when earth fault currents are limited.

The three ways in common use of applying zero-sequence discrimination

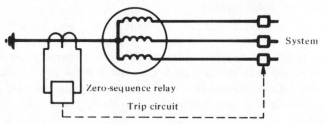

Fig. 2.1.2A   *Zero-sequence relay connection using system neutral current*

are shown in Figs. 2.1.2A, B and C. Arrangement A consists of putting a suitable current-sensitive device in the connection between the power system star (neutral) point and earth. Any current arising from a fault to earth anywhere on the power system must return via this connection and will operate the device. This arrangement can only be used at points near an earthed neutral, and it may be necessary to eliminate the effect, in the relay, of the third harmonic current liable to be present in some neutral-point earthing conditions.

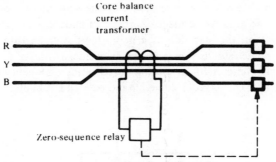

Fig. 2.1.2B *Zero-sequence relay connection using core balance current transformer*

The core-balance arrangement of Fig. 2.1.2B, can be used anywhere on a power system. Here the three phase conductors are passed through the opening of a core-balance transformer. Only if zero-sequence current is flowing will any resultant e.m.f in the transformer core produce a secondary current. It is important to ensure that in any application of this arrangement, no other conductor, such as a cable sheath, which may carry current is passed through the transformer; this may cause incorrect operation unless its effect is deliberately neutralised by bringing the sheath earthing conductor back through the transformer core opening.

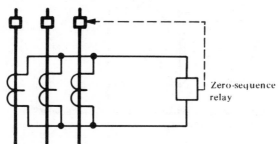

Fig. 2.1.2C *Zero-sequence relay connection using residual connection of line current transformers*

In Fig. 2.1.2C, which illustrates a current-balance system, each of the three conductors of the three phase system has a current transformer, and the secondaries of these are connected in residual connection, with a relay in the fourth wire. Only zero-sequence current in the main circuit will cause current in this 'fourth wire', and therefore tend to operate the relay. The use of this arrangement involves careful choice of relay burden and setting, but these points are dealt with in a later chapter.

(b)   *Negative-phase sequence networks:* Negative-sequence discrimination is sometimes necessary in unusual cases to secure otherwise unattainable discrimination. Negative-sequence currents occur only when system conditions are unbalanced, as between phases; and this is an indication of such system abnormalities as phase-to-phase faults other than three-phase faults, broken conductors, and zero-sequence currents in one winding of a power transformer appearing as negative sequence currents in another, for example a phase-to-earth fault on the star side of a delta/star power transformer appears as a phase-to-phase fault as seen from the delta side.

A typical circuit for measuring negative phase sequence current is shown in Fig. 2.1.2.D. This is considered in more detail in Chapter 12.

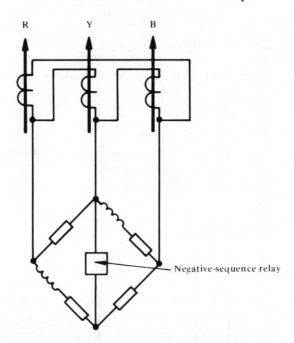

Fig. 2.1.2D   *Illustrating the use of phase shifting circuits to provide a negative phase-sequence current relay.*

(c)   *Positive-phase sequence networks:* It will be clear that it is possible to construct the inverse of negative-sequence networks which will be sensitive only to the positive-sequence components of the currents in a three-phase circuit, and protective devices based on such positive-sequence networks would not respond to negative-sequence conditions. They are used mainly to derive a reliable comparison quantity for phase comparison discriminating systems.

2.1.3 Combined overcurrent and earth fault relays

As shown earlier (Section 2.1.1.(*e*)), combinations of the time and distance discrimination methods achieve results not possible by using either by itself. Similarly, by combining fault type discrimination systems with systems discriminative to location of fault, the effectiveness of the protection can be greatly improved. Indeed, most of the practical protection schemes in later chapters are the result of such combinations.

A common combination is that of a zero-sequence device with current magnitude and time discrimination; and this produces the well known 'two-overcurrent and earth-fault' arrangement illustrated in Fig. 2.1.3A. Using two over-current relays and one zero-sequence relay, all with inherent time lag characteristics, this relatively simple arrangement will permit current magnitude discrimination for phase-to-phase and earth faults, with different time and current settings for the two types of fault.

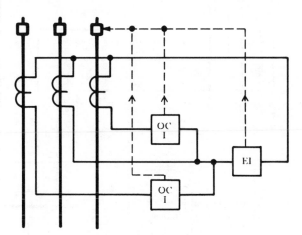

Fig. 2.1.3A *Combined overcurrent and earth-fault protection*

Most of the protective systems to be dealt with later give different settings for phase and earth faults. They include the Translay, Solkor and phase comparison systems. Distance relays invariably make a separate measurement for phase and earth faults using different relay connections in each case.

2.1.4 Derivation of a representative single-phase quantity from a three-phase system

With the longitudinal, differential comparison, discriminative methods, where an auxiliary channel is used to convey from one end to the other detailed 'information' of instantaneous current, the auxiliary channel illustrated was essentially single phase, so that in default of further treatment, three separate such channels would be needed to deal with a normal three-phase system. With a direct-wire channel this would involve high costs, and in the case of voice-frequency, carrier, or radio link channels, even when three channels are technically feasible, the cost and complexity are considerable.

The difficulty can be overcome by providing at each end of the auxiliary channel a means of deriving a single-phase quantity which under both normal and fault conditions will be representative of the three-phase conditions, thereby permitting comparison over a single channel.

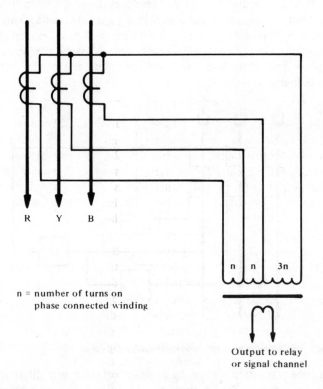

R   Y   B

n = number of turns on
phase connected winding

n n   3n

Output to relay
or signal channel

Fig. 2.1.4A *Use of auxilary summation transformer to provide single-phase output from a three-phase system of currents*

Fig. 2.1.4A shows a typical three-phase to single-phase conversion arrangement. It consists essentially of a summation transformer (an auxiliary current transformer) with a tapped primary winding connected to the three current transformers in the manner shown, together with a secondary winding suitable for the required duty. The output of the summation transformer for any given set of phase currents, I_R, I_Y and I_B, is dependent upon the relative numbers of turns on the three sections of the primary winding and is proportional to a fixed combination of the three phase currents. Thus, for the typical case shown the output is seen to be proportional to the algebraic sum of the phasors $5I_R + 4I_Y + 3I_B$ because the red-phase current can be considered to flow through $5n$ $(= n + n + 3n)$ turns, the yellow-phase current through $4n$ $(= n + 3n)$ turns and the blue-phase current through $3n$ turns.

Table 2.1.4.A

Type of fault	Relative output of summation transformer
R – E	$5I_f$
Y – E	$4I_f$
B – E	$3I_f$
R – Y or Y – B	I_f
R – B	$2I_f$
R – Y – B or R – Y – B – E	$\sqrt{3}I_f$

It will be evident, therefore, that the output obtained for a given type of fault and given phase-current magnitude is dependent on the particular phase or phases involved in the fault condition. Table 2.1.4A shows the relative magnitude of the output for a number of different types of fault, it being assumed that the summation transformer primary winding has a 1:1:3 turns distribution as in Fig. 2.1.4.A. The outputs given in the table ignore the effects of currents which might be present in the phases not involved in the fault condition.

The design of a summation transformer for a given application must be such as will ensure a satisfactory output under all the conditions to be catered for in service. It will be noted that the blue-to-neutral section of the summation transformer primary winding carries the c.t. residual current and is therefore only effective under earth-fault conditions. Hence, by giving a relatively large number of turns to the blue-to-neutral section of the winding, the sensitivity of the device to earth-faults, as compared with phase faults, can be increased as required. This feature is important in applications involving limited earth-fault current. The relative number of turns on to the blue-to-neutral section of the primary winding, compared with the red-to-yellow and yellow-to-blue sections, is also important in that insufficient turns on the blue-to-neutral section can result in a blue-phase earth-fault condition being masked by the currents flowing in the healthy red and yellow phases.

Considered in more general terms, a single phase relaying quantity may be derived from any combination of sequence currents. The advantage of using phase sequence components lies in the fact that, when the whole range of fault currents is considered, it is found that currents in non-faulted phases can give rise to low or misleading outputs from the single phase quantity. The use of a controlled proportion of sequence quantities permits these 'blind spots' to be avoided, and gives a control of output levels for different types of fault. Fig. 2.1.4.B illustrates the general principle of phase sequence network combinations showing the phase

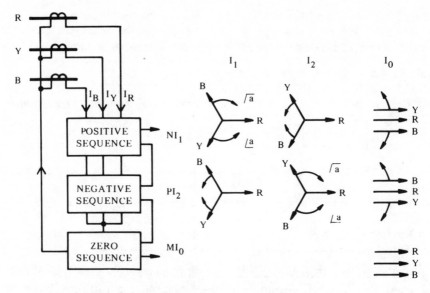

I_0, I_1, I_2 – Zero positive and negative sequence currents.

M, N, P – Proportions of I_0, I_1 and I_2 used for comparison signal.

I_R, I_Y, I_B – Phase currents.

$$\overline{a} = \underline{/\,120^\circ} \text{ operator } (-\frac{1}{2} + j\,\frac{\sqrt{3}}{2})$$

$$\underline{/a} = \overline{/a^2} = \underline{/\,240^\circ} \text{ operator } (-\frac{1}{2} - j\,\frac{\sqrt{3}}{2})$$

Fig. 2.1.4B *Use of combined phase-sequence current networks to provide single-phase output from a three-phase system of currents*

shifts necessary within the network to produce response only to the chosen sequence. Thus to measure positive sequence current:

Phasor I_Y must be advanced by $\underline{/120^\circ}$
Phasor I_B must be retarded by $\overline{/\,120^\circ}$

which ensures that output is only obtained for positive sequence currents.

Similarly, for negative sequence measurement

Phasor I_Y must be retarded by $\underline{/120^\circ}$
Phasor I_B must be advanced by $\overline{/120^\circ}$

giving an output only for negative sequence.

It will be seen in Chapter 10 that a relaying quantity of $NI_1 - PI_2$, where P/N is large gives a reliable output in both phase and magnitude for all types of system fault condition.

2.2   Components of protection

This Section gives an introduction to the wide range of components used to build up a protective system. Extensive description is not intended, as later chapters will deal more fully with most of the items. In the case of circuit-breakers only those features concerned with protection are described.

2.2.1   Relays

Originally, in telegraphy, a relay had a coil which was energised by a weak, received signal current, and this coil, attracting an armature, closed a contact in the line ahead, giving a 'relayed' signal of renewed 'strength'. Relays, which are at the heart of protective schemes, are now of many diverse designs, each aimed at achieving particular results. They are not nowadays exclusively electromagnetic in principle, and may often be solid state devices.

Relays associated with protection are divisible into two main groups. The first are relays designed to detect and to measure abnormal conditions, and having achieved this, to close contacts in an auxiliary circuit to cause some other function to take place. This type of relay is often called a 'comparator' as its function is to compare electrical quantities. The second group are auxiliary relays, designed to be connected in the auxiliary circuits controlled by the measuring relay contacts, and to close (or open) further contacts usually in much heavier current circuits. This second group is also called 'all or nothing' relays.

2.2.2   Current transformers

It will be clear from what has been said already that protection is concerned with the detection and measurement of fault currents in various system components. This measurement would be dangerous and expensive, and indeed impossible, to achieve if the actual load and fault currents, often very large, and at a very high voltage, had to be taken through the measuring relays. A practical way of overcoming these difficulties is to use current transformers. These make available from their secondary windings currents of manageable proportions which are replicas (within limits which will be discussed in Chapter 4) of the currents in the primary windings which carry the actual power system currents under normal and fault conditions.

The construction of current transformers in general follows the pattern of having a core of ferrous material which is magnetised by current in the primary winding — insulation appropriate for the system voltage is used between primary winding and core and secondary winding — inducing a current in a secondary winding having an appropriate number of turns.

Current transformers for protection are essentially similar to those used for the operation of ammeters, watthourmeters and other instruments. In the interests of standardisation nearly all such transformers are designed for a rated secondary current of either 5 A or 1 A.

Current transformers for measurement are not usually required to function (that is, the secondary current is not required to be a replica of the primary current) at current in excess of normal load, but for protection , because it is concerned with fault conditions, the current transformers must reproduce with acceptable accuracy the primary conditions on the secondary sides, both in magnitude and phase, up to much higher currents. This is dealt with more fully in later chapters.

In addition to these main current transformers, use is frequently made in protection of 'auxiliary' or 'interposing' current transformers as a convenient means of performing such functions as summing the secondary currents in more than one circuit.

2.2.3   Voltage transforming devices

In high voltage systems (that is, exceeding 650 V) it is not practicable to connect the voltage coils of protective devices direct to the system. It is necessary to transform the voltage down to a manageable value and also to insulate the protective equipment from the power system. Voltage transforming devices are designed to serve these purposes. For protection they do not differ appreciably from those commonly used for measurement; in fact, the same device usually serves both purposes, but often an additional secondary winding is needed for protection. The voltage on the secondary (relay) side is usually 110 V between phases and 63·5 V between phase and neutral.

For both measurement and protection the secondary voltage must be an exact reproduction in magnitude and phase of the primary voltage; but for protection the range of variation over which exact reproduction is needed is much wider than it need be for instruments.

The term 'voltage transforming device' embraces all the means for deriving a supply from a high voltage source for measurement and protection purposes. It includes specifically:

(i)   wound (electromagnetic) type voltage transformers

(ii)   capacitor voltage devices, which incorporate an electromagnetic unit.

(a)   *The wound-type voltage transformer* is virtually a small power transformer, from which it differs little in design and in appearance, especially in the three-phase pattern. At voltages higher than 33 kV it is usually made in single-phase units, to maintain phase segregation and because many forms of protection require a voltage transformer capable of reproducing the primary phase-to-earth voltage. This can be done very conveniently by combining three single-phase units, whereas special construction, that is a shell-type core or equivalent would be required in a three-phase type.

In the wound-type, outputs of up to 500 VA, which is adequate for all ordinary protection and measurement purposes, are easily obtained.

In this country, for safety reasons, voltage transformers at 132 kV and in some cases at lower voltages are fitted with Buchholz protectors. This complication is avoided in the capacitor voltage device, and partly for this reason the latter type replaces the wound-type at 275 kV and above.

(b)   *In capacitor voltage devices* the wound primary is replaced by a capacitor divider, but the secondary voltage is taken from the secondary winding of a conventional wound-type transformer with its primary winding connected between a tapping on the main (primary) capacitor and earth. The tapping is at a voltage of about 12 kV (measured with the wound transformer primary disconnected). The lower (earthed) capacitor, if necessary, with a capacitor across it, and a reactor in series with it, constitutes a tuned circuit which corrects the phase angle error (displacement) of the secondary voltage at system frequency.

In the United Kingdom, the capacitor voltage device has two important advantages; it obviates the need for a Buchholz protector, as safety considerations are adequately met without a Buchholz protector (there being neither oil in quantity, nor a high voltage winding); and secondly, the h.v. capacitors can be used for the dual purpose of voltage measurement and as injection channels for h.f. carrier-current protection schemes.

The output of a capacitor voltage device is determined largely by the value of capacitance adopted. For practical reasons this limits the output with reasonable accuracy to about 200 VA.

2.2.4   Capacitor dividers

One serious problem met with in the application of high speed distance protection is that the transient performance of capacitor v.t.s following fault inception can introduce serious errors in transformation.

These are mainly caused by the fact that the c.v.t is a device tuned to system frequency; the use of a capacitor divider eliminates this tuned circuit and gives accurate transient performance. The output circuit to the relays is still derived from the lower capacitor but is associated with a voltage amplifier to provide the correct voltage and power levels for relay equipment. This replaces the reactor and wound (electromagnetic) transformer unit of the conventional c.v.t.

2.2.5   H.F. capacitor couplers

H.F. capacitor couplers are used to couple the h.f. receivers and transmitters of carrier-current protective systems into a high voltage line at its terminations. They are something more than mere coupling capacitors, as they include means for tuning the coupling circuits to the frequency of the injected signal. Even when the capacitor portion forms part of a capacitor voltage device, the design and the capacitance values, and also the necessary 'surge' protection, are decided more by the requirements of the coupling function than by those of the capacitor voltage device. In this latter event it is described as a combined h.f. coupler and capacitor voltage device. Fig. 2.2.5.A shows a typical circuit with a combined unit in one leg and a straight coupler in the other; hence the two 'legs' referred to. Any one or more of the legs may include a voltage transforming function, as required by the protection or other measuring devices.

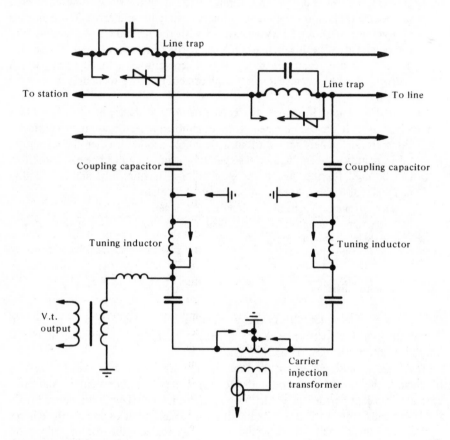

Fig. 2.2.5A *High-frequency line coupling equipment with capacitor voltage transformer*

2.2.6   Line traps

Fig. 2.2.5.A also shows line traps connected in series with the h.v. power line. Their purpose is to direct the h.f. signal along the line to the distant station and to prevent it from being dissipated in the terminal equipment, including adjacent lines, at each local end. To achieve this, the line trap is tuned by means of a parallel-connected capacitor to the frequency of the injected h.f. current, to which it then presents a high impedance, but a low impedance to power frequency current.

The line trap, consisting of an air-cored coil wound with stranded conductor, or equivalent, of cross-section adequate to carry the line load and short-circuit currents, is usually mounted with its integral tuning capacitor on top of the h.v. capacitor 'stack' of the coupler; but at 400 kV the size and weight of the trap make separate mounting desirable.

2.2.7 Circuit-breakers

To disconnect a fault from the power system, one or more circuit-breakers are required in conjunction with the protection.

It is outside the scope of this book to deal with the construction of circuit-breakers, but they all have certain features in common, some of which are of importance to the protection engineer.

The design of the opening mechanism is such that when opening (tripping) is required a trip coil is energised, which releases energy stored in the mechanism, thus causing the main contacts to part. The trip coil is usually energised from a battery by the closing of the protective relay contacts, either direct or via an auxiliary relay. For the smaller circuit-breakers where the operating current of the trip coil is not greater than the rating of the protective relay contacts, the protective relay would be used to energise the trip coil direct. When more than one breaker is to be tripped, or where the trip coil current is in excess of the relay-contact rating, an intermediate (auxiliary) relay having the necessary contact rating must be used.

Trip coils may be operated by either d.c. or a.c., the former is more usual the latter being sometimes employed on the less important distribution systems. In the U.K., the nominal tripping voltage is 110 or occasionally 240 V d.c. for the larger installatons (transmission and generating stations), and 30 V for the smaller distribution substations. Trip coils are highly inductive but when energised do not impose a very onerous duty on the relay contacts. Considerable damage would be done to these contacts, however, if they were arranged to break the trip coil current. In consequence, an auxiliary switch, operated by the circuit-breaker mechanical link mechanism, is connected in series with the trip coil and relay contacts. This auxiliary switch opens when the circuit-breaker opens, before the relay contacts open, and closes again as the circuit-breaker closes.

Auxiliary switches may also be used in the protection circuits, and in alarm and indication circuits. It is important to ensure that the sequence of make or break of the auxiliary switches, in relation to the circuit-breaker and relay contacts, is correct for the duty required.

Another matter which must be taken into account is the time for the breaker to open, that is the time interval between the trip coil being energised, and the arc being extinguished. This time is usually between 0·05 and 0·25 s, depending on the design of the breaker, and must be allowed for in calculating final fault clearance times.

2.2.8 Tripping and other auxiliary supplies

Because protective equipment must at all times be ready to remove faulty elements from power systems, it follows that its reliability cannot be too strongly emphasised. This reliability will not be achieved without an absolutely reliable source of supply to operate the circuit-breaker trip coils, and the related auxiliary relays concerned with tripping.

In generating stations and major substations, the source of tripping supplies is a nominal 110 V lead-acid battery of suitable ampere-hour capacity. Connected in parallel with the battery is a charger. At one time the charger comprised two sections, the first being sufficient for the standing load (for example indicating lamps) and for the normal losses of the battery (that is the trickle charge). The second section was separately switched and for use when boost charging. This type of charger has been superseded by the constant voltage charger which will automatically cater for heavy emergency drains on the battery.

The same battery may be used for tripping and closing, and in such cases the closing requirements usually dictate the ampere-hour rating of battery required. A typical rating for a substation with 132 kV bulk oil circuit-breakers solenoid operated is 250 Ah. If used for tripping only the rating might be 150 Ah.

In smaller substations the tripping supply is often derived from a 30 V lead-acid or nickel-iron battery. The latter is preferred because of its reduced maintenance needs. Such batteries may or may not be provided with continuous charging facilities.

It is usual to arrange for the whole tripping supply, including the battery and its charging means, to operate without a direct earth connection. The advantage in earthing the positive pole of a d.c. supply is that it reduces the risk of failure of fine wire relay coils as a result of electrolytic action. On the other hand, operating without an earth reduces the risk of loss of tripping supply arising from faults on the tripping circuits.

Negative biasing of the positive pole overcomes the electrolysis hazard of the unearthed battery. The principle of negative biasing will be clear from Fig. 2.2.8.A. The bias on a 110 V battery applied to its positive pole is about 30 V, with the result that the positive pole of the battery has a voltage of -30 to earth and the negative pole has a voltage of over -140 V to earth. The negative biasing scheme illustrated also provides earth-fault supervision of the d.c. wiring. The disadvantage of the scheme is that it increases the danger of auxiliary relays mal-operating for faults at F because the driving voltage in such cases is the actual battery voltage plus the bias voltage. It is possible to overcome this danger by ensuring that all auxiliary relays are designed not to operate under such conditions.

Where negative biasing is not employed, adequate supervision of the d.c. wiring can be achieved with the scheme shown in Fig. 2.2.8.B.

Where there are only one or two circuit-breakers to be tripped at any given location this can be achieved by deriving the tripping from an electrolytic capacitor normally kept energised from the local a.c. supply through a rectifier.

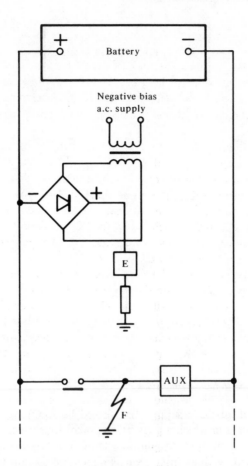

Fig. 2.2.8A *Negative biasing device with combined battery earth-fault alarm relay*

So important is the reliability of the tripping supply that arrangements are often made to supervise it so as to obtain early warning of failure. In one scheme, a separate 'trip supply healthy' indicating lamp is provided, either one per panel, or one per section of switchgear. In another, the circuit of the normal green 'breaker closed' lamp fulfils the same duty. The most comprehensive schemes employ relays of very high resistance with back contacts, that is those closing when the relay is de-energised, completing an alarm circuit. In unattended substations, the trip circuit supervision relay is arranged to give a 'trip-circuit faulty' alarm at the nearest attended point.

Ultimately, however, where the consequences of a failure of tripping are severe, as on the British Supergrid 400 kV and 275 kV systems, arrangements must be made for duplication of relaying equipment, tripping relays, circuit-breaker trip coils and, of course, tripping batteries so that two quite independent lines of tripping are available.

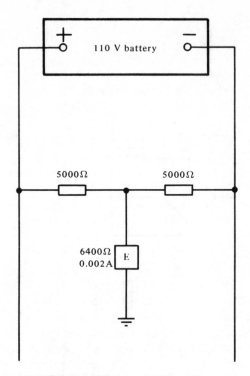

Fig. 2.2.8B   *Battery earth-fault alarm device*

Another form of auxiliary supply that should be mentioned is used for those forms of inter-tripping in which a relay at one point trips a local breaker and must also trip a remote one in order to remove a fault. This requires a pilot circuit, and in some arrangements such an inter-tripping circuit would result in paralleling the tripping supplies at the two separated stations. This is undesirable, because system earth-faults can impress high voltages momentarily between station earths, and if the tripping supplies are paralleled by a pilot circuit, the whole of the tripping circuits may thereby be subjected to a considerable or even hazardous voltage stress to earth, with consequent risk of breakdown. In such circumstances, therefore, the inter-trip circuit supply may be derived from a small independent unearthed and insulated battery.

2.2.9   Fuses, small wiring, terminals and test links

These components play an essential part in protection, and although seemingly 'pedestrian' in character, they must be carefully chosen, carefully installed, and well looked after if they are not to be sources of weakness in the maintenance of the reliability of the protection.

(*a*)   *Fuses:* Apart from the fuses which are themselves primary protection (see Chapter 5), fuses are used in protection for two main duties.

The first is in connection with a.c. voltage supplies, either derived from local 400 V circuits for various auxiliary purposes, or in connection with voltage supplies taken from voltage transformers for relays requiring such supplies, for example directional and distance relays. These fuses have the primary function of protecting the source of supply and the wiring from faults, and a secondary one of acting as a convenient means of isolating sub-circuits when testing or other work is in progress on a relay panel. The form of fuse and its holder must be of an intrinsically safe design and approved for the purpose.

The second use of fuses is in connection with tripping supply wiring, and here their function is similar to those just mentioned for a.c. circuits. Again, reliability is the prime requirement.

Rewireable type fuses were used for many years for the above functions, because they were more reliable than the early type of HRC cartridge fuse. The latter type, however, has now replaced the rewireable fuse in modern installations.

(b) *Small wiring:* 'Small wiring' is a term which covers the very large number of connections needed between relays, current and voltage transformers, trip coils and auxiliary circuits.

Panel wiring must be of high quality, and it must be so installed that it is not unduly strained and no risk of damage exists. Particular care should be given to points where the wiring passes across hinges to swing panels. Modern practice, used by both the Central Electricity Generating Board and Area Boards, proved reliable by long service, is to use for panel wiring either 32/0·20 mm or 7/0·67 mm stranded wire, depending on rating requirements. Included in the term 'small wiring' will be multicore cable runs, and these must also be protected from mechanical damage and the risk of penetration of moisture. Multicore conductor sizes are normally 7/0·67 mm diameter, but where conditions so require, 7/1·35 mm diameter, or two paralleled 7/1·35 mm conductors are used.

In large installations, the small wiring associated with protective gear alone is very extensive, and means of identification by the use of colours, or numbered ferrules, or both is a necessity for the task of checking every wire originally, in the tracing of any wiring faults which may later occur, and for any tests or modifications.

(c) *Terminals:* Of the very large number of terminations, every one needs to be numbered for identification, to avoid inadvertent earthing or energisation which could have disastrous results. Terminals must be mechanically strong enough not to shear, or to be otherwise damaged, when the nuts securing the terminations are being tightened. These requirements can be met by the use of 6, 5, 4 and 3 mm terminals.

Relays which are traditionally panel mounted and back connected often have many terminals. It is present practice to provide terminals at points where wires enter and leave relay panels, at the ends of multicore cables, and at points on switchgear where secondary connections enter and leave, or connect to the terminations of current and voltage transformers. All this seeming complexity has been found necessary for the tidy and safe installation and maintenance of this small wiring. The terminals themselves are usually grouped on standardised moulded terminal boards, the moulding being arranged to provide a barrier between terminals which are usually about 30 mm apart, so that the risk of inadvertent contact when working on the terminal board with spanners is minimised. Insulation type moulded blocks are also used.

(d)   *Test links:* a valuable feature found necessary for expeditious and trouble-free routing testing of protective gear is the provision of test links designed to permit the insertion of injection sets (portable adjustable sources of test current) into current circuits without risk of open-circuiting current transformers, which, besides, being dangerous on account of the high voltages which such open-circuiting can cause, also involves a risk of damage to the current transformers themselves, and of causing inadvertent operation of zero-sequence relays. Fig. 2.2.9.A shows a typical test link board. It will be seen that by manipulating the double links in turn the current transformer can be short-circuited and the test set put safely into the circuit. The covers of such test link boards should preferably be sealed against unauthorised interference, and should be clearly labelled to indicate the circuit with which they are connected.

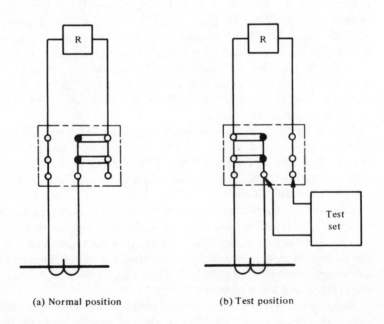

(a) Normal position   (b) Test position

Fig. 2.2.9A   *Illustrating the use of c.t. test links*

An alternative approach uses test blocks which perform a similar function but which also include 'built in' safeguards against wrong use.

With many of the highly complex primary circuit configurations now in use comprehensive protection testing can only be performed by using 'built in' disconnection points which provide a plug connection (or disconnection) facility between incoming and outgoing wires on the associated terminal block.

2.2.10   Pilot circuits

Reference has already been made to these as integral components of some forms of discriminative protection. There are four arrangements in common use.

The first is privately-owned pilot wires, which consist of metallic circuits, run in an auxiliary cable and often laid with the main cable to be protected. Alternatively, the pilot cable may be suspended from a catenary wire on wood poles. In either case the pilot cable may be exposed to high induced voltages.

The requirements for protection pilots are stringent in two particular respects. First, they must not break down between cores and sheath under fault conditions and secondly, induced voltages must not appear between cores to disturb the balance of the relaying signals under through fault conditions. Either of these factors will give rise to incorrect tripping under through fault conditions.

It follows, therefore, that a high insulation level must be provided between pilot cores and sheath and levels of 5 kV or 15 kV are standard, the higher level being used where pilots are in close proximity to the primary circuit. The use of fully transposed (i.e. twisted) pairs is also recommended for all protection functions to minimise induced voltages between cores.

Where high core to sheath voltages are possible, it is essential to provide similar insulation levels to earth on the relay equipment at each end. This is done preferably by using a pilot isolating transformer between relays and pilot wires (Fig. 2.2.10A) but, where undirectional signalling is used this insulation must be included directly in the relaying equipment.

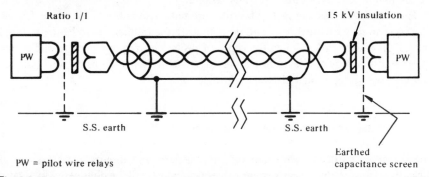

Fig. 2.2.10A   *Illustrating the use of pilot isolating transformers with differential protection*

The use of spark gap (or similar) protectors is not possible because, on operation, they short circuit the pilot wires which then precludes correct operation of the protection.

Privately-owned metallic circuits are a convenient arrangement for protection systems which require the transmission from end to end of a 'sample', both in magnitude and phase, of the current (longitudinal differential protection).

Circuits rented from the Post Office fall broadly into two categories; direct metallic circuits between ends over which some form of 50 Hz comparison may be possible, and audiofrequency communication circuits. The former may be used with special agreement for pilot wire differential protection whereas audiofrequency signalling is widely used for direct intertripping or distance protection signalling, and for phase comparison differential protection.

The Post Office impose limitations on current and voltage levels and require insulation between the secondary protective equipment and the Post Office line capable of withstanding momentarily 15 kV for 132 kV and higher voltage circuits, and 5 kV for 33 kV circuits, these being the values which might be impressed on the secondary equipment by the breakdown of primary insulation.

The third type of pilot circuit makes use of the power lines being protected, by using them as a channel for a superimposed high-frequency carrier current. This carrier current is generated, and detected, by electronic means. Carrier channels are extensively used for phase comparison systems and for distance protection signalling and direct intertripping.

The fourth type of pilot circuit is the microwave radio link. This is of value when other forms of pilot circuit are impracticable, or as emergency circuits when others fail. It can also be used to advantage where a line includes a long river crossing; in this case, not because it is necessarily superior to 'carrier' on the power line, but because the radio link will simultaneously provide multiple channels for telemetering and control which cannot always be obtained with 'carrier' channels. The equipment concerned consists of a line-of-sight radio circuit, if need be with repeater stations, working at very high or ultra-high frequency. As with 'carrier' there are electronic transmitters and receivers, and these are switched on as the protection and other services using the link require.

The use of radio links in Britain is not at present encouraged by the Home Office, who have to agree to such use, and who allocate the frequencies to be used. Radio links, like 'carrier', are suitable for types of protection requiring end-to-end signalling, as distinct from the transmission of current 'samples', as is required, for example, with longitudinal differential protection.

2.3   Consideration of the protection problem

The foregoing sections have examined, in a general and discursive way, some of those basic aspects of power system protection which will be considered in greater depth in subsequent chapters.

Before pursuing these matters in greater detail, however, it is helpful to summarise in general terms the kind of difficulties met with in providing a reliable protection system so that the particular elegance of individual methods may more readily be appreciated.

Because the 'protection problem' is most intractable in the context of high speed fault clearance for large interconnected power systems, this will be the major consideration in the following summary though, of course, many of these problems will arise to some degree for slower protection for smaller power systems.

The basic objective of power system protection is to maintain continuity of supply which it does by rapid and discriminative isolation of faulted items of plant from the rest of the system thereby reducing damage to the plant itself and also reducing the effect of the faulted item of plant upon the rest of the system.

The requirement of the protection equipment, therefore, is to pass an operating signal to the tripping coil of a circuit breaker in the event of a power system fault legitimately within the zone of protection controlled by that equipment. For large power systems where system stability is at risk the detection must take place within one or two cycles of the inception of the fault (i.e. 20 - 40 ms).

In order to determine the location of the fault, the protection scheme must make a comparison of the a.c. quantities available at the time of fault, and the protective relay setting must be such that it can detect the difference between fault conditions required to cause operation and all other external fault or normal healthy system conditions for which operation must not take place. This difference is known as the discrimination margin and there are many factors which tend to reduce it, and thereby to invalidate the provision of fully discriminative protection.

(*a*)   The fault represents a sudden discontinuity; there is, therefore, no guidance available from previous history, and relaying quantities must be measured during the transient fault period.

(*b*)   Comparison of relaying quantities must be completed at high speed, typically within one cycle (20 ms) of fault inception.

(*c*)   The fault current waveform during this transient period is unpredictable, particularly with regard to the degree of exponential and harmonic components present.

(*d*)   Conventional current and voltage transducers possess inherent errors in transformation during the first cycle. These are not readily predictable.

(*e*)   Because of widely varying load and generation conditions on the power system the protection must effect its comparison over a large range of current (and voltage) levels.

(*f*)   Availability and performance of communication channels imposes limitations on protection performance. Normally, only a single phase quantity derived from the three-phase system can be transmitted, which may result in loss of discriminative information.

(*g*)   Signalling levels must be limited to values acceptable to the telephone company and others to prevent unacceptable interference. When considered in relation to the high noise levels often associated with the power system

Table 2.3.A

	Apparatus protection - Differential	Line protection - Distance	Line protection - Differential
Power system quantities	Simple fault conditions confined to apparatus being protected. Special factors - magnetising inrush, tap changing.	Complex fault conditions - Intercircuit faults, mutual induction, fault resistance, line capacitance, system X/R, source impedance, maximum circuit loads, power swings, multiended circuits.	
Transformation devices	Balanced current system permits design of relay circuit to permit controlled CT saturation.	CTs must not saturate under balance point conditions - errors proportional to CT errors. VTs must not produce spurious output for high speed protection.	CTs must be similar at all ends - controlled saturation permissible under through fault conditions for 2 ended circuit. Limits determined by heavy current testing.
Derivation of relaying quantities	Separate comparison of three phase currents in phase and amplitude.	Local derivation of relaying quantities proportional to voltage, current and phase angle to give optimum output to comparator.	Use of summation device to give single-phase relaying quantity. Often restricted to phase angle only.
Comparators	Usually simple level detector. Comparator required only for load and harmonic bias features on transformer circuits.	Comparator characteristic requires optimisation with signal quantities to give ideal shaped zone of protection. Multi-input comparators Use of logic and sampling techniques.	Comparator characteristic requires correlation with summation device. Present methods use phase comparison principles extensively.
Communication	Fundamental frequency current comparison over short pilot circuits.	High speed protection requires use of a command signal over pilot circuit or carrier channel. D.C. over short pilot circuits, coded high frequency over carrier channels and long pilot circuits.	Information derived from power system quantities. Fundamental frequency over pilot circuit. Modulated carrier signal for longer lines.
Logical decisions	Complex logic system required for tripping particularly for busbar protection.	Comprehensive logic functions within the protection scheme. Simple tripping logic.	Simple logic for pilot wire protection. More complex for carrier system. Tripping logic straightforward.

fault, this tends to give an unfavourable signal/noise ratio for the communication channel.

(*h*) The high fault currents produced by the power system fault return to the substation earth electrode system in close proximity to the low current secondary wiring associated with protection circuits. Protection equipment must, be designed to be immune from the mutual coupling effects of these currents.

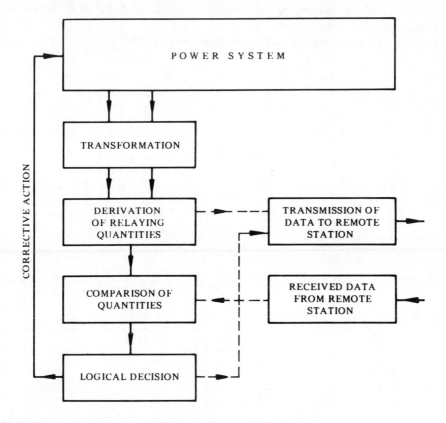

Fig. 2.3A *Summary of requirements for high-speed protection systems*

The impact of all these additional disturbing influences must be taken into account in the design and application of protective systems.

Fig. 2.3A summarises in a generalised form the more important aspects of the protection process and Table 2.3.A itemises important design considerations in meeting practical requirements for some of the more widely used forms of main protection.

Subsequent chapters will describe in detail the implications of many of these problems and will show how modern protection practice contrives acceptable solutions.

2.4   Bibliography

Books

Protective relays: their theory and practice (2 Vols) by A R Van C Warrington (Chapman & Hall, 3rd Ed., 1977)
Protective relays application guide (GEC Measurements, 1975)

Chapter 3

Fault calculation

by J.H.Naylor

3.1 Introduction

3.1.1 Purpose of fault calculation

Fault calculation is the analysis of power system electrical behaviour under fault conditions, with particular reference to the effects of these conditions on the power system current and voltage values. Together with other aspects of system analysis, fault calculation forms an indispensable part of the whole function and process of power system design. Correct design depends essentially on a full knowledge and understanding of system behaviour and on the ability to predict this behaviour for the complete range of possible system conditions. Accurate and comprehensive analysis, and the means and methods of achieving it, are therefore of essential importance in obtaining satisfactory power system performance and in ensuring the continued improvement in performance which results from the development and application of new methods and techniques.

The applications of power system analysis cover the full range of possible system conditions, these being divisible into two main classes, namely conditions in which the power system is operating in a normal healthy state, and others in which it is subjected to one or more of a wide variety of possible fault conditions. The analysis of these conditions and their effects on the power system is of particular relevance to such considerations as:

(a) the choice of a suitable power system arrangement, with particular reference to the configuration of the transmission or distribution network
(b) the determination of the required load and short-circuit ratings of the power system plant
(c) the determination of the breaking capacity required of the power system switchgear and fusegear
(d) the design and application of equipment for the control and protection of the power system
(e) the operation of the system, with particular reference to security of supply and economic considerations

(*f*)   the investigation of unsatisfactory performance of the power system or of individual items of power system plant.

The present chapter is concerned principally with the analysis of system fault conditions, these conditions being of direct and particular relevance to the design and application of power system protection. The methods of analysis employed, however, are essentially applications of general analysis and, as such have equal application to a wide range of other problems whose solution is dependent on electrical network analysis.

3.1.2   Types of fault

In the context of electrical fault calculation, a power system fault may be defined as any condition or abnormality of the system which involves the electrical failure of primary equipment, the reference to primary (as opposed to ancillary) equipment implying equipment such as generators, transformers, busbars, overhead lines and cables and all other items of plant which operate at power system voltage. Electrical failure generally implies one or the other (or both) of two types of failure, namely insulation failure resulting in a short-circuit condition or conducting-path failure resulting in an open-circuit condition, the former being by far the more common type of failure.

The principal types of fault are listed and classified in Table 3.1.2A, and are discussed in greater detail below.

Table 3.1.2A   *Types of fault*

Short-circuited phases	Three-phase fault clear of earth Three-phase-to-earth fault Phase-to-phase fault Single-phase-to-earth fault Two-phase-to-earth fault Phase-to-phase plus single-phase-to-earth fault
Open-circuited phases	Single-phase open-circuit Two-phase open-circuit Three-phase open-circuit
Simultaneous faults	A combination of two or more faults at the same time, the faults being of similar or dissimilar type and occurring at the same or different locations. Typical examples are the cross-country earth-fault and the open-circuit-with-earth-fault condition
Winding faults	Winding-to-earth short-circuit Winding-to-winding short-circuit Short-circuited turns Open-circuited winding

Short-circuited phases: Faults of this type are caused by insulation failure between phase conductors or between phase conductors and earth, or both, the result being the short-circuiting of one or more phases to earth or to one another, or both. The full range of possible fault conditions of this type is illustrated in Fig. 3.1.2A. The three-phase fault, which may be to earth or clear of earth, is the only balanced or symmetrical short-circuit condition, the presence or absence of the earth connection being normally of little or no significance unless the fault occurs simultaneously with a second unbalanced fault involving earth. The three-phase short-circuit is commonly used as a standard fault condition as, for example, in the determination of system fault-levels, these levels being normally quoted as three-phase short-circuit values.

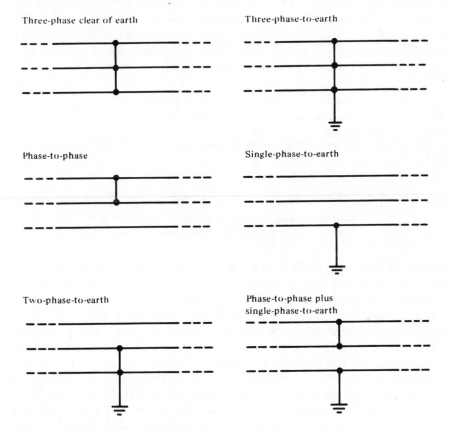

Three-phase clear of earth

Three-phase-to-earth

Phase-to-phase

Single-phase-to-earth

Two-phase-to-earth

Phase-to-phase plus single-phase-to-earth

Fig. 3.1.2A   *Short-circuited-phase faults*

Open-circuited phases: This type of fault, illustrated in Fig. 3.1.2B, is the failure of one or more phases to conduct. The more common causes of this type of fault are joint failures on overhead lines and cables, and the failure of one or more phases of a circuit-breaker or isolator to open or close. The single-phase and two-phase conditions are of particular interest because they both tend to produce unbalance of the power system currents and voltages with consequent risk of damage to rotating plant.

Simultaneous faults: A simultaneous fault condition, sometimes termed a multiple fault condition, is defined as the simultaneous presence of two or more faults of similar or dissimilar types at the same or different points on the power system. Such conditions may result from a common cause, from different but consequential causes or, extremely rarely, from quite separate and independent causes. The commonest simultaneous fault condition is undoubtedly the double-circuit overhead-line fault in which a common cause (for example lightning or accidental contact) results in a fault on each of the two circuits concerned. These

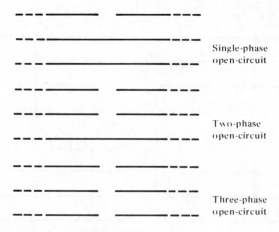

Fig. 3.1.2B   *Open-circuited-phase faults*

two faults, although possibly geographically coincident, will be electrically separate to an extent determined by the point of fault and the particular power system configuration. A simultaneous fault condition of particular interest is that known as the cross-country earth-fault, in which a single-phase-to-earth fault at one point in the power system occurs coincidentally with a second single-phase-to-earth fault on another phase and at some other point in the system. This condition is most commonly experienced on impedance-earthed systems where the second earth-fault may be initiated by the increased healthy-phase voltage resulting from the neutral displacement produced by the first. As already stated, a simultaneous fault condition may consist of two different types of fault at the same point, and one example of this is the open-circuit-with-earth-fault condition in which two faults, namely a single-phase open-circuit and a single-phase-to earth fault, occur coincidentally on the same phase and at the same point in the power system. Such a condition can occur on an overhead line for example, due to a phase conductor breaking at a point near to a tower, the conductor on the tower side of the break being held by the suspension insulator and that on the other side falling to ground.

The fault conditions described are divisible into two distinct classes, namely balanced or symmetrical fault conditions and unbalanced or unsymmetrical fault conditions, the former class comprising all conditions which are symmetrical with respect to the three phases and the latter class the remainder. Of the faults listed. only the three-phase short circuit (to earth or clear of earth) and the three-phase open-circuit are balanced fault conditions, the normal balanced three-phase load condition being a further example of the balanced or symmetrical condition.

Winding faults: The types of fault which can occur on machine and transformer windings are illustrated in Fig. 3.1.2C and consist mainly of short-circuits, from one phase winding to earth, from one phase winding to another or from one point to another on the same phase winding. The last mentioned condition is known as a short-circuited turns fault, and is of particular interest from the protection standpoint in that the fault current in the short-circuited turns may be very large and that in the remainder of the winding very small. The open-circuited winding condition is quite rare in practice and is usually the result of damage to the winding as a consequence of a preceding winding short-circuit at or near the point of fault. Open circuits in transformers may also occur as a result of failure of the tap-change equipment.

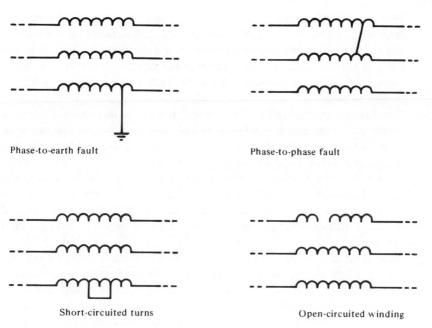

Phase-to-earth fault   Phase-to-phase fault

Short-circuited turns   Open-circuited winding

Fig. 3.1.2C   *Winding faults*

Changing-fault conditions: The types of fault which have been referred to can all be regarded as fixed fault conditions, in that the type of fault remains unchanged for the duration of the fault. The great majority of fault conditions are of this type but there are others, known as changing-fault conditions, in which the type of fault changes during the course of the fault. Such changing-fault conditions can result from a number of causes, the most common being the spreading of a fault arc, or of the ionised gases from a fault arc, to other phases and even to other circuits. A typical example is a single-phase-to-earth fault which develops into a two-phase-to-earth fault and possibly, later, into a three-phase fault. The analysis of a changing fault condition presents no particular difficulty, since the condition can be considered as a succession of fixed fault conditions, each of which can be analysed individually.

3.1.3   Factors affecting fault severity

The severity of a power system fault condition may be assessed in terms of the disturbance produced and the fault damage caused, the magnitude of the fault current and its duration being of particular interest, especially in relation to the design and application of power system protection. The factors which affect fault severity must therefore be given due consideration in all aspects of power system analysis in order to ensure results which are truly representative of the conditions which can occur in practice. The factors which normally require to be considered are:

(*a*)   *Source conditions:* These relate to the amount and disposition of all connected generation (including all other power sources such as interconnections with other systems), the two extremes of minimum and maximum connected plant being of particular interest. The minimum and maximum plant conditions are normally those corresponding to the conditions of minimum and maximum connected load.

(*b*)   *Power system configuration:* This is determined by the items of plant, namely generators, transformers, overhead-line and cable circuits etc., assumed to be in service for the particular condition being investigated and by such other factors as have a bearing on the topology of the equivalent system network. The system configuration may change during the course of a fault with consequent changes in the magnitude and distribution of the fault current, typical causes being the sequential tripping of the circuit-breakers at the two ends of a faulted transmission line and the sequential clearance of multiple fault conditions.

(*c*)   *Neutral earthing:* Faults which involve the flow of earth current (for example, a single-phase or two-phase fault to earth, a single-phase or two-phase open circuit, etc.) may be influenced considerably by the system neutral-earthing arrangements, particularly by the number of neutral earthing points and the presence or absence of neutral earthing impedances. Power systems may be single-point or multiple-point earthed and such earthing may be direct (that is, solid earthing) or via impedance, typical examples being the direct multiple-earthing employed on the British 132 kV, 275 kV and 400 kV systems and the single-point and sometimes multiple-point resistance-earthing commonly employed at 66 kV and below. Earthing impedance can be used to limit the earth-fault current to a very low and even negligibly small value, as in the case of a system earthed through a Petersen coil or a generator earthed through a voltage transformer.

(d) *Nature and type of fault:* From what has already been said, it will be evident that the type of fault and its position in the power system may have a considerable effect on the magnitude and distribution of the system fault current, this being particularly the case in respect of earth-faults as compared with phase faults, open-circuits as compared with short-circuits and faults within machine and transformer windings as compared with similar faults at the winding phase-terminals. Similarly, the effects of a given fault condition may be considerably modified by the simultaneous presence of one or more other fault conditions as, for example, in the combination of a short-circuit and an open-circuit phase condition. A further factor which may require consideration is the possible effect of fault impedance (for example, fault-arc resistance and the ohmic resistance of any metallic or non-metallic fault path, etc.), this being of particular importance in matters relating to the design and application of distance protection.

The wide range of possible system fault conditions and the many factors which influence them result in a wide range of possible levels of fault severity, ranging from extremely low levels up to the maximum levels possible for the system being considered. It is therefore of value, in referring to fault severity generally, to be able to refer to a standard fault condition, namely the three-phase short-circuit, and to the level of fault severity produced by this particular fault condition, namely the three-phase fault level. This level may be expressed in amperes or, as is more usual, in three-phase MVA corresponding to the rated system voltage and the symmetrical value of the three-phase fault current. The three-phase short-circuit can normally be regarded as the most severe condition from the point of view of fault severity, and it is accordingly the maximum possible value of the three-phase fault level which normally determines the required short-circuit rating of the power-system switchgear. A factor which may also have to be taken into account is the maximum value of the single-phase-to-earth fault current which, in a solidly-earthed system, may exceed the maximum three-phase fault current.

The three-phase fault levels experienced in this country range up to 35 MVA at the lowest distribution voltage of 415 V up to some 35 000 MVA at the highest supergrid transmission voltage of 400 kV, the maximum fault current in the latter case being of the order of 50 000 A for a three-phase fault and 60 000A for a single-phase-to-earth fault. Fault clearance times range from less than a tenth of a second to one second or more depending on the protective arrangements employed, low clearance times being of particular importance at the higher fault levels.

3.1.4 Methods of fault calculation

The information normally required from a fault calculation is that which gives the values of the currents and voltages at stated points in the power system when the latter is subjected to a given fault condition, the fault location and system operating conditions being specified. Fault calculation is therefore essentially a matter of network analysis and can be achieved by a number of alternative methods, namely:

(a)   direct solution of the network equations obtained from the mesh-current or nodal-voltage methods,

(b)   solution by network reduction and back-substitution and,

(c)   solution by simulation using a fault calculator or network analyser.

The choice of method will normally depend on the size and complexity of network and on the amount of information required from the analysis, a further important factor being the availability of suitable computing facilities. Direct solution of the network equations is now commonly employed using suitable digital-computer facilities and appropriate computer programs, such use of the computer making it possible to study a wide range of system and fault conditions speedily and economically, particularly in the case of the larger networks.

Solution by network reduction using manual (that is slide rule or desk-calculator computation) is widely used for such problems as involve, or can be represented by, a network of limited size and complexity, there being a large number of fault calculations which fall into this class. Its use in more complicated cases, however, is limited only by the amount of time required to obtain a solution, the cost of such time being a not altogether unimportant consideration. Solution by simulation using a fault calculator or network analyser has the advantage of simplicity of application due to the one-to-one correspondence between the real and the simulated system, but although widely used in the past, prior to the advent of computer methods, its use is now generally limited to smaller networks and to situations where computer facilities may not be readily available.

An essential part of power system analysis and fault calculation is that which concerns the determination of the equivalent system network for the system operating conditions and fault conditions under consideration. As already seen, the fault conditions to be analysed normally fall into one or other of two classes, namely balanced or symmetrical fault conditions (for example the three-phase short-circuit) and unbalanced or unsymmetrical fault conditions, the latter class being normally analysed by the symmetrical-component method. As will be seen later, both classes of fault are analysed by reducing the power system, with its fault condition, to an equivalent single-phase network.

3.2   Basic principles of network analysis

3.2.1   Fundamental network laws

The great majority of fault calculations are concerned with the behaviour of the power system under steady-state conditions or conditions which, from the point of view of analysis, may be regarded as steady-state conditions. It can also usually be assumed that all the power system currents and voltages vary sinusoidally with time at a common constant frequency and can therefore be treated as vector quantities and be expressed, together with the power system impedances and admittances, in complex-number form.

The relationship between the currents, voltages and impedances in any linear network is governed by the three basic network laws, namely Ohm's Law and the two laws of Kirchhoff, a formal statement of these laws in terms of vector quantities being given below.

Ohm's Law: Ohm's Law states that the vector voltage drop V produced by a vector current I flowing through a complex impedance Z is given by the vector equation

$$V = IZ \qquad\qquad 3.2.1.1$$

An alternative form is

$$I = VY \qquad\qquad 3.2.1.2$$

where Y is the reciprocal of Z and is the complex admittance. The law is illustrated in Fig. 3.2.1A from which it will be noted that the sense of the voltage-drop V is in opposition to that of the current I.

Kirchhoff's First Law: Kirchhoff's First Law states that the vector sum of all the currents entering any junction or node in a network is zero or, stated in equation form

$$\sum_i I_i = 0 \qquad\qquad 3.2.1.3$$

where I_i is the vector current flowing into the node from branch i, the summation extending over all the branches connected to the node. Outflowing currents with respect to the node are simply treated as negative inflowing currents.

The law, also known as the Junction Law is illustrated in Fig. 3.2.1B.

Kirchhoff's Second Law: Kirchhoff's Second Law states that the vector sum of all the driving voltages (that is source voltages) acting round any closed path or mesh in a network is equal to the vector sum of the voltage drops in the impedances of the component branches of the path. Thus, in equation form

$$\sum_i E_i = \sum_i I_i Z_i \qquad\qquad 3.2.1.4$$

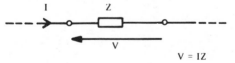

$$V = IZ$$

Fig. 3.2.1A   *Ohm's Law*

where E_i is the vector driving voltage in branch i, I_i the vector current in the branch and Z_i the complex impedance of the branch, the summation extending over all the component branches of the path or mesh. The driving voltages and currents must all be measured in the same direction round the path. Expressed in another way, the law simply states that the vector sum of all the voltages (that is driving voltages and voltage drops) acting round a closed path or mesh is zero.

The law, illustrated in Fig. 3.2.1C, is also known as the Mesh Law.

These three basic network laws applied to the branches, nodes and meshes of any linear network (that is, a network in which the impedances are constant and independent of the currents through them), enable the branch currents to be found if the branch driving voltages and branch impedances are known.

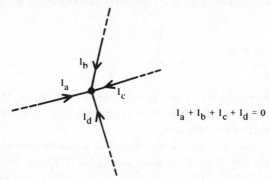

$$I_a + I_b + I_c + I_d = 0$$

Fig. 3.2.1B   *Kirchhoff's First Law*

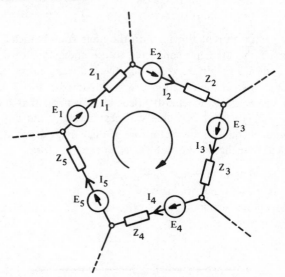

$$E_1 + E_2 + E_3 + E_4 + E_5 = I_1 Z_1 + I_2 Z_2 + I_3 Z_3 + I_4 Z_4 + I_5 Z_5$$

Fig. 3.2.1C   *Kirchhoff's Second Law*

As a simple example consider the elementary two-machine system shown in Fig. 3.2.1D and comprising a generator and a synchronous motor, the former represented by a driving voltage of $118 + j24$ V behind an impedance of $1 + j4$ Ω and the latter by a driving voltage of $100 + j0$ V behind an impedance of $2 + j5$ Ω. The current flowing from the generator to the motor is $3 - j1$ A, and this satisfies Kirchhoff's Second Law because the total voltage drop in the path is

$(3 - j1)(3 + j9)$ V, that is $18 + j24$ V, this being equal to the total driving voltage acting round the path, namely $118 + j24$ V minus $100 + j0$ V.

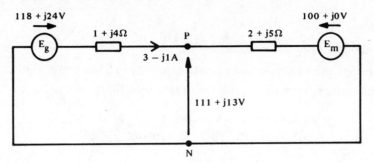

Fig. 3.2.1D

Assume now that a short-circuit occurs at the generator terminals, this short-circuit path having an impedance of $1 + j0$ Ω. The conditions are then as shown in Fig. 3.2.1E where I_1 is the current from the generator, I_2 the current from the motor (now acting as a generator) and I_3 the current through the impedance of the short-circuit path.

It is required to determine I_1, I_2 and I_3, and hence applying Kirchhoff's First Law we obtain the equation

$$I_1 + I_2 - I_3 = 0 \qquad 3.2.1.5$$

while application of the Second Law to each of the two meshes in turn gives the equations

$$(1 + j4)I_1 + (1 + j0)I_3 = 118 + j24 \qquad 3.2.1.6$$
$$(2 + j5)I_2 + (1 + j0)I_3 = 110 + j0 \qquad 3.2.1.7$$

the first of these equations relating to the generator mesh and the second to the motor mesh.

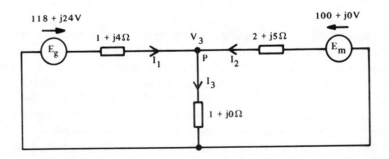

Fig. 3.2.1E

Eliminating I_3 from eqns. 3.2.1.6 and 3.2.1.7 by use of eqn. 3.2.1.5, we obtain the two equations

$$(2 + j4)I_1 + (1 + j0)I_2 = 118 + j24 \qquad\qquad 3.2.1.8$$
$$(1 + j0)I_1 + (3 + j5)I_2 = 110 + j0 \qquad\qquad 3.2.1.9$$

these being a pair of simultaneous equations in the two unknowns I_1 and I_2.

Eliminating I_2 from these equations so as to solve for I_1 we obtain

$$[(3 + j5)(2 + j4) - (1 + j0)(1 + j0)] I_1$$
$$= [(3 + j5)(118 + j24) - (1 + j0)(100 + j0)]$$

which reduces to

$$(-15 + j22)I_1 = 134 + j662$$

giving

$$I_1 = 17 \cdot 7 - j18 \cdot 1 \text{ A}$$

The value of I_1 can now be used in eqn. 3.2.1.9 to obtain I_2, thus

$$I_2 = \frac{(100 + j0) - (1 + j0)(17 \cdot 7 - j18 \cdot 1)}{3 + j5}$$

$$= \frac{82 \cdot 3 + j18 \cdot 1}{3 + j5}$$

giving

$$I_2 = 9 \cdot 9 - j10 \cdot 5 \text{A}$$

Finally, substituting the values of I_1 and I_2 in eqn. 3.2.1.5 gives

$$I_3 = 27 \cdot 6 - j28 \cdot 6 \text{ A}$$

The voltage at the point of fault, namely the product of I_3 and Z_3, is seen to be

$$V_3 = (27 \cdot 6 - j28 \cdot 6)(1 + j0)$$

giving

$$V_3 = 27 \cdot 6 - j28 \cdot 6 \text{ V}$$

This simple example has been solved by treating the network branch currents as the unknowns in the network equations, and while this is obviously the most direct approach, it nevertheless suffers from certain disadvantages if the number of meshes in the network is at all large. These disadvantages stem from the fact that the number of unknowns, namely the branch currents, will generally be larger than is necessary for the solution of the problem and that the equations containing these unknowns will not generally be amenable to a systematic method of solution. To avoid these difficulties, network analysis is better carried out using mesh-current analysis and nodal-voltage analysis. These methods are briefly described in the following two Sections.

3.2.2 Mesh-current analysis

This method of analysis can be understood by considering the simple network shown in Fig. 3.2.2A. It will be noted that each mesh of the network is assumed to carry a circulating current, and it is these so-called mesh currents which are treated as the unknowns in the problem, the current in any given branch being readily obtained once the mesh currents associated with that branch have been determined. Because the mesh currents associated with any given node flow through that node it can easily be seen that they satisfy Kirchhoff's First Law. We can therefore proceed to write down the equations which result from application of the Second Law, there being one such equation for each mesh of the network.

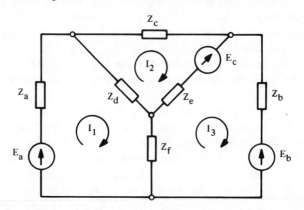

Fig. 3.2.2A   *Mesh-current notation*

Thus, remembering that the current in any branch is the vector sum (taking due account of direction) of the mesh currents flowing in that branch, we obtain the following equations for meshes 1, 2 and 3, respectively:

$$\left. \begin{aligned} Z_a I_1 + Z_d(I_1 - I_2) + Z_f(I_1 - I_3) &= E_a \\ Z_d(I_2 - I_1) + Z_c I_2 + Z_e(I_2 - I_3) &= -E_c \\ Z_f(I_3 - I_1) + Z_e(I_3 - I_2) + Z_b I_3 &= E_c - E_b \end{aligned} \right\} \qquad 3.2.2.1$$

Rearranging these equations in a more systematic form, we obtain

$$\left. \begin{aligned} Z_{11} I_1 + Z_{12} I_2 + Z_{13} I_3 &= E_1 \\ Z_{21} I_1 + Z_{22} I_2 + Z_{23} I_3 &= E_2 \\ Z_{31} I_1 + Z_{32} I_2 + Z_{33} I_3 &= E_3 \end{aligned} \right\} \qquad 3.2.2.2$$

where

$$\left. \begin{aligned} Z_{11} &= Z_a + Z_d + Z_f \\ Z_{22} &= Z_c + Z_d + Z_e \\ Z_{33} &= Z_b + Z_e + Z_f \end{aligned} \right\} \qquad 3.2.2.3$$

$$Z_{12} = Z_{21} = -Z_d$$
$$Z_{23} = Z_{32} = -Z_e \qquad\qquad 3.2.2.4$$
$$Z_{31} = Z_{13} = -Z_f$$

$$E_1 = E_a$$
$$E_2 = -E_c \qquad\qquad 3.2.2.5$$
$$E_3 = E_c - E_b$$

It will be noted that Z_{11} is the sum of the impedances of the branches forming mesh 1, Z_{22} the sum of those forming mesh 2, and Z_{33} the sum of those forming mesh 3. It will also be noted that Z_{12}, equal to Z_{21}, is equal to minus the branch impedance common to meshes 1 and 2, that Z_{23}, equal to Z_{32}, is equal to minus the branch impedance common to meshes 2 and 3, and Z_{31}, equal to Z_{13}, is equal to minus the branch impedance common to meshes 3 and 1. Finally it will be noted that E_1 is the sum of the driving voltages in the branches forming mesh 1, E_2 the sum of those in the branches forming mesh 2, and E_3 the sum of those in the branches forming mesh 3. It should be noted that the branch driving voltages are treated as positive when they act in the same direction as the mesh current in the mesh to which the equation refers, namely, in a clockwise direction, and are treated as negative when they act in the opposite, anti-clockwise direction.

Eqns. 3.2.2.2 are a set of three simultaneous equations in the three unknown mesh currents I_1, I_2 and I_3 and it will be evident that the general case of a network of n meshes will result in a similar set of n simultaneous equations in terms of the n unknown mesh currents. Knowing the branch driving-voltages and impedances, this set of equations can be virtually written down by inspection from the rules already given. The solution of these equations to obtain the mesh currents can be achieved by a number of different methods, each branch current being then obtained from its component mesh currents.

3.2.3. Nodal-voltage analysis

In this method of analysis one of the network nodes is chosen as the reference node and the voltages of the remaining nodes, measured with respect to the reference node, are treated as the unknowns in the problem. The voltage across any branch of a given mesh is equal to the difference between the node voltages at the two ends of the branch in question. It is seen, therefore, that the summation of the component branch voltages round the mesh must be zero because the node voltages, whose difference constitutes any given branch voltage, will be cancelled out in the summation by the contributions which the same node voltages, but reversed in sign, make to the voltages across the adjacent branches of the mesh. The node voltages thus satisfy Kirchhoff's Second Law and we can therefore proceed to apply the First Law to each node of the network, in turn, with the single excepton of the reference node.

Thus, for the simple network shown in Fig. 3.2.3A, we obtain the following equations for nodes 1, 2 and 3, respectively:

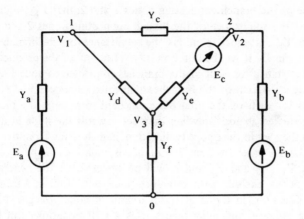

Fig. 3.2.3A *Nodal-voltage notation*

$$
\left.
\begin{array}{l}
(0 + E_a - V_1)Y_a + (V_2 - V_1)Y_c + (V_3 - V_1)Y_d = 0 \\
(0 + E_b - V_2)Y_b + (V_2 - V_2)Y_c + (V_3 + E_c - V_2)Y_e = 0 \\
(0 - V_3)Y_f + (V_1 - V_3)Y_d + (V_2 - E_c - V_3)Y_e = 0
\end{array}
\right\} \qquad 3.2.3.1
$$

It will be noted that these equations are written in terms of the branch admittances as compared with the branch impedances used in the mesh-current method of analysis.

Rearranging the equations in a more systematic form, we obtain

$$
\left.
\begin{array}{l}
Y_{11}V_1 + Y_{12}V_2 + Y_{13}V_3 = I_1 \\
Y_{21}V_1 + Y_{22}V_2 + Y_{23}V_3 = I_2 \\
Y_{31}V_1 + Y_{32}V_2 + Y_{33}V_3 = I_3
\end{array}
\right\} \qquad 3.2.3.2
$$

where

$$
\left.
\begin{array}{l}
Y_{11} = Y_a + Y_c + Y_d \\
Y_{22} = Y_b + Y_c + Y_e \\
Y_{33} = Y_d + Y_e + Y_f
\end{array}
\right\} \qquad 3.2.3.3
$$

$$
\left.
\begin{array}{l}
Y_{12} = Y_{21} = -Y_c \\
Y_{23} = Y_{32} = -Y_e \\
Y_{31} = Y_{13} = -Y_d
\end{array}
\right\} \qquad 3.2.3.4
$$

$$
\left.
\begin{array}{l}
I_1 = E_a Y_a \\
I_2 = E_b Y_b + E_c Y_e \\
I_3 = -E_c Y_e
\end{array}
\right\} \qquad 3.2.3.5
$$

It will be noted that Y_{11} is the sum of the admittances of the branches connected to node 1, Y_{22} the sum of those connected to node 2, and Y_{33} the sum of those connected to node 3. It will also be noted that Y_{12}, equal to Y_{21}, is equal to minus the admittance of the branch connecting nodes 1 and 2, that Y_{23}, equal to Y_{32}, is equal to minus the admittance of the branch connecting nodes 2 and 3, and that Y_{31}, equal to Y_{13}, is equal to minus the admittance of the branch connecting nodes 3 and 1. Finally it will be noted that I_1 is the sum of the products of driving voltage and admittance for each of the branches connected to node 1, I_2 the sum of these products for each of the branches connected to node 2, and I_3 the sum of these products for each of the branches connected to node 3, the branch driving voltages being treated as positive when they act towards the node in question and negative when they act in the opposite direction, namely away from the node.

Eqns. 3.2.3.2 are a set of three simultaneous equations in the three unknown node voltages V_1, V_2 and V_3 and it will be evident that the general case of a network of n nodes, excluding the reference node, will result in a similar set of n simultaneous equations in terms of the n unknown node voltages. Knowing the branch driving voltages and admittances, this set of equations can be virtually written down by inspection from the rules already given.

The set of simultaneous linear equations obtained is identical in general form with that obtained using the mesh-current method of analysis and is amenable to the same methods of solution. Having solved the equations to obtain the node voltages, each branch current is then readily obtained from the node voltages at its two ends, the branch current being given by the product of the branch admittance and the voltage across this admittance. In obtaining this latter mentioned voltage from the node voltages, due account must, of course, be taken of the driving voltage, if any, in the branch in question.

3.2.4   Application of mesh-current and nodal-voltage analysis

The mesh-current and nodal-voltage methods of analysis have both been shown to result in a set of simultaneous linear equations, the solution of which leads to a complete determination of all the network branch currents. As already stated, the rules for the formulation of the equations are such that, with either of the two methods, the resulting set of equations can be virtually written down by inspection once the network meshes or nodes have been numbered.

The solution of a set of simultaneous linear equations is a standard computational procedure and may be achieved by a number of methods including elimination, determinant and matrix methods and iterative methods. Details of these methods will be found in a number of the references given in the bibliography. With all methods of solution, however, the use of manual computation, even with the aid of a desk computer, is not normally a practical proposition if the number of equations is at all large, since the computation time tends to be considerable and increases rapidly with the number of equations. Solution by high-speed digital computer is however, very much a practical proposition, such computers being capable of handling very large sets of equations (that is, simultaneous equations representing a large number of meshes or nodes) and of providing a rapid and accurate solution.

The choice between the mesh-current and nodal-voltage methods will normally be determined by the need to reduce computing time to a minimum. It is of interest to note, therefore, that the great majority of networks have fewer nodes than meshes and are therefore more suited to solution by the nodal-voltage method. This is readily demonstrated by the simple two-machine network of Fig. 3.2.1E which, it will be noted, has two meshes but only one node, apart from the reference node. Thus, applying the mesh-current method we obtain the two equations

$$
\left.
\begin{aligned}
(2 + j4)I_1 - (1 + j0)I_2 &= 118 + j24 \\
-(1 + j0)I_1 + (3 + j5)I_2 &= -100 - j0
\end{aligned}
\right\}
\qquad \text{3.2.4.1}
$$

where I_1 and I_2 are the left-hand and right-hand mesh currents, respectively and are assumed to act in a clockwise direction.

Applying the nodal-voltage method, on the other hand, gives the single equation

$$
\left[\frac{1}{1 + j4} + \frac{1}{1 + j0} + \frac{1}{2 + j5} \right] V_1 = \left[\frac{118 + j24}{1 + j4} + \frac{100 + j0}{2 + j5} \right]
\qquad \text{3.2.4.2}
$$

where V_1 is the voltage at the point of short-circuit, and is denoted by V_3 in Section 3.2.1.

It will be left to the reader to verify that Equation 3.2.4.1 and Equation 3.2.4.2 both give the same results, these having already been obtained in Section 3.2.1.

3.2.5. Network theorems and reduction formulas

The mesh-current and nodal-voltage methods of analysis are both a means of obtaining the complete analytical solution to any linear network problem. They are being used to an increasing extent, their use being limited only by the availability of suitable computing facilities and the fact that an analytical solution can also be achieved by other means, which in many cases may be simpler and more direct. This alternative means of analysis, known as the network-reduction method, depends on the reduction of the network to a simpler equivalent form, the method being particularly useful where the solution is required to give the values of only a limited number of branch currents.

Network reduction is the process of combining network branches so as to reduce the given network to an equivalent network with fewer branches, this equivalent network being amenable to direct and simple solution. Thus, a complete and complex network, as viewed from any given pair of nodes, may be reduced in this way to its simplest equivalent form, namely a single equivalent branch. The network theorems and reduction formulae most commonly required are described below.

Combination of series branches: Taking first the general case of any number of branches connected in series, any given branch i comprising a driving voltage E_i and series impedance Z_i, the equivalent single branch comprises a driving voltage E_r in series with an impedance Z_r where

$$E_r = \sum_i E_i = E_1 + E_2 + \ldots + E_n \qquad 3.2.5.1$$

and

$$Z_r = \sum_i Z_i = Z_1 + Z_2 + \ldots + Z_n \qquad 3.2.5.2$$

and n is the number of branches. The driving voltages are all measured in the same direction with respect to the end nodes of the series combination. These rules, applied to the combination of three series-connected branches, are illustrated in Fig. 3.2.5A.

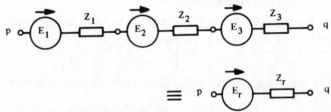

Fig. 3.2.5A   *Combination of series branches*

Combination of parallel branches: Taking, again, the general case of any number of branches but now connected in parallel, any given branch i comprising a driving voltage E_i and series admittance Y_i (that is series impedance $1/Y_i$), the equivalent single branch comprises a driving voltage E_r in series with an admittance Y_r (that is, an impedance $1/Y_r$), where

$$E_r = (1/Y_r) \sum_i E_i Y_i = (1/Y_r)(E_1 Y_1 + E_2 Y_2 + \ldots + E_n Y_n) \qquad 3.2.5.3$$

and

$$Y_r = \sum_i Y_i = Y_1 + Y_2 + \ldots + Y_n \qquad 3.2.5.4$$

and n is the number of branches. The driving voltages are all measured in the same direction with respect to the common nodes of the parallel combination. These rules, applied to the combination of three parallel-connected branches, are illustrated in Fig. 3.2.5B.

Star-to-delta transformation: The star-to-delta transformation permits any set of three star-connected branches with isolated star-point to be replaced by an equivalent set of three delta-connected branches. Thus, let a, b and c denote the three terminals of the star and its equivalent delta, and let the star-connected branches comprise driving voltages E_a, E_b and E_c and impedances Z_a, Z_b and Z_c respectively, the voltages being measured in the direction away from the star point. Then denoting the driving voltages and impedances of the equivalent delta-connected

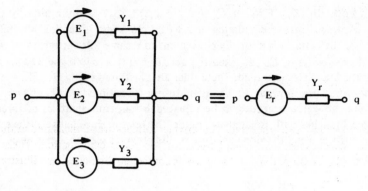

Fig. 3.2.5B *Combination of parallel branches*

branches by E_{ab}, E_{bc} and E_{ca} and Z_{ab}, Z_{bc} and Z_{ca} respectively, the latter values are given in terms of the former by the equations

$$\left.\begin{array}{l} E_{ab} = E_a - E_b + IZ_{ab} \\ E_{bc} = E_b - E_c + IZ_{bc} \\ E_{ca} = E_c - E_a + IZ_{ca} \end{array}\right\} \qquad 3.2.5.5$$

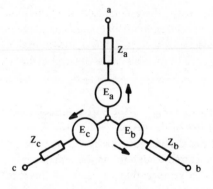

Fig. 3.2.5C *Star and delta circuits*

and

$$\left.\begin{array}{l} Z_{ab} = \dfrac{Z_a Z_b + Z_b Z_c + Z_c Z_a}{Z_c} \\[3ex] Z_{bc} = \dfrac{Z_a Z_b + Z_b Z_c + Z_c Z_a}{Z_a} \\[3ex] Z_{ca} = \dfrac{Z_a Z_b + Z_b Z_c + Z_c Z_a}{Z_b} \end{array}\right\} \qquad 3.2.5.6$$

where I, equal to $(E_{ab} + E_{bc} + E_{ca})/(Z_{ab} + Z_{bc} + Z_{ca})$, is any arbitrarily chosen current assumed to be circulating in an anticlockwise direction through the branches of the delta. It is normally convenient to assume this current to be zero.

The driving voltages E_{ab}, E_{bc} and E_{ca} act from b to a, c to b and a to c, respectively, in the branches concerned. These rules are illustrated in Fig. 3.2.5C.

Delta-to-star transformation: The delta-to-star transformation permits any set of three delta-connected branches to be replaced by an equivalent set of three star-connected branches with isolated star-point, the relationships between the star and delta quantities, using the nomenclature of the previous section, being given by the equations

$$
\begin{aligned}
E_a - E_b &= E_{ab} - IZ_{ab} \\
E_b - E_c &= E_{bc} - IZ_{bc} \\
E_c - E_a &= E_{ca} - IZ_{ca}
\end{aligned}
\qquad 3.2.5.7
$$

and

$$
\left.
\begin{aligned}
Z_a &= \frac{Z_{ab}Z_{ca}}{Z_{ab} + Z_{bc} + Z_{ca}} \\[2ex]
Z_b &= \frac{Z_{bc}Z_{ab}}{Z_{ab} + Z_{bc} + Z_{ca}} \\[2ex]
Z_c &= \frac{Z_{ca}Z_{bc}}{Z_{ab} + Z_{bc} + Z_{ca}}
\end{aligned}
\right\}
\qquad 3.2.5.8
$$

where I, equal to $(E_{ab} + E_{bc} + E_{ca})/(Z_{ab} + Z_{bc} + Z_{ca})$, is the current circulating in an anticlockwise direction through the branches of the delta.

It should be noted that any one of the three driving voltages E_a, E_b or E_c can be chosen quite arbitrarily, this value being then used to determine the remaining two driving voltages. It is normally convenient to arrange that the sum of the three driving voltages is equal to zero, in which case

$$
\left.
\begin{aligned}
E_a &= \tfrac{1}{3}\,[E_{ab} - E_{ca} - I(Z_{ab} - Z_{ca})] \\
E_b &= \tfrac{1}{3}\,[E_{bc} - E_{ab} - I(Z_{bc} - Z_{ab})] \\
E_c &= \tfrac{1}{3}\,[E_{ca} - E_{bc} - I(Z_{ca} - Z_{bc})]
\end{aligned}
\right\}
\qquad 3.2.5.9
$$

where I, as already stated, is given by

$$
I = \frac{E_{ab} + E_{bc} + E_{ca}}{Z_{ab} + Z_{bc} + Z_{ca}}
\qquad 3.2.5.10
$$

For the special case in which $E_{ab} + E_{bc} + E_{ca} = 0$, giving $I = 0$, the star driving voltages then become

$$E_a = \tfrac{1}{3}\,(E_{ab} - E_{ca})$$
$$E_b = \tfrac{1}{3}\,(E_{bc} - E_{ab})$$
$$E_c = \tfrac{1}{3}\,(E_{ca} - E_{bc})$$

3.2.5.11

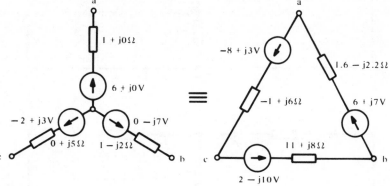

Fig. 3.2.5D *Example of equivalent star and delta circuits*

The transformation rules are illustrated by the circuit shown in Fig. 3.2.5D.

Combination of equal driving-voltages: If two or more branches have a common node and identical driving-voltages with respect to this node, then the individual branch driving-voltages can all be removed and replaced by a single external driving

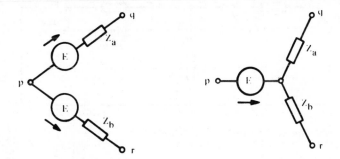

Fig. 3.2.5E *Combination of equal driving voltages*

voltage connected to the common node, the latter driving voltage being equal to the common value of the original branch driving-voltages. The theorem is illustrated in Fig. 3.2.5E and follows readily from the fact that equipotential points can be joined together without any resultant change in the electrical state of the network. The theorem is particularly useful in power system analysis in the reduction of a multiple-source network to its single-source equivalent.

Superposition Theorem: The Superposition Theorem, applicable to any linear network, states that the current which flows in any branch of a network as a result of the simultaneous action of several driving voltages is equal to the vector sum of

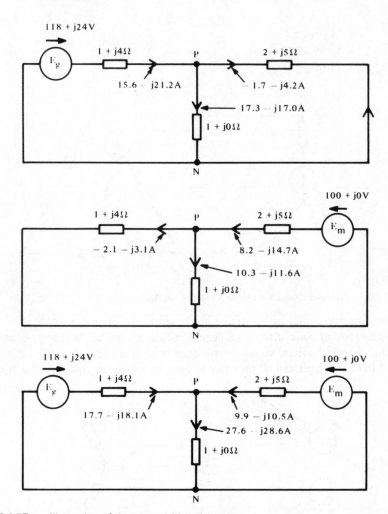

Fig. 3.2.5F   *Illustration of the superposition theorem*

the currents which would flow in the branch in question with each driving voltage acting individually and all the remaining driving voltages equal to zero, that is, short-circuited. The theorem is illustrated in Fig. 3.2.5F using the simple two-machine problem of Section 3.2.1.

Thevenin's Theorem: Thevenin's Theorem, similarly applicable to any linear network, states that any such network containing driving voltages, as viewed from any two terminals, can be replaced by a single driving voltage acting in series with a single impedance. The value of this driving voltage is equal to the open-circuit voltage between the two terminals, and the series impedance is the impedance of the network as viewed from the two terminals with all the driving voltages equal to zero, that is short-circuited. The theorem is illustrated in Fig. 3.2.5G and its application to the simple two-machine circuit of Section 3.2.1 is shown in Fig. 3.2.5H.

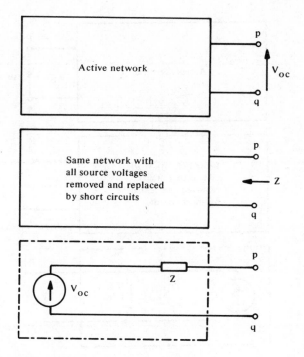

Fig. 3.2.5G   *Thevenin's Theorem*

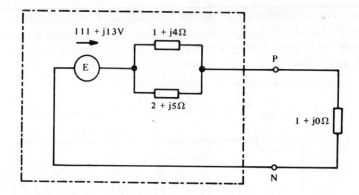

Fig. 3.2.5H   *Thevenin's Theorem applied to the example of Fig. 3.2.1E*

Norton's Theorem: Norton's Theorem is the dual of Thevenin's Theorem and states that any linear network containing driving voltages, as viewed from any two terminals, can be replaced by a single driving current shunted by an impedance. The value of this driving current is equal to the short-circuit current which will flow between the two terminals when connected together, and the shunt impedance is the impedance of the network as viewed from the two terminals with all the driving voltages equal to zero, that is short-circuited. The theorem is illustrated in Fig.

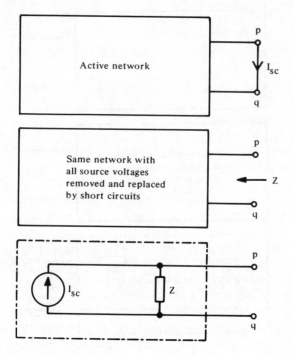

Fig. 3.2.5I   *Norton's Theorem*

3.2.5I and its application to the simple two-machine circuit of Section 3.2.1 is shown in Fig. 3.2.5J. It is important to note that the driving current is constant in value irrespective of the voltage across it, just as a given driving voltage is constant in value irrespective of the current through it. A constant driving current can be

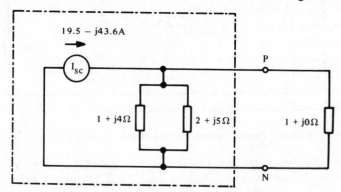

Fig. 3.2.5J   *Norton's Theorem applied to the example of Fig. 3.2.1E*

regarded in physical terms, as the current produced by an infinite voltage acting in series with an infinite impedance, the ratio of the voltage to the impedance being the required driving current.

A number of other useful theorems and reduction formulae will be found in the references given in the bibliography.

3.3 Calculation of balanced fault conditions

3.3.1 Single-phase representation

The component items of electrical plant which together form a three-phase power system, namely generators, transformers, overhead-line and cable circuits, etc., can all be regarded, for most practical purposes, as having electrical characteristics which are balanced or symmetrical with respect to the three phases. Thus, the plant impedance characteristics are usually such that the phase self-impedance values can be regarded as the same for all three phases and the phase-to-phase mutual-impedance values regarded as symmetrical with respect to the three phases. Similarly, the driving voltages produced by the generators and any other synchronous machines are balanced in that the three phase-to-neutral e.m.f.s produced by any given machine are all equal in magnitude and symmetrically spaced, at $120°$ intervals, in time-phase, the phase order being the same for all the machines. This phase order, namely the order in which the instantaneous phase voltages attain their maximum values in the cycle, is termed the positive-sequence phase-order. It readily follows from this system phase-symmetry that conditions which are themselves balanced with respect to the three phases (for example, balanced-load and three-phase short-circuit conditions) will preserve this phase symmetry in that the resulting phase currents and similarly, the resulting phase voltages at any point in the system will also be balanced with respect to the three phases. Thus, for the conditions referred to, the three phase currents and, similarly, the three phase-to-neutral voltages at any given point in the system will be equal in magnitude and equally spaced at $120°$ intervals in time-phase, the phase order being the same as that of the generated phase-to-neutral voltages, namely the positive-sequence phase-order. These currents and voltages are termed positive-sequence currents and voltages and are represented in vector-diagram form in the manner shown in Fig. 3.3.1A.

The mathematical relationships between these balanced (positive-sequence) phase values at any given point in the power system are the same for both current -and voltage, namely

and

$$\left.\begin{aligned} I_b &= a^2 I_a \\ I_c &= a I_a \\ V_b &= a^2 V_a \\ V_c &= a V_a \end{aligned}\right\} \qquad 3.3.1.1$$

where the subscripts a, b and c denote the three phases in positive-sequence phase-order and the symbol a (not to be confused with the phase reference) is a constant

given by

$$a = -\frac{1}{2} + j\frac{\sqrt{3}}{2} = 1 \underline{/120°}$$ 3.3.1.2

and in known as the 120° operator.

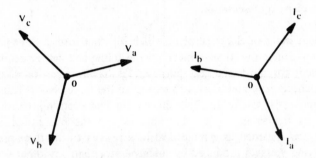

Fig. 3.3.1A   *Phasor-diagram representation of positive-sequence voltages and currents*

It will be noted that multiplication of any given vector by a gives a resultant vector equal in magnitude to the given vector but advanced in phase (that is rotated in an anticlockwise direction) by 120° with respect to the given vector. Similarly multiplication by a^2 give a phase-advance of 240°, because

$$a^2 = \left(-\frac{1}{2} + j\frac{\sqrt{3}}{2}\right)\left(-\frac{1}{2} + j\frac{\sqrt{3}}{2}\right) = -\frac{1}{2} - j\frac{\sqrt{3}}{2} = 1\underline{/240°}$$ 3.3.1.3

Further multiplication gives

$$a^3 = \left(-\frac{1}{2} + j\frac{\sqrt{3}}{2}\right)\left(-\frac{1}{2} - j\frac{\sqrt{3}}{2}\right) = 1\underline{/360°} = 1\underline{/0°}$$ 3.3.1.4

and so on. It should be noted that

$$a = 1 \underline{/120°} = 1 \underline{/-240°}$$
$$a^2 = 1 \underline{/240°} = 1 \underline{/-120°}$$ 3.3.1.5
$$1 + a + a^2 = 0$$

bearing in mind that a vector rotation forward through any given angle is the same as a rotation backwards through an angle equal to 360° minus the given angle.

The balanced conditions referred to are illustrated by Fig. 3.3.1B which shows an 11 kV generator with an impedance of $0 + j1\ \Omega$ per phase supplying a balanced load of $20 + j5\ \Omega$ per phase through a transmission line of $2 + j3\ \Omega$ per phase, the generator neutral point being earthed, as shown, and the transmission line having a three-phase fault clear of earth at the end F remote from the generator. Denoting

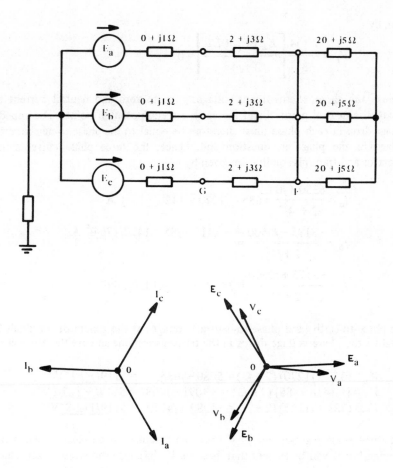

Fig. 3.3.1B *Illustration of a balanced three-phase fault condition*

the three phases, in positive-sequence phase order, by the subscripts a, b and c, the generator phase-to-neutral driving-voltages are given by

$$E_a = 6350 + j0 \quad = 6350\underline{/0°} \text{ V}$$
$$E_b = -3175 - j5500 = 6350\underline{/-120°} \text{ V}$$
$$E_c = -3175 + j5500 = 6350\underline{/120°} \text{V}$$

the magnitude of the phase to neutral voltage namely 6350 V, being the line-to-line voltage of 11 000 V divided by $\sqrt{3}$. It will be noted that e.m.f. E_a has been arbitrarily chosen to have zero phase-angle.

Using the rule given in Section 3.2.5 for the combination of parallel branches it will be seen that the voltage to earth, at F, of the three short-circuited phases is

given by

$$V_F = \frac{2+j4}{3} \left[\frac{E_a + E_b + E_c}{2+j4} \right] = 0$$

because the three phase driving-voltages sum to zero and neutral current being absent, the neutral point N and the earth are equipotential points. The impedance voltage-drop in each phase must therefore be equal to the phase-to-neutral driving-voltage in the phase in question and, hence, the three phase currents in the generator and transmission line are given by

$$I_a = \frac{6350 + j0}{2+j4} = 635 - j1270 = 1420 \underline{/-63\cdot4}^{\circ} \text{A}$$

$$I_b = \frac{-3175 - j5500}{2+j4} = -1418 + j85 = 1420 \underline{/176\cdot6}^{\circ} \text{ A}$$

$$I_c = \frac{-3175 + j5500}{2+j4} = 783 + j1185 = 1420 \underline{/56\cdot6}^{\circ} \text{ A}$$

The phase-to-earth (and phase-to-neutral) voltages at the generator terminals G are equal to the phase voltage drops in the transmission line and are therefore given by

$$V_a = (635 - j1270)(2+j3) = 5080 - j635 \qquad = 5119\underline{/-7\cdot1}^{\circ}\text{V}$$
$$V_b = (-1418 + j85)(2+j3) = -3091 - j4084 = 5119\underline{/-127\cdot1}^{\circ}\text{V}$$
$$V_c = (783 + j1185)(2+j3) = -1989 + j4179 = 5119\underline{/112\cdot9}^{\circ}\text{V}$$

The three-phase short-circuit at F has been assumed to be clear of earth in this example but it will be evident that, because V_F has been shown to be zero, a three-phase-to-earth fault at F would result in zero current in the earth connection and would thus give precisely the same results as those already obtained for the fault clear of earth. The three-phase vector diagrams of the currents and voltages are shown in Fig. 3.3.1B.

Now, it will be evident from Eqns. 3.3.1.1 that a knowledge of the phase currents and voltages relating to any one chosen reference phase will enable the corresponding values of current and voltage in the other two phases to be determined. Thus, if phase-a is chosen as the reference phase then the phase-b values of current and voltage are simply the corresponding phase-a values multiplied by a^2 and the phase-c values the corresponding phase-a values multiplied by a, where a is the 120° operator. For the purposes of analysis, therefore, the power system of Fig. 3.3.1B can be represented by the single-phase network shown in Fig. 3.3.1C, this single-phase network and the associated single-phase vector diagram both relating to the chosen reference phase, namely phase a.

The single-phase representation, although demonstrated for the extremely simple system of Fig. 3.3.1B, is equally applicable to any balanced three-phase network operating under balanced conditions, for example balanced-load or three-phase short-circuit conditions. The single-phase network obtained is termed the system positive-sequence network, and the impedances represented in the network are the impedances appropriate to positive sequence conditions, termed the positive-sequence impedances. It will be noted from Fig. 3.3.1C that the three-phase short-circuit is represented in the positive-sequence network by the short-circuiting connection from the point of fault F to the zero-potential (neutral) bar represented by the thick horizontal line. With this short-circuiting connection absent, the conditions represented are those corresponding to the balanced-load condition existing before the application of the three-phase short circuit.

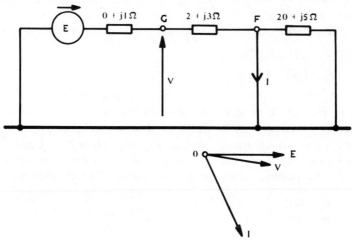

Fig. 3.3.1C   *Single-phase representation of Fig. 3.3.1B*

3.3.2 Use of a common voltage base

The simple example of the previous Section was solved by direct analysis of the given network using actual values of plant impedance together with actual values of the power-system currents and voltages. This direct application of the network laws was possible because the network interconnections were direct (that is, not through transformers) or, put in another way, because the whole system had the same nominal rated voltage for all its component items of plant. The power systems which have to be considered in practice, however, almost invariably consist of a number of sections operating at different nominal rated voltages, the interconnections between sections being by means of transformers. The analysis of such multiple-section systems is achieved by representing the given network by an equivalent network whose several sections all have the same nominal rated voltage. This procedure allows the transformer interconnections to be replaced by equivalent direct interconnections, the resulting network being then amenable to direct solution using the normal methods of network analysis.

The derivation of this so-called common-voltage equivalent network can be readily understood by considering the two network sections, P and Q, shown in Fig. 3.3.2A, the two sections being interconnected by an ideal transformer of turns ratio M (= N_p/N_q) where

$$M = \frac{\text{nominal rated voltage of network-section P}}{\text{nominal rated voltage of network-section Q}} \qquad 3.3.2.1$$

The two network sections are each represented, for simplicity, by a single branch consisting of a driving voltage and an impedance in series, their values being E_p and Z_p for network-section P and E_q and Z_q for network-section Q. The ideal-transformer terminal-voltages and currents are similarly denoted by V_p and I_p and V_q and I_q, where I_p is the current flowing out of network-section P and I_q that flowing into network-section Q. Now, because the transformer is ideal (that is has windings of zero leakage-impedance and takes zero exciting current), it follows that

$$\left. \begin{array}{l} V_p = MV_q = V_q' \text{ say} \\ I_p = I_q/M = I_q' \text{ say} \end{array} \right\} \qquad 3.3.2.2$$

and it is easily seen that these same equations are satisfied by the equivalent system-network of Fig. 3.3.2B in which the ideal transformer is represented by a direct zero-impedance interconnection. This equivalent network has the same nominal rated voltage throughout, namely that of network-section P, and consists of the given network-section P and the equivalent or referred network-section Q'. It will be noted that the referred network-section Q' contains the referred values

$$\left. \begin{array}{l} E_q' = ME_q \\ V_q' = MV_q \\ I_q' = I_q/M \\ Z_q' = M^2 Z_q \end{array} \right\} \qquad 3.3.2.3$$

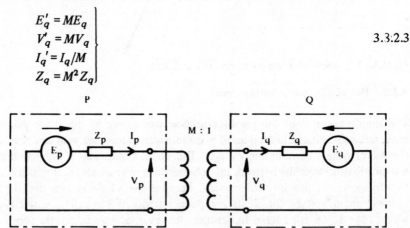

Fig. 3.3.2A   *Simplified representation of two networks with ideal-transformer interconnection*

in place of the actual network values, the expression for the referred impedance following from the fact that the voltages in the referred network are all M times the corresponding voltages in the actual network. Thus, the voltage-drop across Z_q in the actual network is $I_q Z_q$ and the corresponding voltage-drop in the referred net-

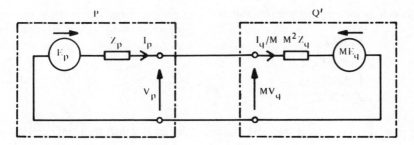

Fig. 3.3.2B *Common-voltage equivalent of Fig. 3.3.2A*

work is $I_q' Z_q'$, so that

$$Z_q' = \frac{MI_q Z_q}{I_q'} = M^2 Z_q$$

Now, eqns. 3.3.2.3 will apply to all the voltages, currents and impedances in network-section Q when the latter is considered as a general network rather than as a single branch. For this general case, therefore, the voltages, currents and impedances given in eqns. 3.3.2.3 can now be regarded as general network values, the equations given representing the relationships between actual values and their referred equivalents. This general case is represented in block-diagram form in Fig. 3.3.2C.

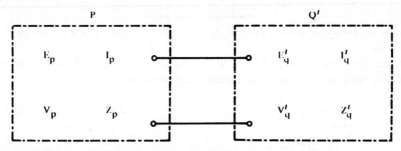

Fig. 3.3.2C *Generalised representation of Fig. 3.3.2B*

Consider, now, an ideal-transformer interconnection between network-section Q and a third network-section S, the turns ration N $(= N_q/N_s)$ of this transformer being given by

$$N = \frac{\text{nominal rated voltage of network section Q}}{\text{nominal rated voltage of network section S}} \qquad 3.3.2.4$$

By similar reasoning to that already described, the two network sections Q and S can be represented by an equivalent network consisting of the given network-section Q and an equivalent or referred network-section S', the referred network-section S' containing the referred values

$$\left.\begin{array}{l} E_s' = NE_s \\ V_s' = NV_s \\ I_s' = I_s/N \\ Z_s' = N^2 Z_s \end{array}\right\} \qquad 3.3.2.5$$

in place of the actual network values. The ideal-transformer interconnection between network-sections Q and S is now represented as previously by a direct zero-impedance interconnection in the equivalent system-network.

The equivalent system-network is shown in block-diagram form in Fig. 3.3.2D.

Suppose, now, that all three network sections are interconnected through the given ideal transformers. Then it will be evident that the equivalent network consisting of Q and S' can itself be replaced by another equivalent network consisting of Q' and S'', this latter equivalent network being directly connected through zero-impedance to the network-section P. Now the values in the network-section Q' are

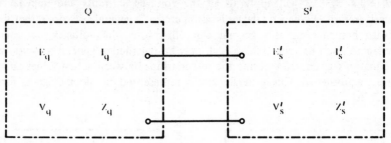

Fig. 3.3.2D

those already given by eqns. 3.3.2.3 while those in S'', are given by applying these same equations to the values in S'. Hence, it follows that

$$\left.\begin{array}{l} E_s'' = MNE_s \\ V_s'' = MNV_s \\ I_s'' = I_s/MN \\ Z_s'' = (MN)^2 Z_s \end{array}\right\} \qquad 3.3.2.6$$

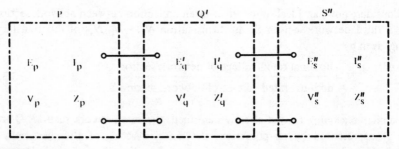

Fig. 3.3.2E

the resulting equivalent network for the full three-section system being represented in block-diagram form by Fig. 3.3.2E.

From eqns. 3.3.2.1 and 3.3.2.4 it is seen that

$$MN = \frac{\text{nominal rated voltage of network section P}}{\text{nominal rated voltage of network section S}}$$

and it thus follows that the rules for referring any given network section to a given common nominal rated voltage, termed the common voltage base, are

$$\left.\begin{array}{l} E' = KE \\ V' = KV \\ I' = I/K \\ Z' = K^2 Z \end{array}\right\} \qquad \text{3.3.2.7}$$

where

$$K = \frac{\text{common voltage base}}{\text{nominal rated voltage of given network section}} \qquad \text{3.3.2.8}$$

and the primed and unprimed symbols represent referred and actual values respectively. It will be noted that these equations are simply a more general statement of eqns. 3.3.2.3 and 3.3.2.5.

Although these conversion equations have been derived by considering network-sections interconnected as a single point it is not difficult to see that they are equally valid for any number of interconnection points.

The process of network analysis by the use of a common voltage base can now be seen to consist of three stages:

(*a*)   the conversion of the given system network to an equivalent network having a single common nominal rated voltage, namely the chosen base voltage, for all its sections

(*b*)   the solution of this equivalent network in terms of its common-base values of voltage, current and impedance

(*c*)   the reconversion of the equivalent network, with its now determined common-base values of current and voltage, to its original actual form containing actual values of current, voltage and impedance.

Eqns. 3.3.2.7, used to determine the referred values of driving voltage and impedance for the equivalent system network, are, of course, equally valid for the final stage of reconversion from referred values to actual values. These equations, rewritten in the form appropriate to this reconversion, are

$$\left.\begin{array}{l} E = E'/K \\ V = V'/K \\ I = KI' \\ Z = Z'/K^2 \end{array}\right\} \qquad \text{3.3.2.9}$$

where the primed symbols represent common-base values and the unprimed symbols actual values. The symbol K is the ratio of common base voltage to actual nominal rated voltage, as already defined.

The use of the common voltage base is illustrated by the simple example shown in Fig. 3.3.2F.

It is important to note that the use of the common voltage base, as so far described, has assumed ideal-transformer interconnections between the different network sections, the voltage-transformation ratios of these transformers being

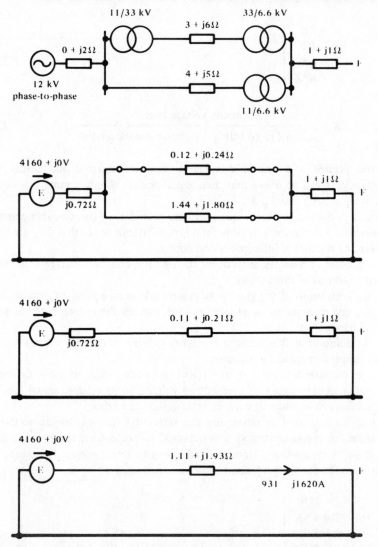

Fig. 3.3.2F   *Application of the common voltage base for a system with ideal-transformer interconnections (common base voltage 6·6 kV)*

identical to the ratios of the nominal rated voltages of their associated network sections. As already shown, such ideal-transformer interconnections are represented in the common-voltage equivalent circuit by direct interconnections of zero impedance. The representation necessary in the case of practical transformers is discussed in the following section.

3.3.3 Representation of nominal-ratio transformer circuits

Practical transformer circuits differ from the ideal transformers of the previous section in that they have non-infinite values of exciting impedance and non-zero values of leakage impedance. From the point of view of their representation in a common voltage equivalent circuit they may in addition, have transformation ratios which differ from the nominal ratios so far considered.

Two-winding transformers: The common-voltage equivalent circuit of two-winding transformer can be derived by considering the single-phase transformer shown in Fig. 3.3.3A, where H and L denote the high-voltage and low-voltage windings, respectively. The transformer is assumed to have a high-voltage-to-low-voltage turns-ratio N ($= N_H/N_L$) equal to the ratio of the nominal rated voltages of the associated network sections. As shown in the figure, the given transformer can be represented completely by an ideal transformer of this same turns-ratio N together with the lumped impedances Z_H, Z_L and Z_e. The impedances Z_H and Z_L are the leakage impedances of the windings H and L, respectively, and Z_e the exciting impedance, $Z_e + Z_H$ being the impedance which would be measured by an open-circuit test on the high-voltage winding.

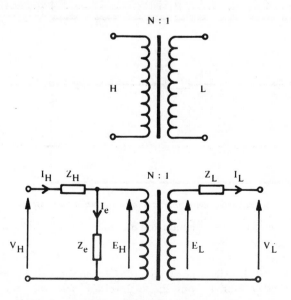

Fig. 3.3.3A *Equivalent circuit of a two-winding transformer*

Now, the voltage E_L across the low-voltage winding of the ideal transformer is given by

$$E_L = V_L + I_L Z_L \qquad\qquad 3.3.3.1$$

where V_L is the voltage and I_L the outflowing current at the terminal of winding L. The voltage across the high-voltage winding of the ideal transformer is therefore

$$E_H = NE_L = N(V_L + I_L Z_L) \qquad\qquad 3.3.3.2$$

which can be rearranged to read

$$E_H = NV_L + (I_L/N)N^2 Z_L \qquad\qquad 3.3.3.3$$

It will be noted that NV_L and I_L/N are the equivalent values of V_L and I_L when referred to the nominal rated voltage of the high-voltage winding, so that

$$E_H = V_L' + I_L' Z_L' \qquad\qquad 3.3.3.4$$

where $Z_L'\ (= N^2 Z_L)$ is the referred value of Z_L.

From Eqn. 3.3.3.4 it will be evident that the equivalent T circuit of Fig. 3.3.3B is the required common-voltage equivalent circuit of the transformer referred to the nominal rated voltage of the high-voltage winding H.

The exciting impedance Z_e can be ignored in the great majority of calculations because the exciting current I_e can normally be considered to be negligibly small.

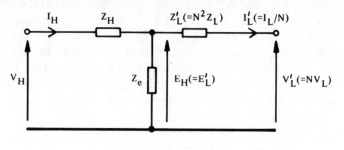

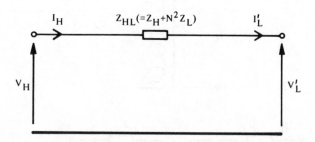

Fig. 3.3.3B   *Common-base equivalent circuits of a two-winding transformer*

In such cases, therefore the common-voltage equivalent circuit reduces to the single series impedance

$$Z_H + N^2 Z_L = Z_{HL} \ , \text{say} \qquad\qquad 3.3.3.5$$

shown in Fig. 3.3.3B. It will be noted that Z_{HL} is the short-circuit impedance of the transformer as measured from the high-voltage side with the low-voltage winding short-circuited. The equivalent impedance of the transformer referred to the nominal rated voltage of the low-voltage winding, namely Z_{LH} is readily

obtained from the fact that
$$Z_{HL} = N^2 Z_{LH}$$
giving
$$Z_{LH} = Z_L + (1/N)^2 Z_H \qquad\qquad 3.3.3.6$$
The impedance Z_{LH} is, of course, the short-circuit impedance of the transformer as measured from the low-voltage side with the high-voltage winding short-circuited.

Auto-transformers: The auto-transformer differs from the two-winding transformer in that a single tapped winding is used in place of two separate windings, the arrangement being as shown in Fig. 3.3.3C. The full winding, which constitutes the high-voltage winding, is assumed to have N_H turns and the common portion, which constitutes the low-voltage winding, is assumed to have N_L turns. As before, the transformer is assumed to have a high-voltage-to-low-voltage turns-ratio N ($= N_H/N_L$) equal to the ratio of the nominal rated voltages of the associated network sections. As shown in the figure, the given transformer can be represented completely by an ideal auto-transformer of this same turns-ratio N together with

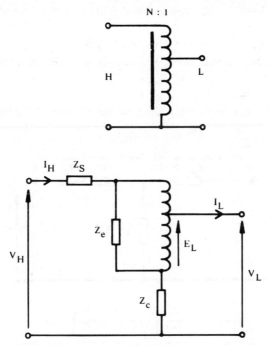

Fig. 3.3.3C *Equivalent circuit of an auto-transformer*

lumped impedances Z_s, Z_c and Z_e. The impedance Z_s is the leakage impedance of that portion of the winding which lies between the high-voltage terminal and the tapping point, the series portion, this portion having $N_H - N_L$ turns. Similarly, Z_c is the leakage impedance of the remaining portion of the winding, namely that between the tapping point and the common terminal. The impedance Z_e is the exciting impedance, $Z_s + Z_e + Z_c$ being the impedance which would be measured by an open-circuit test on the high-voltage winding. The tapping point, it will be noted, constitutes the low-voltage terminal of the transformer.

Now, the voltage E_L across the low-voltage (common) winding of the ideal transformer is given by

$$E_L = V_L + (I_L - I_H)Z_c \qquad 3.3.3.7$$

where V_L is the voltage and I_L the outflowing current at the low-voltage terminal of the winding L and I_H the inflowing current at the high-voltage terminal of winding H. The terminal voltage V_H of the high-voltage winding H is given by

$$V_H = V_L + (N - 1)E_L + I_H Z_S \qquad 3.3.3.8$$

Substituting for E_L in this latter equation using eqn. 3.3.3.7 gives

$$V_H = NV_L + I_H[Z_s - (N - 1)Z_c] + I_L (N - 1)Z_e \qquad 3.3.3.9$$

which, rearranged, gives

$$V_H = NV_L + I_H[Z_s - (N - 1)Z_c] + (I_L/N)N(N - 1)Z_c \qquad 3.3.3.10$$

It will be noted, as before, that NV_L and I_L/N are the equivalent values of V_L and I_L when referred to the nominal rated voltage of the high-voltage winding, so that

$$V_H = V'_L + I_H[Z_s - (N - 1)Z_c] + I'_L N(N - 1)Z_c \qquad 3.3.3.11$$

Now the open-circuit impedance of the auto-transformer as measured from the high-voltage side is

$$Z_s + Z_e + Z_c \qquad 3.3.3.12$$

and that measured from the low-voltage side, but referred to the high-voltage side, is

$$N^2 Z_c + Z_e \qquad 3.3.3.13$$

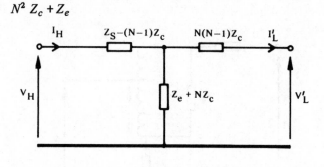

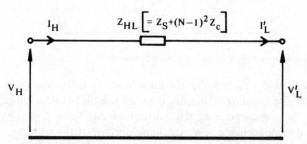

Fig. 3.3.3D   *Common-base equivalent circuits of an auto-transformer*

The required common-voltage equivalent-circuit for the auto-transformer can now be obtained using eqns. 3.3.3.11, 3.3.3.12 and 3.3.3.13 and is as shown in Fig. 3.3.3D, this equivalent circuit being that referred to the nominal rated voltage of the high-voltage winding.

If the magnetising impedance Z_e can be ignored, as is usually the case, the common-voltage equivalent circuit reduces to the single series impedance

$$Z_s + (N-1)^2 Z_c = Z_{HL} \qquad\qquad 3.3.3.14$$

shown in Fig. 3.3.3D. It will be noted that Z_{HL} is the short-circuit impedance of the transformer as measured from the high-voltage side with the low-voltage winding short-circuited. The equivalent impedance of the transformer referred to the low-voltage side is obtained by dividing the above value by N^2, as before, the result being

$$Z_{LH} = (1/N)^2 Z_s + (N-1)^2 Z_c / N^2 \qquad\qquad 3.3.3.15$$

As before, the impedance Z_{LH} is the short-circuit impedance of the transformer as measured from the low-voltage side with the high-voltage winding short-circuited.

Three-winding transformers: The common-voltage equivalent-circuit of a single-phase three-winding transformer can be obtained by similar reasoning to that already employed, the result being the equivalent-star circuit shown in Fig. 3.3.3E. It is assumed, as before, that the turns ratio of each pair of windings is equal to the ratio of the nominal rated voltages of the associated network sections. The letters H, L and T denote the high-voltage, low-voltage and tertiary-voltage windings, respectively, and the component branch impedances Z_H, Z'_L and Z'_T are all assumed to be values referred to the high voltage side. (Note that primed symbols denote referred values.) These component branch impedances are obtained by similar

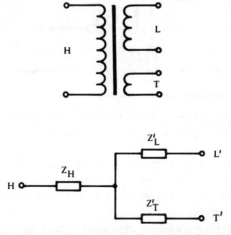

Fig. 3.3.3E   *Common-base equivalent circuit of a three-winding ransformer*

short-circuit impedance measurements to those used for two-winding transformers and autotransformers. Thus, let

Z_{HL} = effective impedance of winding H with winding L short-circuited and winding T open-circuited
Z'_{LT} = effective impedance of winding L with winding T short-circuited and winding H open-circuited
Z'_{TH} = effective impedance of winding T with winding H short-circuited and winding L open-circuited

all three values being referred to the high-voltage side. Then, from the equivalent circuit it is seen that

$$\left. \begin{aligned} Z_{HL} &= Z_H + Z'_L \\ Z'_{LT} &= Z'_L + Z_T \\ Z'_{TH} &= Z'_T + Z_H \end{aligned} \right\} \qquad 3.3.3.16$$

from which

$$\left. \begin{aligned} Z_H &= \tfrac{1}{2}(Z_{HL} + Z'_{TH} - Z'_{LT}) \\ Z'_L &= \tfrac{1}{2}(Z_{HL} + Z'_{LT} - Z'_{TH}) \\ Z'_T &= \tfrac{1}{2}(Z'_{LT} + Z'_{TH} - Z_{HL}) \end{aligned} \right\} \qquad 3.3.3.17$$

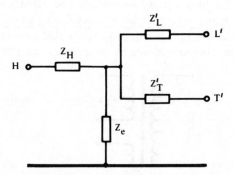

Fig. 3.3.3F   *Common-base equivalent circuit of a three-winding transformer with exciting impedance included.*

The equivalent-star representation of Fig. 3.3.3E is equally valid whether the three windings are electrically separate or not and is therefore also applicable to the quite common case in which two of the windings form an auto-transformer, the third winding only being electrically separate.

If it is required to represent exciting impedance in the equivalent circuit this can be done by adding an impedance of appropriate value between the star-point of the

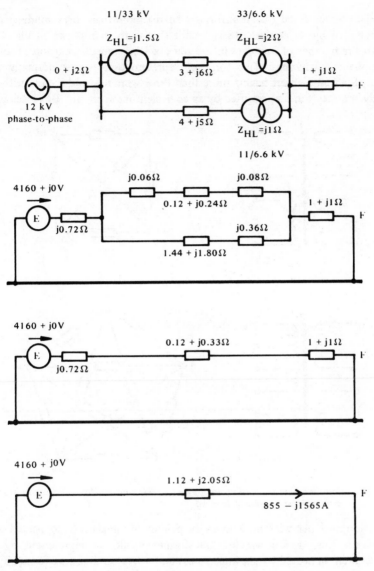

Fig. 3.3.3G   *Example of Fig. 3.3.2F but with practical transformer interconnections.*
(common base voltage 6·6 kV)

impedances Z_H, Z'_L and Z'_T and neutral, as shown in Fig. 3.3.3F. This exciting
impedance must, of course, be to the same common voltage base as the other
impedances.

The representation of transformer impedance is illustrated by the simple
example shown in Fig. 3.3.3G, this being the same as that given in Fig. 3.3.2F
except that the transformers, previously assumed ideal, now have the given values
of winding impedance.

It might be expected that transformers having more than three windings would be represented by an equivalent-star circuit similar to that shown in Fig. 3.3.3E but with the number of branches in the star (exciting impedance ignored) equal to the number of windings. This form of representation is not normally valid, however, for transformers having more than three windings, and such transformers normally require to be represented by an equivalent-mesh circuit. This mesh circuit

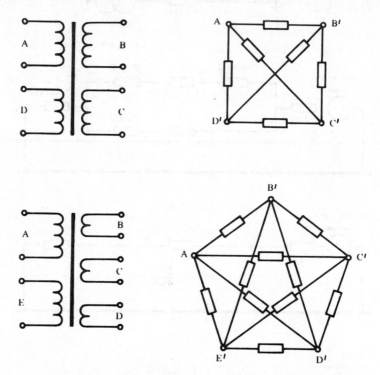

Fig. 3.3.3H   *Common-base equivalent circuits of four-winding and five-winding transformers with exciting impedance ignored*

has one terminal per winding with every pair of terminals interconnected by an impedance. Thus, a four-winding transformer would be represented by four terminals interconnected by six impedances and a five-winding transformer by five terminals interconnected by ten impedances. This form of representation is shown in Fig. 3.3.3H.

3.3.4   Representation of off-nominal-ratio transformer circuits

It has so far been assumed that the transformers are all nominal-ratio transformers, that is that the turns ratio of each transformer is equal to the ratio of the nominal rated voltages of its associated network sections. Put in another way, it has been assumed that the nominal rated voltage of each transformer winding is identical to that of the network section to which it is connected. This assumption is commonly made in fault calculations but it is nevertheless sometimes necessary to consider cases in which the transformer ratio is different from this nominal value, the most common cause of such a difference being the ratio change produced by transformer tap-change equipment. A treatment of off-nominal-ratio transformers is given in Appendix 3.8.1.

3.3.5 Transformer phase-shifts

The single-phase (reference-phase) representation of three-phase transformers, as required for the system positive-sequence network, has so far proceeded on the tacit assumption that all the transformer windings are star connected. It is necessary,

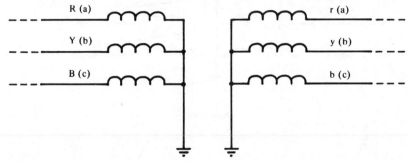

Fig. 3.3.5A

therefore, to examine the validity of this single-phase representation for those cases where other winding connections (for example delta and interconnected-star connections) are employed. The point at issue arises from the fact that, for a power system without transformers, the three system phases have an identity which extends throughout the network. With transformers present, however, the identity of a given phase conductor is limited to the particular network section concerned, this identity terminating at each and every transformer interconnection between that network section and the rest of the system.

The single-phase representation is valid if all the transformers are star connected since the phase references a, b and c can then apply to the corresponding phases of all the network sections, the reference phase (phase a) then having an identity which extends throughout the network. These conditions are shown in Fig. 3.3.5A. Consider, however, the star-delta transformer shown in Fig. 3.3.5B in which the star-side and delta-side phase-terminals are denoted by the phase letters R, Y, B and r, y, b, respectively, allocated as shown. The relationship between the star-side and the delta-side currents and voltages can be obtained by considering each limb of the transformer core and its associated two windings to constitute a single-phase transformer, and combining the delta-side phase-winding voltages and currents to obtain the phase-terminal values. The vector diagrams show the resulting relation-ship between the star-side and delta-side positive-sequence voltages under no-load conditions and that between the star-side and delta-side positive-sequence currents, exciting current ignored. The delta-side currents and no-load voltages, it will be noted, all lag their corresponding star-side values by 30°, this phase shift being caused by the particular star-delta connection of the windings and the given alloca-tion of the phase references. It readily follows, therefore, that with the transformer providing the interconnection between two network sections, the effect of the star-delta connection as compared with the star-star connection is that the currents and voltages at any point in the delta-side network-section are all retarded in phase by 30° with respect to any reference vector in the star-side network. Now, all the

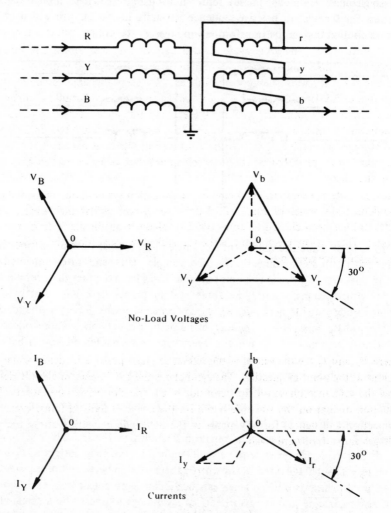

No-Load Voltages

Currents

Fig. 3.3.5B   *Phase-shifts introduced by a star/delta transformer*

transformers in an interconnected power system must have compatible phase-shifts. In other words, the phase-shift introduced between any two network sections as a result of transformer winding-connections must be the same for all the interconnecting paths between the two sections. This means, in effect, that the phase-shifts introduced by the transformer winding-connections have no effect on the magnitudes of the current and voltage values, these magnitudes being identical to those which would be obtained if all the transformer windings were star-connected. The only effect of the transformer winding-connections, therefore, is to shift the vector phase-positions of the currents and voltages in any given network section with respect to those in any other network section or with respect, for example, to the chosen common reference vector for the whole power system. The amount of this phase-shift is known if the winding connections of the interconnecting transformers are known, the total phase-shift introduced by a number of transformers in series being the algebraic sum of their individual phase-shifts.

The effect of transformer winding-connections can now be seen to be readily obtained by simply analysing the system network with all the transformer windings treated as if they were star-connected (that is by using the single-phase equivalent circuits already described) and using the phase reference a, b and c to denote the phases of this hypothetical system, these phase references denoting actual phase conductors in one, or possibly more, of the network sections. The phase currents and voltages so obtained can then be corrected in phase, as necessary, to allow for the transformer phase-shifts, the resulting values then being correct in both magnitude and phase.

Thus, considering the particular case of a two-section system interconnected by the star-delta transformer of Fig. 3.3.5B, let it be assumed that the reference phase (phase a) has been chosen to correspond to phase R on the star side of the transformer. Then, at any given point in the star-side network-section, the phase voltages and currents are given by

$$V_R = V_a \qquad I_R = I_a$$
$$V_Y = a^2 V_a \qquad I_Y = a^2 I_a$$
$$V_B = a V_a \qquad I_B = a I_a$$

where V_a and I_a are the values of the reference-phase positive-sequence voltage and current at the point in question. The symbol a is the $120°$ operator already defined. Now the reference phase on the delta side of the transformer is a hypothetical continuation of that on the star side based on the assumed star-star transformer-interconnection and hence, for any point in the delta-side network-section, the phase voltages and currents are given by

$$V_r = 1\underline{/- 30°} V_a \qquad I_r = 1\underline{/- 30°} I_a$$
$$V_y = 1\underline{/- 30°} a^2 V_a \qquad I_y = 1\underline{/- 30°} a^2 I_a$$
$$V_b = 1\underline{/- 30°} a V_a \qquad I_b = 1\underline{/-30°} a I_a$$

where V_a and I_a are now the values of the reference-phase positive-sequence voltage and current at the point in question in the delta-side network section. The symbol a is the $120°$ operator, as before, the vector multiplier $1\underline{/-30°}$ representing the necessary phase-shift correction.

The phase correction required in any given network-section is determined from a knowledge of the winding connections of the transformers present in any interconnecting path between that particular network-section and the network-section containing the chosen system reference vector. The phase-shifts are normally known from the system phasing diagram but can otherwise be obtained from a knowledge of the vector-symbol reference (for example, Yd1, Dy11, Yy0, etc.) of the transformers concerned and their phase markings. The vector-symbol references are defined in British Standard BS 171:1978, the first (capital) letter denoting the connection of the high-voltage winding (Y for star, D for delta and Z for interconnected-star), the second (small) letter the connection of the low-voltage winding using similar small-letter symbols (y, d and z) and the remaining figure (0, 1, 6 or 11) being the clock-dial reference representing the hour position of the low-voltage phase-vector in relation to that of the corresponding (similarly lettered) high-voltage phase-vector, the latter being assumed to occupy the 0 (that is 12 o'clock) position. In determining the network-section phase-shifts due account must, of course, be taken of the actual phase references employed, usually red, yellow and blue, and their allocation with respect to the B.S. transformer phase-terminal references. The latter are A, B and C for the high-voltage winding and a, b and c for the low-voltage winding and should not be confused with the general phase references a, b and c employed in the network analysis.

In so far as balanced-load and three-phase short-circuit conditions are concerned, it is of interest to note that correction for transformer phase-shifts is not normally of any practical interest or value, since such correction merely ensures the correct relative phase displacements of the currents and voltages in different network-sections. The currents and voltages in any given network-section have correct phase angles with respect to each other whether phase correction is applied or not, since the effect of phase correction is merely to shift all the voltage and current vectors in any network-section by the same fixed amount. In analysing balanced-load or three-phase short-circuit conditions, therefore, phase correction is usually ignored and the network analysed by assuming star-connected transformer windings.

As will be seen in later sections, however, the effect of transformer phase-shifts must be considered in obtaining the correct analysis of unbalanced-fault conditions.

3.3.6   Representation of synchronous machines

The representation of a synchronous machine in the positive-sequence network is by means of the single-phase (reference-phase) circuit shown in Fig. 3.3.6A, the

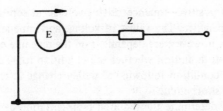

Fig. 3.3.6A *Positive-sequence equivalent circuit of a synchronous machine*

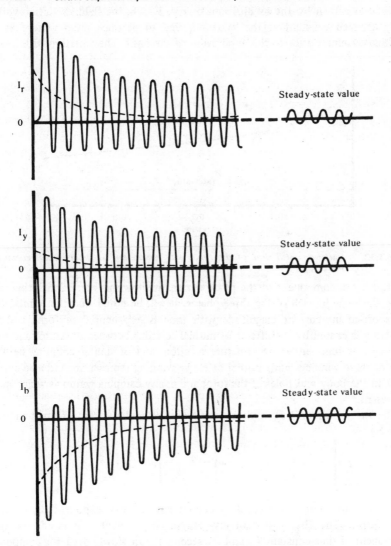

Fig. 3.3.6B *Instantaneous phase-currents of a synchronous machine during a three-phase short-circuit at its terminals*

circuit comprising a positive-sequence driving-voltage in series with the machine positive-sequence impedance. The values of voltage and impedance to be employed in the representation, however, are dependent on the machine operating conditions at the instant in question and on whether the condition to be analysed is a steady-state condition or a condition following a sudden change in electrical conditions, for example a system short-circuit.

The factors which determine the required representation can be understood by considering the effect of a three-phase terminal short-circuit on an unloaded machine as shown by the oscillograms of Fig. 3.3.6B, the field excitation voltage being assumed constant at the value required to produce rated voltage at the machine terminals prior to the application of the fault. The variation with time of

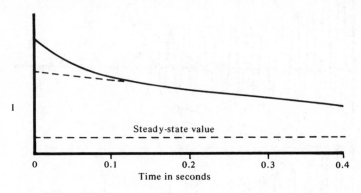

Fig. 3.3.6C *Variation with time of the r.m.s. a.c. component of short=circuit current of Fig. 3.3.6B*

the r.m.s. a.c. component of the phase current is shown in Fig. 3.3.6C, this value being the same in each of the three phases. It will be noted that the reduction in the short-circuit current magnitude with time is exponential in form, and this reduction is caused by the effects of mutual coupling between the stator and rotor windings, as represented by armature reaction, and of similar coupling between each of these windings and another effective winding representing induced-current paths in the body and poles of the rotor and in any damping windings which might be present.

The r.m.s. current magnitude at any time t after the instant of short-circuit is given by

$$I = \left[\frac{E_{st}}{Z_{st}} - \frac{E_t}{Z_t} \right] e^{-\frac{t}{T_{st}}} + \left[\frac{E_t}{Z_t} - \frac{E_s}{Z_s} \right] e^{-\frac{t}{T_t}} + \frac{E_s}{Z_s} \qquad 3.3.6.1$$

and is seen to consist of a constant component and two exponentially-decaying components. The first exponentially-decaying component is a rapidly-decaying component of time-constant T_{st} and the second a more slowly decaying component of time-constant T_t. The machine impedances Z_{st}, Z_t and Z_s are termed the sub-transient, transient and synchronous impedances, respectively, and can be regarded for most practical purposes as purely reactive, that is as jX_{st}, jX_t and jX_s . The voltages E_{st}, E_t and E_s are the voltages behind these impedances, their values being the vector sum of the machine terminal voltage and the appropriate impedance voltage-drop in the machine immediately prior to the short-circuit. The time-constants T_{st} and T_t are termed the sub-transient and transient short-circuit time-constant, respectively, the former usually being of the order of twenty or thirty milli-seconds and the latter of the order of one or two seconds. For the case of a short-circuit on an unloaded machine, the voltages E_{st}, E_t and E_s would, of course, all be equal to the pre-fault value of the open-circuit phase-to-neutral terminal voltage of the machine.

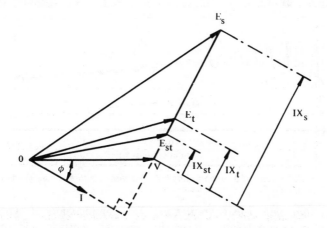

Fig. 3.3.6D *Phasor diagram for a round-rotor synchronous machine*

It will be noted from eqn. 3.3.6.1 that the current at the instant of short-circuit ($t = 0$) is equal to E_{st}/Z_{st} and is thus determined by the sub-transient impedance only. Similarly, the current under steady-state conditions (t much greater than T_{st} and T_t) is given by E_s/Z_s and is determined by the synchronous impedance only. If the initial, rapidly-decaying, transient component is ignored, the initial current is effectively given by E_t/Z_t and is thus determined by the transient impedance only. The vector diagram for a synchronous machine (cylindrical-rotor type assumed) is shown in Fig. 3.3.6D where V represents the phase-to-neutral terminal-voltage of the machine and I the current flowing out of the machine.

In addition to the a.c. components of short-circuit current, two at least of the three phases will have an exponentially-decaying d.c. component of current as shown by the off-set of the current waves with respect to the zero axis in Fig. 3.3.6B. The initial value of this d.c. component in any given phase depends on the instantaneous value of the phase voltage at the instant of short-circuit and is a maximum (equal to the peak value of the initial a.c. component of the phase-current) when the instant of short-circuit ($t = 0$) coincides with an instant at which the voltage behind the sub-transient impedance is instantaneously zero for the phase in question. Conversely, the d.c. component of current will be completely absent when the instant of short-circuit coincides with an instant at which the voltage behind the subtransient impedance is at its maximum (peak) value. The time-constant of the d.c. component of current is practically the same as the sub-transient short-circuit time-constant T_{st}. Because the d.c. currents in the rotor field-winding and damping-circuits are associated with a.c. machine-frequency currents in the stator windings, it follows that the transient d.c. component of current in the stator phases will be associated with a corresponding a.c. machine-frequency component of current in the rotor field winding and damping-circuits. The variation in the field-current of a short-circuited machine operating with constant field voltage is shown in Fig. 3.3.6E.

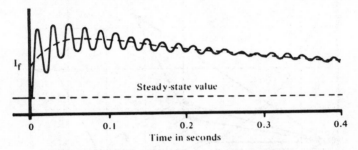

Fig. 3.3.6E   *Field current of a synchronous machine during a three-phase short-circuit at its terminals*

Effect of automatic voltage regulators: The consideration of synchronous-machine performance presented so far has assumed constant field voltage. In practice, however, machines are commonly equipped with automatic voltage regulators whose function is to control the excitation and thereby attempt to maintain the machine terminal-voltage at a constant pre-set value. Under short-circuit conditions, therefore, the regulator will increase the field voltage in an attempt to restore the terminal voltage to its normal pre-fault value and will thus increase the short-circuit current to a higher value corresponding to the higher field current. The effect of a typical regulator for a terminal three-phase short-circuit on an unloaded generator is shown in Fig. 3.3.6F, the variation in the short-circuit current with time being a function of the response characteristics of the regulator, the field-circuit time-constant and the maximum available field-supply voltage.

Saturation effects: The synchronous reactance of a synchronous machine is normally defined, in per-unit value (see Section 3.3.7), as the ratio of the field current required to produce rated armature current on sustained three-phase terminal short-circuit to that which would be required to produce rated armature voltage on no-load if no saturation were present, that is with the open-circuit-voltage/field-current characteristic assumed to be an extrapolation of its initial straight-line form. (See Fig. 3.3.6G.) The synchronous reactance is thus, by definition, an unsaturated value and is therefore applicable to those steady-state conditions in which the main flux paths of the machine can be assumed to be unsaturated.

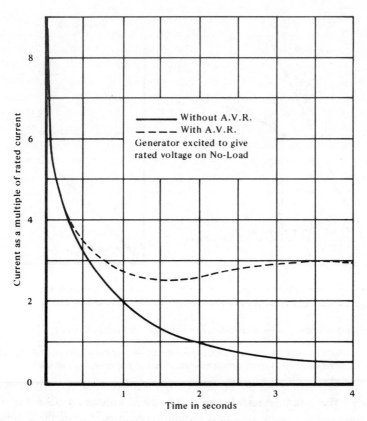

Fig. 3.3.6F

In the case of the sub-transient and transient reactance, the flux paths concerned are leakage-flux paths which are partly in iron and partly in air. These reactances are therefore not strictly constant but are dependent on the degree of saturation of the iron paths, it being necessary, for precision, to know the conditions for which the stated values apply. The values obtained from a terminal short-circuit test with rated pre-fault terminal voltage are known as the rated-voltage values of sub-transient and transient reactance, the values being saturated values because of the high value of armature current for this condition. Unsaturated values are obtained by performing the short-circuit test at reduced pre-fault terminal voltage, for example, at 50% of rated voltage.

Quoted values of sub-transient and transient reactance can usually be assumed to be unsaturated values, unless otherwise stated, these values usually being some 10 or 15% higher than the saturated values.

Salient-pole machines: The equivalent circuit of Fig. 3.3.6A is, strictly speaking, only valid for the case of round-rotor machines, there being no equivalent representation for salient-pole machines, the analysis of which requires the use of the two-

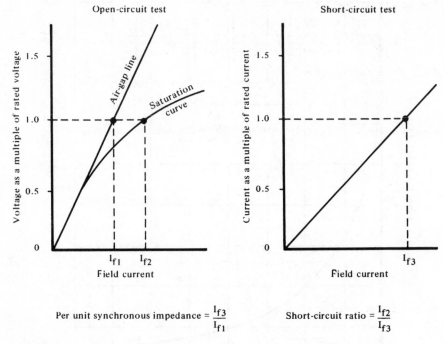

Fig. 3.3.6G   *Open-circuit and short-circuit characteristics of a synchronous machine*

axis theory. The given representation is, however, sufficiently valid for most practical cases of fault calculation provided the impedances used are the direct-axis values.

3.3.7   Use of per-unit and per-cent values

The network analysis described so far has all been in terms of actual or referred values of voltage, current and impedance. In the great majority of cases, however, the plant impedance values are given in per-unit or per-cent value, and it is accordingly normally preferable to employ such values directly in the analysis rather than convert them to their actual or referred ohmic equivalents.

Per-unit values: The basis of the per-unit method can be understood by considering the application of Ohm's Law to a single impedance of Z ohms, the voltage-drop V in volts produced by a current of I amps flowing through the impedance being given by

$$V = IZ \qquad\qquad 3.3.7.1$$

where V and I are vector values and Z is the complex impedance, all values being expressed by complex numbers. Now, letting V_{base} and I_{base} be real numbers representing stated values of voltage in volts and current in amps, the above equation may be written

$$\frac{V}{V_{base}} = \left[\frac{IZ}{V_{base}}\right]\left[\frac{I_{base}}{I_{base}}\right] = \left[\frac{I}{I_{base}}\right]\left[\frac{I_{base}Z}{V_{base}}\right] \qquad 3.3.7.2$$

which, in per-unit notation is written

$$V \text{ p.u.} = (I \text{ p.u.})(Z \text{ p.u.}) \qquad 3.3.7.3$$

The per-unit values of voltage, current and impedance are thus defined by

$$V \text{ p.u.} = \frac{V}{V_{base}} \qquad 3.3.7.4$$

$$I \text{ p.u.} = \frac{I}{I_{base}} \qquad 3.3.7.5$$

$$Z \text{ p.u.} = \frac{Z}{Z_{base}} = \left[\frac{I_{base}}{V_{base}}\right] Z \qquad 3.3.7.6$$

where the base impedance is given by

$$Z_{base} = \frac{V_{base}}{I_{base}} \qquad 3.3.7.7$$

It should be noted that the base values of voltage, current and impedance are all real numbers and it therefore follows that the per-unit values V p.u, I p.u. and Z p.u. are complex numbers with the same arguments as V, I and Z. The per-unit values, being ratios of similar quantities (that is volts, amps or ohms), are dimensionless.

The base values of voltage and current, which must of course be stated, can be any convenient values. In the analysis of three-phase systems the base voltage is always chosen to be equal to the rated phase-to-neutral voltage of the plant item or network section concerned and the base current, the current corresponding to a stated three-phase power-level (usually expressed in MVA), at this same rated voltage. In referring to individual plant items it is usual for the stated power-level to be chosen to be equal to the load rating in MVA of the plant item concerned. Thus considering a 132 kV transmission line with a positive-sequence impedance of $0 \cdot 076 + j0 \cdot 379 \ \Omega$ per km and a load rating of 175 MVA, it follows that

$$V_{base} = \frac{132\,000}{\sqrt{3}} = 76\,300 \text{ V}$$

so that

$$I_{base} = \frac{175 \times 10^6}{\sqrt{3} \times 132\,000} = 765 \cdot 4 \text{ A}$$

from which

$$Z_{base} = \frac{76\,300}{765.4} = 99.7 \ \Omega$$

Hence, the per-unit impedance of the transmission line is given by

$$Z_{p.u.} = \frac{0.076 + j0.379}{99.7} \ \text{per km}$$

from which $Z_{p.u.}$ = 0.000762 + j0.00380 per km to the stated rating of 175 MVA.

The base current for a given base voltage is directly proportional to the chosen MVA base and hence the per-unit impedance of any given item of plant is also directly proportional to the MVA base. Thus the per-unit impedance of the above-mentioned transmission line to a base of 100 MVA is given by

$$Z_{p.u.} = \frac{100(0.000762 + j0.00380)}{175} \ \text{per km}$$

giving $Z_{p.u.}$ = 0.000435 + j0.00217 per km to the new base of 100 MVA.

Per-cent values: It is common practice in power system analysis to express plant impedances in per-cent value rather than per-unit value, the former being simply the latter value multiplied by 100. Expressed in per-cent values, Ohm's Law becomes

$$V\% = \frac{I\%Z\%}{100} \hspace{4cm} 3.3.7.8$$

where the per-cent values of voltage and current are similarly the corresponding per-unit values multiplied by 100. Thus, the transmission line referred to in the previous example has an impedance of 0.0435 + j0.217 per-cent per km to a base of 100 MVA.

Use of common-base per-unit and per-cent values: The use of per-unit or per-cent values of voltage, current and impedance in the analysis of a complete network requires that all such values should be referred to a common MVA base, just as the use of values expressed in volts, amps and ohms requires that these latter-mentioned values, should be referred to a common voltage base. Thus, consider any item of plant, say a transmission line, forming a part of a complete three-phase power system and assume it to have a rated line-to-line voltage of V, and VA rating of S and ohmic impedance of $Z \ \Omega$ per phase. Then, as already shown in Section 3.3.2, this item of plant would be represented in the system positive-sequence network by the referred impedance value

$$Z' = \left[\frac{V_{base}}{V} \right]^2 Z \hspace{4cm} 3.3.7.9$$

where V_{base} is the line-to-line value of the chosen common base voltage. Expressing this referred impedance in per-unit value on its own three-phase VA load-rating S, and remembering that this referred impedance value now represents an equivalent plant item with a rated line-to-line voltage of V_{base}, it is seen from eqn. 3.3.7.6 that

$$Z \text{ p.u.} = \frac{\left[\dfrac{S}{\sqrt{3}V_{base}}\right]\left[\dfrac{V_{base}}{V}\right]^2 Z}{V_{base}/\sqrt{3}} \qquad 3.3.7.10$$

where

$$\frac{S}{\sqrt{3}V_{base}} = I_{base}$$

and
$$V_{base}/\sqrt{3} = \text{phase-to-neutral value of the base voltage}$$
Eqn. 3.3.7.10 reduces to

$$Z \text{ p.u.} = \left[\frac{S}{V^2}\right] Z \qquad 3.3.7.11$$

Eqn. 3.3.7.11, it will be noted, is the per-unit value of the actual plant impedance Z, thus showing that reference to a common voltage base is unnecessary when using per-unit or per-cent values.

Consider, now, the representation of the given plant item in the system positive-sequence network. The positive-sequence network expressed in terms of per-unit or per-cent values of impedance must be identical except for a common multiplier, to the same network expressed in terms of referred ohmic impedances to a common voltage base V_{base}. In other words, the impedances of corresponding branches in the two networks will be in the same constant ratio for all the branches. Now, from eqns. 3.3.7.9 and 3.3.7.11 it is seen that

$$\frac{Z \text{ p.u}}{Z'} = \frac{S}{V_{base}^2} \qquad 3.3.7.12$$

which is seen to be a constant ratio if all the plant items are assumed to have the same VA load rating S. Conversion of all the per-unit or per-cent impedance values to a common MVA base is readily achieved bearing in mind the direct proportionality between MVA rating and per-unit or per-cent impedance. Thus, the required conversion of all the impedance values to a stated common MVA base, which can be arbitrarily chosen, is given by

$$\left[\begin{array}{c} Z \text{ p.u. (or } Z\% \text{) to} \\ \text{common MVA base} \end{array}\right] = \left[\frac{\text{Common MVA base}}{\text{Plant MVA rating}}\right]\left[\begin{array}{c} Z \text{ p.u. (or } Z\% \text{) to} \\ \text{plant MVA rating} \end{array}\right] \qquad 3.3.7.13$$

A frequently used value for the common MVA base is the MVA load rating of the larges individual plant item concerned or some standard value such as 100 MVA, 500 MVA or 1000 MVA appropriate to the system under examination.

3.3.8   Fault-calculation procedure

The analysis of a three-phase balanced-fault condition consists, in general, of three parts, the first being the representation of the given power system with its fault condition by the equivalent positive-sequence network, the second the solution of this network in terms of its common-base values of voltage, current and impedance, and the third the conversion of the resulting common-base values to actual values. The system positive-sequence network as already stated, is the equivalent single-phase (reference-phase) representation of the complete power system. In this network each component item of plant is represented by its equivalent positive-sequence circuit using common-base values of voltage, current and impedance, namely values to a stated common voltage base or, as is more usual, per-unit or per-cent values to a stated common MVA base.

Overhead-line and cable circuits: Overhead-line and cable circuits are represented by their equivalent—π circuits, it being usually sufficient to employ the nominal—π circuit in which the series arm represents the total series impedance of the circuit

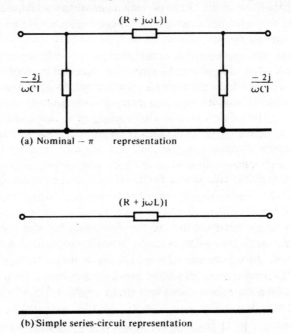

(a) Nominal – π representation

(b) Simple series-circuit representation

Fig. 3.3.8A   *Equivalent circuits of an overhead-line or cable circuit of length l and parameters R, L and C per unit length*

concerned and each of the two shunt arms the impedance corresponding to one half of the total phase-to-neutral capacitance. The shunt-arm impedances are always large in comparison with the series-arm impedance, and representation by the series arm alone is usually sufficiently exact for most practical purposes, particularly for overhead-line circuits.

Transformers and synchronous machines: Transformer and synchronous machine impedances are predominantly reactive with X/R ratios typically between ten and twenty, or sometimes more. It is, therefore, usually sufficiently exact to ignore the resistive component of the impedances and to assume all the impedances to be purely reactive.

Loads: Load impedances are always large in value in comparison with the series impedances of the power system plant and they therefore have only a small effect on the value of the total fault current under short-circuit conditions. Load can therefore be ignored in the majority of short-circuit calculations unless the analysis is particularly concerned with the combined effect of load conditions and short-circuit conditions.

Transformer tap-position: For the great majority of fault calculations it is usually sufficient to ignore actual tap positions and to assume all the transformers to be operating on the nominal-ratio tap-position, the error introduced by this assumption being normally quite small insofar as values of total short-circuit current are concerned. The use of the exact off-nominal-ratio representation, referred to in Section 3.3.4, has many applications in practice, however, where it is required to determine the precise division of load or fault current between transformers operating on different taps.

Equivalent sources: The representation of a complex power-system network can often be simplified considerably by the use of an equivalent generator to represent the whole or certain parts of a given network. Thus, a complete network, as seen from any given point, may be represented, using Thevenin's Theorem, as a single driving voltage in series with a single impedance. This equivalent-generator circuit can often be obtained with sufficient accuracy from an estimated knowledge of the system three-phase fault-level at the point in question, the pre-fault value of the voltage at this point being assumed equal to the nominal rated value.

Treatment of complex impedances: The impedances in the positive-sequence network are all complex impedances and must, therefore, be represented in $R + jX$ form. In many cases, however, the resistance components of the impedances are small compared with the reactance components and in such cases it is often sufficient to treat the impedances as pure reactances, thus ensuring a considerable simplification in computation. The use of such a pure-reactance form of representation, it should be noted, results in a short-circuit current slightly greater than the true value.

Plant-impedance values: The impedance values employed in any particular fault calculation should, wherever possible, be the known values appropriate to the particular items of plant concerned. Where precise actual values are not known, however, it may be permissible to use typical values appropriate to similar plant of similar load and voltage rating. Tables of typical plant impedance values are given in Section 3.4.3.

Neutral earthing: Neutral earthing arrangements have no effect on balanced three-phase conditions, whether load conditions or three-phase short-circuit conditions, and are therefore disregarded in the derivation of the system positive-sequence network.

3.3.9   Example 1

The power system shown in Fig. 3.3.9A develops a three-phase short-circuit on the 132 kV busbars at Station C. Determine the resulting value of the three-phase fault current and its distribution in the 132 kV system, given that the pre-fault value of

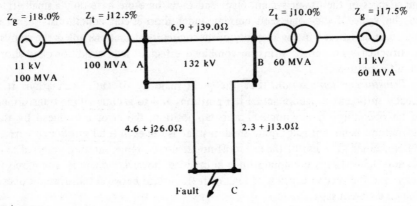

Fig. 3.3.9A

the line-to-line voltage at the point of fault is 140 kV. The system can be assumed to be operating at no-load prior to the fault.

Solution: Using a common voltage base of 132 kV, the resulting positive-sequence network is as shown in Fig. 3.3.9B, the generator and transformer impedances having been converted to equivalent 132 kV Ω. Thus, considering the 100 MVA generator, its rated current is given by

$$I = \frac{100 \times 10^6}{\sqrt{3} \times 11\,000} = 5250 \text{ A}$$

and its rated phase-to-neutral voltage is given by

$$V = \frac{11\,000}{\sqrt{3}} = 6350 \text{ V}$$

from which the corresponding base impedance is seen to be

$$Z_{base} = \frac{6350}{5250} = 1.21 \ \Omega$$

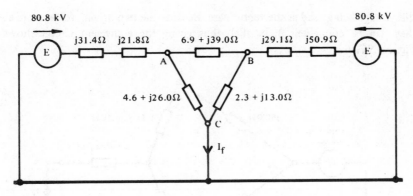

Fig. 3.3.9B

The ohmic impedance of the generator is therefore given by

$$Z = j0.180 \times 1.21 = j0.218 \ \Omega$$

and the value referred to the common base voltage of 132 kV is given by

$$Z' = \left(\frac{132}{11}\right)^2 j0.218 = j31.4 \ \Omega$$

Because the pre-fault conditions have been assumed to be no-load conditions, the generator driving-voltages, referred to the common base voltage of 132 kV, are both given by

$$E = \frac{140\,000}{\sqrt{3}} = 80\,800 \ V$$

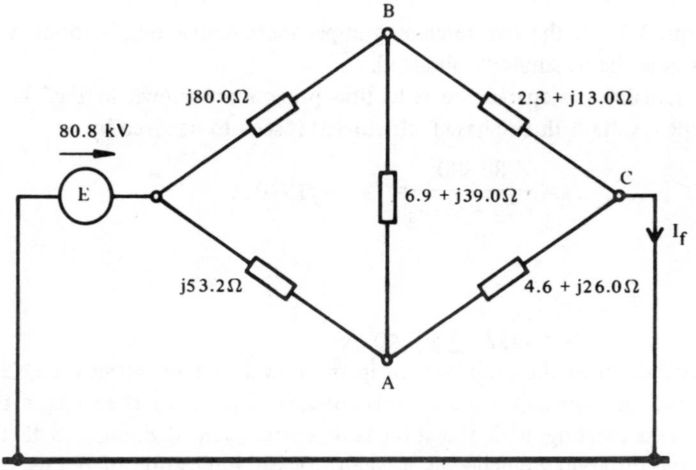

Fig. 3.3.9C

this voltage being used as the vector base. Because the two driving voltages are equal they can be connected in parallel, thus giving the equivalent circuit shown in Fig. 3.3.9C.

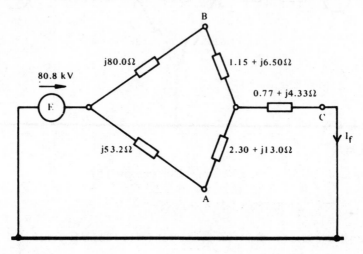

Fig. 3.3.9D

The delta-connected line-impedances $2{\cdot}3 + j13{\cdot}0$, $4{\cdot}6 + j26{\cdot}0$ and $6{\cdot}9 + j39{\cdot}0$ can now be replaced by the equivalent star-connected impedances shown in Fig. 3.3.9D. Thus, the impedance connecting Station C to the star point is given by

$$\frac{(2{\cdot}3 + j13{\cdot}0)(4{\cdot}6 + j26{\cdot}0)}{(2{\cdot}3 + j13{\cdot}0) + (4{\cdot}6 + j26{\cdot}0) + (6{\cdot}9 + j39{\cdot}0)} = 0{\cdot}77 + j4{\cdot}33 \ \Omega$$

using eqn. 3.2.5.8, the two remaining impedances connecting Stations A and B to the star point being similarly obtained.

The remaining steps in the reduction process are shown in Fig. 3.3.9E from which the resultant three-phase fault current is seen to be given by

$$I_f = \frac{80\ 800}{1{\cdot}72 + j41{\cdot}8} = 79{\cdot}7 - j1930 \ \text{A}$$

giving

$$I_f = 1932 \ \underline{/- 87° \ 40'} \ \text{A}$$

The distribution of the fault current in the power system can now be obtained by the process of back-substitution. This consists of retracing the steps in the reduction process starting with the total fault current and dividing this fault current among the different branches by straightforward application of the network laws. Thus, the current fed into the 132 kV system by the generator/transformer unit at

Station A is given by

$$\frac{(1\cdot15 + j86\cdot5)(79\cdot7 - j1930)}{(1\cdot15 + j86\cdot5) + (2\cdot30 + j66\cdot2)} = 55\cdot3 - j1094 \text{ A}$$

$$= 1095 \underline{/- 87°\ 7'} \text{ A}$$

and hence the phase-to-neutral voltage of the reference phase at Station A is given by

$$80\ 800 - j53\cdot2(55\cdot3 - j1094) = 22\ 550 - j2944 \text{ V}$$
$$= 22\ 720 \underline{/- 7°\ 26'} \text{ V}$$

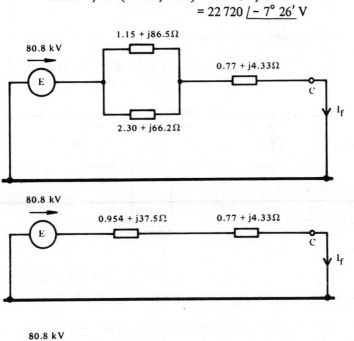

Fig. 3.3.9E

Similarly, the current fed into the 132 kV system from Station B is given by

$$(79\cdot7 - j1930) - (55\cdot3 - j1094) = 24\cdot4 - j836 \text{ A}$$
$$= 836 \underline{/- 88°\ 19'} \text{ A}$$

giving a voltage at Station B of

$$80\,800 - j80 \cdot 0(24 \cdot 4 - j836) = 13\,920 - j1952 \text{ V}$$
$$= 14\,050 \underline{/- 7° 58'} \text{ V}$$

Now, since the voltage at Station C is zero because of the fault, the current flowing from Station A to Station C is

$$\frac{22\,550 - j2944}{4 \cdot 6 + j26 \cdot 0} = 38 \cdot 9 - j860 \text{ A}$$
$$= 861 \underline{/-87° 25'} \text{ A}$$

Also, the current flowing from Station B to Station C, by subtraction, is

$$(79 \cdot 7 - j1930) - (38 \cdot 9 - j860) = 40 \cdot 8 - j1070 \text{ A}$$
$$= 1071 \underline{/- 87° 49'} \text{ A}$$

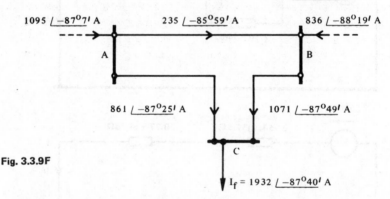

Fig. 3.3.9F

Finally, the current flowing from A to B is

$$(55 \cdot 3 - j1094) - (38 \cdot 9 - j860 = 16 \cdot 4 - j234 \text{ A}$$
$$= 235 \underline{/- 85° 59'} \text{ A}$$

The required fault-current distribution is thus as shown in Fig. 3.3.9F.

The voltage at the generator terminal at Station A, to the common base voltage of 132 kV, is

$$80\,800 - j31 \cdot 4(55 \cdot 3 - j1094) = 46\,430 - j1737 \text{ V}$$

the actual value, transformer phase-shift ignored, being

$$\frac{11(460\,430 - j1737)}{132} = 3870 - j145 \text{ V}$$
$$= 3870 \underline{/- 2° 8'} \text{ V}$$

Similarly, the actual generator current at Station A, transformer phase-shift ignored, is

$$\frac{132(55\cdot3 - j1094)}{11} = 663\cdot5 - j13\,130 \text{ A}$$

$$= 13\,150 \underline{/- 87°\,7'}\text{ A}$$

The corresponding values of voltage and current for the generator at Station B can be similarly shown to be $3190 - j103\cdot6$V (=$3190 \underline{/- 1°\,51'}$ V) and $293 - j10\,030$ A (= $10\,030 \underline{/- 88°\,19'}$ A), respectively.

3.3.10 Example 2

The power system shown in Fig. 3.3.10A develops a three-phase short-circuit at the point F on the h.v. terminals of one of the two auto-transformers at Station B, the pre-fault voltage at the 132 kV busbars of Station B being 138 kV. The load supplied by the 132 kV busbars can be assumed to be passive (that is, to contain no

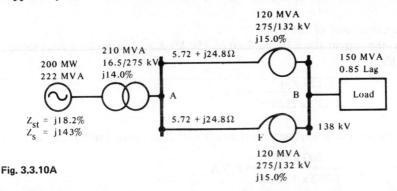

Fig. 3.3.10A

driving voltages) and to be representable by a constant impedance. Determine the value of the short-circuit current and the network branch currents at the instant of fault. Determine also the final steady-state value of the fault current and the network branch currents assuming the fault to remain on the system and there to be no voltage-regulator action.

Solution: Using the per-unit method and a common base of 200 MVA, the system positive-sequence network for the pre-fault load condition is as shown in Fig. 3.3.10B, the branch impedances having all been converted to common-base per-unit values. The generator driving-voltage and impedance depend on the fault condition being investigated, as already mentioned, and the values are therefore denoted by per-unit values E_g and Z_g as shown, the symbol V_g denoting the generator terminal voltage.

The conversion to common-base per-unit values has already been described in Section 3.3.7. Thus, the impedance of the generator step-up transformer, namely $j14.0$ per-cent on its own rating of 210 MVA, becomes

$$\frac{200 \times j0.140}{210} = j0.133 \text{ p.u. on 200 MVA}$$

Similarly, the impedance of each auto-transformer, namely $j15.0$ per-cent on their rating of 120 MVA, becomes

$$\frac{200 \times j0.150}{120} = j0.250 \text{ p.u. on 200 MVA}$$

The 275 kV transmission-line impedances, each of which corresponds to 76.5 km of a twin-conductor-bundle line design, are given in ohmic value in Fig. 3.3.10A and these have been converted by the use of eqn. 3.3.7.11, the resulting per-unit impedance of each line being given by

$$\frac{200 \times 10^6 \times (5.72 + j24.8)}{(275\,000)^2} = 0.015 + j0.0655 \text{ p.u.}$$

to the common base of 200 MVA.

Now, the current taken by the load of 150 MVA at the stated pre-fault voltage of 138 kV is

$$\frac{150 \times 10^6}{1.732 \times 138\,000} = 628 \text{ A}$$

and the current corresponding to the base MVA of 200 at a rated voltage of 132 kV is

$$\frac{200 \times 10^6}{1.732 \times 132\,000} = 875 \text{ A}$$

Hence, the scalar value of the load current in per-unit value is

$$\frac{628}{875} = 0.718 \text{ p.u. on 200 MVA}$$

The scalar value of the voltage across the load, namely 138 kV, is

$$\frac{138}{132} = 1.045 \text{ p.u.}$$

and hence the scalar value of the load impedance is given by

$$\frac{1.045}{0.718} = 1.455 \text{ p.u. on 200 MVA}$$

Now the power factor of the load is 0·850, lagging, corresponding to a load-impedance phase-angle of 31·8°, the sine and cosine of this phase angle being 0·527 and 0·850 respectively. The complex value of the load impedance is therefore given by

$$1·455(0·850 + j0·527) = 1·236 + j0·767 \text{ p.u.}$$

Adopting the pre-fault reference-phase voltage at the 132 kV busbar as the vector base, its complex value thus being $1·045 + j0$ p.u., the current supplied to the load is given by

$$\frac{1·045 \underline{/0°}}{1·455 \underline{/31·8°}} = 0·718 \underline{/- 31·8°}$$

$$= 0·610 - j0·379 \text{ p.u.}$$

This is also the current supplied by the generator through its step-up transformer, the current dividing equally between the two transformer-feeder circuits.

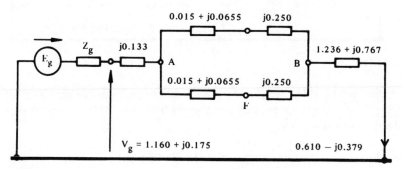

Fig. 3.3.10B

The generator terminal voltage is given by

$$V_g = (1·045 + j0) + [\tfrac{1}{2}(0·015 + j0·3155) + j0·133] \, (0·610 - j0·379)$$

giving

$$V_g = 1·160 + j0·175 \text{ p.u.}$$

The pre-fault conditions are thus as shown in Fig. 3.3.10B, and the fault analysis can now proceed by applying the fault connection between the point of fault F and the neutral bar with appropriate values of E_g and Z_g for the condition under investigation.

Considering, first, the conditions at the instant of short-circuit, the required generator impedance is the sub-transient value, namely $j18·2$ per-cent on the machine rating of 222 MVA, the required common-base per-unit value being

$$\frac{200 \times j0·182}{222} = j0·164 \text{ p.u. on 200 MVA}$$

The generator driving-voltage is the pre-fault value of the generator terminal-voltage plus the pre-fault impedance drop in the machine sub-transient impedance, giving

$$E_g = E_{st} = (1 \cdot 160 + j0 \cdot 175) + j0 \cdot 164(0 \cdot 610 - j0 \cdot 379)$$

from which

$$E_g = 1 \cdot 222 + j0 \cdot 275 \text{ p.u.}$$

The positive-sequence network for the conditions at the instant of fault is shown in Fig. 3.3.10C and this can be solved for the network branch currents by the process of network reduction and back-substitution, the reduction procedure being shown in Fig. 3.3.10D.

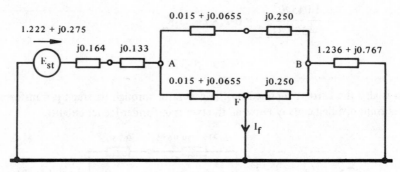

Fig. 3.3.10C

From Fig. 3.3.10D, the given network is seen to reduce to the generator driving-voltage E_{st} in series with the single impedance $0 \cdot 0124 + j0 \cdot 356$ p.u. and, hence, the generator current is given by

$$\frac{1 \cdot 222 + j0 \cdot 275}{0 \cdot 0124 + j0 \cdot 356} = 0 \cdot 892 - j3 \cdot 405 \text{ p.u}$$

Applying the process of back-substitution to obtain the remaining branch currents, the voltage at the point A is obtained from

$$V_A = (0 \cdot 892 - j3 \cdot 405)(0 \cdot 0124 + j0 \cdot 0590)$$

giving

$$V_A = 0 \cdot 2105 + j0 \cdot 00983 \text{ p.u.}$$

The current flowing from A to F through the 275 kV line associated with the faulted transformer can now be obtained and is

$$\frac{0 \cdot 2105 + j0 \cdot 00983}{0 \cdot 015 + j0 \cdot 0655} = 0 \cdot 842 - 3 \cdot 020 \text{ p.u.}$$

The current flowing from A to B through the other 275 kV line is the generator current minus the current just obtained and is given by

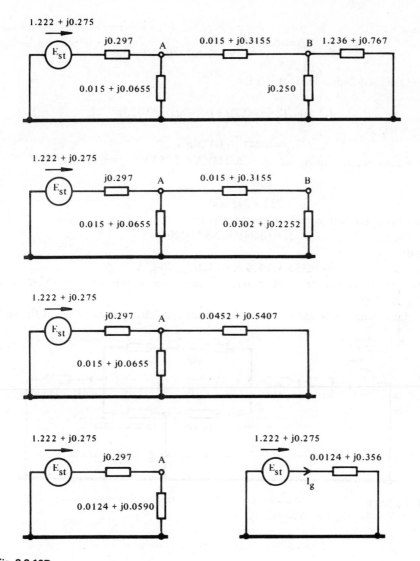

Fig. 3.3.10D

$$(0.892 - j3.405) - (0.842 - j3.020)$$
$$= 0.050 - j0.385 \text{ p.u.}$$

The voltage at B can now be obtained and is given by

$$(0.2105 + j0.00983) - (0.050 - j0.385)(0.015 + j0.3155)$$
$$= 0.0882 - j0.00027 \text{ p.u.}$$

The current flowing to the fault through the transformer on the faulted circuit is

given by

$$\frac{0 \cdot 0882 - j0 \cdot 00027}{j0 \cdot 250} = \sim 0 \cdot 001 - 0 \cdot 353 \text{ p.u.;}$$

and the total fault current at F is thus:

$$I_f = (0 \cdot 842 - j3 \cdot 020) + (- 0 \cdot 001 - j0 \cdot 353)$$

from which

$$I_f = 0 \cdot 841 - j3 \cdot 373 \text{ p.u.}$$

The base current corresponding to 200 MVA at 275 kV is given by

$$\frac{200 \times 10^6}{1 \cdot 732 \times 275\,000} = 420 \text{ A}$$

and hence the fault current in amps is given by

$$I_f = (0 \cdot 841 - j3 \cdot 373)420$$

giving

$$I_f = 353 - j1416 \text{ A} = 1460 \,\underline{/- 76 \cdot 0^\circ}\,\text{A}$$

The fault current and the branch currents are shown in per-unit value in Fig. 3.3.10F.

Considering now the determination of the final steady-state values of the fault

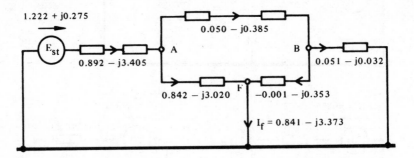

Fig. 3.3.10E

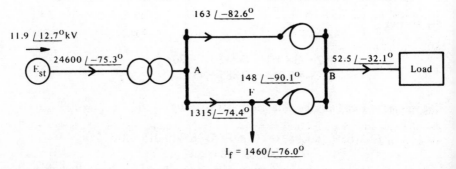

Fig. 3.3.10F

current and the network branch-currents, the generator impedance applicable to this condition is the synchronous value, namely $j143$ per-cent on the machine rating of 222 MVA. The required common-base per-unit value is thus

$$\frac{200 \times j1 \cdot 43}{222} = j1 \cdot 288 \text{ p.u. on 200 MVA}$$

The required generator driving-voltage is the pre-fault voltage behind the synchronous impedance (the excitation being assumed to remain unaltered) and this is given by

$$E_g = E_s = (1 \cdot 160 + j0 \cdot 175) + j1 \cdot 288(0 \cdot 610 - j0 \cdot 379)$$

from which $E_g = 1 \cdot 648 + j0 \cdot 961$ p.u.

The positive-sequence network for the final steady-state condition, therefore, is as shown in Fig. 3.3.10G and this can be solved for the network branch currents, as before, by the process of network reduction and back-substitution. Because the

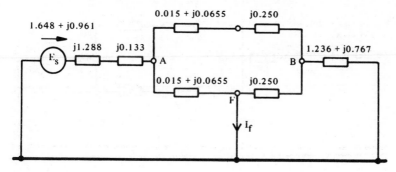

Fig. 3.3.10G

positive-sequence network external to the generator terminal is the same as for the previous case, its equivalent impedance as seen from the generator terminal is the same as before, namely

$$j0 \cdot 133 + (0 \cdot 0124 + j0 \cdot 0590) = 0 \cdot 0124 + j0 \cdot 192 \text{ p.u.}$$

The equivalent positive-sequence network, as seen from the generator, is therefore as shown in Fig. 3.3.10H and comprises a driving voltage of $1 \cdot 648 + j0 \cdot 961$ p.u. in series with an impedance of

$$j1 \cdot 288 + (0 \cdot 0124 + j0 \cdot 192) = 0 \cdot 0124 + j1 \cdot 480 \text{ p.u.}$$

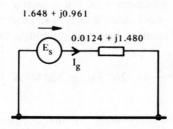

Fig. 3.3.10H

The current supplied by the generator, therefore, is given by

$$\frac{1 \cdot 648 + j0 \cdot 951}{0 \cdot 0124 + j1 \cdot 480.} = 0 \cdot 659 - j1 \cdot 108 \text{ p.u}$$

and, using the process of back-substitution, the network branch currents are found as shown in Fig. 3.3.10I, the fault current at F now being given by

$$I_f = 0 \cdot 637 - j1 \cdot 101 \text{ p.u.}$$

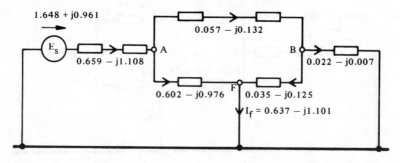

Fig. 3.3.10I

The fault current value in amps, therefore, is given by

$$I_f = (0 \cdot 637 - j1 \cdot 101)420$$

giving

$$I_f = 268 - j463 \text{ A} = 535 \underline{/- 60 \cdot 0°} \text{ A}$$

The values of the network branch currents in amps are shown in polar form, in Fig. 3.3.10J.

It should be noted that the results obtained by the method of solution employed above could have been obtained equally well by the use of Thevenin's Theorem and the Superposition Theorem. Thus, the impedance of the network of Fig. 3.3.10C, as measured between point F and the neutral bar with the fault connection removed and the driving voltage E_{st} short-circuited, is $0 \cdot 0549 + j0 \cdot 310$ p.u., as can be seen from the network reduction shown in Fig. 3.3.10K. Also the pre-fault

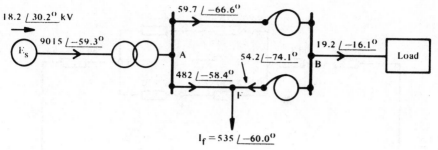

Fig. 3.3.10J

voltage E_f at the point of fault F is given by

$$E_f = (1 \cdot 045 + j0) + 0 \cdot 500(0 \cdot 610 - j0 \cdot 379)(j0 \cdot 250)$$

giving

$$E_f = 1 \cdot 092 + j0 \cdot 076 \text{ p.u.}$$

Hence, applying Thevenin's Theorem, the fault current for a short-circuit at F is given by

$$I_f = \frac{1 \cdot 092 + j0 \cdot 076}{0 \cdot 0549 + j0 \cdot 310}$$

giving

$$I_f = 0 \cdot 841 - j3 \cdot 373 \text{ p.u.}$$

This is seen to be identical to the value obtained by direct solution for the network branch currents.

Knowing the total fault current and the pre-fault branch currents, the network branch currents with the fault condition present are readily obtained by use of the Superposition Theorem as shown in Fig. 3.3.10L. Thus considering the pre-fault load condition represented by diagram (a) of this figure let E_f denote the pre-fault voltage at the point of fault, the value of E_f being $1 \cdot 091 + j0 \cdot 076$ p.u. as already computed. It will be evident that the network branch currents in diagram (a) will be undisturbed if a fictitious driving voltage of value E_f is assumed to be connected between the neutral bar and the point F, the direction of E_f being from the neutral bar to the point F. The pre-fault load condition indicated by diagram (a) can therefore be regarded as caused by the joint action of the driving voltages E_{st} and E_f. By Thevenin's Theorem, however, the fault current at F is obtained by applying a driving voltage E_f between the neutral bar and the point of fault F, as shown in diagram (b), with the driving voltage E_{st} removed (that is short-circuited). It should be noted in this diagram that the voltage E_f acts from the point F to the neutral bar, as is necessary to obtain the correct direction for the fault current, this being the same as an applied driving voltage of $-E_f$ acting from the neutral bar to the point of fault. Diagram (c) represents the required fault-plus-load condition for which it is required to determine the values of the network branch currents and it will be noted that this corresponds to diagram (a) with the assumed fictitious driving

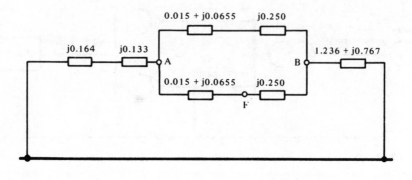

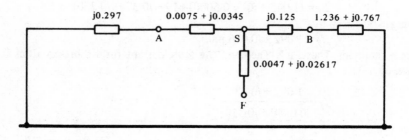

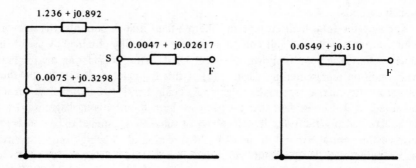

Fig. 3.3.10K

voltage E_f short-circuited.

Let the current in any given branch in diagrams (*a*), (*b*) and (*c*) be denoted by I_{load}, I_{fault} and $I_{load\text{-}plus\text{-}fault}$, respectively. Then by the Superposition Theorem it readily follows that:

$$I_{load} = I_{load\text{-}plus\text{-}fault} - I_{fault}$$

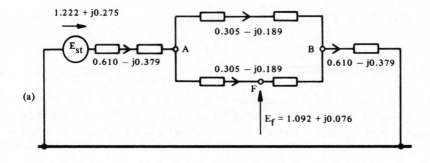

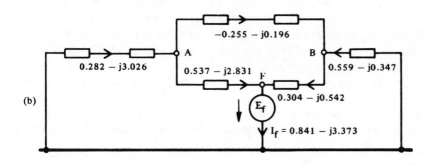

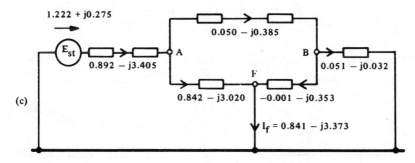

Fig. 3.3.10L

from which the required value of branch current for the load-plus-fault condition is given by:

$$I_{load\text{-}plus\text{-}fault} = I_{load} + I_{fault}$$

This relationship is true for each branch of the network as is easily seen from Fig. 3.3.10L. The use of the Superposition Theorem in this manner is particularly useful in cases where fault analysis is required to take due account of a known pre-fault load condition.

3.4   Calculation of unbalanced fault conditions

3.4.1   Symmetrical components

A full and proper analysis of unbalanced conditions in a three-phase network is made possible by the fact that any given set of unbalanced three-phase vectors, which may be voltages or currents, can be represented by the sum of three sets of balanced or symmetrical vectors, namely: *the positive-sequence set*, consisting of three vectors all equal in magnitude and symmetrically spaced, at 120° intervals, in time-phase with a stated phase order (termed the positive-sequence phase-order) equal to the phase order of the system generated voltages; *the negative-sequence set*, consisting of three vectors all equal in magnitude and symmetrically spaced, at 120° intervals, in time-phase, their phase-order being the reverse of the positive-sequence phase-order; and finally, *the zero-sequence set*, consisting of three vectors, all of which are equal in both magnitude and phase.

These three sets of component vectors are called the positive, negative and zero phase-sequence components of the given set of vectors, and are represented vectorially in the manner shown in Fig. 3.4.1A. The assumed direction of rotation for all voltage and current vectors is the anti-clockwise direction, and it thus follows

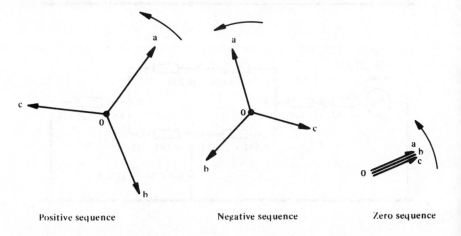

Positive sequence   Negative sequence   Zero sequence

Fig. 3.4.1A   *Phase-diagram representation of phase-sequence components*

that the positive-sequence vectors rotate in the positive-sequence phase-order a, b, c and the negative-sequence vectors in the phase-order a, c, b.

Relations between phase vectors and their sequence components: Let I_a, I_b and I_c be any set of unbalanced three-phase vectors, where the subscripts a, b and c denote the three phases in positive-sequence phase-order. Then denoting the positive, negative and zero phase-sequences by the second subscripts 1, 2 and 0, respectively, the three sets of component vectors are the positive-sequence set

$$I_{a1}, I_{b1} \; (= a^2 I_{a1}) \text{ and } I_{c1} (= a I_{a1})$$ 3.4.1.1

the negative-sequence set

$$I_{a2}, I_{b2} \; (= a I_{a2}) \text{ and } I_{c2} \; (= a^2 I_{a2})$$ 3.4.1.2

and finally, the zero sequence set

$$I_{ao}, I_{bo} \; (= I_{ao}) \text{ and } I_{co} \; (= I_{ao})$$ 3.4.1.3

where the symbol a (not to be confused with the phase reference) is the 120° operator already referred to in Section 3.3.1.

It will be noted that the nine sequence components can all be expressed in terms of the three components of any one chosen reference phase, here denoted by phase a.

From what has already been said, therefore, we have that

$$
\begin{aligned}
I_a &= I_{a1} + I_{a2} + I_{ao} \\
I_b &= I_{b1} + I_{b2} + I_{bo} \\
I_c &= I_{c\mathfrak{z}} + I_{c2} + I_{co}
\end{aligned}
$$ 3.4.1.4

and rewriting these equations in terms of the reference-phase (phase-a) sequence components only, we get

$$
\begin{aligned}
I_a &= I_1 + I_2 + I_0 \\
I_b &= a^2 I_1 + a I_2 + I_0 \\
I_c &= a I_1 + a^2 I_2 + I_0
\end{aligned}
$$ 3.4.1.5

the phase a subscript being omitted from the sequence components because phase-a is understood.

From these equations, the sequence components of the reference phase (phase a) can be obtained in terms of the three phase currents, the resulting equations being

$$
\begin{aligned}
I_1 &= \tfrac{1}{3} (I_a + a I_b + a^2 I_c) \\
I_2 &= \tfrac{1}{3} (I_a + a^2 I_b + a I_c) \\
I_0 &= \tfrac{1}{3} (I_a + I_b + I_c)
\end{aligned}
$$ 3.4.1.6

as can readily be checked by substituting for I_a, I_b and I_c in this latter set of eqautions using the values (expressed in terms of the phase-a sequence components) given by Eqns. 3.4.1.5.

The validity of these relationships between phase vectors and their sequence components can be demonstrated by the three vectors

$$
\begin{aligned}
I_a &= 0 + j14 \\
I_b &= 5 + j5 \\
I_c &= 4 - j8
\end{aligned}
$$

shown in Fig. 3.4.1B. Applying eqns. 3.4.1.4, 3.4.1.5 and 3.4.1.6 to these phase values we obtain

$$I_{a1} = \frac{(0+j14)+(-0\cdot5+j0\cdot866)(5+j5)+(-0\cdot5-j0\cdot866)(4-j8)}{3}$$

$$I_{a2} = \frac{(0+j14)+(-0\cdot5-j0\cdot866)(5+j5)+(-0\cdot5+j0\cdot866)(4-j8)}{3}$$

$$I_{a0} = \frac{(0+j14)+(5+j5)+(4-j8)}{3}$$

from which
$$I_{a1} = -5\cdot253+j5\cdot455$$
$$I_{a2} = 2\cdot253+j4\cdot878$$
$$I_{a0} = 3\cdot000+j3\cdot667$$

Using these values to obtain those for the other two phases gives

$$I_{b1} = (-0\cdot5-j0\cdot866)(-5\cdot253+j5\cdot455) = 7\cdot350+j1\cdot822$$
$$I_{b2} = (-0\cdot5+j0\cdot866)(2\cdot253+j4\cdot878) = -5\cdot350-j0\cdot488$$
$$I_{b0} = 3\cdot000+j3\cdot667$$

and
$$I_{c1} = (-0\cdot5+j0\cdot866)(-5\cdot9253+j5\cdot455) = -2\cdot101-j6\cdot976$$
$$I_{c2} = (-0\cdot5-j0\cdot866)(2\cdot253+j4\cdot878) = 3\cdot098-j4\cdot390$$
$$I_{c0} = 3\cdot000+j3\cdot667$$

These sequence components, rewritten in polar form, are

$I_{a1} = 7\cdot573\underline{/133\cdot9°}$,	$I_{a2} = 5\cdot372\underline{/65\cdot2°}$,	$I_{a0} = 4\cdot737\underline{/50\cdot7°}$
$I_{b1} = 7\cdot573\underline{/13\cdot9°}$,	$I_{b2} = 5\cdot372\underline{/-178\cdot8°}$,	$I_{b0} = 4\cdot737\underline{/50\cdot7°}$
$I_{c1} = 7\cdot573\underline{/-106\cdot1°}$,	$I_{c2} = 5\cdot372\underline{/-54\cdot8°}$,	$I_{c0} = 4\cdot737\underline{/50\cdot7°}$

The sequence components are shown in vector-diagram form in Fig. 3.4.1B.

The relationships between phase values and sequence-component values, although applied to current vectors in eqns. 3.4.1.1 to 3.4.1.6, are, of course, equally applicable to voltage vectors, the resulting equation being

$$\left.\begin{array}{l} V_a = V_1 + V_2 + V_0 \\ V_b = a^2 V_1 + a V_2 + V_0 \\ V_c = a V_1 + a^2 V_2 + V_0 \end{array}\right\} \qquad 3.4.1.7$$

for the phase values in terms of the reference-phase (phase-a) sequence components and

$$\left.\begin{array}{l} V_1 = \tfrac{1}{3}(V_a + a V_b + a^2 V_c) \\ V_2 = \tfrac{1}{3}(V_a + a^2 V_b + a V_c) \\ V_0 = \tfrac{1}{3}(V_a + V_b + V_c) \end{array}\right\} \qquad 3.4.1.8$$

for the converse relationships giving the sequence components of the reference phase (phase a) in terms of the phase values.

Because the symmetrical components of current and voltage in each of the three phases can be expressed in terms of those of the chosen reference phase (phase a), it

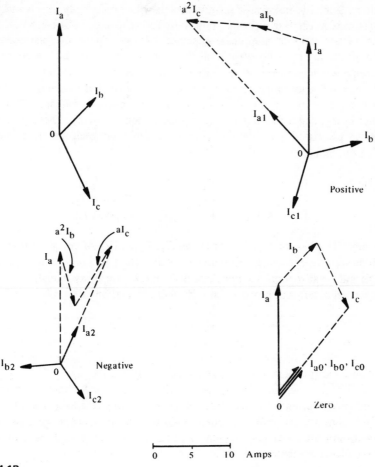

Fig. 3.4.1B

is usual to perform symmetrical-component analysis in terms of the sequence components of this reference phase. This permits the phase subscripts to be deleted from the sequence quantities, it being understood that, in the absence of the phase subscript, the sequence quantities referred to are the phase-a values.

3.4.2 Phase-sequence networks and impedances

The balanced nature of power-system plant impedances has already been referred to in Section 3.3.1, and it follows directly from this characteristic phase symmetry that, in any such balanced-impedance circuit, the voltage-drops produced in the three phases by phase currents of any given phase-sequence will themselves be of that same phase-sequence. Thus, the flow of positive sequence currents through such a circuit will produce positive-sequence voltage-drops in the three phases and no others. Similarly, negative-sequence currents will produce only negative-sequence voltage-drops and zero-sequence currents only zero-sequence voltage-drops.

The vector ratio of the phase-sequence voltage-drop to the phase-sequence current producing it is the same in all three phases and is termed the appropriate phase-sequence impedance of the circuit concerned. There are thus, in general, three phase-sequence impedances for any given three-phase circuit, namely the positive-sequence impedance denoted by Z_1, the negative sequence impedance denoted by Z_2, and the zero-sequence impedance denoted by Z_0. These impedances and their associated phase-sequence currents and voltage-drops are related by Ohm's Law, giving:

$$\left.\begin{array}{lll} V_{a1} = Z_1 I_{a1} & V_{a2} = Z_2 I_{a2} & V_{a0} = Z_0 I_{a0} \\ V_{b1} = Z_1 I_{b1} & V_{b2} = Z_2 I_{b2} & V_{b0} = Z_0 I_{b0} \\ V_{c1} = Z_1 I_{c1} & V_{c2} = Z_2 I_{c2} & V_{c0} = Z_0 I_{c0} \end{array}\right\} \qquad 3.4.2.1$$

In general, the phase-sequence impedances Z_1, Z_2 and Z_0 of any given three-phase circuit have different values, although for static (that is, non-rotating) plant the positive and negative sequence impedances Z_1 and Z_2 are always equal.

Expressed in terms of phase a, the voltage-drop equations are

$$\left.\begin{array}{l} V_1 = Z_1 I_1 \\ V_2 = Z_2 I_2 \\ V_0 = Z_0 I_0 \end{array}\right\} \qquad 3.4.2.2$$

the phase subscript being deleted since phase a is understood.

Considering, now, any balanced-impedance three-phase circuit carrying unbalanced phase currents I_a, I_b and I_c, the corresponding reference-phase (phase a) sequence currents are given by eqns. 3.4.1.6 and the resulting phase-sequence voltage-drops (phase-a values) by eqns. 3.4.2.2. The resulting total voltage-drops in the three phases are therefore

$$\left.\begin{array}{l} V_a = I_1 Z_1 + I_2 Z_2 + I_0 Z_0 \\ V_b = a^2 I_1 Z_1 + a I_2 Z_2 + I_0 Z_0 \\ V_c = a I_1 Z_1 + a^2 I_2 Z_2 + I_0 Z_0 \end{array}\right\} \qquad 3.4.2.3$$

these equations being obtained by substituting from equations 3.4.2.2. into eqns. 3.4.1.8.

Phase-sequence networks: The analysis of balanced-load and three-phase short-circuit conditions has already been discussed in Section 3.3 where use was made of the equivalent single-phase (reference-phase) representation of the power system appropriate to such balanced conditions. This equivalent network, termed the system positive-sequence network, is valid for the balanced conditions in question since, under such conditions, the power system voltages and currents, and the appropriate power system impedances, are all positive-sequence quantities. In order to be able to analyse unbalanced fault conditions, therefore, it is necessary first to consider the equivalent system networks appropriate to such unbalanced conditions, bearing in mind that the system voltages, currents and impedances to be taken into account now include, in general, both negative and zero sequence values in addition to positive-sequence values.

In balanced-impedance circuits, as already stated, currents of any given phase-sequence produce voltage-drops of that same sequence only, the value of the voltage drop for a given value of phase-sequence current being fixed by the appropriate phase-sequence impedance of the circuit concerned and being quite independent of the presence of currents of any other phase sequence in the circuit in question. This independence of the phase-sequence quantities means that in any power system consisting of balanced circuits:

(*a*)   the positive-sequence currents are determined solely by the positive-sequence driving voltages produced by the power sources, the positive-sequence voltage at the point of fault and the system positive-sequence impedances;

(*b*)   the negative-sequence currents are determined solely by the negative-sequence voltage at the point of fault and the system negative-sequence impedances; and,

(*c*)   the zero-sequence currents are determined solely by the zero-sequence voltage at the point of fault and the system zero-sequence impedances.

It is important to note that the e.m.f.s produced by the generators and other synchronous machines are positive-sequence voltages, there being no generated negative- or zero-sequence voltages in the power system. Hence, any negative- or zero-sequence currents present in the power system exist solely as a result of the negative-sequence and zero-sequence voltages, respectively, at the point of fault.

It will now be evident from the above-mentioned considerations that the analysis of unbalanced fault conditions requires, in general, the use of three single-phase (reference-phase) networks, one for each of the three phase-sequences. These networks are termed the system positive, negative and zero sequence networks, the several items of plant which constitute the given power system being represented in each network by their appropriate phase-sequence equivalent circuits.

Positive-sequence network: The system positive-sequence network, already referred to in Section 3.3.1, is a single-phase network representing the reference phase (phase a) of the given power system in so far as positive-sequence quantities are concerned. Each three-phase circuit is therefore represented by its positive-sequence impedance or impedances and, in the case of a power source, by a driving voltage representing the generated e.m.f. behind the source positive-sequence impedance.

Negative-sequence network: The system negative-sequence network is a single-phase network representing the reference phase (phase a) of the given power system in so far as negative-sequence quantities are concerned. Each three-phase circuit is therefore represented by its negative-sequence impedance or impedances. Because there are no generated negative-sequence e.m.f.s in the power system, every power source is represented simply by its negative-sequence impedance, there being no driving voltages corresponding to those in the positive-sequence network. As already pointed out, the positive and negative sequence impedances of any item of static plant are always equal, and it therefore follows that the positive and negative sequence networks differ only in so far as the representation of rotating machines is concerned.

Zero-sequence network: The system zero-sequence network is a single-phase network representing the reference phase of the given power system in so far as zero-sequence quantities are concerned. Each three-phase circuit is therefore represented by its zero-sequence impedance or impedances. Because there are no generated zero-sequence e.m.f.s in the power system, the zero-sequence network, like the negative-sequence network, contains no driving voltages. The zero-sequence network is the only network in which neutral-to-earth connections are shown, the currents in such earthing connections consisting of zero-sequence currents only.

Sequence network representation: It is convenient to depict the three phase-sequence networks, in general terms, by the simple block-diagram form of representation shown in Fig. 3.4.2A, it being appreciated that the rectangle representing any given sequence network is assumed to contain the whole of that sequence network for the particular power system under consideration. Any particular point in the power system (for example, a point of fault F) can be represented by a suitably lettered corresponding point in each of the three sequence networks.

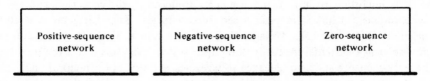

Fig. 3.4.2A   *Block diagram representation of sequence networks*

The thick base line of each rectangle in the block-diagram representation is termed the zero-potential bar and represents the zero-potential reference for the power system, namely earth potential. It is important to note, however, that under fault conditions the earth potential will, in general, be different at different points in the power system, these potential differences being caused by the flow of current through the earth. However, because it is never necessary to determine the values of the phase-sequence voltages at any given point on the system with respect to the earth potential at some other point, any ambiguity is avoided by always interpreting the term 'earth potential' to mean *local* earth potential. Thus, in the case of the zero-sequence network, the voltage at any point in this network, measured with respect to the zero-potential bar, represents the zero-sequence voltage at the corresponding point in the power system, measured with respect to the *local* earth at that point. Similar reasoning is applicable in the case of the positive and negative sequence networks, although for these two networks it is equally valid to regard the zero-potential bar as representing the system neutral.

Considering any short-circuit condition at a point F in the power system, this may be represented by the sequence networks in the manner shown in Fig. 3.4.2B(a), where the phase-a sequence currents flowing in to the fault are denoted by I_{f1}, I_{f2} and I_{f0} and the phase-a sequence voltages at the point of fault by V_{f1}, V_{f2} and V_{f0}. In the case of the open-circuit fault condition, the sequence-network representation is as shown in Fig. 3.4.2B(b), the two sides of the open-circuit in the faulted circuit being denoted by P and Q. In this latter case, the voltages V_{f1}, V_{f2} and V_{f0} are the phase-a sequence voltages produced between the points P and Q by the open-circuit fault condition, I_1, I_2 and I_0 being the resultant phase-a sequence currents in the faulted circuit.

The phase-sequence voltages and currents produced by the different types of fault are determined in Sections 3.4.4 and 3.4.5 together with the sequence-network interconnections necessary to represent these fault conditions.

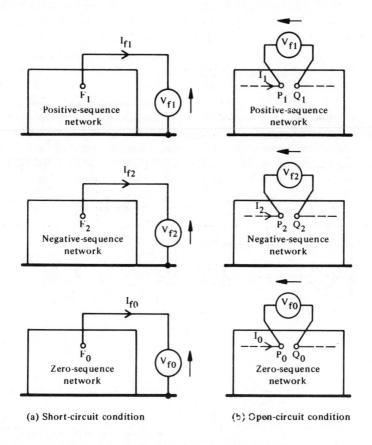

(a) Short-circuit condition   (b) Open-circuit condition

Fig. 3.4.2B   *Representation of fault conditions by sequence networks*

3.4.3　Phase-sequence equivalent circuits

The positive, negative and zero phase-sequence impedances of any given three-phase circuit can be determined by test by applying three-phase voltages of the appropriate phase-sequence and measuring the resultant phase currents, short-circuiting connections being applied to the circuit terminals, as necessary, in order to provide a path

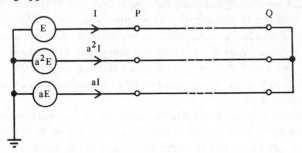

$$Z_1 = Z_2 = E/I$$

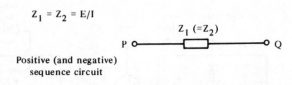

Positive (and negative)
sequence circuit

Fig. 3.4.3A　*Measurement of the positive (and negative) sequence impedance of a transmission line*

for the flow of the phase-sequence currents. Thus, the positive (and negative) sequence impedances of an overhead-line circuit (shunt-admittance ignored) and a star/delta transformer could be measured in the manner shown in Figs. 3.4.3A and

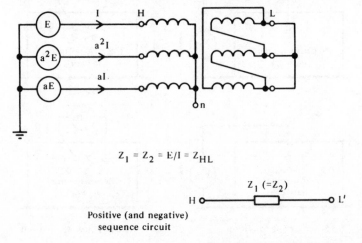

$$Z_1 = Z_2 = E/I = Z_{HL}$$

Positive (and negative)
sequence circuit

Fig. 3.4.3B　*Measurement of positive (and negative) sequence impedance of a transformer*

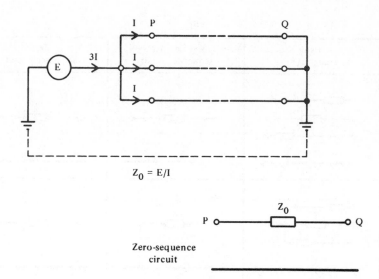

Fig. 3.4.3C *Measurement of the zero-sequence impedance of a transmission line*

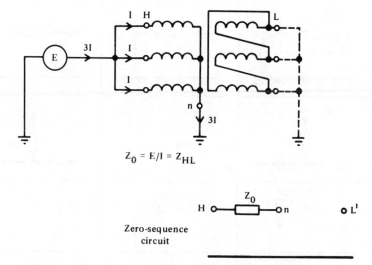

Fig. 3.4.3D *Measurement of the zero-sequence impedance of a transformer*

3.4.3B, respectively, and the zero-sequence impedance in the manner shown in Figs. 3.4.3C and 3.4.3D. Because these are both items of static (that is non-rotating) plant, the negative-sequence impedance is in each case equal to the positive-sequence value.

Table 3.4.3A gives the phase-sequence circuits of a number of arrangements of lumped impedances, the arrangements in question being representative of a number of typical items of power system plant. Thus, the first arrangement shown, namely a simple three-phase series circuit could represent a three-phase series reactor, and the second, namely the star-connected impedances, a three-phase shunt-reactor,

Circuit arrangement	Pos've and neg've sequence circuit	Zero sequence circuit
	Not applicable	

shunt-capacitor or load. The phase-sequence circuits appropriate to the arrangement of delta-connected impedances are obtained by applying the delta-to-star transformation, the resulting positive (and negative) sequence impedance being $Z/3$ as shown, where Z is the value of each impedance in the delta. The zero-sequence impedance of the delta-connected impedances, as seen from the circuit terminals, is obviously infinite since there is no path to earth for the flow of zero-sequence current. The zero-sequence circuit in this case, therefore, is simply an unconnected terminal, as shown.

In obtaining the positive and negative-sequence circuits, it is important to note that the system electrical neutral points are all at zero potential with respect to earth in so far as positive and negative-sequence voltages are concerned. The star point n of the set of three star-connected impedances (all equal) is therefore shown connected to the zero-potential bar in the positive and negative-sequence networks. In the case of the delta-connected impedances, the positive and negative-sequence circuits are the same in form as that for the star-connected impedances, the impedance value being $Z/3$ instead of Z as a result of the delta-to-star transformation. In this case it is the star point of the equivalent-star arrangement which can be regarded as connected to the zero-potential bar.

Neutral earthing impedances: It will be noted from Table 3.4.3A that the zero-sequence circuit for a neutral earthing impedance, of value Z_n is $3Z_n$ and the reason for this can be readily understood from Fig. 3.4.3E. At the neutral point, as

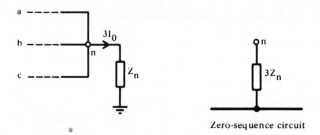

Fig. 3.4.3E *Zero-sequence circuit of a neutral earthing impedance*

shown, the zero-sequence currents I_0 in the three phases combine to give a current of $3I_0$ in the neutral earthing impedance, the three zero-sequence currents being all equal in both magnitude and phase. Now the potential V_0 of the neutral point with respect to earth is the same as the potential of the three phase conductors at the neutral point and hence the zero-sequence voltage at the neutral point, from eqn. 3.4.1.8, is

$$V_0 = \tfrac{1}{3}(V_n + V_n + V_n) = V_n$$

But,

$$V_n = 3I_0Z_n$$

and because the zero-sequence impedance is the zero-sequence voltage-drop divided by the per-phase zero-sequence current, it follows that the zero-sequence impedance of the earthing impedance is given by

$$Z_0 = \frac{3I_0Z_n}{I_0} = 3Z_n$$

and is thus seen to be three times the value of the neutral earthing impedance as shown in the figure.

Synchronous machines: The positive, negative and zero-sequence circuits for a synchronous machine (that is a generator, synchronous motor or synchronous condenser) are shown in Fig. 3.4.3F and require little further comment. The negative-sequence impedance is usually of roughly the same value as the positive-sequence sub-transient impedance, the zero-sequence impedance tending to vary cosiderably from one design of machine to another but being usually less than the negative-sequence impedance. All the machine impedances can generally be regarded, for most practical purposes as pure inductive reactances. It should be noted that the negative and zero sequence impedances have single fixed values for

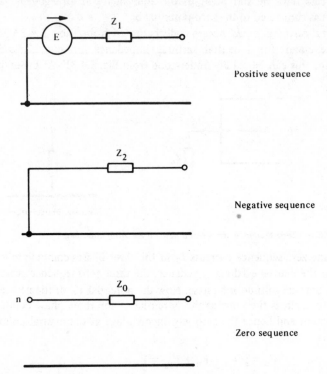

Fig. 3.4.3F   *Phase-sequence circuits of a synchronous machine*

any given machine (subject to slight variation due to saturation effects) whereas there are three values of positive-sequence impedance, as already discussed in Section 3.3.6, namely the subtransient, transient and synchronous values.

Overhead-line and cable circuits: The phase-sequence circuits for an overhead-line or underground cable circuit can generally be represented by the simple series circuits shown in Fig. 3.4.3G, these circuits being valid if the phase-to-phase and phase-to-earth admittances of the circuit are negligibly small. If these shunt admittances are not negligibly small, the phase-sequence circuits may be represented by the norminal-π circuits shown in Fig. 3.4.3H, where Y_1 and Y_0 are, respectively, the positive-sequence and zero-sequence admittances for the total length of the given circuit.

The value of the zero-sequence impedance Z_0 depends on the fact that the

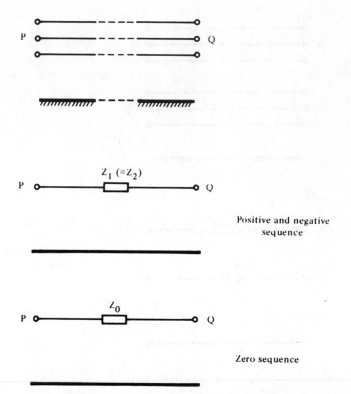

Fig. 3.4.3G   *Phase-sequence circuits of an overhead-line or cable circuit*

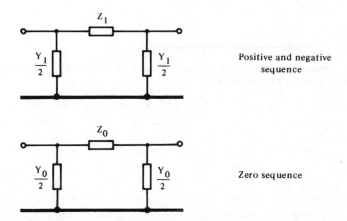

Fig. 3.4.3H   *Phase-sequence circuits of an overhead-line; or cable circuit including shunt-admittances*

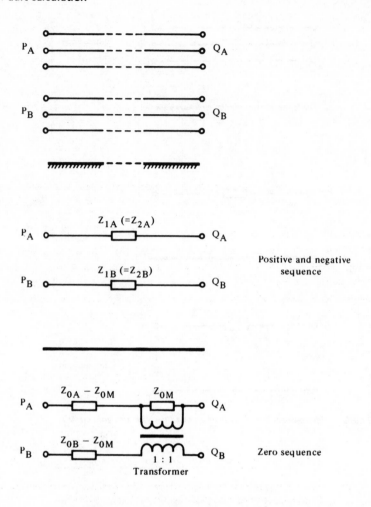

Fig. 3.4.3I   *Phase-sequence circuits of a pair of overhead-line or cable circuits with zero-sequence mutual coupling*

return path for the zero-sequence currents is through earth, the term 'earth' here being meant to refer to the body of the earth together with any circuit earth-wires or cable-sheaths connected to it. The zero-sequence impedance is generally greater than the positive (and negative) sequence impedance being usually in the order of two to three times the positive-sequence value in the case of overhead-line circuits. The zero-sequence circuits of Figs. 3.4.3G and 3.4.3H assume the overhead-line or cable circuit to be sufficiently remote from other circuits as to have no electromagnetic or electrostatic coupling with such circuits. Where this is not the case, as with the two circuits of a double-circuit overhead line, the required zero-sequence circuits (self and mutual shunt-admittances ignored) are as shown in Fig. 3.4.3I, the

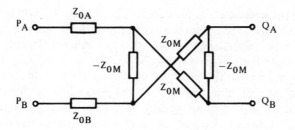

Fig. 3.4.3J   *Alternative form of zero-sequence circuit for the two circuits of Fig. 3.4.3I*

circuits shown taking due account of the zero-sequence mutual impedance Z_{0M}, between the two circuits concerned. The use of the perfect one-to-one ratio coupling-transformer in the zero-sequence circuit can be avoided if the given circuit is replaced by the equivalent circuit shown in Fig. 3.4.3I. If the two circuits are connected to a common busbar at one end, the resultant-zero-sequence circuit is that shown in Fig. 3.4.3K, Fig. 3.4.3L shows the equivalent zero-sequence circuit

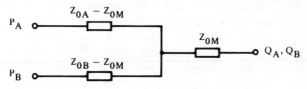

Fig. 3.4.3K   *Alternative form of zero-sequence circuit for the two circuits of Fig. 3.4.3I, the two circuits being connected to a common busbar at end Q*

for the case where the two circuits are connected to common busbars at both ends.

Allowance for shunt-admittance effects can be made in a similar way to that already referred to in connection with single-circuit lines, that is by means of

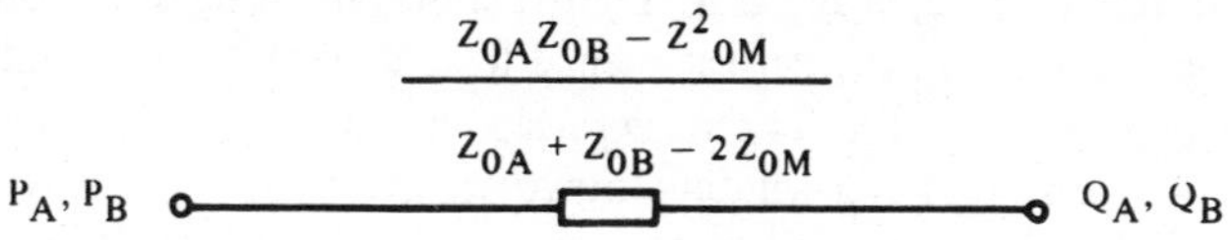

$$P_A, P_B \quad\text{o}\qquad \frac{Z_{0A}Z_{0B} - Z^2_{0M}}{Z_{0A} + Z_{0B} - 2Z_{0M}} \qquad\text{o}\quad Q_A, Q_B$$

Fig. 3.4.3L   *Alternative form of zero-sequence circuit for the two circuits of Fig. 3.4.3I, the two circuits being connected to common busbars at both ends*

shunt-connected impedances at the circuit ends, these impedances including circuit-to-circuit impedances in the zero-sequence circuit to represent the effects of zero-sequence mutual admittance between the two circuits. Positive and negative sequence mutual admittance can usually be assumed to be negligibly small.

Transformer circuits: The positive-sequence circuits of transformers have been considered in some detail in Section 3.3.3 and require little further comment other than to point out that they are equally valid for the negative-sequence network, there being no difference between the positive and negative-sequence circuits in so far as static plant is concerned. As pointed out in Section 3.3.5, the positive-sequence circuit of a transformer is based on the assumption that all the windings are star-connected, and this assumption applies similarly to the negative-sequence circuit. The effect of the actual transformer-winding connections (for example star/delta, star/interconnected-star, etc.) being simply to produce known phase-shifts of the network currents and voltages. This question of transformer phase-shifts is considered further in Section 3.4.5.

The zero-sequence circuit of a transformer is dependent on the paths which the transformer provides for the flow of zero-sequence current, the flow of zero-sequence currents in one winding requiring a balancing flow of zero-sequence currents in one or more other windings. Thus, considering the star/delta transformer of Fig. 3.4.3D, it will be noted that zero-sequence currents can flow in the star winding provided the neutral is earthed, the ampere-turns produced by these currents being balanced by a circulating zero-sequence current in the delta-winding of the transformer. It is important to note that the delta winding of the transformer provides no connection to earth for zero-sequence currents flowing in from the delta-winding terminals. The zero-sequence impedance of the transformer as seen from the delta-winding terminals is therefore infinite.

The zero-sequence circuit for the star/delta transformer is thus as shown in Fig. 3.4.3D, the transformer impedance Z_{HL} being the sum of the star-winding leakage-impedance Z_H per phase, and the referred delta-winding leakage-impedance, Z_L' per phase. For most practical purposes, the impedance Z_{HL} can be assumed to be the same for zero-sequence conditions as for positive (and negative) sequence coditions. The impedance Z_{HL} is the phase-sequence impedance in ohms referred to the nominal rated voltage of winding H and can be referred to any other rated voltage or converted to per-unit or per-cent value by the methods already described.

It is of interest to note, in Fig. 3.4.3D, that short-circuiting of the delta-winding terminals is unnecessary in the zero-sequence test, since the delta winding already provides a closed path for the flow of zero-sequence current. If the delta-winding were replaced by a second star-winding, however, the zero-sequence test would, of course, require the neutral and all three phase terminals of this star winding to be connected together, thus providing the necessary path for the flow of the zero-sequence currents.

The phase-sequence circuits for a star/delta transformer with an impedance-earthed neutral are shown in Fig. 3.4.3M, the zero-sequence circuit being readily derived from Figs. 3.4.3D and 3 4.3E. It will be noted that the earthing impedance affects only the zero-sequence circuit, the positive (and negative) sequence circuit consisting of the transformer impedance only.

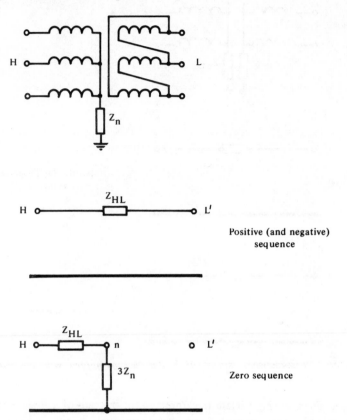

Fig. 3.4.3M *Phase-sequence circuits of a star/delta transformer with impedance-earthed neutral*

Fig. 3.4.3N shows the phase-sequence circuits of a star/star transformer, each of the two neutral points being individually earthed through an impedance. Here again, the given circuits are referred to the nominal rated voltage of winding H. The zero-sequence impedance of the circuit is seen to be

$$Z_{HL} + 3Z_{nh} + 3Z'_{nl}$$

where Z'_{nl} is the neutral impedance Z_{nl} referred to winding H and is therefore given by

$$Z'_{nl} = N^2 Z_{nl}$$

As before, N is the transformation-ratio of the transformer.

The zero-sequence circuit of Fig. 3.4.3N is, strictly speaking, only valid for the case of a five-limb transformer or its equivalent (for example, a three-phase unit

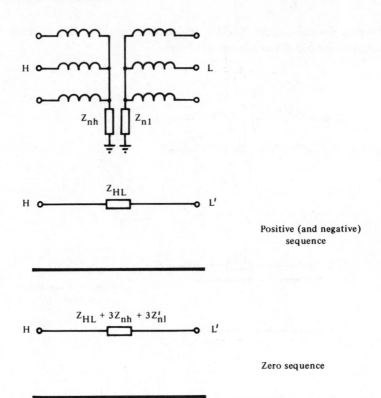

Fig. 3.4.3N   *Phase-sequence circuits of a star/star transformer with impedance-earthed neutrals*

composed of three single-phase transformers). In the case of a three-limb star/star transformer, the zero-sequence fluxes cause currents to be induced in the sides of the transformer tank (ref. Edith Clarke Vol. II) with the result that the latter acts as an effective high-impedance delta winding.

The phase-sequence circuits for a star/star auto-transformer are shown in Fig. 3.4.3P, the transformer neutral being impedance earthed. Here again, the zero-sequence circuit is only valid for the case of a five-limb transformer or its equivalent.

Star/star transformers are commonly provided with a delta-connected tertiary winding, and the phase-sequence circuits for such a transformer are shown in Fig. 3.4.3Q, the two star-winding neutrals being individually earthed through impedances. The zero-sequence circuit applies equally to the case where the delta-winding does not exist physically but is an effective winding formed by the transformer tank. As before, the given phase-sequence circuits are referred to the nominal rated voltage of winding H, referred impedance values being indicated by dashed symbols.

Fig. 3.4.3R shows the phase-sequence circuits for a star/star auto-transformer equipped with a delta-connected tertiary winding, the neutral being again impe-

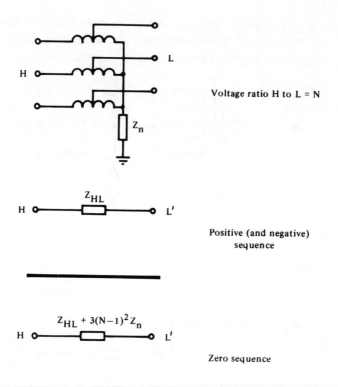

Voltage ratio H to L = N

Positive (and negative)
sequence

Zero sequence

Fig. 3.4.3P *Phase-sequence circuits of a star/delta auto-transformer with impedance-earthed neutral*

dance earthed. The phase-sequence circuits, as previously, are referred to winding H.

In all the zero-sequence circuits which have been given, the case of solid earthing of any given neutral is obtained by simply assuming a zero value for the earthing impedance in question. Similarly, in all cases except that given in Fig. 3.4.3R, the representation of an unearthed neutral is obtained by simply assuming an infinite value (that is an open-circuit) for the earthing impedance concerned. In the case of the star/star auto-transformer of Fig. 3.4.3R, putting Z_n equal to infinity in the given zero-sequence circuit gives an indeterminate result. For this case, therefore, the required zero-sequence circuit with the neutral unearthed is as shown in circuit (*a*) of Fig. 3.4.3S. This latter circuit is obtained by transforming the star circuit of Fig. 3.4.3R into its equivalent delta and then putting Z_n equal to infinity. An alternative form of the zero-sequence circuit is shown in circuit (*b*) of Fig. 3.4.3S.

As already stated, it is common practice to assume the transformer-winding leakage-impedances to be the same for zero and positive (and negative) sequence conditions. This equality of the sequence-impedances is exact for the special case of three-phase banks of single-phase transformers but for the more usual case of three-phase transformers it should be noted that differences may exist between the positive (and negative) and zero-sequence values. These differences are generally small, however, and are usually ignored in the great majority of fault calculations.

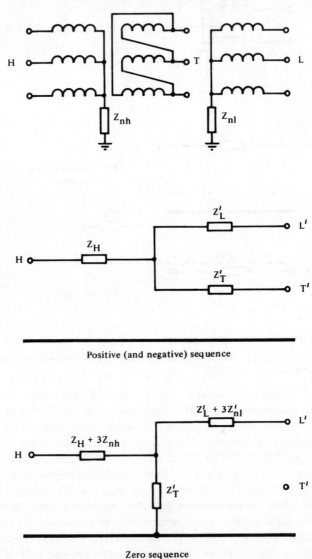

Positive (and negative) sequence

Zero sequence

Fig. 3.4.3Q   *Phase-sequence circuits of a star/star*

In the case of three-winding transformers in which one winding is a permanently connected delta winding, the measurement of the zero-sequence equivalent circuit is complicated slightly by the presence of the delta winding. Thus, consider a transformer with star-connected high-voltage and low-voltage windings and a delta-

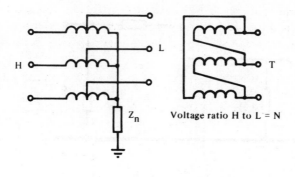

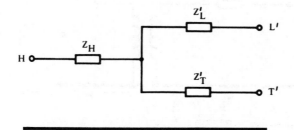

Positive (and negative) sequence

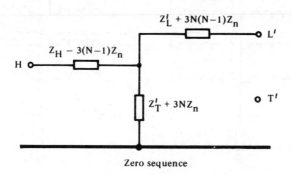

Zero sequence

Fig. 3.4.3R *Phase-sequence circuits of a star/star auto-transformer with delta-tertiary winding*

connected tertiary winding and let the common-base zero-sequence equivalent circuit be the star circuit composed of impedances Z_H, Z_L and Z_T.

Then, let Z_A = zero-sequence impedance measured at the terminals of winding H with winding L an open-circuit

Z_B = zero-sequence impedance measured at the terminals of winding H with winding L short-circuited to neutral

Z_C = zero-sequence impedance measured at the terminals of winding L with winding H on open-circuit

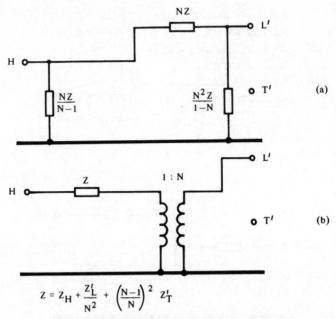

$$Z = Z_H + \frac{Z'_L}{N^2} + \left(\frac{N-1}{N}\right)^2 Z'_T$$

Fig. 3.4.3S   *Alternative forms of zero-sequence circuit for the transformer of Fig. 3.4.3R when the neutral is unearthed*

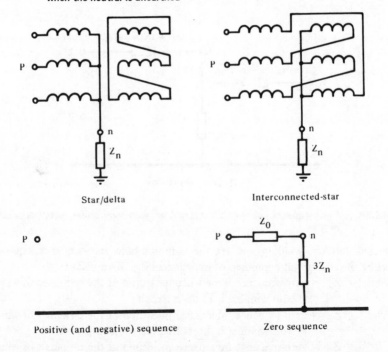

Star/delta   Interconnected-star

Positive (and negative) sequence   Zero sequence

Fig. 3.4.3T   *Phase-sequence circuits of an earthing transformer*

Z_D = zero-sequence impedance measured at the terminals of winding L with winding H short-circuited to neutral

Assuming all impedances to be to a common base, then

$$Z_A = Z_H + Z_T$$

$$Z_B = Z_H + \frac{Z_T Z_L}{Z_T + Z_L}$$

$$Z_C = Z_L + Z_T$$

$$Z_D = Z_L + \frac{Z_T Z_H}{Z_T + Z_H}$$

from which

$$Z_T = \sqrt{(Z_A(Z_C - Z_D))} = \sqrt{(Z_C(Z_A - Z_B))}$$
$$Z_H = Z_A - Z_T$$
$$Z_L = Z_C - Z_T$$

The same test method is applicable to the case of the star/star auto-transformer with delta-tertiary winding.

Earthing transformers: The transformers considered so far have all been of the type required to provide interconnection facilities between network sections and, as already seen, such transformers commonly provide neutral earthing facilities for one or more of the network sections concerned. In certain cases, however, a transformer may be used solely for the provision of a neutral earthing point where such a neutral point would not otherwise exist, for example, on the delta side of a star/delta transformer.

The requirements of a neutral earthing transformer are that it should present a low impedance to the flow of zero-sequence currents but a high impedance (ideally infinitely high) to the flow of positive (and negative) sequence currents. Two commonly used earthing-transformer arrangements are shown in Fig.3.4.3T, namely the star/delta transformer and the inter-connected-star earthing-reactor. In each case, the positive (and negative) sequence impedance can be regarded as infinitely high for most practical purposes, this impedance being the positive (and negative) sequence magnetising-impedance. The positive-sequence circuit thus consists of the unconnected terminal as shown. In the case of the star/delta transformer, the zero-sequence impedance Z_0 is the sum of the star-winding and delta-winding leakage impedances as already explained, while in the case of the interconnected-star earthing reactor it is the sum of the leakage impedances of the two equal half-windings which constitute each leg of the reactor. It will be noted that the flow of zero-sequence current through the earthing reactor produces zero magnetising ampere-turns on each leg of the reactor since the ampere-turns produced by one

Table 3.4.3B *Typical per-cent reactances of synchronous machines at 50 Hz*

Type and rating of machine	Positive sequence			Negative sequence X_2	Zero sequence X_0	Short-circuit ratio
	X_{st}	X_t	X_s			
11 kV salient-pole alternator without dampers	22·0	33·0	110	22·0	6·0	–
11·8 kV 60 MW 75 MVA turbo-alternator	12·5	17·5	201	13·5	6·7	0·55
11·8 kV 56 MW 70 MVA gas-turbine turbo-alternator	10·0	14·0	175	13·0	5·0	0·68
11·8 kV 70 MW 87·5 MVA gas-turbine turbo-alternator	14·0	19·0	195	16·0	7·5	0·55
13·8 kV 100 MW 125 MVA turbo-alternator	20·0	28·0	206	22·4	9·4	0·58
16·0 kV 275 MW 324 MVA turbo-alternator	16·0	21·5	260	18·0	6·0	0·40
18·5 kV 300 MW 353 MVA turbo-alternator	19·0	25·5	265	19·0	11·0	0·40
22 kV 500 MW 588 MVA turbo-alternator	20·5	28·0	255	20·0	6·0 – 12·0	0·40
23 kV 660 MW 776 MVA turbo-alternator	23·0	28·0	207	26·0	15·0	0·50

Table 3.4.3C *Typical impedance values for overhead lines at 50 Hz*

Voltage kV	Conductor size in mm² al.	Series impedance Ω/km			Shunt susceptance $\mu\Omega^{-1}$/km			Charging current amps/km
		Z_1 (and Z_2)	Z_0	Z_{0m}*	Z_1 (and B_2)	B_0	B_{0m}*	
33	75	0·36 + j0·41	0·56 + j1·02	–	–	–	–	–
33	100	0·27 + j0·39	0·48 + j0·98	–	–	–	–	–
33	175	0·15 + j0·37	0·35 + j0·97	–	–	–	–	–
132	175	0·177 + j0·402	0·354 + j1·022	0·178 + j0·509	2·85	1·66	−0·463	0·22
132	400	0·076 + j0·379	0·191 + j0·963	0·115 + j0·474	3·04	1·73	−0·494	0·24
274	2 x 175	0·089 + j0·324	0·198 + j0·854	0·110 + j0·462	3·52	2·04	−0·681	0·58
275	2 x 400	0·038 + j0·320	0·147 + j0·839	0·109 + j0·450	3·59	2·06	−0·682	0·58
400	2 x 400	0·039 + j0·328	0·146 + j0·851	0·107 + j0·445	3·59	2·09	−0·663	0·85
400	4 x 400	0·019 + j0·277	0·105 + j0·790	0·086 + j0·425	4·13	2·33	−0·684	0·98

Table 3.4.3D   Typical impedance data for underground cable circuits at 50 Hz

Rated voltage kV	Conductor size mm²	Sheath type and bonding	Core formation and spacing	Series impedance Ω/km Z_1 (and Z_2)	Z_0	Charging current A/km
11	120	Lead Solid	Three-core	$0.181 + j0.084$	—	1.16
33	120	Lead Solid	Three-core	$0.181 + j0.107$	—	1.77
33	300	Lead Solid	Close-trefoil	$0.071 + j0.106$	—	2.49
66	630	Lead Cross	Flat, 127 mm	$0.037 + j0.152$	$0.568 + j0.245$	10.3
132	500	CSA* Solid	Three-core	$0.050 + j0.088$	—	9.86
132	2600	CSA* Cross	Flat, 520 mm	$0.011 + j0.204$	$0.063 + j0.0396$	20.0
275	1150	Lead Cross	Flat, 205 mm	$0.0206 + j0.169$	$0.323 + j0.117$	19.2
275	2000	CSA* Cross	Flat, 260 mm	$0.0138 + j0.169$	$0.0646 + j0.0507$	23.9
400	2000	Lead Cross	Flat, 145 mm	$0.0140 + j0.132$	$0.224 + j0.0829$	27.8
400	3000	CSA* Cross	Tref., 585 mm	$0.0093 + j0.189$	$0.044 + j0.0490$	33.3

*CSA - Corrugated seamless aluminium

Table 3.4.3E   *Typical per-cent reactances of two-winding transformers at 50 Hz*

Transformer rating in MVA	Nominal voltage of higher-voltage winding								
	3.3 kV	6.6kV	11 kV	22 kV	33 kV	66 kV	132 kV	275 kV	400 kV
1	4.75	4.75–6.0	4.74–6.0	5.0–6.0	5.0–6.0	6.0	—	—	—
5	—	6.0–7.0	6.0–7.0	6.0–7.0	6.0–7.0	7.5	—	—	—
10	—	9.0–11.0	9.0–11.0	9.0–11.0	9.0–11.0	9.0–11.0	10.0	—	—
15	—	12.5–15.0	12.5–15.0	12.5–15.0	12.5–15.0	10.0–11.0	10.0	—	—
30	—	—	—	—	12.5	10.0–11.0	10.0	—	—
45	—	—	—	—	—	10.0–12.5	12.5	—	—
60	—	—	—	—	—	10.0–12.5	12.5	—	—
90	—	—	—	—	—	—	15.0–22.5	15.0–20.0	—
120	—	—	—	—	—	—	—	17.0	—
210	—	—	—	—	—	—	—	17.0	—
425	—	—	—	—	—	—	—	17.0	—
600	—	—	—	—	—	—	—	—	14.0–16.0
800	—	—	—	—	—	—	—	—	14.0–16.0

Table 3.4.3F *Typical per-cent reactances of auto-transformers at 50 Hz*
All transformers equipped with delta-tertiary windings

Transformer rating	Per-cent reactance					
	X_{HL}	X_{HT}	X_{LT}	X_H	X_L	X_T
120 MVA 275/132 kV	15·0	38·0	18·0	17·5	− 2·5	20·5
180 MVA 275/132 kV	15·0	40·0	20·0	17·5	− 2·5	22·5
240 MVA 275/132 kV	20·0	52·0	25·0	23·5	− 3·5	28·5
240 MVA 400/132 kV	20·0	52·0	30·0	21·0	− 1·0	31·0
500 MVA 400/132 kV	12·0	80·0	52·0	20·0	− 8·0	60·0
750 MVA 400/275 kV	12·0	85·0	60·0	18·5	− 6·5	66·5
1000 MVA 400/275 kV	16·0	110·0	84·0	21·0	− 5·0	89·0

half-winding are equal and opposite to those produced by the other.

Plant impedance values: Typical impedance values for synchronous machines, overhead lines, cable circuits and transformers are given in Tables 3.4.3B, 3.4.3C, 3.4.3D, 3.4.3E and 3.4.3F.

3.4.4 Analysis of short-circuit conditions

The analysis of unbalanced fault conditions has already been shown to involve, in general, the three phase-sequence networks of the given power system, namely the positive, negative and zero-sequence networks. It is convenient to represent each sequence network in its simplest form as viewed from the point of short-circuit, F, the positive-sequence network being thus represented by a driving voltage E in series with a positive-sequence impedance Z_1, the negative-sequence network by the negative-sequence impedance Z_2 and the zero-sequence network by the zero-sequence impedance Z_0. In other words, the power system as seen from the point of fault, F, is considered as a single equivalent three-phase generator of terminal voltage E (reference-phase-to-neutral) and phase-sequence impedances Z_1, Z_2 and Z_0. These conditions are shown in Fig. 3.4.4A.

It will be noted that the voltage E is the pre-fault reference-phase voltage at the point of fault and that Z_1, Z_2 and Z_0 are the impedances of the positive, negative and zero-sequence networks, respectively, as measured from the point of fault.

The symmetrical-component equations representing any given fault condition are obtained from a knowledge of the voltage and current constraints at the point of fault, these constraints being expressed in symmetrical component terms. The standard formulae for a number of short-circuit conditions are derived below, phase 'a' being used as the reference phase. The symbols V_1, V_2 and V_0 denote the reference-phase sequence voltages at the point of short-circuit and the symbols I_1, I_2 and I_0 the reference-phase sequence currents flowing into the fault.

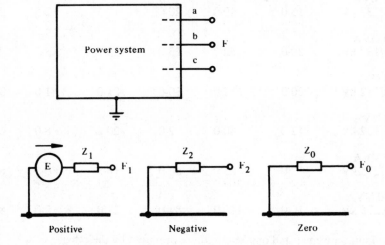

Fig. 3.4.4A *Equivalent phase-sequence circuits of a power system as seen from the point of fault*

(*a*)   *Three-phase fault:* Considering, first, the three-phase fault clear of earth, shown in Fig. 3.4.4B, the conditions at the point of fault are

$$V_a = V_b = V_c = V, \text{ say} \qquad\qquad 3.4.4.1$$

and

$$I_a + I_b + I_c = 0 \qquad\qquad 3.4.4.2$$

Expressing eqn. 3.4.4.2 in terms of symmetrical components gives

$$(I_1 + I_2 + I_0) + (a^2 I_1 + a I_2 + I_0) + (a I_1 + a^2 I_2 + I_0) = 0$$

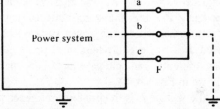

Fig. 3.4.4.B   *Three-phase fault*

from which

$$I_0 = 0$$

because $1 + a + a^2$ is equal to zero.

Expressing eqns. 3.4.4.1 in terms of symmetrical components (with $I_0 = 0$) gives

$$\left.\begin{array}{l} V_a = E - I_1 Z_1 - I_2 Z_2 = V \\ V_b = a^2 E - a^2 I_1 Z_1 - a I_2 Z_2 = V \\ V_c = aE - a I_1 Z_1 - a^2 I_2 Z_2 = V \end{array}\right\} \qquad 3.4.4.3$$

and adding the three equations together we obtain

$$V_a + V_b + V_c = 0 = 3V$$

Hence

$$V_a = V_b = V_c = 0$$

Now, from eqn. 3.4.4.3 it is seen that

$$V_a - aV_b = (a^2 - 1)I_2 Z_2 = (1 - a)V = 0$$

Hence

$$I_2 = 0$$

The required symmetrical-component equations for the three-phase fault are therefore

$$\left.\begin{array}{l} I_1 = \dfrac{E}{Z_1} \\[2mm] I_2 = 0 \\ I_0 = 0 \end{array}\right\} \qquad 3.4.4.4$$

Turning, now, to the three-phase-to-earth fault, the only difference from the conditions just considered is that the three phase conductors, in addition to being connected to each other, are also connected to earth. The conditions at the point of fault are, therefore, now given by

$$\left.\begin{array}{l} V_a = E - I_1 Z_1 - I_2 Z_2 - I_0 Z_0 = 0 \\ V_b = a^2 E - a^2 I_1 Z_1 - a I_2 Z_2 - I_0 Z_0 = 0 \\ V_c = aE - a I_1 Z_1 - a^2 I_2 Z_2 - I_0 Z_0 = 0 \end{array}\right\} \qquad 3.4.4.5$$

Adding these three equations together gives

$$V_a + V_b + V_c = -3 I_0 Z_0 = 0$$

from which

$$I_0 = 0$$

because $1 + a + a^2$ is equal to zero.

Also from these same equations

$$V_a - aV_b = (a^2 - 1)I_2Z_2 = 0$$

from which

$$I_2 = 0$$

The required symmetrical-component equations are therefore precisely the same as those already given by eqns. 3.4.4.4 for the three-phase fault clear of earth. The electrical conditions are thus the same for both types of fault, there being zero current in the earth connection for the three-phase-to-earth fault.

Since the only currents present are positive-sequence currents, the phase currents flowing into the fault are

$$I_a = I_1 = \frac{E}{Z_1}$$

$$I_b = a^2{}_1 = \frac{a^2 E}{Z_1}$$ 3.4.4.6

$$I_c = aI_1 = \frac{aE}{Z}$$

the sum of the three currents being zero as already indicated.

(*b*)   *Phase-to-phase fault:* It is convenient to assume the phase-to-phase fault to be between phases b and c, as shown in Fig. 3.4.4C, the conditions at the point of fault being

$$I_a = 0$$ 3.4.4.7

$$I_b + I_c = 0$$ 3.4.4.8

$$V_b = V_c = V, \text{say}$$ 3.4.4.9

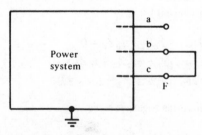

Fig. 3.4.4C   *Phase-to-phase fault*

Writing eqns. 3.4.4.7. and 3.4.4.8 in terms of symmetrical components gives

$$I_a = I_1 + I_2 + I_0 = 0$$
$$I_b + I_c = (a^2 I_1 + aI_2 + I_0) + (aI_1 + a^2 I_2 + I_0) = 0$$

from which

$$I_b + I_c = - I_1 - I_2 + 2I_0 = 0$$

Hence, it is seen that

$$I_a + I_b + I_c = 3I_0 = 0$$

so that

$$I_0 = 0$$

Also, from the equations for I_a and $I_b + I_c$ it is seen that

$$I_a - (I_b + I_c) = 2I_1 + 2I_2 = 0$$

from which

$$I_2 = -I_1$$

Expressing eqns. 3.4.4.9 in symmetrical-component form gives

$$V_b = a^2 E - a^2 I_1 Z_1 - aI_2 Z_2 = V$$
$$V_c = aE - aI_1 Z_1 - a^2 I_2 Z_2 = V$$

from which

$$V_b - V_c = (a^2 - a)E - (a^2 - a)I_1 Z_1 - (a - a^2)I_2 Z_2 = 0$$

giving

$$E - I_1 Z_1 + I_2 Z_2 = 0$$

But $I_2 = -I_1$ and hence it is seen that

$$E - I_1(Z_1 + Z_2) = 0$$

The required symmetrical-component equations for the phase-to-phase fault are therefore

$$\left. \begin{aligned} I_1 &= \frac{E}{Z_1 + Z_2} \\[2ex] I_2 &= \frac{- E}{Z_1 + Z_2} \\[2ex] I_0 &= 0 \end{aligned} \right\} \qquad 3.4.4.10$$

The phase currents flowing into the fault can now be obtained and are given by

$$\left. \begin{aligned} I_a &= I_1 + I_2 = 0 \\[2ex] I_b &= a^2 I_1 + aI_2 = \frac{-j\sqrt{3}E}{Z_1 + Z_2} \\[2ex] I_c &= aI_1 + a^2 I_2 = \frac{j\sqrt{3}E}{Z_1 + Z_2} \end{aligned} \right\} \qquad 3.4.4.11$$

because $a^2 - a$ is equal to $- j\sqrt{3}$.

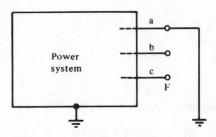

Fig. 3.4.4D   *Single-phase-to-earth fault*

(c)   *Single-phase-to earth fault:* For this fault condition, it is convenient to assume the short-circuit to be between phase a and earth, as shown in Fig. 3.4.4.D, the conditions at the point of fault being

$$V_a = 0 \qquad\qquad\qquad 3.4.4.12$$

$$I_b = I_c = 0 \qquad\qquad\qquad 3.4.4.13$$

Writing eqns 3.4.4.13 in symmetrical-component form, we obtain

$$I_b = a^2 I_1 + a I_2 + I_0 = 0;$$
$$I_c = a I_1 + a^2 I_2 + I_0 = 0$$

and from these equations it is seen that

$$I_b - I_c = (a^2 - a)I_1 + (a - a^2)I_2 = 0$$

from which

$$I_1 = I_2$$

Substituting for I_2 therefore

$$I_b + I_c = - I_1 - I_1 + 2I_0 = 0$$

from which

$$I_0 = I_1$$

Hence

$$I_1 = I_2 = I_0$$

Writing eqn. 3.4.4.12 in symmetrical-component form gives

$$V_a = E - I_1 Z_1 - I_2 Z_2 - I_0 Z_0 = 0$$

but because I_2 and I_0 are both equal to I_1, this can be written

$$E - I_1(Z_1 + Z_2 + Z_0) = 0$$

Hence, the required symmetrical-component equations for the single-phase-to-earth fault are

$$I_1 = I_2 = I_0 = \frac{E}{Z_1 + Z_2 + Z_0}$$

3.4.4.14

The phase currents flowing into the fault can now be obtained and are given by

$$I_a = I_1 + I_2 + I_0 = \frac{3E}{Z_1 + Z_2 + Z_0}$$

$$I_b = a^2 I_1 + a I_2 + I_0 = 0$$
$$I_c = a I_1 + a^2 I_2 + I_0 = 0$$

3.4.4.15

(*d*) *Two-phase-to-earth fault:* It is convenient to assume the two-phase-to-earth fault to be between phases b and c and earth, as shown in Fig. 3.4.4E, the conditions at the point of fault being

$$I_a = 0$$

3.4.4.16

$$V_b = V_c = 0$$

3.4.4.17

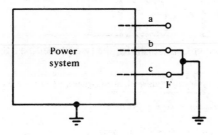

Fig. 3.4.4E   *Two-phase-to-earth fault*

Writing eqn. 3.4.4.17 in symmetrical-component form gives

$$V_b = a^2 E - a^2 E - a^2 I_1 Z_1 - a I_2 Z_2 - I_0 Z_0 = 0$$
$$V_c = aE - a I_1 Z_1 - a^2 I_2 Z_2 - I_0 Z_0 = 0$$

from which

$$V_b - a V_c = (1 - a) I_2 Z_2 - (1 - a) I_0 Z_0 = 0$$

giving

$$I_0 = \frac{I_2 Z_2}{Z_0}$$

Writing eqn. 3.4.4.16 in terms of symmetrical components gives

$$I_a = I_1 + I_2 + I_0 = 0$$

which, on substituting for I_0, becomes

$$I_a = I_1 + \frac{(Z_2 + Z_0)I_2}{Z_0} = 0$$

Hence

$$I_2 = \frac{-Z_0 I_1}{Z_2 + Z_0}$$

$$I_0 = \frac{-Z_2 I_1}{Z_2 + Z_0}$$

Now

$$V_b + V_c = -E + I_1 Z_1 + I_2 Z_2 - 2I_0 Z_0 = 0$$

which on substituting for I_2 *and* I_0, becomes

$$E = I_1 \left[Z_1 - \frac{Z_1 Z_0}{Z_2 + Z_0} + \frac{2Z_2 Z_0}{Z_2 + Z_0} \right]$$

from which

$$E = I_1 \left[Z_1 + \frac{Z_2 Z_0}{Z_2 + Z_0} \right]$$

The symmetrical-component equations for the two-phase-to-earth fault are therefore

$$\left. \begin{array}{l} I_1 = \dfrac{(Z_2 + Z_0)E}{Z_1 Z_2 + Z_2 Z_0 + Z_0 Z_1} \\[2em] I_2 = \dfrac{-Z_0 E}{Z_1 Z_2 + Z_2 Z_0 + Z_0 Z_1} \\[2em] I_0 = \dfrac{-Z_2 E}{Z_1 Z_2 + Z_2 Z_0 + Z_0 Z_1} \end{array} \right\} \qquad 3.4.4.18$$

The phase currents flowing into the fault can now be obtained and are given by

$$\left. \begin{array}{l} I_a = I_1 + I_2 + I_0 = 0 \\[1.5em] I_b = a^2 I_1 + a I_2 + I_0 = \dfrac{-j\sqrt{3}E(Z_0 - aZ_2)}{Z_1 Z_2 + Z_2 Z_0 + Z_0 Z_1} \\[2em] I_c = a I_1 + a^2 I_2 + I_0 = \dfrac{j\sqrt{3}E(Z_0 - a^2 Z_2)}{Z_1 Z_2 + Z_2 Z_0 + Z_0 Z_1} \end{array} \right\} \qquad 3.4.4.19$$

(*e*)   *The phase-to-phase plus single-phase-to-earth fault*: It is convenient to assume the phase-to-phase fault to be between phases b and c and the single-phase-to-earth fault between phase a and earth, as shown in Fig. 3.4.4F, the conditions at the point of fault being

$$V_a = 0 \qquad\qquad\qquad 3.4.4.20$$
$$V_b = V_c = V, \text{say} \qquad 3.4.4.21$$
$$I_b + I_c = 0 \qquad\qquad 3.4.4.22$$

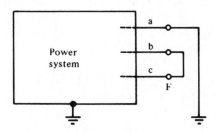

Fig. 3.4.4F   *Phase-to-phase plus single-phase-to-earth fault*

Writing equations 3.4.4.20 and 3.4.4.21 in terms of symmetrical components gives

$$V_a = E - I_1 Z_1 - I_2 Z_2 - I_0 Z_0 = 0$$
$$V_b = a^2 E - a^2 I_1 Z_1 - a I_2 Z_2 - I_0 Z_0 = V$$
$$V_c = aE - a I_1 Z_1 - a^2 I_2 Z_2 - I_0 Z_0 = V$$

Adding these equations together gives

$$V_a + V_b + V_c = -3 I_0 Z_0 = 2V$$

from which

$$V = \frac{-3 I_0 Z_0}{2}$$

Now, from the equations for V_b and V_c

$$V_b - a V_c = (1 - a) I_2 Z_2 - (1 - a) I_0 Z_0 = (1 - a) V$$

giving

$$I_2 Z_2 - I_0 Z_0 = V$$

and substituting for V gives

$$I_2 Z_2 - I_0 Z_0 = \frac{-3 I_0 Z_0}{2}$$

Hence

$$I_0 = \frac{-2I_2 Z_2}{Z_0}$$

Writing eqn. 3.4.4.22 in terms of symmetrical components gives

$$I_b + I_c = (a^2 I_1 + a I_2 + I_0) + (a I_1 + a^2 I_2 + I_0) = 0$$

from which

$$-I_1 - I_2 + 2I_0 = 0$$

Substituting for I_0 gives

$$- I_1 - I_2 - \frac{4I_2 Z_2}{Z_0} = 0$$

from which

$$I_2 = \frac{-I_1 Z_0}{4Z_2 + Z_0}$$

so that

$$I_0 = \frac{2Z_2 I_1}{4Z_2 + Z_0}$$

Substituting for I_2 and I_0 in the expression for V_a gives

$$V_a = E - I_1 \left[Z_1 - \frac{Z_2 Z_0}{4Z_2 + Z_0} + \frac{2Z_2 Z_0}{4Z_2 + Z_0} \right] = 0$$

from which

$$E - I_1 \left[\frac{4Z_1 Z_2 + Z_2 Z_0 + Z_0 Z_1}{4Z_2 + Z_0} \right] = 0$$

The symmetrical-component equations for this fault condition are thus

$$
\left.
\begin{aligned}
I_1 &= \frac{(4Z_2 + Z_0)E}{4Z_1 Z_2 + Z_2 Z_0 + Z_0 Z_1} \\[2mm]
I_2 &= \frac{-Z_0 E}{4Z_1 Z_2 + Z_2 Z_0 + Z_0 Z_1} \\[2mm]
I_0 &= \frac{2Z_2 E}{4Z_1 Z_2 + Z_2 Z_0 + Z_0 Z_1}
\end{aligned}
\right\}
\quad \text{3.4.4.23}
$$

from which the phase currents flowing into the fault are

$$
\left.
\begin{aligned}
I_a &= I_1 + I_2 + I_0 = \frac{6Z_2 E}{4Z_1 Z_2 + Z_2 Z_0 + Z_0 Z_1} \\[2mm]
I_b &= a^2 I_1 + a I_2 + I_0 = \frac{-j\sqrt{3}E(2Z_2 + Z_0)}{4Z_1 Z_2 + Z_2 Z_0 + Z_0 Z_1} \\[2mm]
I_c &= a I_1 + a^2 I_2 + I_0 = \frac{j\sqrt{3}E(2Z_2 + Z_0)}{4Z_1 Z_2 + Z_2 Z_0 + Z_0 Z_1}
\end{aligned}
\right\}
\qquad 3.4.4.24
$$

(*f*)   *Summary of symmetrical-component formulas:* The symmetrical components of fault current for the five short-circuit conditions are summarised in Table 3.4.4B.

The symmetrical components of voltage at the point of fault are obtained from the equations:

$$
\begin{aligned}
V_1 &= E - I_1 Z_1 \\
V_2 &= -I_2 Z_2 \\
V_0 &= -I_0 Z_0
\end{aligned}
\qquad 3.4.4.25
$$

the resulting values being given in Table 3.4.4C. The phase-to-earth voltages at the point of fault are given in Table 3.4.4D.

From the symmetrical components of fault current and fault voltage, given in Tables 3.4.4A and 3.4.4C, it will be seen that the given short-circuit conditions can be represented by interconnection of the sequence networks in the manner shown in Table 3.4.4E.

The analysis of each fault condition is thus seen to reduce to the solution of an equivalent single-phase network, the latter being composed, in general, of the three sequence networks. It is important to note that each sequence network represents the chosen reference phase of the power system, namely phase a, and that the sequence network currents and voltages are, in consequence, all phase a values.

In the case of the three-phase short-circuit, the negative and zero sequence networks are not interconnected with the positive-sequence network and because the latter network is the only one containing driving voltages, the currents and voltages in the negative and zero-sequence networks are all zero. In analysing the three-phase short-circuit condition, therefore, the only network which requires to be considered is the positive-sequence network. Similarly, in the case of the phase-to-phase short-circuit condition, the zero-sequence network has no interconnection with the positive-sequence network and, hence, for this fault condition the only networks which require to be considered are the positive and negative-sequence networks. It will be noted that each of the remaining three fault conditions involves a short-circuit or short-circuits to earth and that in all three cases the analysis requires consideration of all three sequence networks.

Table 3.4.4F shows the phase-sequence components of fault current, in vector-

Table 3.4.4A.   Phase-sequence components of current in fault under short-circuit conditions

Fault condition	I_1	I_2	I_0
Three-phase (a-b-c or a-b-c-e)	$\dfrac{E}{Z_1}$	0	0
Phase-to-phase (b-c)	$\dfrac{E}{Z_1+Z_2}$	$\dfrac{-E}{Z_1+Z_2}$	0
Single-phase-to-earth (a-e)	$\dfrac{E}{Z_1+Z_2+Z_0}$	$\dfrac{E}{Z_1+Z_2+Z_0}$	$\dfrac{E}{Z_1+Z_2+Z_0}$
Two-phase-to-earth (b-c-e)	$\dfrac{(Z_2+Z_0)E}{Z_1Z_2+Z_2Z_0+Z_0Z_1}$	$\dfrac{-Z_0E}{Z_1Z_2+Z_2Z_0+Z_0Z_1}$	$\dfrac{-Z_2E}{Z_1Z_2+Z_2Z_0+Z_0Z_1}$
Phase-to-phase plus single-phase-to-earth (b-c plus a-e)	$\dfrac{(4Z_2+Z_0)E}{4Z_1Z_2+Z_2Z_0+Z_0Z_1}$	$\dfrac{-Z_0E}{4Z_1Z_2+Z_2Z_0+Z_0Z_1}$	$\dfrac{2Z_2E}{4Z_1Z_2+Z_2Z_0+Z_0Z_1}$

Table 3.4.4B. *Phase current values of current in fault under short-circuit conditions*

Fault condition	I_a	I_b	I_c
Three-phase (a-b-c or a-b-c-e)	$\dfrac{E}{Z_1}$	$\dfrac{a^2 E}{Z_1}$	$\dfrac{aE}{Z_1}$
Phase-to-phase (b-c)	0	$\dfrac{-j\sqrt{3}E}{Z_1 + Z_2}$	$\dfrac{j\sqrt{3}E}{Z_1 + Z_2}$
Single-phase-to-earth (a-e)	$\dfrac{3E}{Z_1 + Z_2 + Z_0}$	0	0
Two-phase-to-earth (b-c-e)	0	$\dfrac{-j\sqrt{3}E(Z_0 - aZ_2)}{Z_1 Z_2 + Z_2 Z_0 + Z_0 Z_1}$	$\dfrac{j\sqrt{3}E(Z_0 - a^2 Z_2)}{Z_1 Z_2 + Z_2 Z_0 + Z_0 Z_1}$
Phase-to-phase plus single-phase-to-earth (b-c plus a-e)	$\dfrac{6Z_2 E}{4Z_1 Z_2 + Z_2 Z_0 + Z_0 Z_1}$	$\dfrac{-j\sqrt{3}E(2Z_2 + Z_0)}{4Z_1 Z_2 + Z_2 Z_0 + Z_0 Z_1}$	$\dfrac{j\sqrt{3}E(2Z_2 + Z_0)}{4Z_1 Z_2 + Z_2 Z_0 + Z_0 Z_1}$

Table 3.4.4C. *Phase-sequence components of voltage at point of fault under short-circuit conditions*

Fault condition	V_1	V_2	V_0
Three-phase (a-b-c or a-b-c-e)	0	0	0
Phase-to-phase (b-c)	$\dfrac{Z_2 E}{Z_1 + Z_2}$	$\dfrac{Z_2 E}{Z_1 + Z_2}$	0
Single-phase-to-earth (a-e)	$\dfrac{(Z_2 + Z_0)E}{Z_1 + Z_2 + Z_0}$	$\dfrac{-Z_2 E}{Z_1 + Z_2 + Z_0}$	$\dfrac{-Z_0 E}{Z_1 + Z_2 + Z_0}$
Two-phase-to-earth (b-c-e)	$\dfrac{Z_2 Z_0 E}{Z_1 Z_2 + Z_2 Z_0 + Z_0 Z_1}$	$\dfrac{Z_2 Z_0 E}{Z_1 Z_2 + Z_2 Z_0 + Z_0 Z_1}$	$\dfrac{Z_2 Z_0 E}{Z_1 Z_2 + Z_2 Z_0 + Z_0 Z_1}$
Phase-to-phase plus single-phase-to-earth (b-c plus a-e)	$\dfrac{Z_2 Z_0 E}{4Z_1 Z_2 + Z_2 Z_0 + Z_0 Z_1}$	$\dfrac{Z_2 Z_0 E}{4Z_1 Z_2 + Z_2 Z_0 + Z_0 Z_1}$	$\dfrac{-2Z_2 Z_0 E}{4Z_1 Z_2 + Z_2 Z_0 + Z_0 Z_1}$

Table 3.4.4D. *Phase voltages at the point under short-circuit conditions*

Fault condition	V_a	V_b	V_c
Three-phase (a-b-c or a-b-c-e)	0	0	0
Phase-to-phase (b-c)	$\dfrac{2Z_2 E}{Z_1 + Z_2}$	$\dfrac{-Z_2 E}{Z_1 + Z_2}$	$\dfrac{-Z_2 E}{Z_1 + Z_2}$
Single-phase-to-earth (a-e)	0	$\dfrac{[(a^2 - a)Z_2 + (a^2 - 1)Z_0]E}{Z_1 + Z_2 + Z_0}$	$\dfrac{[(a-a^2)Z_2 + (a - 1)Z_0]E}{Z_1 + Z_2 + Z_0}$
Two-phase-to-earth (b-c-e)	$\dfrac{3Z_2 Z_0 E}{Z_1 Z_2 + Z_2 Z_0 + Z_0 Z_1}$	0	0
Phase-to-phase plus single-phase-to-earth (b-c plus a-e)	0	$\dfrac{-3Z_2 Z_0 E}{4Z_1 Z_2 + Z_2 Z_0 + Z_0 Z_1}$	$\dfrac{-3Z_2 Z_0 E}{4Z_1 Z_2 + Z_2 Z_0 + Z_0 Z_1}$

Table 3.4.4E *Interconnection of the sequence networks for the representation of system short-circuit conditions*

*Closed for three-phase-to-earth fault.

diagram form, for the five short-circuit conditions considered, the impedances Z_1, Z_2 and Z_0 of the power system, as seen from the point of fault, being assumed to be all equal. The three impedances are all assumed to have an X/R ratio of 5, corresponding to a phase angle of $78° \ 42'$. The table also shows the phase values of the fault currents, and it can be readily checked from the vector diagrams that each phase-current vector is the sum of its associated sequence-current vectors. In addition to the current vectors, the table also gives the vector diagrams of the phase-to-earth voltages at the point of fault, the pre-fault phase voltages at the point of fault, $E_a(=E)$, E_b and E_c, being shown by broken lines.

It is important to note that the vector diagrams of Table 3.4.4F refer specifically to the stated case, namely that in which the three phase-sequence impedances are all equal in both magnitude and phase. It will be noted that, for this case, the voltage to earth of any unfaulted phase or phases at the point of fault is equal to the pre-fault voltage of the phase or phases in question. This is not the case, in general, when the sequence impedances are not equal.

3.4.5   Effect of fault impedance

The analysis of short-circuit conditions, as presented in the previous Section, has assumed the short-circuiting connections to be of zero impedance. This assumption is sufficiently accurate for the great majority of fault calculations but it is, nevertheless, sometimes necessary to take due account of fault-path impedance,

Table 3.4.4F   Current and voltage vector-diagrams for the five different short-circuit conditions for a power system in which $Z_1 = Z_2 = Z_0$, the X/R ratio being 5

Fault condition	Positive-sequence currents	Negative-sequence currents	Zero-sequence currents	Phase currents	Phase voltages
Three-phase (a-b-c or a-b-c-e)	I_{c1}, I_{a1}, I_{b1}	Zero	Zero	I_c, I_a, I_b	E_c, E_a, E_b; $v_a = v_b = v_c = 0$
Phase-to-phase (b-c)	I_{c1}, I_{a1}, I_{b1}	I_{c2}, I_{a2}, I_{b2}	Zero	$I_a = 0$, I_c, I_b	E_c, v_c, E_a, v_a, v_b, E_b
Single-phase-to-earth (a-e)	I_{c1}, I_{a1}, I_{b1}	I_{b2}, I_{c2}, I_{a2}	I_{a0}, I_{b0}, I_{c0}	$I_b = I_c = 0$, I_a	E_c, E_a, v_b, $v_a = 0$, E_b
Two-phase-to-earth (b-c-e)	I_{c1}, I_{a1}, I_{b1}	I_{a2}, I_{c2}, I_{b2}	I_{a0}, I_{b0}, I_{c0}	$I_a = 0$, I_c, I_b	E_c, E_a, v_a, $v_b = v_c = 0$, E_b
Phase-to-phase plus single-phase-to-earth (b-c plus a-e)	I_{c1}, I_{a1}, I_{b1}	I_{a2}, I_{c2}, I_{b2}	I_{a0}, I_{b0}, I_{c0}	I_c, I_a, I_b	E_c, v_c, E_a, v_b, $v_a = 0$, E_b

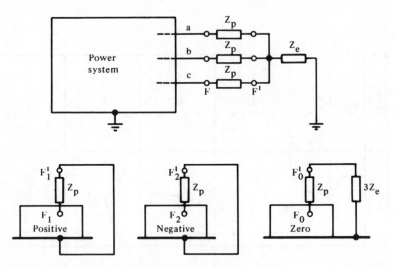

Fig. 3.4.5A   *Three-phase fault with fault impedance*

a particular instance being the consideration of fault-arc resistance in its effect on distance protection.

The effect of fault impedance is most readily understood by considering the phase-sequence impedances which must be added, externally, to the system sequence networks when the latter are interconnected to represent the short-circuit condition in question. Thus, considering the three-phase fault shown in Fig. 3.4.5A, let the fault-path impedances be Z_p in each phase, together with Z_e between the star-point of these three impedances and earth. Considering the position F' as the true short-circuit position, rather than F, it will be evident that the impedances Z_p simply appear as external impedances Z_p connected to the fault points F_1, F_2 and F_0 of the three sequence networks. Similarly, the impedance Z_e, as seen from F', appears as an external impedance $3Z_e$, connected to the zero-potential (earth) bar of the zero-sequence network, as shown in the figure. Now, it will be noted that at F', the three phases are connected together through zero impedance and that this star-point is connected through zero-impedance to the terminal of the impedance Z_e. It follows, therefore, that the sequence-network connections appropriate to this fault condition are as shown in the figure, the points F_1' and F_2' being connected to the zero-potential bar of the positive and negative-sequence networks, respectively, and the point F_0' being connected to the terminal of the impedance $3Z_e$ associated with the zero-sequence network. As already pointed out in the previous Section, the inclusion of the negative and zero-sequence networks in the representation of the three-phase short-circuit is only of academic interest, since the currents and voltages present in the system are all positive-sequence values.

Considering, now, the phase-to-phase fault shown in Fig. 3.4.5B, let the fault-path impedance between the faulted phases b and c be $2Z_p$ and let this be represented by an impedance Z_p in each of the two phases. Now, there is no flow of

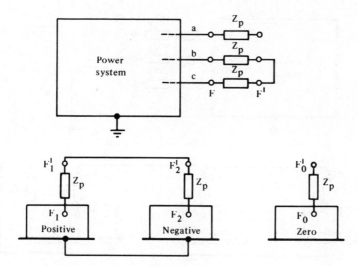

Fig. 3.4.5B *Phase-to-phase fault with fault impedance*

current from phase a into the fault, and hence the electrical conditions will be quite unaltered by the insertion of a fictitious impedance Z_p in series with phase a, as shown. Each phase now contains an impedance Z_p between the fault position F and the position F', and at this latter position, it will be noted, the phase b and c are connected together through zero impedance. The fault condition, now considered as being at F', can therefore be analysed by applying the results of Section 3.4.4 with the three sequence networks augmented by the added impedance Z_p connected to the fault points F_1, F_2 and F_0, as shown in the figure.

The remaining fault conditions, namely the single-phase-to-earth fault, the two-

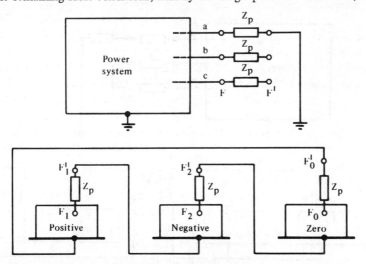

Fig. 3.4.5C *Single-phase-to-earth fault with fault impedance*

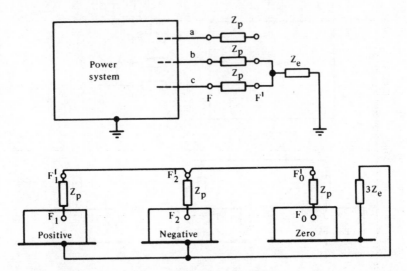

Fig. 3.4.5D   *Two-phase-to-earth fault with fault impedance*

phase-to-earth fault and the phase-to-phase plus single-phase-to-earth fault, are treated in a similar manner, the resulting sequence-network interconnections being given in Figs. 3.4.5C, 3.4.5D and 3.4.5E.

The treatment of fault impedance described above is based on the assumption that the fault-path impedances are known fixed values. This assumption is acceptable for many purposes but it is important to note that in a particularly important case, namely that of a fault arc, the fault-path impedance (normally regarded as a pure resistance) is a function of the fault current and the arc length. Warrington

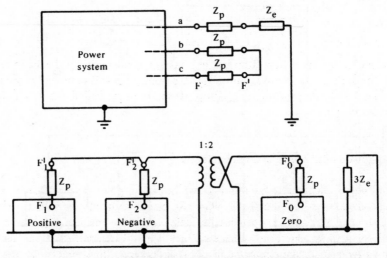

Fig. 3.4.5E   *Phase-to-phase plus single-phase-to-earth fault with fault impedance*

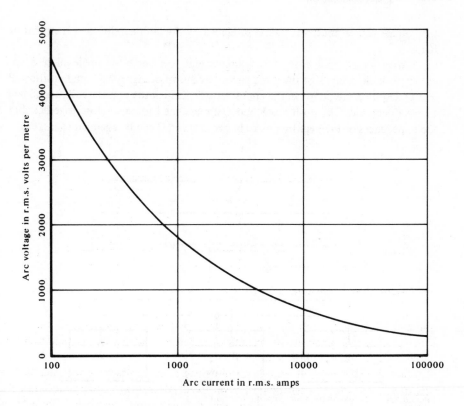

Fig. 3.4.5F   *A.C. arc voltage as a function of arc current*

expresses the characteristic of such a.c. arcs, in air, by the formula

$$V = \frac{8750L}{I^{0\cdot 4}}$$

where V is the arc voltage-drop in r.m.s. volts, L is the length of the arc in feet and
I is the arc current in r.m.s. amps. This arc characteristic is represented graphically
in Fig. 3.4.5F in terms of voltage-drop per metre of arc length as a function of arc
current in amps.

3.4.6   Analysis of open-circuit conditions

The open-circuit conditions normally of interest in power-system analysis are the
single-phase open-circuit and the two-phase open-circuit, the remaining possibility,
namely the three-phase open-circuit, being of little practical significance. The
analysis of these conditions is achieved by the use of symmetrical components in a
similar manner to that employed for short-circuit conditions, that is by considering

the voltage and current constraints produced by the fault condition at the point of fault.

(*a*)   *Single-phase open-circuit:* It is convenient to assume the single-phase open-circuit to be in phase a of the given circuit, as shown in Fig. 3.4.6A, the positions P and Q denoting the points in the circuit between which the open-circuit is assumed to have occurred. The positions P and Q are assumed to be so close together that the impedances of the healthy phases between P and Q can be assumed to be zero.

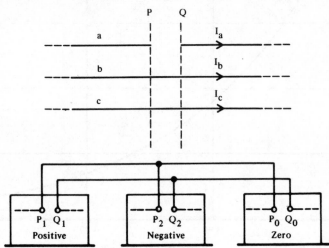

Fig. 3.4.6A   *Single-phase open-circuit condition*

Writing down the voltage and current constraints at the point of fault gives the equations

$$\left.\begin{array}{l} (V_a)_{PQ} = (V_a)_P - (V_a)_Q \neq 0 \\ (V_b)_{PQ} = (V_b)_P - (V_b)_Q = 0 \\ (V_c)_{PQ} = (V_c)_P - (V_c)_Q = 0 \end{array}\right\} \qquad 3.4.6.1$$

$$\left.\begin{array}{l} I_a = 0 \\ I_b \neq 0 \\ I_c \neq 0 \end{array}\right\} \qquad 3.4.6.2$$

The symbols $(V_a)_{PQ}$, $(V_b)_{PQ}$ and $(V_c)_{PQ}$, it will be noted, represent the series voltage-drops along the phase conductors from P to Q.

The phase sequence components of the voltage-drops are given by

$$\left.\begin{array}{l} (V_1)_{PQ} = \frac{1}{3}[(V_a)_{PQ} + a(V_b)_{PQ} + a^2(V_c)_{PQ}] = \frac{1}{3}(V_a)_{PQ} \\ (V_2)_{PQ} = \frac{1}{3}[(V_a)_{PQ} + a^2(V_b)_{PQ} + a(V_c)_{PQ}] = \frac{1}{3}(V_a)_{PQ} \\ (V_0)_{PQ} = \frac{1}{3}[(V_a)_{PQ} + (V_b)_{PQ} + (V_c)_{PQ}] = \frac{1}{3}(V_a)_{PQ} \end{array}\right\} \qquad 3.4.6.3$$

because $(V_b)_{PQ}$ and $(V_c)_{PQ}$ are both zero. The positive, negative and zero-sequence voltage-drops between P and Q are thus seen to be all equal.

Considering, now, the phase-sequence components of the currents, because $I_a = 0$ it follows that

$$\left.\begin{array}{l} I_1 = \tfrac{1}{3}(I_a + aI_b + a^2 I_c) = \tfrac{1}{3}(aI_b + a^2 I_c) \\[2mm] I_2 = \tfrac{1}{3}(I_a + a^2 I_b + aI_c) = \tfrac{1}{3}(a^2 I_b + aI_c) \\[2mm] I_0 = \tfrac{1}{3}(I_a + I_b + I_c) = \tfrac{1}{3}(I_b + I_c) \end{array}\right\} \qquad 3.4.6.4$$

It is thus seen that

$$I_1 + I_2 + I_0 = 0 \qquad\qquad 3.4.6.5$$

because $1 + a + a^2$ is equal to zero, and hence

$$I_2 + I_0 = -I_1 \qquad\qquad 3.4.6.6$$

The constraints imposed by the fault condition, as expressed by eqns. 3.4.6.3 and 3.4.6.6, are seen to be satisfied by the interconnection of the sequence networks shown in Fig. 3.4.6A. It should be noted that, in each sequence network, the branch representing the given crcuit is open-circuited between the points corresponding to the positions P and Q in the given circuit, that is the points P_1 and Q_1, P_2 and Q_2 and P_0 and Q_0.

Now let Z_1, Z_2 and Z_0 be the impedances of the positive, negative and zero-sequence networks as measured between P_1 and Q_1, P_2 and Q_2 and P_0 and Q_0, respectively, in Fig. 3.4.6A. Then, the positive-sequence network, as seen from the points P_1 and Q_1, reduces to a positive-sequence voltage in series with the impedance Z_1, the positive-sequence voltage being given (by Thevenin's Theorem) by $Z_1 I_{1pf}$, where I_{1pf} denotes the pre-fault value of the positive-sequence current in phase a of the given circuit.

From Fig. 3.4.6A, it follows that the required phase-sequence currents in the faulted circuit are given by

$$\left.\begin{array}{l} I_1 = \dfrac{Z_1 I_{1pf}}{Z_1 + \dfrac{Z_2 Z_0}{Z_2 + Z_0}} \\[8mm] I_2 = \dfrac{-Z_0 I_1}{Z_2 + Z_0} \\[6mm] I_0 = \dfrac{-Z_1 I_1}{Z_2 + Z_0} \end{array}\right\} \qquad 3.4.6.7$$

from which the phase currents in the faulted circuit can be shown to be given by

$$I_a = 0$$

$$I_b = \left[\frac{(a^2 - 1)Z_2 + (a^2 - a)Z_0}{Z_1 Z_2 + Z_2 Z_0 + Z_0 Z_1} \right] Z_1 I_{1pf}$$

$$I_c = \left[\frac{(a - 1)Z_2 + (a - a^2)Z_0}{Z_1 Z_2 + Z_2 Z_0 + Z_0 Z_1} \right] Z_1 I_{1pf}$$

3.4.6.8

It will be noted that the sequence currents and phase currents are zero if the pre-fault condition is one n which the circuit in question is carrying zero current.

(*b*)   *Two-phase open-circuit:* For this case it is convenient to assume the open-circuits to be in phases b and c of the given circuit, as shown in Fig. 3.4.6B.

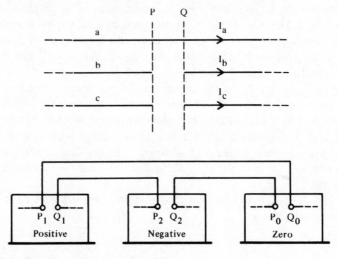

Fig. 3.4.6B   *Two-phase open-circuit condition*

Proceeding as in the previous case, the voltage and current constraints at the point of fault are

$$\left. \begin{array}{l} (V_a)_{PQ} = (V_a)_P - (V_a)_Q = 0 \\ (V_b)_{PQ} = (V_b)_P - (V_b)_Q \neq 0 \\ (V_c)_{PQ} = (V_c)_P - (V_c)_Q \neq 0 \end{array} \right\}$$

3.4.6.9

$$\left. \begin{array}{l} I_a \neq 0 \\ I_b = 0 \\ I_c = 0 \end{array} \right\}$$

3.4.6.10

As before, the symbols $(V_a)_{PQ}$, $(V_b)_{PQ}$ and $(V_c)_{PQ}$ represent the series voltage-drops along the phase conductors from P to Q.

The phase-sequence components of the voltage-drops are given by

$$(V_1)_{PQ} = \tfrac{1}{3}[(V_a)_{PQ} + a(V_b)_{PQ} + a^2(V_c)_{PQ}] = \tfrac{1}{3}[a(V_b)_{PQ} + a^2(V_c)_{PQ}]$$
$$(V_2)_{PQ} = \tfrac{1}{3}[(V_a)_{PQ} + a^2(V_b)_{PQ} + a(V_c)_{PQ}] = \tfrac{1}{3}[a^2(V_b)_{PQ} + a(V_c)_{PQ}] \quad 3.4.6.11$$
$$(V_0)_{PQ} = \tfrac{1}{3}[(V_a)_{PQ} + (V_b)_{PQ} + (V_c)_{PQ}] = \tfrac{1}{3}[(V_b)_{PQ} + (V_c)_{PQ}]$$

because $(V_a)_{PQ} = 0$. From these equations it is seen that:

$$(V_1)_{PQ} + (V_2)_{PQ} + (V_0)_{PQ} = 0 \qquad\qquad 3.4.6.12$$

because $1 + a + a^2$ in equal to zero.

Considering, now, the phase-sequence components of the currents it follows that

$$\left. \begin{aligned} I_1 &= \tfrac{1}{3}(I_a + aI_b + a^2 I_c) = \tfrac{1}{3} I_a \\ I_2 &= \tfrac{1}{3}(I_a + a^2 I_b + a I_c) = \tfrac{1}{3} I_a \\ I_0 &= \tfrac{1}{3}(I_a + I_b + I_c) = \tfrac{1}{3} I_a \end{aligned} \right\} \qquad 3.4.6.13$$

because I_b and I_c are both zero. The positive, negative and zero-sequence currents in the faulted circuit are thus seen to be equal.

The constraints imposed by the fault condition as expressed by eqns. 3.4.6.12 and 3.4.6.13, are seen to be satisfied by the interconnection of the sequence networks shown in Fig. 3.4.6B. As before, the branch representing the given circuit in each sequence network is open-circuited between the points corresponding to the positions P and Q in the given circuit, that is the points P_1 and Q_i, P_2 and Q_2 and P_0 and Q_0.

Proceeding as in the previous case, it follows from Fig. 3.4.6B that the required phase-sequence currents in the faulted circuit are given by

$$I_1 = I_2 = I_0 = \frac{Z_1 I_{1pf}}{Z_1 + Z_2 + Z_0} \qquad\qquad 3.4.6.14$$

from which the phase currents in the faulted circuit are seen to be given by

$$\left. \begin{aligned} I_a &= \frac{3Z_1 I_{1pf}}{Z_1 + Z_2 + Z_0} \\[1em] I_b &= 0 \\ I_c &= 0 \end{aligned} \right\} \qquad 3.4.6.15$$

It will again be noted that the sequence currents and phase currents are zero if the pre-fault condition is one in which the circuit in question is carrying zero current.

3.4.7 Transformer phase-shifts

The representation of a given power system by its positive, negative and zero-sequence networks, all of which represent the chosen reference phase, namely phase a, implies that the phase references a, b and c can be regarded as applying to the whole of the power system, even though the latter may consist of a number of network sections interconnected through transformers. This continuity of the phase references through the transformer interconnections results from the assumption, for the positive and negative-sequence networks, that all the transformer windings are star-connected, this assumption having been the basis for the derivation of the transformer positive and negative-sequence circuits obtained in Section 3.3.3. Since not all transformer windings are star-connected, the phase references a, b and c, which denote actual phase conductors in a given network section (for example that containing the point of fault), must be regarded as denoting hypothetical phase conductors in the remaining network sections. It is therefore necessary, for complete analysis, to be able to obtain the sequence currents and voltages applicable to the *actual* phase conductors in any given network section, given the corresponding reference-phase (phase-a) values obtained from the sequence networks and taking due account of the actual transformer-winding connections employed in the power system.

The effect of transformer-winding connections has already been discussed in Section 3.3.5 for the particular case of the system positive-sequence network, the assumption of star-connected transformer windings having been shown to give valid results provided that the positive-sequence currents and voltages obtained from the sequence network (that is the phase-a values) are suitably corrected in phase, as necessary, to take due account of the actual transformer-winding connections. This reasoning is similarly applicable in the case of the negative-sequence network, the negative-sequence currents and voltages obtained from the negative sequence network (that is the phase-a values) being also required to be suitably corrected in phase, as necessary, to take due account of the actual transformer-winding connections.

Insofar as negative-sequence quantities are concerned, the phase-shift introduced by a particular star/delta transformer is illustrated in Fig. 3.4.7A, the transformer in question being identical to that given in Fig. 3.3.5B. It will be noted that the delta-side negative-sequence currents and no-load voltages all *lead* their corresponding star-side values by 30°. It has already been shown in Fig. 3.3.5B, however, that the delta-side positive-sequence currents and no-load voltages all *lag* their corresponding star-side values by 30°. The phase-shift produced is thus seen to be the same in magnitude for both positive and negative sequence quantities, the direction of the phase-shift in the case of the negative-sequence vectors being the reverse of that applicable in the case of the positive-sequence vectors. Although illustrated for a particular case, this relationship between the positive and negative-sequence phase-shifts is true in general, the two phase-shifts being always equal in magnitude and opposite in direction. The magnitude of the phase-shifts and their respective directions are, of course, dependent on the particular transformer-winding connections and the allocation of the phase-references.

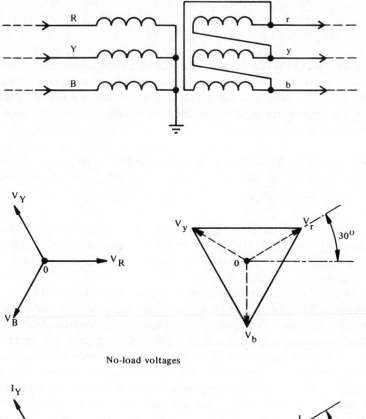

No-load voltages

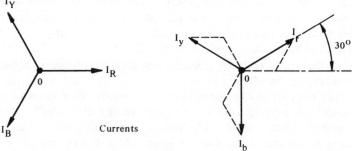

Currents

Fig. 3.4.7A *Phase-shifting effect of a star/delta transformer on negative-sequence currents and voltages*

Considering, again, the star/delta transformer of Fig. 3.4.7A, let the phase references, a, b and c correspond to the given star-side phase-references R, Y and B, respectively, and let I_1 and I_2 denote the phase-a positive and negative-sequence currents at any point in the star-side network section. Then, the corresponding sequence currents in the actual phases R, Y and B at the point in question are given by:

$$
\begin{array}{ll}
I_{R1} = I_1 & I_{R2} = I_2 \\
I_{Y1} = a^2 I_1 & I_{Y2} = a I_2 \\
I_{B1} = a I_1 & I_{B2} = a^2 I_2
\end{array} \Bigg\} \qquad 3.4.7.1
$$

with a similar set of equations relating the sequence voltages.

At any point in the delta-side network section, however, the positive and negative-sequence currents in the actual phases r, y and b must be obtained by applying the appropriate phase correction to the phase-a sequence currents I_1 and I_2 at the point in question, giving

$$
\begin{array}{ll}
I_{r1} = 1\underline{/-30^\circ}\, I_1 & I_{r2} = 1\underline{/+30^\circ}\, I_2 \\
I_{y1} = 1\underline{/-30^\circ}\, a^2 I_1 & I_{y2} = 1\underline{/+30^\circ}\, a I_2 \\
I_{b1} = 1\underline{/-30^\circ}\, a I_1 & I_{b2} = 1\underline{/+30^\circ}\, a^2 I_2
\end{array} \qquad 3.4.7.2
$$

with, again, a similar set of equations relating the sequence voltages. The vector multipliers $1\underline{/-30^\circ}$ and $1\underline{/+30^\circ}$ represent the positive and negative-sequence phase-shift correction which must be applied to take due account of the transformer-winding connections.

The effect of transformer phase-shift is illustrated in Fig. 3.4.7B for the case of the given star/delta transformer, the transformer being assumed to be supplying current to a red-phase earth-fault on the star-winding side, the yellow and blue phase currents on that side being both zero. The positive, negative and zero-sequence currents on the star-winding side are as shown (per-unit values being assumed) and, since the transformer is identical to that already considered in Figs. 3.3.5B and 3.4.7A, it follows that the delta-side positive-sequence currents are identical (in per-unit value) to the corresponding star-side values, but retarded in phase by 30°, while the delta-side negative-sequence currents are identical to the corresponding star-side values but advanced in phase by 30°. The star-side and delta-side sequence currents are thus as shown in Fig. 3.4.7B, there being no zero-sequence currents on the delta-side of the transformer.

The phase currents on the two sides of the transformer are obtained by vector summation of the sequence currents, the results being as shown with current in the red and yellow phases only on the delta side of the transformer. These delta-side phase currents are seen to be equal in magnitude and 180° apart in phase, the magnitude (in per-unit value) being $1/\sqrt{3}$ times that of the red-phase current on the star-side of the transformer. The validity of this phase-current distribution is readily verified by considering the flow of current in the transformer phase-windings, as shown by the arrows.

The question of transformer-winding connections has so far been considered solely in relation to the phase-shift corrections which must be applied to the quantities obtained from the positive and negative sequence networks. In fact, the positive and negative-sequence networks are the only ones in which phase-shift correction is required, the zero-sequence quantities requiring no such correction. This is due to the fact that the flow of zero-sequence current from one network section to another can only occur if each of the associated transformer windings is connected in star or inter-connected-star with both the neutral points earthed, such a winding arrangement producing no phase-shift of the zero-sequence currents on one side of the transformer with respect to those on the other. In the case of the star/delta transformer already referred to, the transformer-winding connections limit the zero-sequence currents to the network-section connected to the star winding and hence, since there is no flow of zero-sequence current through the transformer, the question of phase-shift correction does not arise.

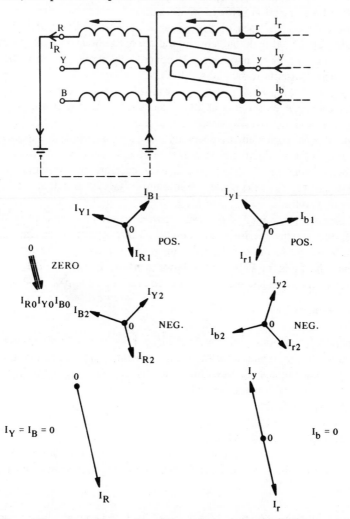

Fig. 3.4.7B   *Effect of transformer phase-shifts on fault-current distribution*

3.4.8   Fault-calculation procedure

The analysis of a power-system fault condition consists, in general, of the following steps:

(*a*)   The representation of the given power system by its positive, negative and zero-sequence networks, as required for the particular fault condition under consideration, the zero-sequence network being omitted for faults which do not involve earth, and both the negative and zero-sequence networks being omitted for the balanced three-phase fault condition. This representation is achieved by the adoption of common-base values, that is, amps, volts and ohms to a common base-voltage or per-unit or per-cent values to a common MVA base, the latter being the more usual.

(*b*)   The reduction of each of the sequence networks concerned to its simplest form, namely a single branch, and the use of the branch values so obtained in the appropriate symmetrical-component equations to give the phase-a sequence currents at the point of fault.

(*c*)   The use of the process of back-substitution to obtain the distribution of the phase-a sequence currents in their respective sequence networks, the resulting positive and negative-sequence voltages and currents in the sequence networks being phase-corrected, as necessary, to give the values appropriate to the actual phase conductors in each of the network sections concerned.

(*d*)   The summation of the phase-sequence currents and voltages to give the resultant values of the phase currents and voltages at any desired points in the power system.

The procedure outlined above will provide a complete analysis of the given power system for the specified fault condition, but in many cases the information required is limited to the conditions at the point of fault or in the network section containing the point of fault. In the latter-mentioned cases, the network analysis is obviously very much less than would be required for a complete analysis.

3.4.9   Example 3

The generator/transformer unit shown in Fig. 3.4.9A develops a short-circuit on the h.v. terminals of the step-up transformer, the generator and transformer impedances having the values indicated. Determine the short-circuit currents at the point of fault, assuming the fault condition to be

(*a*)   a three-phase fault,
(*b*)   a phase-to-phase fault,
(*c*)   a single-phase-to-earth fault.

It can be assumed that the pre-fault voltage at the point of fault is 70 kV phase-to-phase and that the generator/transformer unit is not connected to the rest of the power system.

Solution: Adopting a common base MVA of 100, the common-base values of the

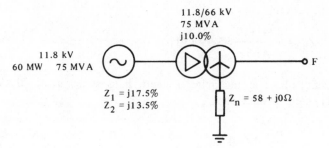

11.8/66 kV
75 MVA
j10.0%

11.8 kV
60 MW   75 MVA

$Z_1 = j17.5\%$
$Z_2 = j13.5\%$

$Z_n = 58 + j0\,\Omega$

F

Fig. 3.4.9A

generator impedances are given by

$$Z_{g1} = \frac{j0\cdot175 \times 100}{75} = j0\cdot234 \text{ p.u.}$$

$$Z_{g2} = \frac{j0\cdot135 \times 100}{75} = j0\cdot180 \text{ p.u.}$$

and the transformer impedances are given by

$$Z_{t1} = Z_{t2} = Z_{t0} = \frac{j0\cdot100 \times 100}{75} = j0\cdot133 \text{ p.u.}$$

The zero-sequence impedance of the neutral earthing resistor is given by

$$Z_{n0} = 3Z_n = 174 + j0 \ \Omega$$

which must be converted to per-unit value to the common base MVA of 100. Now, the rated current corresponding to 100 MVA at 66 kV is given by

$$\frac{100 \times 10^6}{\sqrt{3} \times 66\,000} = 874\text{A}$$

Also, the phase to neutral voltage corresponding to 66 kV is

$$\frac{66\,000}{\sqrt{3}} = 38\,100\text{V}$$

and hence, the base impedance corresponding to the base MVA of 100 at 66 kV is

$$\frac{38\,100}{874} = 43\cdot6 \ \Omega$$

The required per-unit zero-sequence impedance of the earthing resistor is therefore

given by

$$Z_{no} = \frac{174 + j0}{43 \cdot 6.} = 3 \cdot 99 + j0 \text{ p.u}$$

The pre-fault voltage at the point of fault, F, is stated to be 70 kV and this expressed in per-unit value is

$$\frac{70}{66} = 1 \cdot 060 \text{ p.u.}$$

The positive, negative and zero-sequence networks for the system are thus as shown in Fig. 3.4.9B from which it is seen that

$$E = 1 \cdot 060 + j0 \text{ p.u. (the vector reference)}$$
$$Z_1 = j0 \cdot 367 \text{ p.u.}$$
$$Z_2 = j0 \cdot 313 \text{ p.u.}$$
$$Z_0 = 3 \cdot 99 + j0 \cdot 133 \text{ p.u.}$$

where E is the pre-fault voltage of phase a at the point of fault and Z_1, Z_2 and Z_0 are the positive, negative and zero-sequence impedances of the system as would be measured from the point of fault.

These values can now be used in the appropriate symmetrical-component formulae of Table 3.4.4A as follows:

Case (a)   *Three-phase fault:* For this fault condition the sequence currents at the point of fault are

$$I_1 = \frac{E}{Z_1}$$

$$I_2 = 0$$
$$I_0 = 0$$

from which

$$I_1 = \frac{1 \cdot 060 + j0}{j0 \cdot 367} = -j2 \cdot 89 \text{ p.u.}$$

The required phase-current values at the point of fault are thus seen to be given by

$$I_a = I_1 = 0 - j2 \cdot 89 \text{ p.u.}$$
$$I_b = a^2 I_1 = -2 \cdot 50 + j1 \cdot 445 \text{ p.u.}$$
$$I_c = a I_1 = 2 \cdot 50 + j1 \cdot 445 \text{ p.u.}$$

Multiplying these values by the base current corresponding to 100 MVA at 66 kV (874 A) gives the required phase currents in amps, the resultant values, expressed in

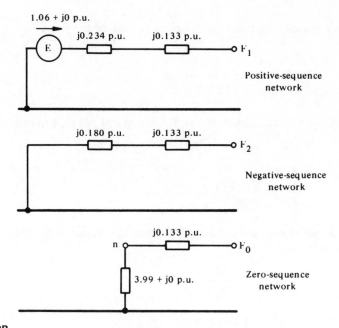

1.06 + j0 p.u.

j0.234 p.u.   j0.133 p.u.   F₁

E

Positive-sequence
network

j0.180 p.u.   j0.133 p.u.   F₂

Negative-sequence
network

j0.133 p.u.   F₀

n

3.99 + j0 p.u.   Zero-sequence
network

Fig. 3.4.9B

polar form, being

$$I_a = 2526\underline{/-90°} \text{ A}$$
$$I_b = 2526\underline{/+150°} \text{ A}$$
$$I_c = 2526\underline{/+30°} \text{ A}$$

Case (b)   Phase-to-phase fault: For this fault condition the sequence currents at the point of fault are given by

$$I_1 = \frac{E}{Z_1 + Z_2}$$

$$I_2 = \frac{-E}{Z_1 + Z_2}$$

$$I_0 = 0$$

from which

$$I_1 = \frac{1 \cdot 060 + j0}{j0 \cdot 680} = -j1 \cdot 560 \text{ p.u.}$$

$$I_2 = \frac{-1 \cdot 060 - j0}{j0 \cdot 680.} = j1 \cdot 560 \text{ p.u}$$

The required phase-current values at the point of fault are therefore

$$I_a = I_1 + I_2 = 0 \text{ p.u.}$$
$$I_b = a^2 I_1 + a I_2 = -2 \cdot 70 + j0 \text{ p.u.}$$
$$I_c = a I_1 + a^2 I_2 = 2 \cdot 70 + j0 \text{ p.u.}$$

Multiplying by 874 to convert to amps, the required values, expressed in polar form, are

$$I_a = 0$$
$$I_b = 2360 \underline{/+180^\circ} \text{ A}$$
$$I_c = 2360 \underline{/0^\circ} \text{ A}$$

Case (c)   Single-phase-to-earth fault: The sequence currents at the point of fault for this condition are

$$I_1 = I_2 = I_0 = \frac{E}{Z_1 + Z_2 + Z_0}$$

$$= \frac{1 \cdot 060 + j0}{3 \cdot 99 + j0 \cdot 813} \text{ p.u.}$$

$$= 0 \cdot 255 - j0 \cdot 052 \text{ p.u.}$$

The required phase currents at the point of fault are therefore given by

$$I_a = I_1 + I_2 + I_0 = 0 \cdot 765 - j0 \cdot 156 \text{ p.u.}$$
$$I_b = a^2 I_1 + a I_2 + I_0 = 0$$
$$I_c = a I_1 + a^2 I_2 + I_0 = 0$$

Multiplying by 874 to convert to amps, the resulting values, expressed in polar form, are

$$I_a = 683 \underline{/-11^\circ \ 31'} \text{ A}$$
$$I_b = 0$$
$$I_c = 0$$

3.4.10   Example 4

The system shown in Fig. 3.4.10A develops a single-phase-to-earth fault at the point F on the 275 kV terminals of the auto-transformer, the plant impedance values being as indicated. Determine the value of the fault current at F assuming the pre-fault phase-to-phase voltage at F to be the rated value, namely 275 kV.

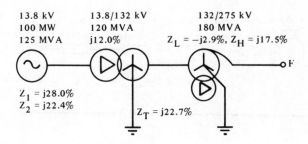

Fig. 3.4.10A

Solution: Adopting a common base MVA of 100, the required common-base values of the plant impedances are

$$Z_{g1} = \frac{j0 \cdot 280 \times 100}{125} = j0 \cdot 244 \text{ p.u.}$$

$$Z_{g2} = \frac{j0 \cdot 224 \times 100}{125} = j0 \cdot 179 \text{ p.u.}$$

$$Z_t = \frac{j0 \cdot 120 \times 100}{120} = j0 \cdot 100 \text{ p.u.}$$

$$Z_H = \frac{j0 \cdot 175 \times 100}{180} = j0 \cdot 0972 \text{ p.u.}$$

$$Z_L = \frac{-j0 \cdot 029 \times 100}{180} = -j0 \cdot 0161 \text{ p.u.}$$

$$Z_T = \frac{j0 \cdot 227 \times 100}{180} = j0 \cdot 126 \text{ p.u.}$$

Because the pre-fault voltage at F is equal to the rated voltage its per-unit value is unity. The system positive, negative and zero-sequence networks are thus as shown in Fig. 3.4.10B from which it will be seen that the resultant sequence impedances, as seen from the point of fault are

$$Z_1 = j0 \cdot 405 \text{ p.u.}$$
$$Z_2 = j0 \cdot 360 \text{ p.u.}$$
$$Z_0 = j0 \cdot 148 \text{ p.u.}$$

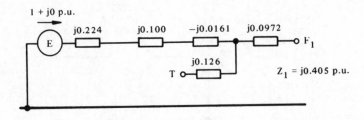

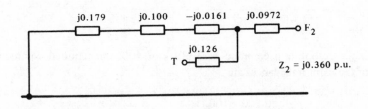

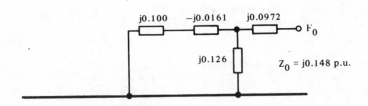

All impedances in per-unit on 100 MVA

Fig. 3.4.10B

The sequence currents flowing into the fault at F are therefore

$$I_1 = I_2 = I_0 = \frac{E}{Z_1 + Z_2 + Z_0}$$

$$= \frac{1 + j0}{j0.913} \text{ p.u.}$$

$$= -j1.095 \text{ p.u.}$$

from which

$$I_a = I_1 + I_2 + I_0 = -j3.29 \text{ p.u.}$$

the remaining phase currents I_b and I_c being both zero.

Now the current corresponding to 100 MVA at 275 kV is

$$\frac{100 \times 10^6}{\sqrt{3} \times 275\,000} = 210 \text{ A}$$

and hence, multiplying the given per-unit value by 210, the resulting value of the fault current at F is

$$I_a = -j3 \cdot 29 \times 210 = -j689 \text{ A}$$

or, expressed in polar form

$$I_a = 689\underline{/-90°} \text{ A}$$

3.4.11 Example 5

The power system shown in Fig. 3.4.11A develops a two-phase-to-earth fault at the point F on the 132 kV overhead-line transmission system, the pre-fault phase-to-phase voltage at F being equal to the rated value, namely 132 kV. Determine the current and voltage conditions at the point of fault and the values of the phase

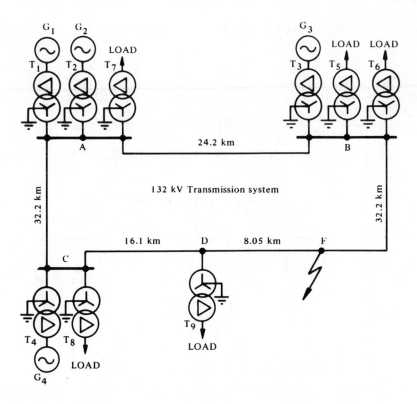

Fig. 3.4.11A

currents which flow to the point of fault from the directions of stations B and D. Determine also the phase-to-earth voltages at station B. It can be assumed that the system loads are all zero. What is the three-phase fault level at F?

The plant impedance values are given in Table 3.4.11A, the generator positive-sequence impedances being the transient values

Table 3.4.11A   *Plant impedance data for Example 5*

Plant unit	Rating	Per-cent impedance	
		to MVA rating	to 100 MVA base
G_1, G_2	60 MW	$Z_1 = j17 \cdot 0$	$Z_1 = j22 \cdot 7$
	75 MVA	$Z_2 = j12 \cdot 0$	$Z_2 = j16 \cdot 0$
G_3, G_4	30 MW	$Z_1 = j15 \cdot 0$	$Z_1 = j40 \cdot 0$
	37·5 MVA	$Z_2 = j11 \cdot 5$	$Z_2 = j30 \cdot 7$
T_1, T_2	75 MVA	$j12 \cdot 0$	$j16 \cdot 0$
T_3, T_4	37·5 MVA	$j10 \cdot 0$	$j26 \cdot 7$
T_5, T_6	30 MVA	$j10 \cdot 0$	$j33 \cdot 3$
T_7, T_8, T_9	60 MVA	$j12 \cdot 0$	$j20 \cdot 0$
O.H. Line	–	–	$Z_1 = Z_2 = 0 \cdot 089 + j0 \cdot 236$
per km	–	–	$Z_0 = 0 \cdot 197 + j0 \cdot 589$

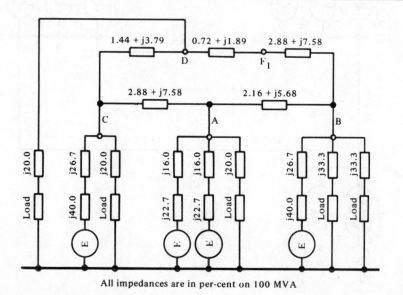

All impedances are in per-cent on 100 MVA

Fig. 3.4.11B   *Positive-sequence network*

Solution: Using a common MVA base of 100, the required common-base per-cent impedance values are as given in Table 3.4.11A, the positive, negative and zero-sequence networks being as shown in Figs. 3.4.11B, 3.4.11C and 3.4.11D. Ignoring the load impedances (that is assuming them to be infinite) the steps in the network reduction process are as shown in Figs. 3.4.11E, 3.4.11F and 3.4.11G, for the positive, negative and zero-sequence networks, respectively.

From the network reduction, the sequence impedances as seen from the point of fault are

$$Z_1 = 1 \cdot 69 + j16 \cdot 7 \text{ per-cent} = 0 \cdot 0169 + j0 \cdot 167 \text{ p.u.}$$
$$Z_2 = 1 \cdot 71 + j14 \cdot 9 \text{ per-cent} = 0 \cdot 0171 + j0 \cdot 149 \text{ p.u.}$$
$$Z_0 = 1 \cdot 90 + j9 \cdot 25 \text{ per-cent} = 0 \cdot 0190 + j0 \cdot 0925 \text{ p.u.}$$

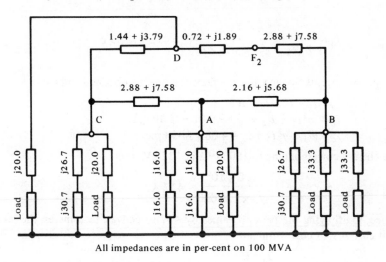

All impedances are in per-cent on 100 MVA

Fig. 3.4.11C   *Negative-sequence network*

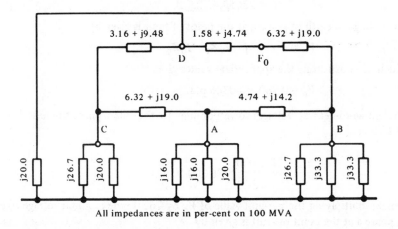

All impedances are in per-cent on 100 MVA

Fig. 3.4.11D   *Zero-sequence network*

The pre-fault voltage at F is equal to the rated voltage. Hence,

$$E = 1 + j0 \text{ p.u. (the vector reference)}$$

The sequence currents at the point of fault can now be obtained from the equations for the two-phase-to-earth fault in Table 3.4.4A, namely

$$I_1 = \frac{(Z_2 + Z_0)E}{Z_1 Z_2 + Z_2 Z_0 + Z_0 Z_1} = 0 \cdot 521 - j4 \cdot 40 \text{ p.u.}$$

$$I_2 = \frac{-Z_0 E}{Z_1 Z_2 + Z_2 Z_0 + Z_0 Z_1} = - 0 \cdot 109 + j1 \cdot 71 \text{ p.u.}$$

$$I_0 = \frac{-Z_2 E}{Z_1 Z_2 + Z_2 Z_0 + Z_0 Z_1} = - 0 \cdot 412 + j2 \cdot 69 \text{ p.u.}$$

The phase currents flowing into the fault can now be obtained and are

$$I_a = I_1 + I_2 + I_0 = 0$$
$$I_b = a^2 I_1 + a I_2 + I_0 = - 5 \cdot 91 + j3 \cdot 49 \text{ p.u.}$$
$$I_c = a I_1 + a^2 I_2 + I_0 = 4 \cdot 68 + j4 \cdot 58 \text{ p.u.}$$

The current corresponding to 100 MVA at 132 kV is

$$\frac{100 \times 10^6}{\sqrt{3} \times 132\,000} = 437 \text{ A}$$

Hence, multiplying the per-unit values by 437 to convert to amperes, the resultant fault currents, in polar form, are

$$I_a = 0$$
$$I_b = 3000 \underline{/149° \ 26'} \text{ A}$$
$$I_c = 2865 \underline{/44° \ 23'} \text{ A}$$

The voltage to earth of phase a at the point of fault is given by

$$V_a = E - I_1 Z_1 - I_2 Z_2 - I_0 Z_0$$

which on substituting the appropriate values gives

$$V_a = 0 \cdot 780 - j0 \cdot 0386 \text{ p.u.}$$

The phase-to-neutral voltage corresponding to the rated phase-to-phase value of 132 kV is

$$\frac{132\,000}{\sqrt{3}} = 76\,300 \text{ V}$$

Hence, multiplying the per-unit value of V_a by 76 300 the required voltage to earth of phase a at the point of fault is given by

$$V_a = 59\,500 - j2940 \text{ V}$$

or, in polar form, by

$$V_a = 59 \cdot 6 \underline{/-2° \ 50'} \ \text{kV}$$

Now, by the process of back-substitution, the sequence currents which flow to the

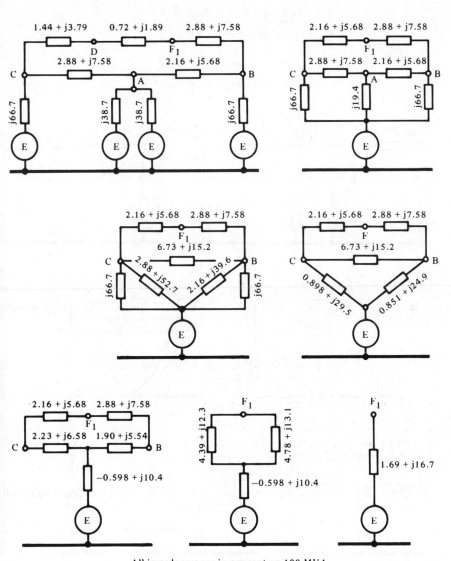

All impedances are in per-cent on 100 MVA

Fig. 3.4.11E *Reduction of the positive-sequence network*

fault from the direction of station B are, from Figs. 3.4.11E, 3.4.11F and 3.4.11G

$$I_1 = \frac{(4\cdot39 + j12\cdot3)(0\cdot521 - j4\cdot40)}{(4\cdot39 + j12\cdot3) + (4\cdot78 + j13\cdot1)} \text{p.u.}$$

$$I_2 = \frac{(4\cdot34 + j12\cdot2)(-0\cdot109 + j1\cdot71)}{(4\cdot34 + j12\cdot2) + (4\cdot74 + j13\cdot1)} \text{p.u.}$$

$$I_0 = \frac{(2\cdot80 + j13\cdot8)(-0\cdot412 + j2\cdot69)}{(2\cdot80 + j13\cdot8) + (7\cdot05 + j25\cdot4)} \text{p.u.}$$

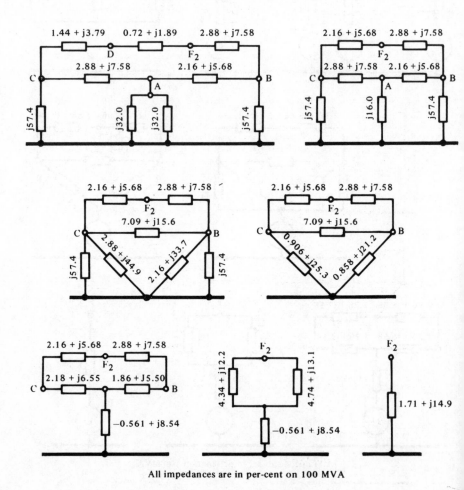

All impedances are in per-cent on 100 MVA

Fig. 3.4.11F   *Reduction of the negative-sequence network*

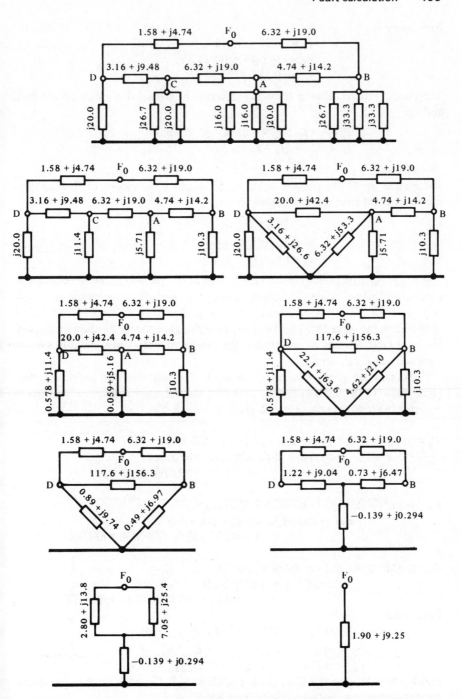

All impedances are in per-cent on 100 MVA

Fig. 3.4.11G *Reduction of the zero-sequence network*

from which

$$I_1 = 0\cdot259 - j2\cdot13 \text{ p.u.}$$
$$I_2 = -0\cdot0546 + j0\cdot823 \text{ p.u.}$$
$$I_0 = -0\cdot187 + j0\cdot930 \text{ p.u.}$$

The phase currents flowing from the direction of station B can now be obtained and are

$$I_a = I_1 + I_2 + I_0 = 0\cdot0174 - j0\cdot377 \text{ p.u.}$$
$$I_b = a^2 I_1 + aI_2 + I_0 = -2\cdot84 + j1\cdot31 \text{ p.u.}$$
$$I_c = aI_1 + a^2 I_2 + I_0 = 2\cdot27 + j1\cdot86 \text{ p.u.}$$

Multipyling by 437 to convert to amps, the required phase currents flowing from the direction of station B are, in polar form

$$I_a = 165\underline{/-87°\ 22'} \text{ A}$$
$$I_b = 1370\underline{/155°\ 14'} \text{ A}$$
$$I_c = 1280\underline{/39°\ 21'} \text{ A}$$

The phase currents flowing from the direction of station D can now be obtained by subtraction of the values just obtained from the total phase-current values at the point of fault. The required current and voltage conditions at the point of fault are therefore as shown in Fig. 3.4.11H. The figure also gives the vector diagram showing the total fault currents I_b and Ic, and the phase-a voltage V_a in relation to the pre-fault voltages E_a, E_b and E_c.

To obtain the phase voltages at station B, the sequence voltage-drops in each phase between F and B must be added to the corresponding phase voltages at F, giving the following per-unit voltages at B

$$V_a = (0\cdot780 - j0\cdot0386) + (0\cdot259 - j2\cdot13)(0\cdot0288 + j0\cdot0758)$$
$$+ (-0\cdot0546 + j0\cdot823)(0\cdot0288 + j0\cdot0758)$$
$$+ (-0\cdot187 + j0\cdot930)(0\cdot0632 + j0\cdot190)$$

$$V_b = 0 + a^2(0\cdot259 - j2\cdot13)(0\cdot0288 + j0\cdot0758)$$
$$+ a(-0\cdot0546 + j0\cdot823)(0\cdot0288 + j0\cdot0758)$$
$$+ (-0\cdot187 + j0\cdot930)(0\cdot0632 + j0\cdot190)$$

$$V_c = 0 + a(0\cdot259 - j2\cdot13)(0\cdot0288 + j0\cdot0758)$$
$$+ a^2(-0\cdot0546 + j0\cdot823)(0\cdot0288 + j0\cdot0758)$$
$$+ (-0\cdot187 + j0\cdot930)(0\cdot0632 + j0\cdot190)$$

from which

$$V_a = 0\cdot697 - j0\cdot0374 \text{ p.u.} = 53\cdot3\underline{/-3°\ 4'} \text{ kV}$$
$$V_b = -0\cdot293 - j0\cdot168 \text{ p.u.} = 25\cdot8\underline{/-150°\ 10'} \text{ kV}$$
$$V_c = -0\cdot189 + j0\cdot236 \text{ p.u.} = 23\cdot1\underline{/128°\ 40'} \text{ kV}$$

Finally, to determine the three-phase fault level at F, the scalar value of the system positive-sequence impedance as seen from F is

$$\sqrt{0\cdot0169^2 + 0\cdot167^2} = 0\cdot168 \text{ p.u. on 100 MVA}$$

and hence the scalar value of the fault current from a three-phase fault at F is given by

$$I = \frac{E}{0 \cdot 168} = 5 \cdot 96 \text{ p.u.}$$

since $E = 1 \cdot 00$ p.u.

Multiplying by 437 to convert to amps

$$I = 2604 \text{ A}$$

and hence the required three-phase short-circuit level is

$$\sqrt{3} \times 132 \times 2 \cdot 604 \text{ MVA} = 596 \text{ MVA}$$

It should be noted that this result could have been obtained directly from the fact that the fault MVA for a three-phase short-circuit at rated voltage is equal to the ratio of the base MVA (that is 100) to the per-unit scalar value of the system positive-sequence impedance (that is 0·168).

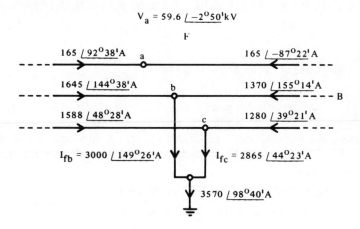

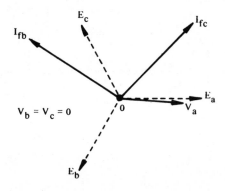

Fig. 3.4.11H

3.4.12   Example 6

The power system shown in Fig. 3.4.12A develops a single-phase open-circuit at the point F on one of the two 80·5 km 132 kV transmission lines connecting stations A and B, each line having positive and zero sequence impedances, per km, of $0·089 + j0·236$ per-cent and $0·197 + j0·589$ per-cent, respectively, on 100 MVA. Determine the resulting phase currents in the two 132 kV circuits immediately after the open-circuiting, given that the load voltage on the 33 kV side of the transformer at station B is 32 kV. The load can be assumed to be wholly passive and to contain no rotating plant, its positive and negative-sequence impedances thus being equal.

Solution: Using the load voltage as the vector reference, its value in per-unit is given by

$$\frac{32}{33} + j0 = 0·970 + j0$$

Adopting 100 MVA as the common base, the scalar value of the load power is

$$\frac{85}{100} = 0·85 \text{ p.u.}$$

and the scalar value of the load current is therefore

$$\frac{0·85}{0·97} = 0·876 \text{ p.u.}$$

Now, the phase-angle of the load impedance, that is the angle whose cosine is 0·950, is 18° 12′, the sine of this angle being 0·312. The complex value of the load current is therefore

$$0·876(0·950 - j0·312) = 0·832 - j0·274 \text{ p.u.}$$

and, hence, the complex value of the load impedance is

$$\frac{0·970 + j0}{0·832 - j0·274} = 1·051 + j0·346 \text{ p.u.}$$

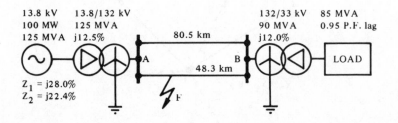

13.8 kV   13.8/132 kV   132/33 kV   85 MVA
100 MW   125 MVA   90 MVA   0.95 P.F. lag
125 MVA   j12.5%   80.5 km   j12.0%

A   B   LOAD
                            48.3 km

$Z_1 = j28.0\%$
$Z_2 = j22.4\%$ F

Fig. 3.4.12ᴊ

The positive, negative and zero-sequence networks of the power system, open-circuited at the point of fault, are shown in Fig. 3.4.12B, the plant impedance values having been all converted to the common base of 100 MVA. Considering the positive-sequence network, the effective impedance of the network, as would be

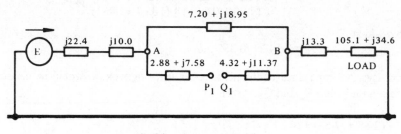

Positive-sequence network

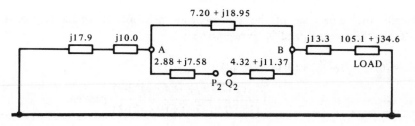

Negative-sequence network

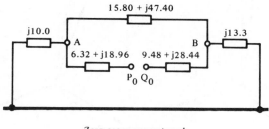

Zero-sequence network

All impedances in per-cent on 100 MVA

Fig. 3.4.12B

measured between the points P_1 and Q_1, is seen to be

$$Z_1 = (2\cdot88 + j7\cdot58) + (4\cdot32 + j11\cdot37)$$
$$+ \frac{(7\cdot20 + j18\cdot95)(105\cdot1 + j80\cdot3)}{(7\cdot20 + j18\cdot95) + (105\cdot1 + j80\cdot3)} \text{ per-cent}$$

from which
$$Z_1 = 0\cdot147 + j0\cdot352 \text{ p.u.}$$

Similarly, the impedance of the negative-sequence netwok, as would be measured between the points P_2 and Q_2, is seen to be

$$Z_2 = (2\cdot88 + j7\cdot58) + (4\cdot32 + j11\cdot37)$$
$$+ \frac{(7\cdot20 + j18\cdot95)(105\cdot1 + j75\cdot8)}{(7\cdot20 + j18\cdot95) + (105\cdot1 + j75\cdot8)} \text{ per-cent}$$

from which
$$Z_2 = 0\cdot148 + j0\cdot351 \text{ p.u.}$$

Finally the impedance of the zero-sequence network, as would be measured between the points P_0 and Q_0, is seen to be

$$Z_0 = (6\cdot32 + j18\cdot96) + (9\cdot48 + j28\cdot44)$$
$$+ \frac{(15\cdot80 + j47\cdot4)(0 + j23\cdot3)}{(15\cdot80 + j47\cdot4) + (0 + j23\cdot3)} \text{ per-cent}$$

from which
$$Z_0 = 0\cdot174 + j0\cdot634 \text{ p.u.}$$

Now, the pre-fault value of the positive-sequence current in the circuit containing

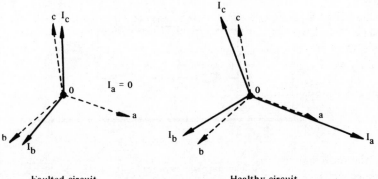

Faulted circuit   Healthy circuit

Fig. 3.4.12C

the point of fault, F, is equal to one half the current taken by the load, giving

$$I_{1pf} = 0.416 - j0.137 \text{ p.u.}$$

Hence, using the values obtained above in eqns. 3.4.6.7, the required positive, negative and zero-sequence currents in the faulted circuit are

$$I_1 = \cfrac{Z_1 I_{1pf}}{Z_1 + \cfrac{Z_2 Z_0}{Z_2 + Z_0}} = 0.2535 - j0.0884 \text{ p.u.}$$

$$I_2 = \frac{-Z_0 I_1}{Z_2 + Z_0} = -0.1633 + j0.0484 \text{ p.u.}$$

$$I_0 = \frac{-Z_2 I_1}{Z_2 + Z_0} = -0.0902 + j0.0400 \text{ p.u.}$$

The phase currents in the faulted circuit can now be obtained and are

$$I_a = I_1 + I_2 + I_0 = 0 \text{ p.u.}$$
$$I_b = a^2 I_1 + a I_2 + I_0 = -0.254 - j0.301 \text{ p.u.}$$
$$I_c = a I_1 + a^2 I_2 + I_0 = -0.0167 + j0.421 \text{ p.u.}$$

the direction of flow being from A to B. The base current corresponding to the base MVA of 100 at 132 kV is 437 A and, hence, multiplying the above values by 437 to convert to amps, the resulting phase currents, in polar form, are

$$I_a = 0$$
$$I_b = 172\underline{/-130°10'} \text{ A}$$
$$I_c = 185\underline{/92°16'} \text{ A}$$

Now the effective impedance of the faulted circuit to the flow of positive-sequence current is seen, from Fig. 3.4.6A, to be its normal healthy positive-sequence impedance (7·20 + j18·95 per-cent) plus the impedance formed by the parallel combination of Z_2 and Z_0, that is

$$(0.072 + j0.1895) + \frac{(0.148 + j0.351)(0.174 + j0.634)}{(0.148 + j0.351) + (0.174 + j0.634)} \text{ p.u.}$$

$$= 0.155 + j0.416 \text{ p.u.}$$

With the open-circuit fault present, therefore, the positive-sequence voltage (reference-phase value) of point A with respect to point B is

$$(0.2535 - j0.0884)(0.155 + j0.416) = 0.0761 + j0.0917 \text{ p.u.}$$

The positive-sequence current flowing from A to B in the other, healthy, 132 kV circuit is therefore

$$I_1 = \frac{0.0761 + j0.0917}{0.072 + j0.1895} = 0.556 - j0.190 \text{ p.u.}$$

Also, knowing the negative sequence current flowing in the faulted circuit, the negative-sequence current flowing from A to B in the healthy circuit is, from Fig. 3.4.12B,

$$\frac{-(-0.1633 + j0.0484)(105.1 + j75.8)}{(105.1 + j75.8) + (7.20 + j18.95)} \text{ p.u.}$$

from which

$$I_2 = 0.140 - j0.0535 \text{ p.u.}$$

Similarly, the zero-sequence current flowing from A to B in the healthy circuit is

$$I_0 = \frac{-(-0.0902 + j0.0400)(j23.3)}{(15.80 + j47.40) + (j23.3)}$$

from which

$$I_0 = 0.0311 - j0.00621 \text{ p.u.}$$

The phase currents flowing from A to B in the healthy circuit are therefore

$$I_a = I_1 + I_2 + I_0 = 0.727 - j0.250 \text{ p.u.}$$
$$I_b = a^2 I_1 + a I_2 + I_0 = -0.435 - j0.245 \text{ p.u.}$$
$$I_c = a I_1 + a^2 I_2 + I_0 = -0.199 + j0.476 \text{ p.u.}$$

Multiplying these values by 437 to convert to amps, the required phase currents in the healthy circuit are, in polar form;

$$I_a = 336 \underline{/-18° \ 59'} \text{ A}$$
$$I_b = 218 \underline{/-150° \ 36'} \text{ A}$$
$$I_c = 226 \underline{/112° \ 41'} \text{ A}$$

The phase currents in the two circuits are shown in vector-diagram form in Fig. 3.4.12C, the pre-fault values being shown by the broken lines. It will be noted that the missing phase-a current in the faulted circuit produces an increased phase-a current in the parallel healthy circuit.

It is important to note that the generator impedance used in the given calculations is the transient value and that, in consequence, the phase currents obtained are those appropriate to the conditions obtaining immediately after the instant of fault.

3.5   Calculation of simultaneous fault conditions

3.5.1   Sequence networks

The fault conditions so far considered have all been single fault conditions occurring at a stated single point on the power system, the analysis of these conditions having been achieved by considering the positive, negative and zero-sequence networks of the given power system and reducing these networks to their simplest form as seen from the point of fault. A similar procedure is used in dealing with two faults which occur simultaneously at, say, two different points on the power system, the requirement now being that the three sequence networks must be considered in relation to the two points of fault, namely A and B, instead of the single point F considered previously.

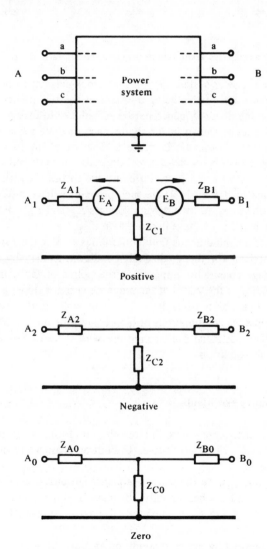

Fig. 3.5.1A *Equivalent phase-sequence networks for a system subjected to two simultaneous faults at points A and B*

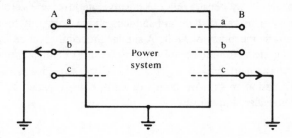

Fig. 3.5.2A *Block diagram representation of the cross-country earth-fault condition*

The three-phase power system is shown in block-diagram form in Fig. 3.5.1A, the phase references a, b and c being the same at the two points of fault, A and B. The corresponding phase-sequence networks, reduced to their simplest form, are the equivalent-T circuits shown in the figure, each of these networks representing the chosen reference phase, namely phase a. The use of the two driving voltages E_A and E_B in the positive-sequence network permits the treatment of cases in which the pre-fault voltages at A and B are different due to the network pre-fault conditions (for example load flows). Where such pre-fault voltage difference is zero or can be ignored, however, the two driving voltages E_A and E_B can be removed and replaced by a single driving voltage in series with Z_{C1}.

The analysis of a simultaneous fault condition is achieved in a similar manner to that already described for the single fault condition, namely by considering the current and voltage constraints imposed at the points of fault, these constraints being used to determine the values of the sequence currents flowing from the power system into the two points of fault. It is not possible, in the space available, to consider all the possible combinations of fault conditions and the treatment given is therefore limited to particular fault conditions with special reference to the cross-country earth-fault condition.

3.5.2   Cross-country earth-fault

This fault condition is represented, in block-diagram form, in Fig. 3.5.2A, the fault condition at A being a single-phase-to-earth fault on phase b and that at B a similar fault, but on phase c.

Let I_{A1}, I_{A2} and I_{A0} be the phase-a sequence currents flowing into the fault at A and let I_{B1}, I_{B2} and I_{B0} be, similarly, the phase-a sequence currents flowing into the fault at B. Let E_A and E_B be the pre-fault phase-a voltages at the points A and B, respectively.

The constraints imposed by the fault condition at A are

$$\left. \begin{array}{l} (I_a)_A = (I_c)_A = 0 \\ (V_b)_A = 0 \end{array} \right\} \qquad \text{3.5.2.1}$$

and writing the current constraints in symmetrical-component form gives

$$(I_a)_A = I_{A1} + I_{A2} + I_{A0} = 0 \\ (I_c)_A = aI_{A1} + a^2 I_{A2} + I_{A0} = 0 \Big\} \qquad 3.5.2.2$$

from which it follows that

$$I_{A2} = aI_{A1} \\ I_{A0} = a^2 I_{A1} \Big\} \qquad 3.5.2.3$$

The fault current at A is thus given by

$$(I_b)_A = a^2 I_{A1} + aI_{A2} + I_{A0}$$

from which

$$(I_b)_A = 3a^2 I_{A1} \qquad 3.5.2.4$$

Similarly, the constraints imposed by the fault condition at B are

$$(I_a)_B = (I_b)_B = 0 \\ (V_c)_B = 0 \Big\} \qquad 3.5.2.5$$

and, again, writing the current constraints in symmetrical-component form gives

$$(I_a)_B = I_{B1} + I_{B2} + I_{B0} = 0 \\ (I_b)_B = a^2 I_{B1} + aI_{B2} + I_{B0} = 0 \Big\} \qquad 3.5.2.6$$

from which it follows that

$$I_{B2} = a^2 I_{B1} \\ I_{B0} = aI_{B1} \Big\} \qquad 3.5.2.7$$

The fault current at B is thus given by

$$(I_c)_B = aI_{B1} + a^2 I_{B2} + I_{B0}$$

from which

$$(I_c)_B = 3aI_{B1} \qquad 3.5.2.8$$

Considering the voltage constraint at A, it follows from Fig. 3.5.2A that

$$(V_b)_A = a^2 E_a - a^2 I_{A1}(Z_{A1} + Z_{C1}) - aI_{A2}(Z_{A2} + Z_{C2}) \\ - I_{A0}(Z_{A0} + Z_{C0}) - a^2 I_{B1} Z_{C1} \\ - aI_{B2} Z_{C2} - I_{B0} Z_{C0} = 0 \qquad 3.5.2.9$$

which reduces to

$$E_A = I_{A1}[(Z_{A1} + Z_{A2} + Z_{A0}) + (Z_{C1} + Z_{C2} + Z_{C0})] \\ + I_{B1}[Z_{C1} + aZ_{C2} + a^2 Z_{C0}] \qquad 3.5.2.10$$

Similarly, considering the voltage constraint at B, it is seen that

$$(V_c)_B = aE_B - aI_{B1}(Z_{B1} + Z_{C1}) - a^2 I_{B2}(Z_{B2} + Z_{C2}) \\ - I_{B0} + (Z_{B0} + Z_{C0}) - aI_{A1} Z_{C1} \\ - a^2 I_{A2} Z_{C2} - I_{A0} Z_{C0} = 0 \qquad 3.5.2.11$$

which reduces to

$$E_B = I_{B1}[(Z_{B1} + Z_{B2} + Z_{B0}) + (Z_{C1} + Z_{C2} + Z_{C0})] \\ + I_{A1}[Z_{C1} + a^2 Z_{C2} + aZ_{C0}] \qquad 3.5.2.12$$

Solving the simultaneous equations 3.5.2.10 and 3.5.2.12 gives

$$I_{A1} = \frac{GE_A - HE_B}{GJ - HK} \qquad\qquad 3.5.2.13$$

$$I_{B1} = \frac{JE_B - KE_A}{GJ - HK} \qquad\qquad 3.5.2.14$$

where

$$G = (Z_{B1} + Z_{B2} + Z_{B0}) + (Z_{C1} + Z_{C2} + Z_{C0})$$
$$H = Z_{C1} + aZ_{C2} + a^2 Z_{C0}$$
$$J = (Z_{A1} + Z_{A2} + Z_{A0}) + (Z_{C1} + Z_{C2} + Z_{C0})$$
$$K = Z_{C1} + a^2 Z_{C2} + aZ_{C0}$$

The required fault currents at A and B can now be obtained from eqns. 3.5.2.4 and 3.5.2.8, giving:

$$(I_b)_A = 3a^2 \left[\frac{GE_A - HE_B}{GJ - HK} \right] \qquad\qquad 3.5.2.15$$

$$(I_c)_B = 3a \left[\frac{JE_B - KE_A}{GJ - HK} \right] \qquad\qquad 3.5.2.16$$

The resulting current distribution in the power system is obtained by the process of back-substitution in the manner already described.

The treatment of other simultaneous fault conditions can be achieved in a similar manner to that described above, assuming, as in the case treated, that the two faults both occur on the same network section. The treatment of simultaneous faults in which the two faults occur on different network sections (that is, are separated by transformer interconnections) is given by Edith Clarke in the book referred to in the Bibliography. This book gives a full treatment of a wide range of simultaneous fault conditions.

3.5.3   Sequence network interconnections

The treatment of single fault conditions in Sections 3.4.4, 3.4.5 and 3.4.6 has shown that any given fault condition may be represented by an appropriate interconnection of the sequence networks. Such interconnection of the sequence networks can also be used for the representation of simultaneous fault conditions, the required interconnection for any given fault condition being that which applies the appropriate constraints to the sequence currents and voltages at the two points of fault.

In interconnecting the sequence networks it is important to note that

(a)   the three sequence networks represent the chosen reference phase, namely phase a of the power system (*b*)   the interconnections applied must be such as will satisfy the fault constraints at the two points of fault, those applied to achieve the necessary constraints at one point of fault being applied in such a way as not to introduce additional constraints at the other point of fault.

Fig. 3.5.3A shows the required interconnection of the sequence networks to represent

(i)   a three-phase fault at A plus a three-phase fault at B

(ii)   a single-phase-to-earth fault (a—e) at A plus a three-phase fault at B

(iii)   a phase-to-phase fault (b—c) at A plus a three-phase fault at B.

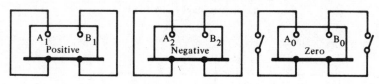

Three-phase faults at A and B

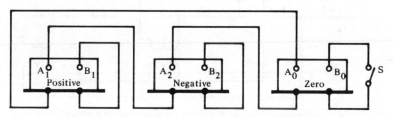

Phase-a earth-fault at A with three-phase fault at B

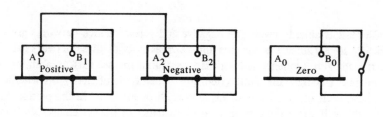

Phase-to-phase fault (b to c) at A with three-phase fault at B

Fig. 3.5.3A   *Representation of simultaneous fault conditions by interconnection of the sequence networks*

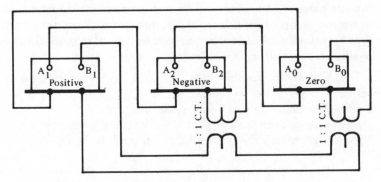

Phase-a earth-faults at A and B

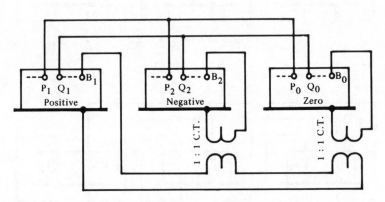

Phase-a open-circuit at A(P,Q) with a phase-a earth-fault at B

Fig. 3.5.3B *Representation of simultaneous fault conditions by interconnection of the sequence networks and the use of real-ratio interposing transformers*

For the reasons already given, the negative and zero-sequence networks are superfluous in case (i) since the currents and voltages in both these networks are zero. Similarly, the zero-sequence network is superfluous in case (iii). It is important to note in case (ii) that the fault condition depends significantly on whether the three-phase fault at B is clear of earth (switch open) or to earth (switch closed), because this will affect the zero-sequence impedance of the system as seen from the other point of fault, A.

Fig. 3.5.3B shows the required interconnection of the sequence networks to represent

(iv) a single-phase-to-earth fault (a–e) at A plus a single-phase-to-earth fault (a–e) at B

(v)   a single-phase open-circuit in phase a at A (P, Q) plus a single-phase-to-earth fault (a—e) at B.

It will be noted that in both the latter-mentioned cases the interconnections have required the use of perfect 1:1 interposing transformers, these being necessary to avoid the introduction of additional constraints at the points of fault over and above those necessary to represent the stated fault conditions.

The sequence-network interconnections shown in Figs. 3.5.3A and 3.5.3B result from applying the known relations between the phase-a sequence currents and voltages at the points of fault, the interconnections necessary being a combination of those required to satisfy the two fault conditions considered individually. Other simultaneous fault conditions can be similarly represented by appropriate interconnection of the sequence networks. It is important to note, however, that the sequence currents and voltages represented in the sequence networks are the phase-a values, and the sequence network interconnections which must be applied are those required to satisfy the known relations between the phase-a sequence quantities at the two points of fault.

In certain cases the required interconnection of the sequence networks will involve the use of ideal phase-shifting transformers of ratio $1:a$ and $1:a^2$, where $a = 1\underline{/120^\circ}$, and this can be illustrated for a particular case, namely that of a phase-a earth fault at A plus a phase-b earth-fault at B. At the point A the relationship between the phase-a sequence currents is

$$(I_1)_A = (I_2)_A = (I_0)_A$$

and at point B the relationship is

$$a^2(I_1)_B = a(I_2)_B = (I_0)_B$$

At the point B, therefore, it is required that

$$(I_2)_B = a(I_1)_B$$
$$(I_0)_B = a^2(I_1)_B$$

It will be noted that these constraints are satisfied by the interconnection of the sequence networks shown in Fig. 3.5.3C.

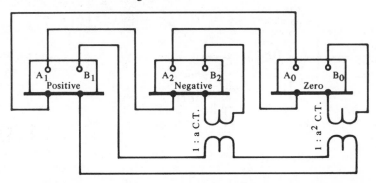

Fig. 3.5.3C   *Representation of a simultaneous fault condition (phase-a earth-fault at A with phase-b earth-fault at B) by interconnection of the sequence networks and the use of complex-ratio interposing transformers*

3.5.4 Example 7

The 33 kV system shown in Fig. 3.5.4A develops a phase-b earth-fault at the point A and a phase-c earth-fault at the point B, the positive and zero sequence impedances of the 33 kV overhead lines being $0 \cdot 155 + j0 \cdot 367 \ \Omega$ per km and $0 \cdot 9354 + j0 \cdot 969 \ \Omega$ per km, respectively. Determine the values of the fault currents at A and B and the value of the current in the neutral-earthing resistor. It can be assumed that the load currents are zero and that the pre-fault phase-to-phase voltages at two points of fault are equal to the rated value of 33 kV. It can also be assumed that the negative-sequence impedance of the 132 kV system is the same as the positive-sequence value.

Solution: Using a common MVA base of 100, the 132 kV system impedance is seen to be

$$\frac{100}{1500} = 0 \cdot 0667 \text{ p.u.} = 6 \cdot 67 \text{ per-cent}$$

the stated X/R ration of 5 corresponding to an impedance phase-angle of $78° \ 41'$. The complex value of the 132 kV system impedance is therefore given by

$$6 \cdot 67 \ (\cos 78° \ 41' + j \sin 78° \ 41') = 1 \cdot 31 + j6 \cdot 53 \text{ per-cent}$$

The impedance of the 60 MVA transformer to the common 100 MVA base is

$$\frac{100 \times j12 \cdot 5}{60} = j20 \cdot 8 \text{ per-cent}$$

Using the nomenclature of Fig. 3.5.1A, therefore, it follows that

$$Z_{C1} = Z_{C2} = (1 \cdot 31 + j6 \cdot 53) + (j20 \cdot 8) = 1 \cdot 31 + j27 \cdot 3 \text{ per-cent}$$

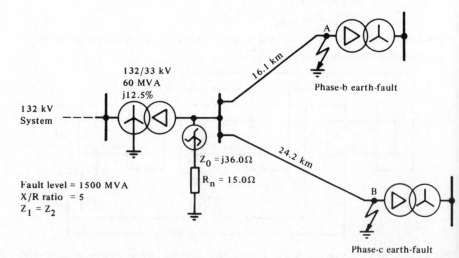

Fig. 3.5.4A

The impedance Z_{C0} is the zero-sequence impedance of the earthing transformer plus the zero-sequence impedance of the earthing resistor, giving

$$Z_{C0} = 45 \cdot 0 + j36 \cdot 0 \ \Omega$$

Now the base current corresponding to 100 MVA at 33 kV is

$$\frac{100 \times 10^6}{\sqrt{3} \times 33\,000} = 1750 \ \text{A}$$

the rated phase-to-neutral voltage being

$$\frac{33\,000}{\sqrt{3}} = 19\,050 \ \text{V}$$

The base impedance for the 33 kV system is therefore

$$\frac{19\,050}{1750} = 10 \cdot 88 \ \Omega$$

and the common-base value of Z_{C0} is therefore

$$\frac{45 \cdot 0 + j36 \cdot 0}{10 \cdot 88} = 4 \cdot 135 + j3 \cdot 31 \ \text{p.u.}$$

giving

$$Z_{C0} = 413 \cdot 5 + j331 \cdot 0 \ \text{per-cent}$$

The common-base values of the line impedances are

$$\text{Positive-sequence impedance} = \frac{0 \cdot 155 + 0 \cdot 367}{10 \cdot 88} \ \text{p.u. per km}$$

$$= 1 \cdot 42 + j3 \cdot 37 \ \text{per-cent per km}$$

$$\text{Zero-sequence impedance} = \frac{0 \cdot 354 + j0 \cdot 969}{10 \cdot 88} \ \text{p.u. per km}$$

$$= 3 \cdot 25 + j8 \cdot 91 \ \text{per-cent per km}$$

From the given line lengths, therefore, it is seen that

$$Z_{A1} = Z_{A2} = 23 \cdot 0 + j54 \cdot 2 \ \text{per-cent}$$
$$Z_{A0} = 52 \cdot 4 + j143 \cdot 4 \ \text{per-cent}$$
$$Z_{B1} = Z_{B2} = 34 \cdot 5 + j81 \cdot 3 \ \text{per-cent}$$
$$Z_{B0} = 78 \cdot 6 + j215 \cdot 1 \ \text{per-cent}$$

The positive, negative and zero-sequence networks for the power system are thus as shown in Fig. 3.5.4B. Combining the impedance values for use in the fault-current equations gives

$$G = (Z_{B1} + Z_{B2} + Z_{B0}) + (Z_{C1} + Z_{C2} + Z_{C0})$$

giving

$$G = 5.64 + j7.63 \text{ p.u.}$$
$$H = Z_{C1} + aZ_{C2} + a^2 Z_{C0} = 0.570 - j5.09 \text{ p.u.}$$
$$J = (Z_{A1} + Z_{A2} + Z_{A0}) + (Z_{C1} + Z_{C2} + Z_{C0})$$

giving

$$J = 5.15 + j6.37 \text{ p.u.}$$
$$K = Z_{C1} + a^2 Z_{C2} + aZ_{C0} = -4.69 + j2.05 \text{ p.u.}$$

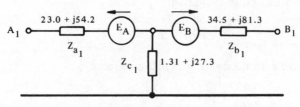

Positive-sequence network

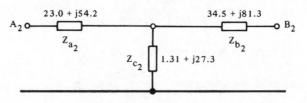

Negative-sequence network

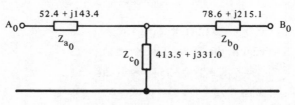

Zero-sequence network

$$E_A = E_B = 1 + j0 \text{ p.u.}$$

All impedance values are in per-cent on 100 MVA

Fig. 3.5.4B

Substituting these values into eqns. 3.5.3.15 and 3.5.3.16, with $E_A = E_B = 1 + j0$, gives

$$(I_b)_A = -0.710 - j0.122 \text{ p.u.}$$
$$(I_c)_B = 0.511 + j0.240 \text{ p.u.}$$

Multiplying by the base current of 1750 A to convert to amps, the required fault currents, expressed in polar form, are

$$(I_b)_A = 1262 \underline{/-170° \ 15'} \text{ A}$$
$$(I_c)_B = 987 \underline{/25° \ 10'} \text{ A}$$

The current flowing from earth into the neutral earthing resistor is

$$I_n = (I_b)_A + (I_c)_B = -0.199 + j0.118 \text{ p.u.}$$

which multiplied by 1750 and converted to polar form gives

$$I_n = 405 \underline{/149° \ 20'} \text{ A}$$

The fault currents are shown in vector-diagram form in Fig. 3.5.4C.

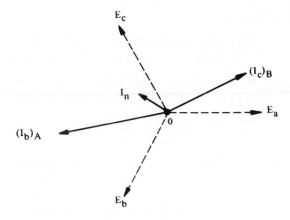

Fig. 3.5.4C

3.5.5 Example 8

The power system shown in Fig. 3.5.5A develops a single-phase (phase a) earth-fault at the point F on the h.v. terminals of the 132/33 kV transformer, together, with a phase-a open-circuit immediately on the line side of the earth fault. Determine the value of the fault current at F and compare this with the value obtained with the open-circuit absent. The line can be assumed to have a positive-sequence impedance of $0.089 + j0.236$ per-cent per km and a zero-sequence impedance of $0.197 + j0.589$ per-cent per km on a 100 MVA base. It can be assumed that the system load is zero.

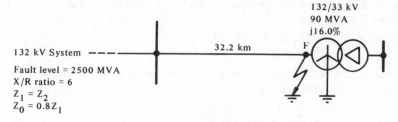

Fig. 3.5.5A

Solution: Adopting a common base MVA of 100, the sequence impedances of the 132 kV system are

$$Z_1 = Z_2 = \frac{100}{2500}(\cos 80° \; 32' + j \sin 80° \; 32') \text{ p.u.}$$

$$= 0.00658 + j0.0395 \text{ p.u.}$$
$$Z_0 = 0.8Z_1 \;\; = 0.00526 + j0.0316 \text{ p.u.}$$

and those of the 132 kV line are

$$Z_1 = Z_2 = 0.0288 + j0.0758 \text{ p.u.}$$
$$Z_0 = 0.0632 + j0.190 \text{ p.u.}$$

The common-base impedance of the transformer is

$$Z_t = \frac{100 \times j16.0}{90} = j17.8 \text{ per-cent}$$

$$= j0.178 \text{ per-unit}$$

The positive, negative and zero-sequence networks thus reduce to the circuits shown in Fig. 3.5.5B, it being assumed that the pre-fault phase-to-phase voltage at F is equal to the rated value of 132 kV.

Considering, now, the conditions at the point of fault, these are shown in Fig. 3.5.5C, the currents flowing into the transformer consisting of zero-sequence currents only, I per phase, as shown.

The phase currents which flow in the transmission line towards the point of fault are thus

$$I_a = 0$$
$$I_b = I$$
$$I_c = I$$

the corresponding sequence currents in the line thus being

$$I_{s1} = \tfrac{1}{3}(I_a + aI_b + a^2 I_c) = -\tfrac{1}{3}I$$
$$I_{s2} = \tfrac{1}{3}(I_a + a^2 I_b + aI_c) = -\tfrac{1}{3}I$$
$$I_{s0} = \tfrac{1}{3}(I_a + I_b + I_c) = \tfrac{2}{3}I$$

Let the sequence impedances of the power system to the left of the point of fault, as seen from P, be Z_{s1}, Z_{s2} and Z_{s0}. Then, the phase-to-earth voltages at F are given by

$$(V_a)_F = 0$$
$$(V_b)_F = (V_b)_P = a^2 E - a^2 I_{s1} Z_{s1} - a I_{s2} Z_{s2} - I_{s0} Z_{s0}$$
$$(V_c)_F = (V_c)_P = a E - a I_{s1} Z_{s1} - a^2 I_{s2} Z_{s2} - I_{s0} Z_{s0}$$

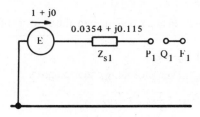

Positive-sequence network

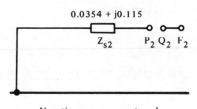

Negative-sequence network

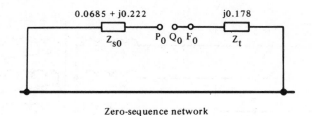

Zero-sequence network

All impedances are in per-unit on 100 MVA

Fig. 3.5.5B

and, hence, the zero-sequence voltage at the point F is

$$(V_0)_F = \tfrac{1}{3}[(V_a)_F + (V_b)_F + (V_c)_F]$$
$$= \tfrac{1}{3}[-E + I_{s1}Z_{s1} + I_{s2}Z_{s2} - 2I_{s0}Z_{s0}]$$

But

$$I_{s1} = I_{s2} = -\tfrac{1}{3}I$$

and

$$I_{s0} = \tfrac{2}{3}I$$

and hence

$$(V_0)_F = -\tfrac{1}{9}[3E + I(Z_{s1} + Z_{s2} + 4Z_{s0})]$$

Now, the zero-sequence voltage at F must be equal to the zero-sequence voltage-drop in the transformer, so that

$$(V_0)_F = IZ_t$$

and, hence, substituting for $(V_0)_F$ in the preceding equation gives

$$9IZ_t = -3E - I(Z_{s1} + Z_{s2} + 4Z_{s0})$$

from which

$$I = \frac{-3E}{9Z_t + Z_{s1} + Z_{s2} + 4Z_{s0}}$$

The fault current I_f which flows from phase a to earth at F is equal to minus I, hence the required equation for the fault current is

$$I_f = \frac{3E}{9Z_t + Z_{s1} + Z_{s2} + 4Z_{s0}}$$

Substituting the values of voltage and impedance for the given example, shown in Fig. 3.5.5B, gives

$$I_f = \frac{3(1 + j0)}{0{\cdot}345 + j2{\cdot}721} \text{ p.u.}$$

The base current corresponding to the base MVA of 100 at 132 kV is 437 A and,

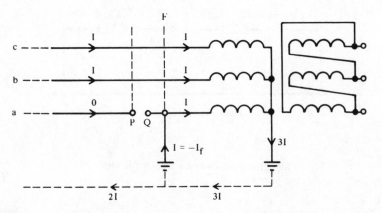

Fig. 3.5.5C

hence, multiplying the per-unit value of the fault current by 437 to convert to amps, the required fault current, expressed in polar form, is

$$I_f = 479\underline{/-82°\ 43'}A$$

With the open-circuit absent, the value of the fault current is

$$I_f = \frac{3E}{Z_1 + Z_2 + Z_0}$$

where Z_1, Z_2 and Z_0 are the sequence impedances of the complete system as seen from the point of fault F. With the open-circuit removed in the sequence networks of Fig. 3.5.5B, therefore, it is seen that the above-mentioned impedances values are

$$Z_1 = Z_{s1} = 0.0354 + j0.115 \text{ p.u.}$$
$$Z_2 = Z_{s2} = 0.0354 + j0.115 \text{ p.u.}$$
$$Z_0 = \frac{Z_{s0}Z_t}{Z_{s0} + Z_t} = 0.0132 + j0.101 \text{ p.u.}$$

The value of the fault current with the open-circuit absent is therefore

$$I_f = \frac{3(1 + j0)}{0.084 + j0.331} \text{ p.u.}$$

giving

$$I_f = 2.16 - j8.52 \text{ p.u.}$$

Multiplying by 437 and converting to polar form, the required current is

$$I_f = 3840\underline{/-75°\ 47'}\ A$$

It will be noted that the open-circuit produces a considerable reduction in the value of the earth-fault current.

3.6 Practical network analysis

It will be evident from the examples already given that network analysis by manual computation may involve considerable expenditure of time and effort if the network under examination has many nodes and branches, the method becoming virtually impracticable if the network is particularly large as may often be the case in some of the studies required to be carried out for the larger power systems. Accordingly, recourse may sometimes necessarily have to be made to alternative methods of analysis to overcome this difficulty, the first, based on the analogue principle, being the use of a network analyser and the second, and now much more common method, the use of a digital computer.

3.6.1 Network analysers

The network analyser provides, through analogue simulation, a means of network analysis by which the required power-system currents and voltages can be obtained by direct measurement carried out on an appropriate electrical model of the network under consideration.

The simulation principle can be understood by considering a given network and assuming it to be represented by a second similar network in which the voltages, currents and impedances are fixed multiples of the corresponding voltages, currents and impedances in the given network. The second network is said to be a simulated equivalent of the given network in that the electrical behaviour of the model network is identical in form to that of the given network. The response of the given network can therefore be obtained by direct measurement of the currents and voltages in the model network, the values so obtained being then multiplied by known constants to obtain the actual values appropriate to the given network. Thus, let V, I and Z denote actual voltages, currents and impedances in the given network and let V_m, I_m and Z_m be corresponding values in the model network. Then the relationships between actual and model values can be written

$$V = K_e V_m$$
$$I = K_i I_m$$
$$Z = K_z Z_m = (K_e/K_i) Z_m$$

where K_e, K_i and K_z are constants. (It should be noted that the constants K_e, K_i and K_z are not independent in that a given choice of values for any two of these constants automatically determines the value of the third).

The simulation principle is illustrated by the simple example shown in Fig. 3.6.1A in which the per-unit quantities in the given network correspond to actual

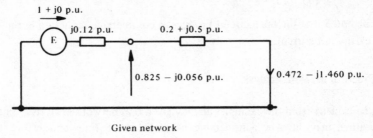

Given network

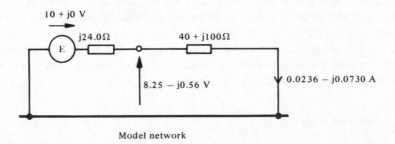

Model network

Fig. 3.6.1A   *Illustration of network simulation*

Fig. 3.6.1.1A   *Typical a.c. network-analyser installation*

voltages, currents and impedances in the model network, the relationships between the two sets of quantities being:

$$\begin{aligned}
1 \text{ per-unit voltage} &= 10\text{V} \\
1 \text{ per-unit current} &= 0.050 \text{ A} \\
1 \text{ per-unit impedance} &= 200 \ \Omega
\end{aligned}$$

It will be noted that the values of voltage, current and impedance used in the model are such as can be easily provided in the required physical model of the given network.

3.6.1.1   A.C. analyser

Using the simulation principle described in the previous Section, a given single-phase a.c. network (for example, the positive-sequence network shown in Fig. 3.4.11B) may be represented by an equivalent single-phase model network, the latter consisting of

(a)   an appropriate number of single-phase voltage sources, adjustable in magnitude and phase, for the simulation of the given network driving-voltages

(b)   an appropriate number of impedance units built up from resistors, inductors, and capacitors, as required, for the simulation of the network branch impedances

(c)   suitable interconnection facilities

(d)   suitable metering facilities to permit the measurement of currents and voltages in complex-number form with respect to some common reference phase

An equipment providing the above-mentioned facilities is termed an a.c. network analyser, and such equipment has been widely used for fault calculation and network analysis generally. A typical installation is shown in Fig. 3.6.1.1A, the racks in the background being used to accommodate the source units and impedance units. Interconnection facilities are provided by a patch panel shown in the middle of the racks, the metering facilities being housed in the two consoles shown in the foreground. The equipment shown is termed a universal network analyser in that it may be used to represent any given network by suitable interconnection of the individual source units and impedance units. The impedance units are arranged so that they can be set at will to any desired impedance value, this being achieved by the use of plug-in components or decade switches. The source units, similarly, are provided with means of setting the driving-voltage values in both magnitude and phase. The impedances are equipped with jack-in points to which the metering (that is current and voltage measuring facilities) can be connected when required.

In simulating a given power system fault condition it is generally necessary to represent all three sequence networks and to interconnect these in the network analyser to represent the particular fault condition being investigated. The sequence currents and voltages at any point in the network can then be measured at the corresponding points in the sequence networks, the values obtained being then used to obtain the required power-system currents and voltages. Using a network analyser, therefore, the steps in the fault calculation process are

(a) the representation of the given power system by its positive, negative and zero-sequence networks to a chosen common base

(b) the physical representation of these sequence networks by means of the network analyser

(c) the interconnection of the sequence networks in the network analyser to represent the power system fault conditions under consideration

(d) the measurement of the required sequence currents and voltages in the network analyser

(e) the calculation of the required power system currents and voltages from the measured sequence quantities.

The network analyser thus replaces computation of the sequence-network currents and voltages by direct measurement of these quantities in the model network, the resultant saving in time and labour being usually very considerable. The accuracy obtained from a network analyser depends essentially on the accuracy of calibration of the analyser components and that of the associated measuring equipment, overall error limits of ±2% being typical for modern installations.

3.6.1.2   D.C. analyser

In many cases, fault calculations can be achieved with sufficient accuracy by treating all the impedances as scalar quantities rather than complex quantities, this simplification being usually restricted to those cases in which the network impedances can all be regarded as having the same phase angle. This assumption makes it possible to represent all the network impedances by resistors in the network analyser and also enables the network driving-voltages to be simulated in the analyser by d.c. voltage sources. In this simplified method of representation, therefore, the given a.c. network is simulated by an equivalent, or approximately equivalent, d.c. model, the a.c. currents and voltages in the given network being represented by d.c. values in the model network. An analyser of this type is termed a d.c. network analyser or d.c. fault calculator.

3.6.2   Digital-computer analysis

Network analysis by solution of the relevant network equations is readily achieved by the use of digital-computer methods of analysis, the availability of suitable large-capacity computers and appropriate analysis programs making it possible to analyse even the largest networks with required speed and accuracy. Computer-based methods of analysis are accordingly now very widely used for load-flow studies, fault calculations and system stability investigations to the extent that they have now largely superseded the previous use of network analysers for such work.

The use of a computer requires the adoption of an orderly and logical method of description of the network to be studied, in terms of its nodes and branches, the appropriate data defining the network being passed to the computer by means of punched cards or directly from a keyboard. The information so provided is handled by a program management system, the function of which is to store, retrieve and generally manipulate the network data for input and transfer to any of the several analysis programs which may require to be used in the solution of any particular problem. Such a program management system, developed and used by the CEGB and named TRAM, is capable of handling problems involving up to 1000 nodes and 15000 branches. The network equations involved in any particular problem are solved by appropriate direct or iterative computational procedures within the computer using the necessary analysis programs, the latter covering such standard needs as load-flow determination, three-phase short-circuit studies, unbalanced-fault studies, network reduction and system stability studies. Analysis programs are available which also have provision for the inclusion of power-system protection data, thus making it possible, in fault studies, to investigate also the response of the protection to the fault conditions under study and thereby assist, for example, in the determination of required protection settings and the assessment of expected fault clearance times.

3.6.3 Transient analysis

The methods of analysis so far considered have all been concerned with determination of the power-frequency components of current and voltage on the assumption of steady-state conditions, it being sufficient for most studies to assume that only power-frequency components are present or that such transient components as may be present, for example in fault conditions, are of only negligible significance in the particular study in question. Such an assumption may not always be admissible, however, particularly in studies concerned with the performance of high-speed protection, recognising that such protection is required to perform its function within a very short time after the instant of fault when significant transient non-power-frequency components of current and voltage can also be expected to be present.

The transient components in question which may need to be considered in such studies include both d.c. and a.c. components, with the latter possibly ranging in frequency from below fundamental frequency (particularly if large underground-cable systems are involved) up to several kHz and with decay time-constants, for both d.c. and a.c. components, of up to a few hundreds of milliseconds.

The accurate analysis of power-system fault conditions to include such transient phenomena is recognised to present particular difficulties, the first requirement being a much more detailed specification of the system under study, including both lumped and distributed parameters and, where relevant, an appropriate modelling of non-linear parameters. The second requirement is a suitable method of transient analysis of the resulting network, the methods employed to date including both analogue simulation through use of a transient network analyser and digital analysis by means of a computer. Details of such methods will be found in the relevant references contained in the Bibliography.

3.7 Winding faults

3.7.1 General considerations

The analysis of faults in machine and transformer windings presents particular difficulty in that the effective impedances of the affected windings under internal fault conditions are not normally known. The methods of analysis which may be employed are, therefore, severely limited and are usually concerned with obtaining a reasonable estimate based on certain simplifying assumptions. A particular case in which simplifying assumptions can yield quite accurate results is that concerned with the analysis of earth faults on impedance-earthed windings, where the neutral-earthing impedance can be regarded as large compared with the winding impedance.

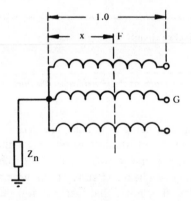

Fig. 3.7.2A *Synchronous machine with fault position F, a per-unit distance x from the neutral point*

3.7.2 Generator-winding faults

Consider the generator shown in Fig. 3.7.2A and let it be assumed that a short-circuit condition occurs at the point F, a per-unit distance x from the generator neutral point. Let it be further assumed that the generated e.m.f. (phase-a value) in that portion of the winding between the neutral point and the point of fault is xE, where E is the value appropriate to the full winding, the e.m.f. in the remaining

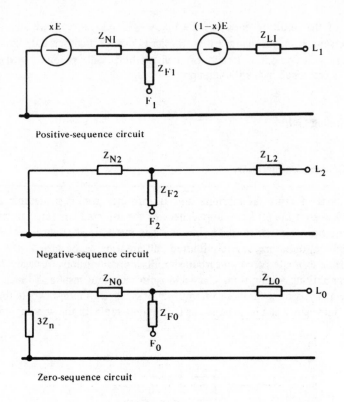

Positive-sequence circuit

Negative-sequence circuit

Zero-sequence circuit

Fig. 3.7.2B   *Phase-sequence circuits of the synchronous machine of Fig. 3.7.2A*

portion of the winding thus being $(1 - x)E$. The generator winding can now be regarded as a three-ended circuit, these three ends being the neutral end N, the line or phase-terminal end L and the point of fault F. It follows, therefore, that the positive, negative and zero-sequence circuits of the generator will have the form shown in Fig. 3.7.2B. It will be noted that there are now three generator impedance values to be considered for each of the three phase-sequence circuits, namely Z_N, Z_L and Z_F, respectively, with appropriate phase-sequence suffixes, the values of these impedances depending on the fault position x and the normal full-winding values of the generator phase-sequence impedances Z_1, Z_2 and Z_0.

In order to apply the generator phase-sequence circuits of Fig. 3.7.2B it is, of course, necessary to determine the required impedance values, given the values of x, Z_1, Z_2 and Z_0. Some supposition must, therefore, be made to obtain these values and the simplest of these is to assume that there is no mutual coupling between the neutral-to-fault and fault-to-line sections of the winding, and that the impedances appropriate to each of these two winding sections are proportional to lengths of these sections. The phase-sequence circuits which result from these

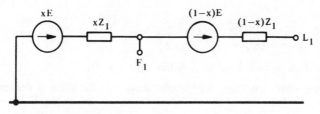

Positive-sequence circuit

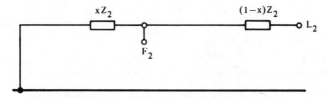

Negative-sequence circuit

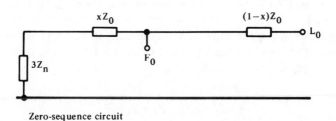

Zero-sequence circuit

Fig. 3.7.2C *Phase-sequence circuits of the synchronous machine of Fig. 3.7.2A assuming a linear winding-impedance distribution*

assumptions are shown in Fig. 3.7.2C, from which it will be seen that

$$\left.\begin{array}{ll} Z_{N1} = xZ_1 & Z_{L1} = (1 - x)Z_1 \\ Z_{N2} = xZ_2 & Z_{L2} = (1 - x)Z_2 \\ Z_{N0} = xZ_0 & Z_{L0} = (1 - x)Z_0 \end{array}\right\} \qquad 3.7.2.1$$

the remaining impedances Z_{F1}, Z_{F2} and Z_{F0} all being zero.

Considering the simple case in which there is assumed to be no infeed to the fault from the generator terminals, the phase-sequence impedance values as seen from the point of fault are xZ_1, xZ_2 and xZ_0, the pre-fault voltage at the point of fault (phase-a value) being xE.

Hence, considering a three-phase fault at F, the resultant fault current value is given by

$$I_f = \frac{xE}{xZ_1} = \frac{E}{Z_1} \qquad 3.7.2.2$$

the value of the fault current thus being seen to be independent of fault position.

Similarly, for a phase-to-phase fault at F, the value of the phase-fault current is

given by

$$I_f = \frac{\sqrt{3}xE}{xZ_1 + xZ_2} = \frac{\sqrt{3}E}{Z_1 + Z_2} \qquad 3.7.2.3$$

which is also seen to be independent of the fault position.

Considering now, a single-phase-to-earth fault at F, the value of the fault current is given by

$$I_f = \frac{3xE}{xZ_1 + xZ_2 + xZ_0 + 3Z_n} \qquad 3.7.2.4$$

and if Z_n is very much greater than Z_1, Z_2 and Z_0, the expression for the fault current reduces to the approximate form

$$I_f = \frac{xE}{Z_n} \qquad 3.7.2.5$$

The case of the short-circuited turns condition can be treated by assuming the short-circuited portion of the winding to constitute a fraction x of the full winding, as shown, in Fig. 3.7.2D, it being further assumed that the short-circuit current I_f is quite independent of the position of the short-circuited turns within the winding. With these assumptions, the value of the fault current will be precisely the same as for a phase-to-*neutral* fault at a per-unit distance x from the neutral point, the fault current being therefore given by

$$I_f = \frac{3xE}{xZ_1 + xZ_2 + xZ_0} = \frac{3E}{Z_1 + Z_2 + Z_0} \qquad 3.7.2.6$$

The value of the fault current is thus seen to be independent of the fraction of the winding spanned by the short-circuit.

In all the above-mentioned fault conditions, the effect of fault infeed from the generator terminals can be taken into account by connecting the generator phase-sequence circuits of Fig. 3.7.2C to those applicable to the rest of the system.

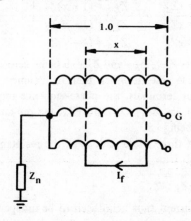

Fig. 3.7.2D

It is important to note that the generator phase-sequence circuits of Fig. 3.7.2C are based on a particular and somewhat arbitrary supposition regarding the subdivision of the generator impedance values. The results obtained must not, therefore, be regarded as anything more than a very rough approximation to the actual conditions.

It should be noted also that this simple treatment is applicable only to the case of a generator with a single-conductor stator winding. A more rigorous treatment, applicable to generators with stator windings having a number of paths in parallel, is given by V.A. Kinitsky.

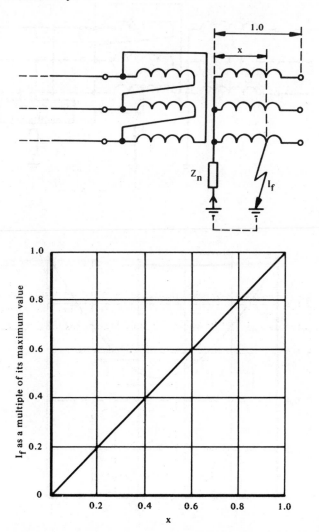

Fig. 3.7.3A *Variations of fault current with fault position for an impedance-earthed star winding*

3.7.3 Transformer-winding faults

In dealing with earth faults on transformer windings, the special case of impedance-earthed windings is amenable to the simplified treatment already described in the previous Section, the value of the fault current being the pre-fault phase-to-earth voltage at the point of fault divided by the effective value of the system earthing impedance. The two cases of most common interest are shown in Figs. 3.7.3A and 3.7.3B, namely the star-connected winding and the delta-connected winding.

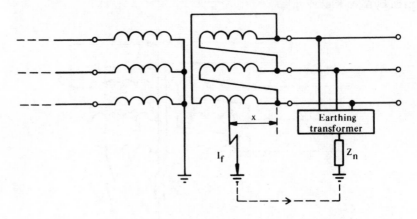

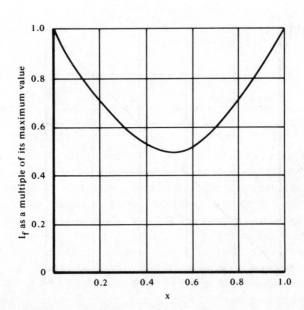

Fig. 3.7.3B *Variation of fault current with fault position for an impedance-earthed delta winding*

It is of interest to note, in the case of the delta-connected winding, that the pre-fault phase-to-earth voltage has a minimum value when the fault is at the centre of the affected winding, this minimum value being one half the phase-to-neutral voltage. As will be seen from Fig. 3.7.3C, the magnitude of the pre-fault phase-to-neutral voltage, E_f, at the point of fault is

$$E_f = E\sqrt{1 + 3x(x - 1)}$$

where E is the phase-to-neutral voltage of the winding and x is the per unit distance of the fault from one terminal of the winding.

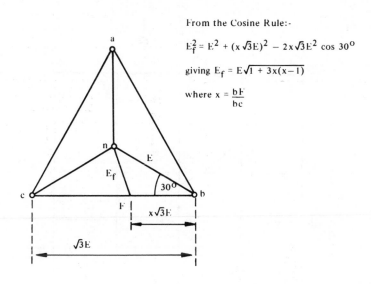

From the Cosine Rule:-

$$E_f^2 = E^2 + (x\sqrt{3}E)^2 - 2x\sqrt{3}E^2 \cos 30^0$$

giving $E_f = E\sqrt{1 + 3x(x-1)}$

where $x = \dfrac{bF}{bc}$

Fig. 3.7.3C *Prefault phase-to-neutral voltage in a delta winding and its dependence on fault position*

The case of an earth fault on a solidly-earthed star-connected transformer-winding is of particular interest, and has been investigated by tests on a 132/33 kV 45 MVA star/delta transformer, the results being as shown in Fig. 3.7.3D. It will be noted that, within the limited range of fault positions investigated (accessible by virtue of the tap-change connections), the earth-fault current is a maximum for a fault close to the neutral point, the current flowing into the winding from the phase terminal having a minimum value of zero for a fault in this position. Extending these results to the case of short-circuited turns it is not difficult to see that the fault current in the short-circuited turns can be expected to be high if the fraction of the winding which is short-circuited is small, the high value of current in the short-circuited turns being accompanied by a relatively low value of current in the remainder of the winding.

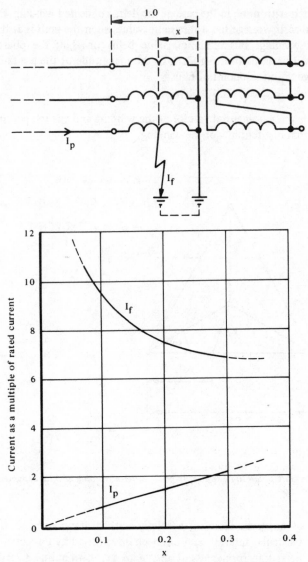

Fig. 3.7.3D *Variation of fault current with fault position for an earth fault in the solidly-earthed star-connected winding of a star/delta transformer*

3.8   Appendixes

3.8.1   Representation of off-nominal-ratio transformers

The representation of transformer circuits given in Section 3.3.3 was on the basis that the transformer windings could be assumed to have the same rated voltage as their associated network sections, such transformers being termed nominal-ratio transformers. Thus, a transformer interconnecting a 132 kV system and a 33 kV system would, on this basis, be assumed to have a transformation ratio of exactly 132 kV to 33 kV with a corresponding turns ratio (star/star windings assumed) of exactly 4 to 1. It is, however, sometimes necessary to consider cases in which the transformer voltage ratio is not the same as the ratio of the rated voltages of the associated network sections, the most common instance being that in which the effect of transformer tap-change equipment must be taken into account.

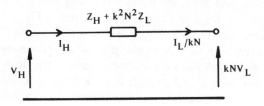

Fig. 3.8.1A   *Representation of an off-nominal-ratio transformer*

In considering the representation of such an off-nominal-ratio transformer, let it be assumed that the two-winding transformer of Fig. 3.3.3A has a turns ratio (star/star windings assumed) of kN instead of N, so that

$$kN = \frac{\text{rated voltage of winding H}}{\text{rated voltage of winding L}}$$

and N, as before, is the ratio of the nominal rated voltages of the network sections to which the windings H and L are connected. Thus, considering the case of a 118·8/33 kV transformer interconnecting a 132 kV system and a 33 kV system it is seen that

$$kN = \frac{118·8}{33} = 3·60$$

$$N = \frac{132}{33} = 4·00$$

so that

$$k = \frac{3·60}{4·00} = 0·90$$

The symbol k thus denotes a positive real number whose value may be less than, equal to, or greater than unity, its value being unity when the transformer ratio is exactly equal to the ratio of the nominal rated voltages of the associated network sections.

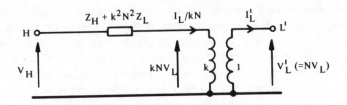

Fig. 3.8.1B   *Equivalent circuit of the off-nominal-ratio transformer*

Proceeding as in Section 3.3.3, the equivalent circuit may be obtained directly by replacing N by kN in the equivalent-T circuit shown in Fig. 3.3.3B, the resulting circuit with magnetising impedance ignored being as shown in Fig. 3.1.8A. It will be noted, however, that the low-voltage-side values, previously NV_L and I_L/N, are now kNV_L and I_L/kN and are therefore no longer compatible with the referred values of the other voltages and currents in the low-voltage network section. These latter values, it will be remembered, are referred to the nominal rated voltage of the high-voltage network section by multiplication by N and division by N respectively, not by kN. To overcome this difficulty, therefore, the referred values NV_L and I_L/N must be obtained by applying the values kNV_L and I_L/kN in Fig. 3.8.1A to an ideal transformer of turns-ratio k as shown in Fig. 3.8,1B, the low-voltage-side values obtained from the transformer being the true referred values $V_L'(= NV_L)$ and I_L' $(= I_L/N)$. Fig. 3.8.1B is therefore the required off-nominal-ratio equivalent circuit of the transformer.

It is important to note in Fig. 3.8.1B that the impedance $Z_H + k^2N^2Z_L$ is the short-circuit impedance Z_{HL} of the transformer, as measured from the high-voltage side H, with the given transformation ratio of kN. If the non-unity value of k is due to the effect of tap-changer equipment, it is of interest to know the relationship between this off-nominal-ratio impedance and the value applicable for the nominal-ratio ($k = 1$) tap-position, the latter-mentioned value being the one normally known. To obtain this relationship let

$$k = k_H/k_L$$

where

$$k_H = \frac{\text{rated voltage of winding H for given tap-position}}{\text{rated voltage of winding H for nominal-ratio tap-position}}$$

and

$$k_L = \frac{\text{rated voltage of winding L for given tap-position}}{\text{rated voltage of winding L for nominal-ratio tap-position}}$$

the values of k_H and k_L being each identical to the ratio of the numbers of turns on the winding referred to for the given and nominal-ratio tap-positions.

Now the leakage impedances Z_H and Z_L are predominantly reactive and can be assumed to be approximately proportional, within limits, to the square of the

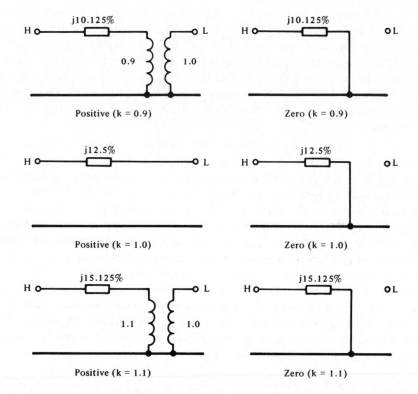

Fig. 3.8.1C *Effect of off-nominal-ratio operation of a 132/33 kV 60 MVA star/delta transformer on the transformer phase-sequence circuits*

number of turns on the windings concerned. It therefore follows that, to a close approximation

$$\left.\begin{array}{l} Z_H = k_H^2 (Z_H)_{nom} \\ Z_L = k_L^2 (Z_L)_{nom} \end{array}\right\} \qquad 3.8.1.1$$

where $(Z_H)_{nom}$ and $(Z_L)_{nom}$ are the nominal-ratio values of the two impdeances.

The value of the transformer impedance Z_{HL}, referred to the high-voltage winding is therefore

$$\begin{aligned} Z_{HL} &= Z_H + k^2 N^2 Z_L \\ &= k_H^2 (Z_H)_{nom} + (k_H/k_L)^2 N^2 k_L^2 (Z_L)_{nom} \\ &= k_H^2 [(Z_H)_{nom} + N^2 (Z_L)_{nom}] \end{aligned}$$

giving

$$. \; Z_{HL} = k_H^2 (Z_{HL})_{nom} \qquad 3.8.1.2$$

where $(Z_{HL})_{nom}$ is the nominal-ratio impedance of the transformer referred to the high-voltage winding.

The application of these results to the representation of an off-nominal-ratio transformer is illustrated in Fig. 3.8.1C for the case of a 60 MVA star/delta transformer with a nominal ratio of 132/33 kV and a nominal-ratio impedance of $j12.5\%$, the star connected 132 kV winding being solidly earthed. The tap changer is assumed to be on the 132 kV winding so that $k_H = k$ and $k_L = 1$, the equivalent circuits shown in Fig. 3.8.1C representing k values of 0.9, 1.0 and 1.1, corresponding to transformation ratios of 118.8/33 kV, 132/33 kV and 145.2/33 kV, respectively.

The representation of off-nominal-ratio transformers by means of circuits containing ideal transformers, as shown in Fig. 3.8.1C, has the disadvantage that such circuits, although suitable for network analyser use, are not satisfactory for normal network analysis by computation. To overcome this difficulty, therefore, the ideal transformer of turns-ratio k must be replaced by a suitable equivalent circuit. The derivation of this equivalent circuit can be understood by considering the ideal transformer of Fig. 3.8.1D with a primary-to-secondary turns-ratio k and an impedance Z in series with the primary winding. Let it be assumed that this circuit can be replaced by an equivalent-π circuit consisting of a primary-side shunt-impedance A, a secondary-side shunt-impedance B and a series impedance C. For the two circuits to be electrically equivalent the no-load transformation-ratios, the short-circuit impedances and the open-circuit impedances must each be the same for both circuits. Considering, first, the no-load voltage-transformation ratios, it is seen that the primary-to-secondary ratio is

$$k = \frac{A}{A + C} \qquad\qquad 3.8.1.3$$

and the secondary-to-primary ratio

$$\frac{1}{k} = \frac{B}{B + C} \qquad\qquad 3.8.1.4$$

Similarly, the impedance measured at the primary terminals with the secondary terminals short-circuited is

$$Z = \frac{AC}{A + C} \qquad\qquad 3.8.1.5$$

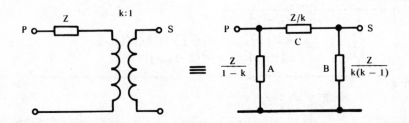

Fig. 3.8.1D

and that measured at the secondary terminals with the primary terminals short-circuited is

$$\frac{Z}{k^2} = \frac{BC}{B+C}$$

3.8.1.6

From eqns. 3.8.1.3 and 3.8.1.5 it is seen that

$$C = \frac{Z}{k}$$

3.8.1.7

and substituting this value of C in eqns. 3.8.1.3 and 3.8.1.4 gives

$$A = \frac{Z}{1-k}$$

3.8.1.8

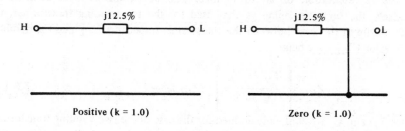

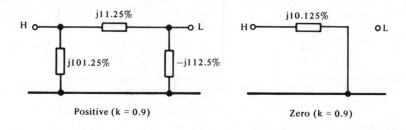

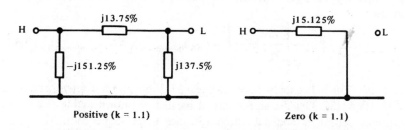

Fig. 3.8.1E *Application of the equivalent-π representation to the phase-sequence circuits of Fig. 3.8.1C*

and

$$B = \frac{Z}{k(k-1)}$$ 3.8.1.9

These values of A, B and C are the required equivalent-π values and it can easily be checked that they satisfy the remaining condition, namely that the open-circuit impedances as measured from the two sides should both be equal to infinity. Applying these results to the phase-sequence circuits shown in Fig. 3.8.1C, the resulting circuits are as shown in Fig. 3.8.1E.

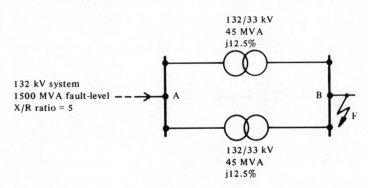

Fig. 3.8.1F

The representation of an off-nominal-ratio auto-transformer is achieved by precisely the same reasoning as that used for the two-winding transformer, the relationship in this case between the transformer impedance Z_{HL} and the nominal-ratio value $(Z_{HL})_{nom}$ being

$$Z_{HL} = \left[\frac{k_H N - k_L}{N - 1} \right]^2 (Z_{HL})_{nom}$$ 3.8.1.10

where k_H and k_L are as already defined for the case of the two-winding transformer.

If tap-changing is effected by variation of the low-voltage-winding tapping-point, as is commonly the case, then $k_H = 1$ and $k_L = 1/k$ so that Equation 3.8.1.10 becomes

$$Z_{HL} = \left[\frac{kN - 1}{k(N - 1)} \right]^2 (Z_{HL})_{nom}$$ 3.8.1.11

Example: The bulk-supply point feeding a 33kV distribution network consists of two 45 MVA 132/33 kV transformers in parallel, as shown in Fig. 3.8.1F, each transformer having a nominal-ratio impedance of $j12\cdot5$ per-cent. The 132 kV system, as seen from the 132 kV busbars of the bulk-supply point can be assumed to have an impedance corresponding to a three-phase short-circuit level of 1500 MVA and an X/R ratio of 5, the generated voltage behind the system impedance

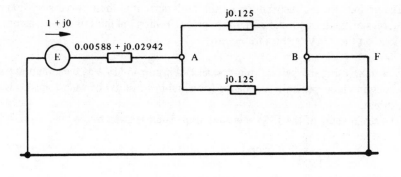

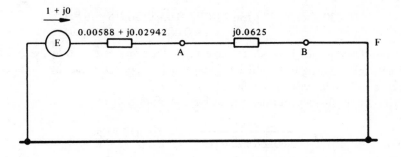

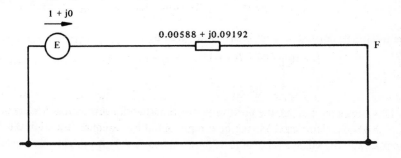

Fig. 3.8.1G

being the nominal phase-to-phase value of 132 kV. Determine the value of the three-phase fault current for a fault on the 33 kV busbars, assuming:

(a)   that both transformers are on the nominal-ratio tap-position

(b)   that one transformer, T_1, is on the nominal-ratio tap-position and the other T_2, is on the tap-position corresponding to a voltage-ratio of 145·2/33 kV, the tap-changer being on the h.v. winding.

Determine also the distribution of the fault current in these two cases. What are the values of the transformer currents in case (*b*) when the fault is absent, assuming the load on the 33kV busbars to be zero?

Solution: using the per unit method and adopting 45 MVA as the common base, the common-base per-unit impedance (nominal-ratio value) of each transformer is $j0.125$ p.u.

The scalar value of the 132 kV system impedance is given by

$$\frac{45}{1500} = 0.0300 \text{ p.u.}$$

the phase-angle of this impedance being the angle whose tangent is 5, that is $78.7°$. The complex value of the 132 kV system impedance is therefore given by

$$0.0300(\cos 78.7° + j\sin 78.7°) = 0.0300(0.1959 + j0.9806)$$
$$= 0.00588 + j0.02942 \text{ p.u.}$$

The positive-sequence network for case (*a*) is therefore as shown in Fig. 3.8.1G, the network reducing to the driving voltage of $1 + j0$p.u., used as the vector base, in series with an impedance of $0.00588 + j0.09192$ p.u.

The current flowing into the fault at F is therefore given by

$$I_f = \frac{1 + j0}{0.00588 + j0.09192} = 0.693 - j10.83 \text{ p.u.}$$

The current corresponding to the common base of 45 MVA at 33kV is

$$\frac{45 \times 10^6}{1.732 \times 33\,000} = 788 \text{ A}$$

The total fault current in amps is therefore given by

$$I_f = (0.693 - j10.83)788 = 546 - j8537 \text{ A}$$

giving

$$I_f = 8552\underline{/-86.33°} \text{ A}$$

Turning, now, to case (*b*), the positive-sequence network for the system is shown in Fig. 3.8.1H, transformer T2 being now represented by its equivalent-π circuit. The nominal-ratio impedance value of $j0.125$ p.u. becomes the off-nominal-ratio value

$$(1.1)^2 (j0.125) = j0.15125 \text{ p.u.,}$$

since

$$k = \frac{145.2}{132} = 1.1$$

and hence the series arm of the equivalent-π circuit has the value

$$\frac{j0.15125}{1.1} = j0.1375 \text{ p.u.}$$

The left-hand shunt arm of the equivalent-π circuit has the value

$$\frac{j0.15125}{1-1.1} = -j1.5125 \text{ p.u.}$$

and the right-hand shunt arm the value

$$\frac{j0.15125}{1.1(1.1-1)} = j1.375 \text{ p.u.}$$

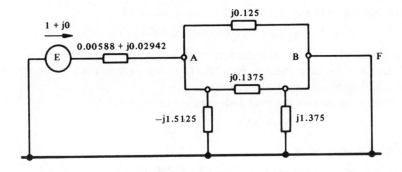

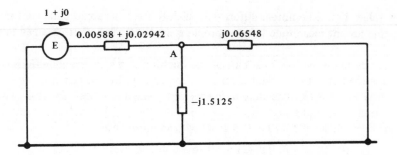

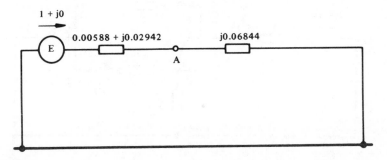

Fig. 3.8.1H

The reduction of the positive-sequence network is shown in Fig. 3.8.1H from which it will be seen that the equivalent circuit, as seen from the 132 kV system, is a driving voltage of $1 + j0$ p.u. in series with an impedance of

$$(0.00588 + j0.02942) + j0.06844 = 0.00588 + j0.09786 \text{ p.u.}$$

The current flowing into the station, from the system, at the 132 kV busbars is therefore

$$\frac{1 + j0}{0.00588 + j0.09786} = 0.612 - j10.18 \text{ p.u.}$$

and hence the voltage at A, namely the 132 kV busbars, is given by

$$(0.612 - j\,10.18)\,(j0.06844) = 0.6967 + j0.04189 \text{ p.u.}$$

The currents in the remaining network branches can now be readily obtained and are shown in per-unit value in Fig. 3.8.1I, the currents in amps being shown in Fig. 3.8.1J along with those for case (a).

It will be noted that the total fault current at F is given by

$$I_f = 0.640 - j10.641 \text{ p.u.}$$

the value in amps being

$$I_f = (0.640 - j10.641)788 = 504 - j8385 \text{ A}$$

giving

$$I_f = 8400\underline{/-86.56°} \text{ A}$$

This value, it will be noted, differs only slightly from the value obtained for case (a), the current magnitude being approximately 1·8% below that obtained in case (a).

Considering, now, the final part of the question in which the conditions are as for case (b) but with the fault absent, the required positive-sequence network is as shown in Fig. 3.8.1K. The steps in the network reduction process are as shown and these lead to an equivalent circuit, as seen from the 132 kV system, consisting of the driving voltage of $1 + j0$ p.u. in series with an impedance of

$$(0.00588 + j0.02942) + j30.26 = 0.00588 + j30.29 \text{ p.u.}$$

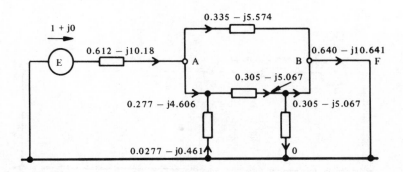

Fig. 3.8.1I

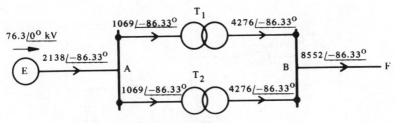

a) Transformers on same tap position

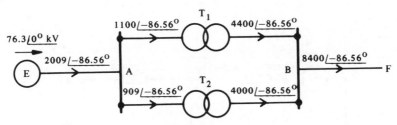

b) Transformers on dissimilar tap positions

Fig. 3.8.1J

The current flowing from the 132 kV system into the 132 kV busbars is therefore

$$\frac{1 + j0}{0.00588 + j30.29} = 0.0000064 - j0.03301 \text{ p.u. on 45 MVA,}$$

and the voltage at A, namely the 132 kV busbars, is therefore

$$(0.0000064 - j0.03301)(j30.26) = 0.9989 + j0.000194 \text{ p.u.}$$

The current flowing to neutral through the shunt impedance of $-j1.5125$ p.u. is thus

$$\frac{0.9989 + j0.000194}{-j1.5125} = -0.000128 + j0.6604 \text{ p.u.}$$

and hence the current flowing from A to B through the series impedance of $j0.06548$ p.u. is

The voltage at

$$(0.0000064 - j0.0331) - (-0.000128 + j0.6604)$$
$$= 0.000134 - j0.6935 \text{ p.u.}$$

The voltage at B, namely the 33 kV busbars is therefore

$$(0.9989 + j0.000194) - (0.000134 - j0.6935)(j0.06548)$$
$$= 0.9535 + j0.000185 \text{ p.u.}$$

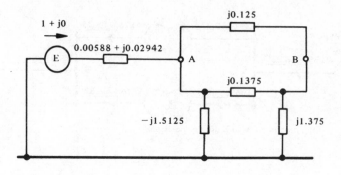

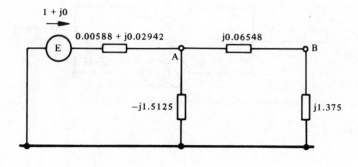

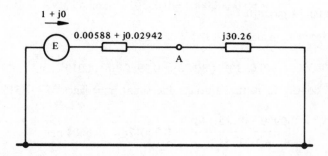

Fig. 3.8.1K

The remaining branch currents can now be readily obtained and are shown in per-unit value in Fig. 3.8.1L. The currents in amperes are given in polar form in Fig. 3.8.1M.

3.8.2   Effects of overhead-line asymmetry

In the great majority of network calculations by symmetrical components, it is sufficient to assume that all the items of plant concerned have balanced impedances,

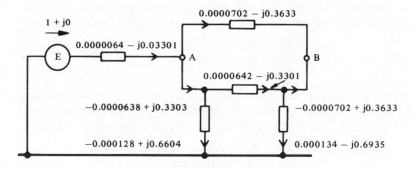

Fig. 3.8.1L

that is that the impedance presented to current of any given phase sequence is the same for all three phases. Although this assumption is valid for all practical purposes in so far as generators, transformers, reactors and cable-circuits are concerned, it is not strictly true for overhead-line circuits and occasions may arise in which the effect of this phase unbalance may have to be assessed.

For the general unbalanced three-phase circuit, the following equations relate the sequence voltage-drops to the sequence currents producing them

$$\left.\begin{aligned} V_1 &= I_1 Z_{11} + I_2 Z_{12} + I_0 Z_{10} \\ V_2 &= I_1 Z_{21} + I_2 Z_{22} + I_0 Z_{20} \\ V_0 &= I_1 Z_{01} + I_2 Z_{02} + I_0 Z_{00} \end{aligned}\right\} \qquad 3.8.2.1$$

The impedances Z_{11}, Z_{22} and Z_{00} are known as the positive, negative and zero-sequence self-impedances, respectively, of the given circuit, and are the values normally quoted as Z_1, Z_2 and Z_0 when unbalance effects are not being considered. The impedances Z_{12}, Z_{10}, Z_{21}, Z_{20}, Z_{01} and Z_{02} are known as the sequence mutual-impedances. Thus, the impedance Z_{01} represents the zero-sequence voltage-drop produced in the circuit when unit value of positive-sequence current flows through it.

For static plant

$$\left.\begin{aligned} Z_{11} &= Z_{22} \\ Z_{01} &= Z_{20} \\ Z_{10} &= Z_{02} \end{aligned}\right\} \qquad 3.8.2.2$$

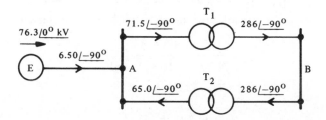

Fig. 3.8.1M

It is important to note that the sequence mutual-impedance values are not reciprocal; in other words

$$Z_{10} \neq Z_{01}$$
$$Z_{12} \neq Z_{21}$$
$$Z_{20} \neq Z_{02}$$

Values of the sequence self and mutual impedances for 132 kV overhead lines have been given by Butterworth, the following values referring to one circuit of a 132 kV 0·175 in^2 e.c. (175 mm^2 al.) double-circuit line with a single earth-wire.

$$Z_{11} = Z_{22} = 0·158 + j0·406 \ \Omega \ \text{per km}$$
$$Z_{00} = 0·359 + j1·10 \ \Omega \ \text{per km}$$
$$Z_{10} = Z_{02} = -0·00143 - j0·0206 \ \Omega \ \text{per km}$$
$$Z_{12} = -0·0214 + j0·0172 \ \Omega \ \text{per km}$$
$$Z_{21} = 0·0220 + j0·0168 \ \Omega \ \text{per km}$$
$$Z_{01} = Z_{20} = 0·0111 - j0·0240 \ \Omega \ \text{per km}$$

It will be noted that the sequence mutual-impedances are small compared with the sequence self-impedances, the largest sequence mutual-impedance having a magnitude equal to about 6% of the positive-sequence self-impedance. In a perfectly balanced circuit, all the sequence-mutual impedances are zero and the phase-sequence voltage-drop equations given in eqns. 3.8.2.1 then reduce to the form shown in eqns. 3.4.2.6.

The following example illustrates the use of the sequence self and mutual impedances.

Example :   Two stations A and B are interconnected by a 32·2 km 132 kV overhead line, the latter having a three-phase fault clear of earth at end B. Determine the zero-sequence current in the line, assuming station A to have a positive-sequence source-impedance of $j8·70 \ \Omega$, stations A and B both having zero-sequence impedances of $j6·96 \ \Omega$ at 132 kV. The overhead line can be assumed to have the sequence self and mutual impedance values already quoted.

Solution: An exact solution of the problem will not be attempted because of the cosiderable arithmetic involved. The following approximate solution is acceptable, however, because of the relatively small magnitudes of the sequence mutual-impedances, compared with the sequence self-impedances.

From the given data, the positive-sequence self-impedance of the overhead line is

$$Z_{11} = 32·2 \ (0·158 + j0·406) \ \Omega = 5·10 + j13·06 \ \Omega$$

The positive-sequence current flow through the line to the three-phase fault is therefore

$$I_1 = \frac{76 \, 300 + j0}{j8·70 + (5·10 + j13·06)}$$

$$= 780 + j3330 \ \text{A}$$

giving

$$I_1 = 3420\underline{/-76° \ 45'} \ \text{A}$$

The appropriate sequence mutual-impedance of the overhead line, from the given data, is

$$Z_{01} = 32 \cdot 2 \, (0 \cdot 0111 - j0 \cdot 0240) \, \Omega = 0 \cdot 356 - j0 \cdot 774 \, \Omega$$

The zero-sequence voltage-drop produced in the line by the positive-sequence current is therefore given by

$$V_0 = I_1 Z_{01}$$
$$= (780 - j3330) \, (0 \cdot 356 - j0 \cdot 774)$$

giving

$$V_0 = -2302 - j1789 \text{ V}$$

Now, the zero-sequence self-impedance of the overhead line, from the given data, is

$$Z_{00} = 32 \cdot 2 \, (0 \cdot 359 + j1 \cdot 10) \, \Omega = 11 \cdot 54 + j35 \cdot 4 \, \Omega$$

and hence, the total impedance presented to the flow of the zero-sequence current in the line is

$$Z_0 = 2(j6 \cdot 96) + (11 \cdot 54 + j35 \cdot 4) = 11 \cdot 54 + j49 \cdot 3 \, \Omega$$

The zero-sequence current in the line is therefore

$$I_0 = \frac{V_0}{Z_0}$$

$$= \frac{-2302 - j1789}{11 \cdot 54 + j49 \cdot 3} \text{ A}$$

$$= -44 \cdot 8 + j36 \cdot 2 \text{ A}$$

giving

$$I_0 = 57 \cdot 6 \underline{/141° \, 4'} \text{ A}$$

This zero-sequence current, which flows in the opposite direction to the positive-sequence current in the line, is seen to have a magnitude equal to about 1·7% of the positive-sequence current.

3.9   Bibliography

British Ştandards

BS.171 : 1978, 'Power transformers'

Books

Symmetrical components by C F Wagner and R D Evans (McGraw Hill, 1933)
Circuit analysis of a.c. power systems by Edith Clarke (John Wiley & Sons, 1950)
Power system analysis by J R Mortlock and M W Humphrey Davies (Chapman & Hall, 1952)

The general theory of electrical machines by B Adkins (Chapman & Hall, 1957)
Advanced studies in electrical power system design by R A Hore (Chapman & Hall, 1966)
Electric energy systems theory by O Elgard (McGraw Hill, 1971)
Protective relays application guide (GEC Measurements, 1975)
Power system planning by R L Sullivan (McGraw Hill, 1976)
Computation of power-system transients by J P Bickford, N Mullineux and J R Reed (Peter Peregrinus, 1976)

Articles

'Digital computers in power system analysis' by P P Gupta and M W Humphrey Davies (*Proc. IEE*, 1961, **108**, pp. 383-398)
'Some improved methods for digital network analysis' by A Brameller and J K Denmead (*Proc. IEE*, 1962, **109**, pp. 109-116)
'A conjugate-impedance network analyser operating at 50 c/s' by W Casson and A W Hales (*Proc. IEE*, 1958, **105**, pp. 295-303)
'Electrical characteristics of overhead lines' by S Butterworth (ERA Report 0T4, Pt. I, 1950 and Pt. II, 1951)
'Calculations of internal fault currents in synchronous machines' by V A Kinitsky (IEEE Int. Conf. Record, Pt. III - Power, 23rd-26th March 1964, pp. 13-31)
'Digital simulation of faulted e.h.v. transmission lines with particular reference to very high speed protection' by A T Johns and R K Aggarwal (*Proc. IEE*, 1976, **123**, pp. 353-359)
'Developments in techniques for simulating faults in e.h.v. transmission systems' by A T Johns and M M T El-Kateb (*Proc. IEE*, 1978, **125**, pp. 221-229)

Chapter 4

Protective transformers

by N.Ashton, revised by E.J.Mellor

4.1 General

4.1.1 Introduction

This chapter deals with instrument transformers, both current and voltage intended for the operation of protective relays. Such transformers are necessary for the reasons explained in Chapter 2, that is, to isolate the voltage and current coils of the relays from the high voltages of the power system, and to supply standard values of current and voltage to the relays, for example 5A or 1A for current coils and 110 V for voltage coils, thus enabling standard relays to be 'matched' to any power system.

4.1.2 Basic transformer principles

It is assumed that the student is already familiar with elementary transformer theory to the extent that he understands that when an alternating current flows in the primary winding, that current creates a magneto-motive force (m.m.f) which results in an alternating flux in the core, which, in turn, induces an electromotive force (e.m.f) in the primary winding and in any other windings wound on, or linked with, the core.

A transformer, consisting of a core of magnetic material on which are wound two windings, can be operated in two basic modes, shunt and series.

In the shunt mode, as in power or voltage operation, a voltage is applied to the terminals of the primary windings, which, since the inducted e.m.f. in the primary winding is sensibly equal to this applied voltage, determines the magnitude of the core flux and, therefore, for a given sectional area of core, the flux density in the core. With no burden (load) connected to the secondary terminals the current flowing in the primary winding will be that necessary to excite the core. With a burden connected to the secondary terminals current will flow in the secondary winding, its value depending on the impedance of the burden, and additional current will flow in the primary winding depending on the turns-ratio of the transformer. The ampere-turns (a.t.) of the primary winding always exceed those of the secondary winding by the amount necessary to excite the core.

In the series mode, that is, in current operation, the primary winding is connected in series with the power system whose relatively high impedance determines the magnitude of the primary current and a component of this current excites the core to the flux density necessary to induce in the secondary winding an e.m.f. sufficient to drive the secondary current through the total impedance of the secondary circuit.

In power and voltage transformers, therefore, the core flux density is substantially constant under normal operating conditions; but in current transformers it is dependent on the magnitude of the primary current and the impedance of the secondary circuit.

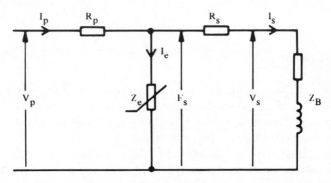

Fig. 4.1.2A   *Equivalent circuit for a transformer of 1/1 turns ratio and negligible leakage flux*

Fig. 4.1.2A shows a simplified equivalent circuit for a two-winding transformer of 1/1 turns ratio, the leakage inductances having been omitted, (See Section 4.2.4). In voltage operation we are interested in the magnitude and phase differences between the primary and secondary voltages V_p and V_s, caused by the currents I_p and I_s flowing in the primary and secondary windings, the resistances of which are denoted by R_p and R_s, respectively.

In current operation, however, we are not usually interested in these voltage relationships at all but in the relationship between the primary current I_p and the secondary current I_s. It will be noted that these currents differ by the amount of the core exciting current I_e which is, of course, a component of I_p.

4.2   Steady-state theory of current transformers

4.2.1   Equivalent circuit, vector diagram, errors

Referring to Fig. 4.1.2A it will be seen that the errors of a current transformer are caused by a component of the primary current being utilised to excite the core, with the result that only the remainder of the primary current is available for 'passing on' to the secondary circuit. Thus, for a 1/1 turns ratio, $I_s = I_p - I_e$ where I_e is dependent on the induced e.m.f. E_s (equal to $I_s(R_s + Z_B)$), and on the exciting impedance Z_e. In this circuit R_s is the resistance of the secondary winding and Z_B the impedance of the secondary burden.

Treating Z_e as a linear impedance, the vectorial relationship between the fundamental frequency currents are typically as in Fig. 4.2.1A. This shows that the vector difference between I_p and I_s is I_e, and that I_r, the component of I_e in phase with I_p, constitutes the current (magnitude) error and I_q, the component of I_e in quadrature with I_p, results in the phase error θ. The relative values of the current error component I_r and the phase error component I_q depend on the phase displacement of I_s and I_e, the current error being a maximum and the phase error zero when I_s and I_e are in phase, that is when the total impedance of the secondary circuit and the exciting impedance Z_e are of like power factor. Under such conditions the current error of a transformer with no turns correction, that is, with its turns ratio equal to the nominal current ratio, is equal to the fundamental frequency component of the exciting current (usually expressed as a percentage of the primary current).

Composite error: This term is defined in connection with protective current transformers in BS 3938 : 1973.

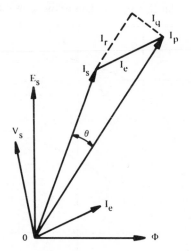

Fig. 4.2.1A   *Phasor diagram for circuit of Fig. 4.1.2A*

'Composite error' is the r.m.s. value of the difference between the ideal secondary current and the actual secondary current, including the effects of phase displacement and harmonics of the exciting current. In a c.t. with negligible leakage flux and no turns correction, that is, with turns ratio equal to the nominal current ratio, composite error corresponds to the r.m.s. value of the exciting current (usually expressed as a percentage of the primary current).

Again referring to Fig. 4.1.2A., if Z_e was in fact a linear impedance the vectorial error I_e of Fig. 4.2.1A would be the composite error. In practice the magnetising impedance Z_e is non-linear, with the result that the exciting current I_e contains some harmonics of the fundamental frequency which increase its r.m.s. value and thus increase the composite error. This effect is most noticeable in the region approaching saturation of the core.

It will be noted that the composite error is greater than the vectorial error, the current error or the phase (quadrature) error. For example, if a transformer with no turns correction had an exciting current, in terms of primary current of 5% fundamental frequency component plus 5% harmonics, the composite error would be $\sqrt{(5^2 + 5^2)} = 7.07\%$. The vectorial error would be 5% the current error would not exceed 5% and the phase error would not exceed 5 centiradians, that is, 2.87 degrees.

It should also be noted that composite error, because it includes harmonics, cannot carry a plus or minus sign.

4.2.2   Influence of the core, magnetic materials and magnetisation curves

It has been shown that the errors of a current transformer (c.t.) result from the core exciting current, so it is obviously of first importance when considering the performance of a c.t. to be able to calculate or measure the exciting current.

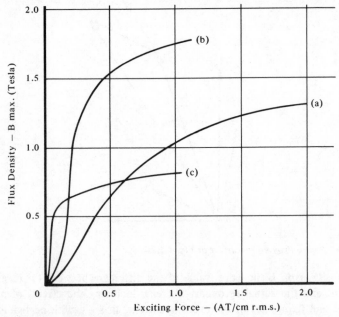

Fig. 4.2.2A   *50 Hz magnetisation curves*
(a) Hot-rolled non-oriented silicon steel
(b) Cold-rolled oriented silicon steel
(c) Nickel-iron (80% nickel)

The excitation or magnetisation characteristics of a c.t. depend on the cross-sectional area and length of magnetic path of the core, the number of turns in the windings and the magnetic characteristics of the core material. Fig. 4.2.2A shows typical magnetisation curves for three core materials commonly employed in instrument transformers, namely (a) hot-rolled non-oriented silicon steel, (b) cold-rolled oriented silicon steel, (c) nickel-iron. The curves show the exciting force (m.m.f.) in r.m.s. a.t./cm (ampere-turns per cm length of magnetic path) against peak flux density B_{max} in tesla of net-sectional core area. It will be seen that at low flux densities (a) has the lowest permeability and (c) the highest permeability, whereas (b) comes in between but has an outstandingly high permeability at high flux densities. A characteristic lying between those of the individual materials can be obtained by building composite cores of two or more materials.

The core peak flux density B_{max} can be calculated from the formula

$$B_{max} = -\frac{E_s}{4.44 T_s A f}$$

where E_s = the secondary e.m.f. in volts

T_s = the number of turns in the secondary winding

A = the net core section in sq. metres

and f is the frequency.

Reference to Fig. 4.1.2A shows that $E_s = I_s(R_s + Z_B)$, where Z_B is the impedance of the external secondary circuit or the burden, so that for a constant burden Z_B the core flux density varies directly as the secondary current. It will thus be apparent from Fig. 4.2.2A that as the primary, and therefore the secondary, currents are increased, a point is reached at which the core material starts to saturate and the exciting current becomes excessive, thus resulting in excessive current error. The exciting current is, of course, equal to the m.m.f. in a.t./cm multiplied by the length of the core path (in cm) and divided by the number of turns in the winding to which it is referred, either primary or secondary.

Reference to Fig. 4.2.2A shows that if the flux density at rated secondary current is 0.1 Tesla a c.t. with a nickel-iron core to curve (c) would have good accuracy up to five times the rated current. If, however, cold-rolled silicon steel with characteristics to curve (b) is used, the accuracy would be reasonably good up to 10 or 15 times the rated current although not as good below five times rated current as it would be with core material to curve (c).

Fig. 4.2.2B shows typical curves relating primary to secondary current using the materials whose magnetisation characteristics are given in Fig. 4.2.2.A.

When considering the performance to be expected from a given c.t., the exciting current can be measured at various values of e.m.f. For this it is usually more convenient to apply a varying voltage to the secondary winding, the primary winding being open-circuited. Fig. 4.2.2C shows a typical relationship between secondary e.m.f. and exciting current determined in this manner.

The point K_p on the curve is arbitrarily called the knee-point, and is defined as

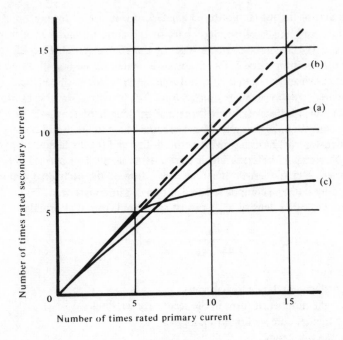

Fig. 4.2.2B   *Typical performace curves with the magnetic materials of Fig. 4.2.2A*

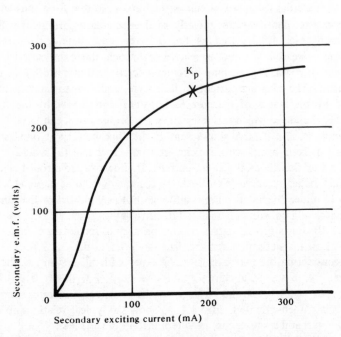

Fig. 4.2.2C   *Magnetising curve for a c.t. turns-ratio 500/1; secondary resistance 2Ω*

the point at which an increase of 10% in the exciting e.m.f. produces an increase of 50% in the exciting current.

From the information given in Fig. 4.2.2C the percentage exciting current, which is equal to the maximum composite error in a c.t. with no turns correction and negligible leakage flux, can be calculated for any operating condition.

For example, with a burden impedance of 15 Ω (15 VA at 1 A) of 0·8% power factor, the total secondary circuit impedance, adding the 2 Ω winding resistance vectorially, would be approximately 16·6Ω and the secondary e.m.f. at 1 A (500 A primary current) would be 16·6 V. At 10 times this current E_s would be 166 V (assuming no saturation) and the exciting current approximately 70 mA, which is 0·7% of the ideal secondary current of 10 A. This means that the current and composite errors would not exceed 0·7% and the phase error could not exceed 0·7 centiradians equal to 0·7 x 34·38 = 24 min. (Note: With a burden power factor of 0·8 lagging, the phase error would be unlikely to exceed 10 min because the exciting and secondary currents would be almost in phase. See Fig. 4.2.1A).

At 7500 A primary current the secondary e.m.f. would be approximately 250 V, giving an exciting current of 200 mA which is 1·33% of the nominal secondary current of 15A.

4.2.3 Single-turn primary current transformers

Toroidally wound ring core c.t.s are commonly used because they can conveniently be mounted on a bushing in switchgear or a power transformer, which then serves as an insulated single-turn primary. At low primary currents, however, it may be difficult to obtain sufficient output VA at the desired accuracy because, not only is a large core section required to induce the required secondary e.m.f. in the small number of secondary turns associated with the single-turn primary, but also the exciting a.t., and, therefore, the errors, are large as a percentage of the small value of primary a.t. available. In particular, this effect is pronounced when the core diameter is made large in order to fit over a large diameter h.v. bushing, because this increases the length of the flux path and hence the a.t. necessary to excite the core.

4.2.4 Flux leakage

In the foregoing, flux leakage effects have been assumed to be neglibile, which fortunately is substantially true for a ring core with uniformly wound secondary winding and centrally positioned primary conductor which does not bend round the outside of the core at a small radius. In wound primary c.t.s, particularly when the primary and secondary windings are not closely coupled, there may be considerable leakage flux adding to the mutual flux in the parts of the core where the influence of the m.m.f, due to the primary a.t. predominates over that due to the opposing a.t. of the secondary winding, so that the core flux density is non-uniform along the core flux path. An extreme example of this effect, chosen merely for illustration, is shown in Fig. 4.2.4A, where the primary and secondary windings are positioned on two opposite limbs of a rectangular core. It will be seen that leakage flux ϕ_L adds to the mutual flux ϕ_M in the left-hand portion of the core on which the primary coil is wound. Even in designs with concentric primary and secondary windings, such as the shell-type core illustrated in Fig. 4.2.4B, the leakage flux passing between the primary and secondary windings and returning to increase the flux density in the outer limbs and yokes of the core is appreciable.

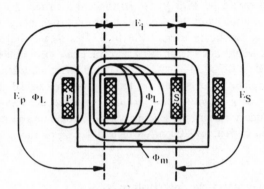

Fig. 4.2.4A   *Flux leakage in wound-primary current transformer*

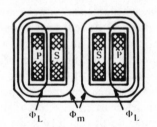

Fig. 4.2.4B   *Flux leakage in wound-primary current transformer*

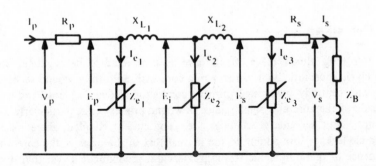

Fig. 4.2.4C   *Equivalent circuit including flux leakage effects*

Under conditions such as these, the performance can not be calculated without a detailed knowledge of the flux distribution throughout the core, since, in order to arrive at the total exciting current which constitutes the error in current transformation, it is necessary to assess the sum of the exciting a.t. required for the various values of flux density existing along the core flux path. Fig. 4.2.4C shows a simplified equivalent circuit which takes such flux leakage into account. In theory the core flux path would have to be divided into an infinite number of small lengths and the flux density and exciting a.t. calculated for the flux density of each length In Fig. 4.2.4C, however, the core is considered in three zones having flux densities corresponding to induced e.m.f.s E_p, E_i (intermediate) and E_s for the three zones indicated in Fig. 4.2.4A. These zones have exciting impedances Z_{e1}, Z_{e2} and Z_{e3} taking exciting currents I_{e1}, I_{e2} and I_{e3} respectively. The effects can be reduced by increasing the core section in the parts of the core carrying the leakage flux, and in shell-type cores such as that shown in Fig. 4.2.4B it is beneficial to increase the section of the outer limbs or yokes to obtain a flux density comparable with that in the centre limb of the core.

This subject is very involved and cannot be treated adequately here, but it might be noted that the concept of representing flux leakage by so-called 'secondary reactance', which is considered to add to the burden and therefore to increase the flux density throughout the core, is completely erroneous, and cannot be applied satisfactorily for core flux densities outside the linear portion of the magnetisation characteristic, that is at low and high flux densities.

Although, in general, leakage flux should be avoided in protective c.t.s, it can be beneficial in c.t.s for the operation of metres, instruments and certain forms of protection for the following reasons:

In a c.t. supplying a resistive burden the additional core exciting current due to the leakage flux leads the exciting current due to the mutual flux by 90 degrees. Thus the total exciting current is brought more nearly into phase with the primary current, and this reduces the phase error, while the reduction in secondary current magnitude, due to the same effect, can be compensated by an increase in turns correction, that is a reduction in the number of secondary turns.

Secondly, an increase in leakage flux is accompanied by a decrease in the mutual air flux, so that at primary currents above the value at which the core saturates the increase in secondary current, for a given increase in primary current, is reduced. Thus in c.t.s with high leakage flux the secondary current is more effectively limited at high system fault currents and this affords protection to the windings and movements of instruments, meters and relays.

4.2.5 Balancing windings and eddy-current shielding

It has been shown in the previous Section that when leakage flux links the primary winding and not the secondary winding the resultant increase in exciting current results in a reduction of secondary current, that is in a negative current error. When part of the secondary winding is much more closely coupled with the primary winding than the remainder of the secondary winding, so that some core flux links both the primary winding and the more closely coupled part but not the loosely coupled part of the secondary winding, a counter effect occurs which tends to increase the secondary current above the nominal value. This is shown in Fig. 4.2.5A where a ring core with a uniformly spaced secondary winding is linked with an unsymmetrically disposed primary winding, ϕ_L being the leakage flux.

Severe leakage flux effects, whether resulting in positive or negative current errors, are undesirable in c.t.s required for certain forms of balanced protection. In wound primary transformers these effects are under the control of the c.t. designer and can be minimised by suitable disposition of the windings. Also, in the majority of applications where ring core c.t.s with uniformly spaced secondary windings are mounted on bushings, the spacing of the neighbouring phase conductor, which

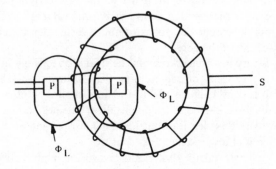

Fig. 4.2.5A   *Flux leakage in a ring core with a concentrated primary winding*

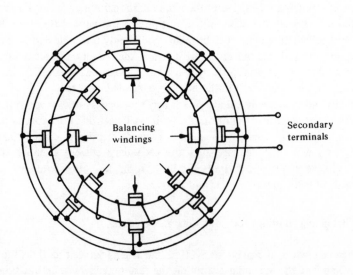

Fig. 4.2.5B   *Parallel connection of balancing windings*

forms the return loop of the primary winding, is such that up to the values of fault current envisaged the leakage flux effects are of little or no consequence. However, there are certain applications where the fault current may be extremely high and the effect of the proximity of the return conductors is not readily accessible by the c.t. designer, and in such instances it may be necessary to employ balancing windings or eddy-current shielding to reduce the leakage flux to an acceptable level.

The arrangement of balancing windings is shown diagramatically in Fig. 4.2.5B. This consists of a number of uniformly disposed windings connected in parallel and having identical turns. The illustration shows the balancing windings wound over the secondary winding but it may be convenient to locate the balancing windings next to the core.

The action of balancing windings is as follows. With uniform flux throughout the core, that is, no flux leakage, equal e.m.f.s are induced in all the windings and because the windings are in parallel no current flows in them. When flux leakage occurs the flux is no longer uniform throughout the core and unequal e.m.f.s are therefore induced in these windings, resulting in circulating currents and local m.m.f.s which counteract the unbalanced m.m.f.s responsible for the flux leakage, thus reducing it.

The secondary winding itself may be arranged to perform the balancing function by forming it from a number of parallel connected coils but, since this would require each coil to have a large number of turns of fine wire, it is usually preferable to employ separate balancing windings each of a few turns of a conductor of comparatively large section. The number of turns in the balancing windings is unimportant, the lower limit being a single turn for each, connected in parallel by heavy copper rings. It is an obvious step from such an arrangement to enclose the core in a split tubular sheath of conducting material; the gap at the split prevents it forming a short-circuited turn on the core. In effect this is an infinite number of single-turn coils connected in parallel and is more correctly termed an eddy-current shield.

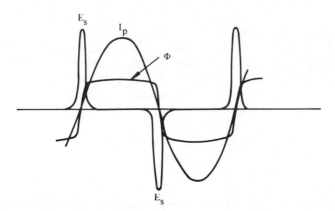

Fig. 4.2.6A *Wave-shapes of primary current I_p core flux Φ and induced e.m.f. E_s with open-circuited secondary winding*

4.2.6   Open-circuit secondary voltage

It is shown in Section 4.2.2. that the e.m.f. induced in the secondary winding is that required to drive the secondary current through the total impedance of the secondary circuit, and that the core flux inducing this e.m.f. is provided by a small difference between the primary and secondary a.t. With the secondary circuit open, however, there are no secondary a.t.s to oppose those due to the primary current and the whole of the primary a.t. act on the core as an excessive exciting force, which might drive the core into saturation on each half-wave of current. Typical flux and induced e.m.f. wave shapes for this condition are shown in Fig. 4.2.6A and it will be seen that the high rate of change of the flux ϕ in the region of the primary current zero induces an e.m.f., E_s of high peak value in the secondary winding. With rated current in the primary winding this peak value may be as low as a few hundred volts in a small measuring c.t. with a 5A secondary winding, but it might reach many kilovolts in the case of, say a 2000/1A protective c.t. with a large core section. With system fault currents flowing through the primary winding even higher voltages would be induced. Such voltages not only constitute a hazard to the insulation of the c.t. itself and to connected instruments, relays and associated wiring, but also to life. It is thus important to prevent this condition arising and if the secondary circuit has to be broken for any reason, it is essential first to short-circuit the secondary terminals of the c.t. with a conductor securely connected and capable of carrying the c.t. secondary current.

4.2.7   Secondary currents, burdens and connecting lead resistance

A standard rated secondary current of 5 A has been in use for many years. In applications for which the resistance of the leads between the c.t. and the instruments or relays results in an excessive VA burden, rated secondary currents of 2 A or even 1 A have to be used. For example, if a c.t. is required to supply relays taking 10 VA through a loop lead resistance of 0·1 Ω the total burden at 5 A is $10 + 5^2 \times 0\cdot1$ = 12·5 VA, and a c.t. with a standard output rating of 15 VA would be satisfactory. If, however, the lead resistance, due to the distance between the c.t. and relays, is 2Ω, the output required at 5A would be $10 + 5^2 \times 2 = 60$ VA which would require an excessively large and expensive transformer. By using 1 A rated secondary current the output required would be reduced to $10 + 1^2 \times 2 = 12$ VA which could be provided by a c.t. of reasonable dimensions and cost.

These lower rated secondary currents, however, should not be used indiscriminately because they require an increased number of secondary turns with some increase in dimensions and cost. Further, their use, particularly with c.t.s of high rated primary currents results in increased transient and secondary open-circuit voltages. Fortunately, at the higher primary currents, say in excess of 1000 A, comparatively high VA outputs are readily obtained, even with single-turn primary c.t.s and an intermediate value of rated secondary current such as 2 A may be used.

Auxiliary c.t.s are sometimes used to reduce the current in high resistance leads but the auxiliary c.t. itself imposes an additional burden of several VA on the main c.t. and tends to offset the reduction in burden caused by the reduced current in the leads.

4.2.8   Test windings

To test the overall operation of a c.t. and its associated instruments or relays, it is necessary to inject current into the primary circuit from a test supply transformer. In certain situations, for example where a ring c.t. is mounted over the bushing of high voltage equipment, it may be difficult or inconvenient to inject into the main primary circuit, and test primary windings would be required. Test windings are usually rated at 10A, corresponding to the rated primary current, and are usually insulated from the secondary windings and earth to withstand a 2 kV one-minute test. They are usually short-time rated, capable of carrying their rated current for an hour without overheating.

When using a test primary winding it is essential to ensure that the main primary winding is not short-circuited through any of the system connections and, conversely, when the c.t. is energised normally through its main primary winding, the test winding must be open-circuited. It is desirable to earth one terminal of the test winding when not in use.

4.3   Current transformers for protection

4.3.1   Saturation of the core and ratio on overcurrents. BS 3938

Unlike measuring c.t.s, which are required to be accurate over the normal working range of currents, protective c.t.s are usually required to maintain their ratio up to several times the rated primary current, although in many applications their accuracy at currents below the rated value is unimportant. It has been shown in Section 4.2.2 that at some value of primary current above the rated value, the core will commence to saturate, resulting in an increase in secondary current error. The value of primary current at which this error reaches or approaches a certain limiting value is termed the accuracy limit primary current.

C.t.s. for most forms of protection are covered by BS 3938 : 1973 and guidance in the application of c.t.s is given in Appendix B of this British Standard. Accuracy classes 5P and 10P are intended to apply to c.t.s for simple forms of protection, such as the operation of overcurrent relays and trip coils, and of low-impedance earth-fault relays with time-lag characteristics. These classes specify limits of current error at rated primary current and limits of composite error at the 'accuracy limit primary current'; in addition the phase displacement at rated primary current is specified for Class 5P only. The ratio between the accuracy limit primary current and the rated primary current is known as the 'rated accuracy limit factor', the standard factors being 5, 10, 15, 20 and 30. For convenience, the limits of errors for classes 5P and 10P are given in Table 4.3.1.A below.

In passing, it might be noted that a c.t. rated at 15 VA provides an output of about 6 kVA at 20 times the rated current.

Table 4.3.1.A   *BS 3938:1973 Limits of error for accuracy Class 5P and Class 10P*

Accuracy class	Current error at rated primary current	Phase displacement at rated primary current		Composite error at rated accuracy limit primary current
		minutes	centiradians	
	%			%
5P	±1	±60	±1·8	5
10P	±3			10

4.3.2 Trip-coil operation

Class 10P will generally be sufficiently accurate for this purpose, but the question of VA rating and saturation factor may present some problems. Trip coils are usually so constructed that a considerable change in the impedance of the coil results from the movement of the coil plunger, the impedance at the conclusion of the operating stroke being several times that at the commencement of the operation. This means that the burden imposed on the c.t. may change from, say, 10 VA to 40 VA, referred to the rated secondary current; for example, 0·4 to 1·6 Ω for a 5 A c.t. during the operation of the trip coil. Fortunately, the current required to operate the device usually decreases with the armature movement and the application of a constant voltage somewhat in excess of the 'pick-up' voltage will usually result in firm operation. The c.t. should be capable of supplying this voltage without saturation of its core and should have the required accuracy, say Class 10P at the nominal operating (pick-up) current of the trip coil. For a trip coil operating in the overcurrent range, between 100 and 200% of the c.t. rated current, a VA rating corresponding to the low impedance or unoperated position of the trip coil plunger and a rated accuracy limit factor of 5 will usually be adequate.

4.3.3 Overcurrent-relay operation

For the operation of instantaneous overcurrent relays the c.t. requirements are similar to those for trip coils, and Class 10P accuracy with a rated accuracy-limit factor of 5 should again be adequate. For overcurrent relays with inverse-time characteristics, however, Class 10P accuracy should be specified together with a rated accuracy-limit factor corresponding to the maximum overcurrent at which reasonable accuracy of the relay time characteristic is required.

When considering the VA rating to be specified, account must be taken of the reduced impedance of the relay on its higher current settings and any further reduction in impedance which may occur due to saturation of the relay magnetic circuit at currents in excess of the nominal setting values.

4.3.4   Earth-fault relays with inverse-time characteristics

To ensure adequate phase-fault stability and accurate time grading, relays of this type with low settings, when connected in the residual circuit of a three-phase set of c.t.s, usually require c.t.s of Class 5P accuracy. This is because on the occurrence of an earth fault the earth-fault relay is shunted by the exciting impedances of three c.t.s. (four if there is a neutral c.t.). The primary current to operate the relay is calculated by adding the relay operating current to the sum of the secondary exciting currents of the three (or four) c.t.s, the whole being multiplied by the c.t. turns ratio. It is thus essential to employ c.t.s with low exciting currents to secure reasonably low earth-fault settings. These are characteristic of Class 5P.

4.3.5   Relay settings and primary operating currents

In considering the settings of low-impedance earth-fault relays it should be borne in mind that, since the operating VA of the relay will be approximately the same value for all its settings, a lower current setting will require a correspondingly higher operating voltage and thus a higher exciting current in the c.t. or c.t.s. There is thus an optimum relay setting which results in the minimum primary operating current or earth-fault setting. This is obtained approximately when the relay operating current and the sum of the exciting currents of the parallel connected c.t.s are equal; in other words, when the percentage primary operating current is approximately twice the percentage relay setting. To illustrate this point typical current values are given in Table 4.3.5A from which it will be seen that, for the particular case considered, the 20% relay setting results in the lowest overall earth-fault setting of 38%.

Table 4.3.5A

Relay setting—per cent of c.t. rated secondary current	50	40	30	20	10
Sum of c.t. exciting currents—per cent of rated current	8	10	13	18	35
Earth-fault setting—per cent of c.t. rated primary current	58	50	43	38	45

Note. The relay and exciting currents are added arithmetically because they are approximately in phase

4.3.6   Current transformers for balanced differential protective schemes

Class X current transformers: This class is included in BS 3938:1973 to cover protective c.t.s for use in applications where the required characteristics of the c.t.s cannot conveniently be expressed in the terms used for classes 5P and 10P.

The performance of class X c.t.s of the 'low-reactance type', that is having negligible leakage flux, is specified in the following terms:

(*a*)   rated primary current
(*b*)   turns ratio
(*c*)   knee-point e.m.f.
(*d*)   exciting current at the knee-point e.m.f. and/or at a stated percentage thereof.
(*e*)   resistance of the secondary winding, corrected to 75°C or the maximum service temperature, whichever is the greater.

Standard values for (*b*), (*c*), (*d*) and (*e*) are not prescribed. The actual value of (*c*) shall not be less than that specified, while the actual values of (*d*) and (*e*) shall not exceed the specified values. The error in (*b*) shall not exceed ±0·25%.

Class X c.t.s for balanced protective schemes: In differential protective schemes the characteristics of the c.t.s are most conveniently specified in the terms of class X. In general there are two or three modes of operation to be considered, for example through-fault conditions when the protective gear is required to be stable, and faults within the protected zone when the c.t. has to be capable of operating the relay and supplying current to other c.t.s which may be in idle shunt. This means that operation has to be considered not only at greatly different primary currents, but also with widely different secondary circuit impedances. Also the shunting impedance of the secondary winding, in both the saturated and unsaturrated states of the core, may have to be considered. Due allowance usually has to be made for d.c. components in the primary current as will be shown later.

The most satisfactory method is to specify the characteristics required of such a c.t. in terms of turns ratio, secondary winding resistance and exciting currents at appropriate values of secondary e.m.f. These requirements are usually specified to

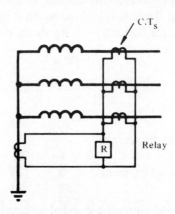

Fig. 4.3.6A   *Restricted earth-fault protection of power transformer windings*

the c.t. designer by the protective gear application engineer, but invariably the secondary winding resistance and the e.m.f.s are interdependent and cannot be decided until the c.t. is designed.

An example commonly met is that of four c.t.s with parallel connected secondary windings operating a high-impedance relay to provide a restricted earth-fault scheme for a power transformer winding, the circuit being as Fig. 4.3.6A. The rated current may be 1000 A and the maximum through-fault current 15 kA, and the prescribed primary operating current for an in-zone fault may have to be not greater than 25%, that is 250 A.

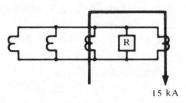

15 kA

Fig. 4.3.6B   *Through-fault condition*

The first requirement to consider is stability under the conditions shown in Fig. 4.3.6B. In order to be sure of stability under transient conditions it is usual to design on the basis that the core of one of the two c.t.s through which the fault current flows may be fully saturated. The secondary winding of this c.t. can then be regarded as a resistance which, in series with the leads to the relay, constitutes a path shunting the relay through which the other c.t. drives a current equal to the fault current divided by the c.t. turns ratio. With a turns ratio of 500/1 the ideal secondary current would be 30A with 15 kA in the primary circuit. Assuming the resistance of the pair of leads between the relay and the 'saturated' c.t. to be 1 Ω the voltage appearing across the relay would be $30(1 + R_s)$, where R_s is the secondary winding resistance. If it were practicable to make R_s equal 0·5 Ω the voltage across the relay would be 45 V and a relay operating voltage of 50 V would ensure stability. If, however, R_s could not conveniently be made less than 2 Ω the relay operating voltage would have to be not less than 90 V and an operating voltage of, say, 100 V would be selected.

The second requirement to be considered is the operation of the relay on an in-zone fault as shown in Fig. 4.3.6C. To ensure speedy operation of the relay it is usually desirable to make the knee-point e.m.f. of the c.t. magnetising curve not less than twice the relay operating voltage, so that with $R_s = 0·5$ Ω the knee-point

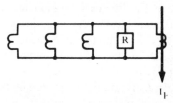

I_1.

Fig. 4.3.6C   *Condition for an earth-fault in the protected zone*

e.m.f. must not be less than 100 V, but with R_s = 2 Ω the minimum knee-point e.m.f. would be 200 V.

A typical magnetising curve for a c.t. having the latter characteristics is shown in Fig. 4.2.2C from which it will be seen that at the relay operating voltage of 100 V the exciting current is 40 mA.

Referring to Fig. 4.3.6A it will be seen that if each c.t. requires 40 mA exciting current (referred to the secondary winding) and the relay operating current is 10 mA then the primary current I_f to trip the relay is equal to $500(10 + 4 \times 40) \times 10^{-3}$ = 85A which is well below the prescribed maximum of 250 A. The knee-point e.m.f of the curve Fig. 4.2.2C is approximately 240 V which is more than double our relay operating voltage. This voltage would correspond to a flux density (B_{max}) in the core of, say, 1·2 tesla which, from formula (i) in Section 4.2.2 would require a net core section of 18 cm^2 and, if we assume a core space-factor of 95%, the required gross core section would be about 19 cm^2.

Considering next the desired exciting current of 40 mA, this corresponds to $40 \times 500 \times 10^{-3}$ = 20 a.t; and if we assume a mean core diameter (for a ring type c.t.) of 12·7 cm the length of the magnetic path will be 40 cm. Thus a core material requiring an exciting force of 0·5 a.t/cm at B_{max} equal to 0·5 tesla would be needed. This corresponds to curve (*a*) of Fig. 4.2.2.A.

A further requirement for through-fault stability in such differential schemes is identical or closely similar turns ratios for all the c.t.s. concerned. In the example given above, the ratio of the primary operating current to the maximum through-fault current is 85/15 000 or 0·57%, which could well be produced by a small difference in the turns ratios of two or more c.t.s and thus cause operation of the relay on a through-fault. To ensure a safe margin the permissible difference in turns ratio between any two c.t.s of such a balanced group is usually specified to be half this amount, that is 0·28% in the example above, which, with a nominal turns ratio of 500/1 would mean a maximum difference of one turn.

4.3.7 Simple transient-state theory

When a system fault occurs the fault current almost invariably contains a transient d.c. component, and for certain balanced schemes of protection it is desirable that the c.t.s should maintain their a.c. ratio under such fault conditions. Fig. 4.3.7A shows the currents, induced e.m.f. and core flux conditions in an ideal c.t. with a 1/1 turns ratio, as indicated in the simplified equivalent circuit where R is the total secondary circuit resistance and L_e the exciting inductance (compare Fig. 4.1.2A). It will be seen that the maximum flux in the core, due principally to the need for flux to induce the transient unidirectional component of E_s, is several times the alternating flux which would be the only flux required if there were no d.c. component in the primary current.

It can be shown that when L_e is infinite the maximum transient flux is governed by the degree of asymmetry of the primary current and by the primary circuit time-constant T_p, in other words, by the area shown shaded in the upper curve.

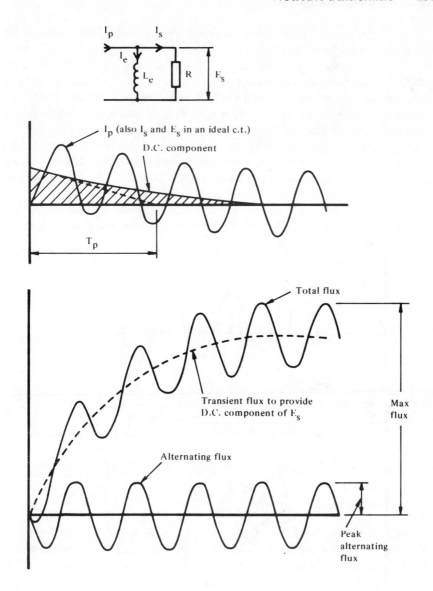

Fig. 4.3.7A *Transient current and flux conditions*

With maximum asymmetry and a resistive secondary circuit, the ratio of the maximum flux to the peak alternating flux is approximately equal to the X/R ratio of the primary circuit, that is of the power system up to the fault position. However, when L has a finite value, as in practice, the d.c. component of I_s becomes less than that of I_p by the amount of the d.c. component of I_e. Thus the d.c. component of E_s and the unidirectional flux required to produce it are reduced.

For the c.t. to maintain accurate a.c. transformation under such conditions its core section must be large enough to accommodate the total flux without saturation of the core material. A practical method of determining the required core section is to calculate the secondary e.m.f. corresponding to the steady-state maximum fault current and to multiply this e.m.f. by the system X/R ratio to give the required knee-point e.m.f. of the c.t. A total flux excursion corresponding to a knee-point e.m.f. derived in this way is in practice not attained because (*a*) the maximum theoretical magnitude of d.c. component of the fault current is never attained, (*b*) as already explained, the d.c. component of exciting current reduces the flux excursion, sometimes by as much as 50% and (*c*) the inductive component of the secondary burden requires no unidirectional e.m.f.

However, the upward swing of the total flux may, in unfavourable circumstances, commence from a remanent flux due to previous magnetisation, thus reducing the

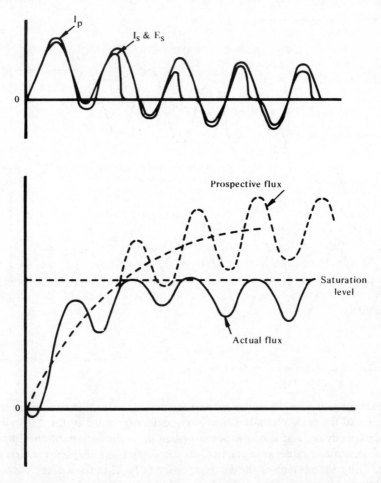

Fig. 4.3.7B   *Effect of core saturation on flux and secondary e.m.f and current*

flux excursion which the core can accommodate without saturating. This possibility prevents the designer from reducing the core section to take advantage of the factors (*a*), (*b*) and (*c*) above.

The effect of saturation in a c.t. with insufficient core section is shown in Fig. 4.3.7B. The flux reaches the saturation region during one of the positive excursions of primary current and the saturated exciting inductance L_e (Fig. 4.3.7A) shunts most of the primary current I_p, thus distorting the secondary current I_s to the wave shape shown. During the negative excursions of current, however, the flux is required to reduce and so the core becomes unsaturated during this negative current and for part of the following positive current excursion before becoming saturated once more, and so on. As the d.c. component of the primary current decays the negative excursions of the current and flux become greater, and the core eventually runs out of saturation during the complete cycle, when the secondary current becomes normal again.

As explained in Section 4.3.6 certain systems of protection are not adversely affected by saturation and it is unnecessary to take special measures in this connection. It is, however, the duty of the protective gear application engineer to decide for which forms of protection and under what conditions of operation the c.t.s should not saturate.

4.4 Construction of current transformers

4.4.1 Basic types

Current transformers can be divided into two major types, the single-turn (bar) primary and the multi-turn wound-primary.

In the former the primary conductor may form part of the c.t. assembly, in which case it must be suitably insulated to withstand the system voltage to earth where it passes through the c.t. core and secondary windings. Such a c.t. is shown in Fig. 4.4.1A, the primary insulation of synthetic resin bonded paper being suitable for service on a 12 kV system.

The majority of single-turn primary c.t.s make use of an insulated conductor provided as part of other equipment such as bushings of switchgear or power transformers, and the c.t. is merely a ring core with a toroidally wound secondary winding.

Wound primary c.t.s may have the primary and secondary windings arranged concentrically, the secondary winding invariably being the inner winding since it is advantageous to keep the resistance of this winding as low as possible, or, in designs intended primarily for operating instruments, meters and simple overcurrent relays, the primary and secondary windings may be disposed on different limbs of the core. Such an arrangement results in minimum weights of windings, and the flux leakage effect resulting from this loose coupling reduces the phase error and limits

Fig. 4.4.1A   *Double-secondary bar-primary current transformer*
(*GEC High Voltage Switchgear Ltd.*)

Fig. 4.4.1B   *12kV cast resin insulated wound-primary current transformer*
(*GEC High Voltage Switchgear Ltd.*)

Fig. 4.4.1C   *12kV current transformer with cast resin insulated primary winding (GEC High Voltage Switchgear Ltd.)*

the secondary current produced by high primary overcurrents. Typical 12 kV designs are shown in Figs. 4.4.1B, C and D.

4.4.2   Forms of cores

The simplest form of core is the ring, composed either of hot-rolled silicon steel stampings or, more usually in recent years, of spirally wound strip of cold-rolled grain-oriented steel or of nickel-iron alloy.

Fig. 4.4.1D   *12kV current transformer with butyl rubber insulated primary winding*
(GEC High Voltage Switchgear Ltd.)

Cores for wound-primary c.t.s are usually assembled from stampings of E, I or L-shape depending on whether the core is a simple rectangle or of the three-limb shell-type, but C-cores of bonded cold-rolled grain-oriented steel are also employed. Some typical shapes are shown in Figs. 4.4.2A, B, C, D and E.

Cores of grain-oriented materials should be arranged as far as possible with the flux direction along the grain as indicated in Fig. 4.4.2C. This requirement is satisfied completely in wound-strip ring cores and in cut C-cores (Fig. 4.4.2E)

4.4.3   Windings and insulation

(a)   *Primary windings (wound primary current transformers):* These usually take the form of edge-wound copper strip because this method of winding results in

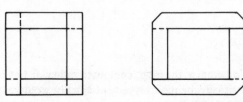

Fig. 4.4.2A   *I-shape*   **Fig. 4.4.2B**   *L-shape stampings*

coils best capable of withstanding the electromagnetic forces produced by high values of primary current. The inter-turn insulation may consist of split washers of pressboard or similar material, of tape applied to the individual turns or a coating of resinous materials.

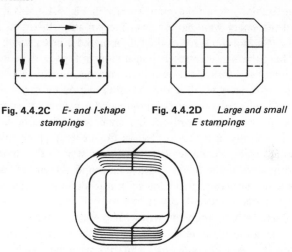

Fig. 4.4.2C   *E- and I-shape*   Fig. 4.4.2D   *Large and small*
stampings   *E stampings*

Fig. 4.4.2E   *Cut C-core*
Basic forms of high voltage c.t.s

The major insulation to earth of c.t.s for use up to 12 kV service, may be formed by taping the primary winding with varnished cloth tape or, more usually in modern designs, by enveloping the winding in cast-resin or moulded butyl rubber. The non-resilient nature of cast-resin necessitates some means of permitting the expansion of the primary winding, which occurs in a fraction of a second during the passage of a fault current, without imposing a strain on the cast-resin sufficient to case cracking. There are various ways of accomplishing this, some protected by patents. Rubber-like compounds are usually sufficiently resilient not to require this precaution.

(*b*)   *Secondary windings:* These are usually wound from round or rectangular section wires of enamelled copper. Coils for assembly on to cores built up of stampings are usually machine wound with paper between layers, the coil being subsequently varnish impregnated and insulated overall with press-paper wraps and tape.

Ring cores are insulated by means of pressboard washers and wraps, covered with varnished cloth or plastic tape, or they may be encased in split channel-section cases of moulded insulation, or coated with resinous compound. The toroidal winding is frequently carried out by hand but where large numbers of turns are required, or a large number of identical windings are to be wound, toroid winding machines are usually employed. Multi-layer windings are usually insulated between layers with varnished-cloth tape and the winding taped overall and reinforced with washers and wraps of pressboard.

4.4.4   High-voltage current transformers

Separately mounted post-type c.t.s suitable for outdoor service are frequently required for use in conjunction with air blast circuit-breakers. There are three basic forms of construction, shown diagrammatically in Fig. 4.4.4A, B and C. In type A, the cores and secondary windings are contained in an earthed tank at the base of a porcelain insulator and the leads of the full-insulated primary winding are taken up to the top helmet through the procelain insulator. In type B, the cores and windings are mounted midway inside the porcelain housing, usually with half the major insulation on the primary winding and the other half on the secondary winding and cores. This form of construction is limited in the volume of cores and windings which can be accommodated without the diameter of the procelain insulator becoming uneconomically large, but for two or three cores and secondary windings of modest output it offers a compact arrangement. In type C, the cores and secondary windings are housed in the helmet or live-tank and the earthed secondary leads brought down the insulator. This form of construction is particularly suitable for use when high primary currents are involved as it permits the use of a short bar primary conductor with consequent easing of the electrodynamic and flux leakage problems. The major insulation may be wholly on the secondary windings and cores or partially on the primary conductor, while the secondary leads require insulating to withstand the system voltage where they pass through the bases of the live-tank and down the porcelain bushing.

The major insulation of such current transformers is usually oil-impregnated paper, in some constructions with interleaved stress control foils, and examples using this form of insulation are shown in Figs. 4.4.4D, E, F, G and H. An alternative method of insulating for high voltages employs a gas, such as sulphur-hexafluoride, usually at a pressure in the region of two or three atmospheres. Unlike oil, such a gas is capable of withstanding high voltages between electrodes spaced

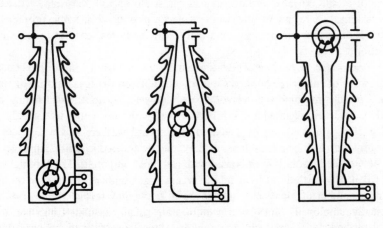

Fig. 4.4.A   Fig. 4.4.B   Fig. 4.4.C

Fig. 4.4.4D *525 kV, 2000A hairpin primary current transformer with several secondary windings (GEC High Voltage Switchgear Ltd.)*

Fig. 4.4.4E *245kV 'cross-coil' type current transformer with series parallel primary links (GEC High Voltage Switchgear Ltd.)*

several inches apart without intervening barriers of solid insulation, so that constructional problems are concerned with the rigid positioning of the high voltage and earthed electrodes and the provision of a housing capable of withstanding the required gas pressure.

Fig. 4.4.4F *245 kV live tank current transformer with oil-impregnated paper insulation (GEC High Voltage Switchgear Ltd.)*

Fig. 4.4.G   *420kV, 4000A hairpin–primary current transformer (GEC High Voltage Switchgear Ltd.)*

4.5   Testing of current transformers

4.5.1   Error measurements

The simplest direct method of measuring current magnitude errors is to use two ammeters, one measuring the primary current and the other the secondary current, and provided the required degree of accuracy is not high this method is satisfactory, and can even be used at currents up to several times the rated values.

Fig. 4.4.4H *420 kV, 4000A live tank current transformer employing SF$_6$ gas insulation (GEC High Voltage Switchgear Ltd.)*

When small errors of less than 1% are to be measured, and when both magnitude and phase errors are to be measured, some form of comparison with a standard current transformer is necessary and bridge circuits, electromagnetic comparators, or differential ammeter methods are then employed.

Current transformers, of the uniformly wound ring core type for use with bar primary arrangements resulting in negligible leakage flux, may have their current errors assessed by the indirect method of measuring the exciting current taken by the secondary winding with an applied voltage equal to the induced e.m.f. under specified burden and current conditions. As explained in Section 4.2.1, the current error in such a current transformer, with no turns correction, cannot exceed the percentage exciting current.

So-called high-reactance current transformers, in which the effect of flux leakage is appreciable, normally have their composite errors measured by a direct method (see Appendix J of BS 3938). A high-reactance current transformer is defined in BS 3938 (Appendix K) as one in which, with a turns ratio equal to the rated current transformation ratio, the composite error measured by a direct test at the rated accuracy limit primary current exceeds 1·3 times the percentage exciting current measured when the rated accuracy limit e.m.f. is applied to the secondary winding. This e.m.f. is taken as that required to pass the rated accuracy limit secondary current through an impedance equal to the vectorial sum of the impedance of the rated burden and the resistance of the secondary winding. For a number of current transformers of the same design BS 3938 (Appendix J) permits the composite errors to be derived from a comparison of their exciting currents with the exciting current of an identical current transformer of which the composite error has been measured by a direct test.

4.5.2   Turns ratio tests

There is no simple and positive method of measuring turns ratio on a completed current transformer. The usual method is to measure the current magnitude error at about the rated current with a low value of secondary burden. The accuracy of measurement depends on the magnitude of the component of the exciting current affecting the current error—see Section 4.2.1—for example there would be no difficulty in detecting an error of one turn in 100 turns, but with 500 or more turns in the secondary winding and a current error component of exciting current in the region of 0·25 to 0·5%, it might be difficult to decide whether a measured current error of −0·5% was due to exciting current alone or due in part to an error in turns ratio.

A more accurate assessment of turns ratio error can be made by measuring the current error at about the rated primary current with two or three different values of unity power-factor burden. These errors are then plotted against the corresponding values of total secondary circuit impedance, that is including that due to the secondary winding resistance, and extrapolated to zero burden to give the error in turns ratio (See BS 3938, Appendix M.)

Because of these difficulties the specified maximum turns ratio error should not be less than that required to ensure correct operation of the protective gear.

4.5.3   Exciting current

For most protective schemes it is necessary to measure the exciting current at one or more values of secondary e.m.f. This is accomplished quite simply by applying the appropriate voltage, and measuring the current taken by the secondary winding, the primary and any other windings being open-circuited. In some cases an excitation curve may be required and sufficient measurements are then made to enable the curve to be plotted. When it is only desired to check that the knee-point e.m.f. is not less than a certain value that value is applied and the exciting current measured. A voltage 10% higher is then applied when the exciting current measured should not exceed that measured at the knee-point e.m.f. by more than 50%.

4.5.4 Current transformers for balanced differential protective schemes

As stated in Section 4.3.6 it is often possible to prove the suitability of c.t.s for such schemes by measurements of exciting current and turns ratio. In some instances it may be desirable to carry out a balance test between pairs of c.t.s as shown in Fig. 4.5.4A. If the object of the test is to prove that the two c.t.s have the same or similar turns ratio the burden. R_B is kept to a minimum, but if the object is to prove the combination of turns ratio and exciting current balance, the burden R_B would represent that expected in service. The ammeter A measures the spill or out-of-balance current. The primary current may be either the rated value for turns balance tests or the relevant through-fault current for turns and exciting current balance tests.

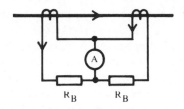

Fig. 4.5.4A *Connections for balance test*

Balance tests with a relay in place of the ammeter are sometimes performed, but such tests prove the combination of the c.t.s and the relay and are not strictly tests of the c.t.s themselves.

4.5.5 Polarity

Various methods are used by manufacturers to prove that the terminal markings are correct. When such a check is necessary to prove the polarity on site it can be carried out as follows. Connect the positive terminal of a low voltage d.c. supply, such as a small battery, to the c.t primary terminal bearing the lowest suffix number and the negative of the supply to the other primary terminal. Connect the negative terminal of a d.c. voltmeter to the c.t. secondary terminal bearing the lowest suffix numeral and the positive terminal of the voltmeter to the other secondary terminal. On breaking the d.c. supply the voltmeter will give a positive deflection if the terminal markings are correct.

4.5.6 Insulation tests

Routine insulation tests specified in BS 3938 consist of applying for one minute the appropriate 50 Hz voltage to the primary or secondary winding, all windings being short-circuited and the one not being supplied with the test voltage connected to the frame and earth. The test voltage for secondary windings is 2 kV r.m.s., while that for primary windings depends on the rated primary voltage of the c.t.

An impulse voltage test may have to be met as a type test if the c.t. is for service in a situation exposed to over-voltages of atmospheric origin, and if for service outdoors a type test under artificial rain may also be specified.

4.6   Voltage-transformer theory

4.6.1   Electromagnetic-type voltage transformers

Referring once more to Fig. 4.1.2A, it will be seen that the errors of a voltage transformer (v.t.) are the difference in magnitude and phase between V_p and V_s and that they consist of the 'no-load' errors, when Z_B is infinity caused by the voltage drop due to the exciting current flowing in the primary winding, and the 'load' errors due to the voltage drops in both windings as a result of the burden current I_s. A simplified vector diagram for the circuit of Fig. 4.1.2A, drawn with particular reference to voltages, is shown in Fig. 4.6.1A. The difference between V_p and V_s is shown for the loaded condition. On no load, the primary current would be I_e only and the primary voltage the vector shown dotted and marked V_p', while there would be no secondary current and V_s would be equal to the induced e.m.f. E_s. It should be noted that, like Fig. 4.1.2A, the vector diagram of Fig. 4.6.1A ignores the effects of leakage flux.

For a constant value of applied voltage V_p it is convenient to plot an error diagram of the form shown in Fig. 4.6.1B in which per cent voltage (ratio)

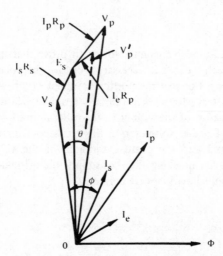

Fig. 4.6.1A *Phasor diagram for circuit of Fig. 4.1.2A with particular reference to voltage errors*

error is plotted horizontally and phase displacement (centriradians) is plotted vertically. With known errors for two loading conditions, such as no-load and 100 VA unity power factor (u.p.f.), the diagram can be constructed to give the errors for any other value of burden and power factor the latter being the cosine of the angle ϕ. For a different value of the applied voltage the no-load errors will be different and the whole diagram will move by the amount of the change in the no-load errors.

It should be noted that the phase error change with u.p.f. burden is the result of flux leakage which, as far as the burden current is concerned, is equivalent to series inductive reactance. See Fig. 4.2.4C.

4.6.2 Capacitor-type voltage transformers

At 132 kV and higher voltages capacitor v.t.s. may be more economic than electromagnetic v.t.s, particularly when the h.v. capacitors can serve also for carrier-current coupling.

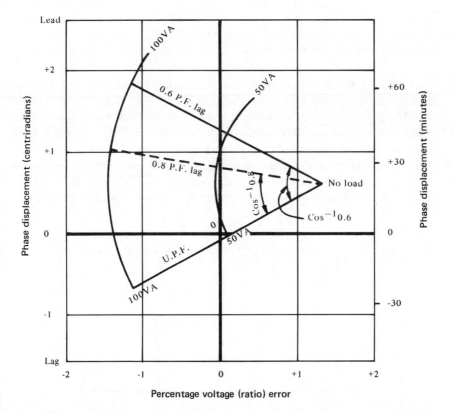

Fig. 4.6.1B *Voltage transformer error diagram*

Fig. 4.6.2A shows the basic circuit usually employed. The line to ground voltage V_p is applied across the capacitor voltage divider comprising C_1 and C_2 and the intermediate voltage V_{c2} is fed to the primary winding of an electromagnetic transformer T via a tuning inductance L which resonates approximately with $C_1 + C_2$ at the system frequency. The transformer T steps down to the secondary voltage V_s.

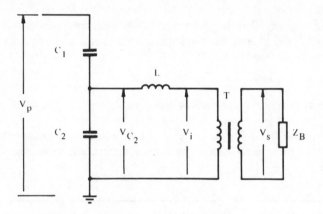

Fig. 4.6.2A   *Basic circuit of a capacitor v.t.*

There are numerous variations of this basic circuit. The inductance L may be a separate unit or it may be incorporated in the form of leakage inductance in the transformer T. Because the capacitors C_1 and C_2 cannot conveniently be made to close tolerances it is necessary to provide adjustments of ratio by means of tappings either on the transformer T or on a separate auto-transformer in the secondary circuit. Adjustment of the tuning inductance L is also necessary and this may be effected variously by tappings, by a separate tapped inductor in the secondary circuit, by adjustment of gaps in iron cores, or by shunting with a variable capacitor.

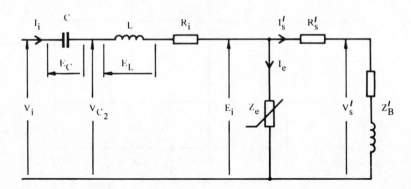

Fig. 4.6.2B   *Equivalent circuit of a capacitor v.t.*

To understand the factors affecting the performance it is convenient to use the equivalent circuit of Fig. 4.6.2B in which V_i is the nominal intermediate voltage equal to V_p divided by $1 + C_2/C_1$, C is a fictitious capacitance numerically equal to $C_1 + C_2$, L the tuning inductance, R_i represents the resistance of the intermediate voltage winding of the transformer T plus the losses in C and L, and Z_e is the exciting impedance of the transformer T. The secondary circuit resistance and the burden impedance, both referred to the intermediate voltage, are represented by R'_s and Z'_B, respectively, and similarly V'_s and I'_s represent the secondary terminal voltage and the output current.

It will be seen that except for C the circuit is the usual equivalent circuit of a transformer (compare with Fig. 4.1.2A), and therefore at the frequency when C and L are resonant and cancel each other the circuit will behave, under steady state conditions, as a conventional transformer. It will also be apparent that provided R'_i and R'_s are not unduly large, and I_e small compared with I'_s the vector difference between V_i and V'_s, which constitutes the overall error of the capacitor v.t., will be small. This is illustrated in Fig. 4.6.2C which is the vector diagram for the circuit of Fig. 4.6.2B. The diagram is drawn for a burden power factor (cos ϕ) close to unity and the voltage error is the difference in magnitude between V_i and V'_s, while the phase error is the angle θ. The voltage V_{C2}, also indicated in Fig. 4.6.2B, is that across capacitor C_2 (Fig. 4.6.2A) and it will be noticed that this voltage increases with output current and could reach a dangerously high value in the event of the

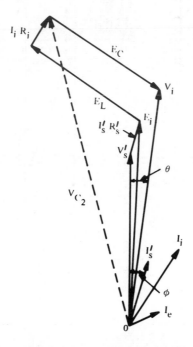

Fig. 4.6.2C *Phasor diagram for circuit of Fig. 4.6.2B*

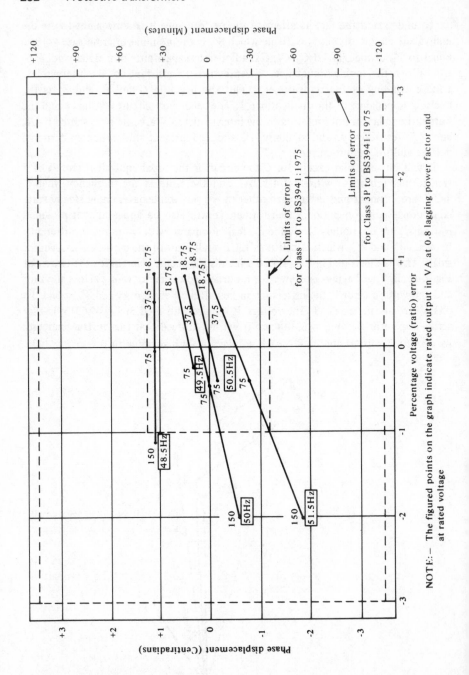

Fig. 4.6.2D *Typical error diagram for a full-range capacitor v.t. of class 1/3P accuracy to BS 3941 : 1975 for frequencies between 48·5 Hz and 51·5 Hz*

secondary terminals being short-circuited. The value of V_{C2} is, however, usually limited by some means, such as a spark-gap connected across C_2 or by arranging the inductance L to saturate at currents above the rated output value.

It will also be seen from Fig. 4.6.2C that at frequencies differing from the resonant value either E_L or E_C will predominate with the result that, with a u.p.f. burden, the phase error θ will be changed. Provided the reactive voltages E_L or E_C are not too high in relation to V_i, the change of phase error with frequency is not excessive. Typical capacitor v.t.s used in this country have h.v. capacitors (C_1) of 2000 pF and V_i of about 12 kV and give a change of phase error at the rated burden (150 VA 0·8 pf) of about 30 minutes per Hz of frequency change in 145 kV transformers and about 10 minutes per HZ in 400 kV transformers. Earlier designs had lower values of C and V_i and hence higher values of L and R_i (Fig. 4.6.2B) with the result that ratio and phase change with burden was considerably greater than in electromagnetic v.t.s and several changes of adjustments were necessary to cover the full burden range with reasonable accuracy. Also, for the ratio and phase adjustments to be independently effective it was necessary to correct inductive burdens to unity power factor by means of shunt capacitors.

Present standard designs used in this country are rated at 150 VA Class 3/3P (BS 3941), and cover the range from 25 to 100% of rated output without any change of adjustments. The performance is comparable with that of electromagnetic v.t.s of the same rating and it is unnecessary to correct the power factor of the burden.

The errors of a capacitor v.t. at a given voltage can be plotted in the same manner as for an electromagnetic v.t. as shown in Fig. 4.6.2D which shows the errors at various frequencies of a transformer giving Class 1·0 accuracy over a ±0·5 Hz frequency range (compare with Fig. 4.6.1B).

4.6.3   Burdens and lead resistances

The resistance of leads connecting the secondary winding to the instruments or relays increases the burden on c.t.s as explained in Section 4.2.7, and thus increases the core flux, the exciting current and, therefore, the errors.

In voltage transformers the secondary lead resistance again affects the errors but in a more direct manner. The principal effect is that the voltage at the terminals of the instruments or relays differs from the voltage at the secondary terminals of the v.t. by the voltage drop (p.d.) in the leads. A second order effect is that there is a slight reduction in effective burden on the v.t.

For example, if the burden on a single-phase v.t. with 110 V secondary is nominally 110 VA so that the nominal output current is 1 A, and the loop resistance of the leads is 1 Ω, an error of approximately 1 V will be introduced into the voltage across the burden. Whether this 1 V is equivalent to $1 \times 100/110 = 0.91\%$ voltage (magnitude) error, or to a combination of voltage and phase error depends on the power factor of the burden. With a pure resistive burden this additional error

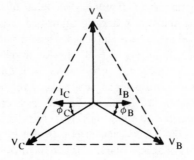

Fig. 4.6.3A   *U.p.f burden across B-C only*

would be approximately -0.9% in voltage magnitude and with a pure inductive burden it would become approximately $+0.9$ centiradians in phase, that is, $+30$ minutes, while with an intermediate burden power factor the errors would become approximately $-I_sR_L \times 100 \times \cos \Phi/V_s$ in voltage and $+I_sR_L \times 3438 \times \sin \Phi/V_s$ in phase, where I_s is the output current, R_L is the loop resistance, V_s is the nominal secondary voltage, and Φ is the angle of lag of the current I_s behind the voltage V_s (see Fig. 4.6.1A).

It should be noted that with leading power-factor burdens the phase error due to leads becomes negative, that is lagging.

The second-order effect mentioned previously can normally be neglected, because it would only be appreciable in the event of large errors introduced by the leads, for example, if a 110 V secondary winding was loaded by a 110 VA u.p.f. burden through a loop lead resistance of 5 Ω, the approximate error would be -5 V or -4.45%. A more accurate assessment of the error would result from taking into account the reduced output, that is, burden + lead resistance = $110 + 5 = 115$ Ω total so that the v.t. output is $110^2/115 = 105$ VA and the additional error due to the leads is $5/115 \times 100 = -4.35\%$. Note that this simple method of comparing the lead and burden resistances is only applicable to resistive burdens.

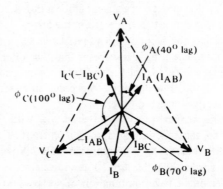

Fig. 4.6.3B   *Effects of unbalanced burdens*

It should also be noted that secondary fuses can have resistance values sufficiently high to cause appreciable errors in high accuracy metering applications. Where a v.t. or a three-phase group of v.t.s is employed to supply through long leads a large output to relays and instruments, in addition to a small output to high accuracy integrating meters, it is preferable to use separate leads and secondary fuses for the metering circuit.

With three-phase v.t.s and three-phase groups of single-phase v.t.s connected in star, the effects of lead resistance become much more complicated because the burden across one pair of phases affects the errors of the voltages across the other two pairs of phases. In extreme cases of unbalanced loading of the v.t., the power flow can be reversed in one phase to neutral winding. This results in a positive voltage error in this phase to neutral voltage, not only because of the lead resistance but also due to the winding resistances.

Fig. 4.6.3A shows the burden on phases B and C of a three-phase v.t. or group due to a u.p.f. burden across BC. If the burden across BC is 100 VA the burden on phase B is $100/\sqrt{3}$ VA at 0·866 p.f. (30°) leading, and the same numerical value on phase C but at 0·866 p.f. (30°) lagging.

Fig. 4.6.3B shows the burdens on the phases for burdens each of 100 VA at 0·342 p.f. (70°) lagging across phases AB and BC with no burden across phases CA. The burden on phase A is $100 /\sqrt{3}$ VA at 0·766 p.f. (70° – 30° = 40°) lagging, that on phase B is 100 VA at 0·342 p.f. (70°) lagging and that on phase C is $100/\sqrt{3}$ VA at 70° + 30° = 100° lagging, that is a power *input* on the secondary winding of phase C of $100/\sqrt{3}$ VA at 180° – 100° = 80° leading (0·174 p.f.).

Power factor correction of inductive burdens: As mentioned in Section 4.6.2, early designs of capacitor v.t.s, many of which are still in use in this country, have relatively poor basic accuracy; a combination of tapped secondary windings, variable series inductance, and correction of the burden power factor to unity being employed to provide reasonably good accuracy over the usual range of 25 to 100% of rated output. The settings required to cover the various steps of the total burden range are usually selected as a result of tests by the manufacturer and are indicated on the rating plate. These settings apply to unity power factor burdens on the single-phase unit, that is phase to neutral loading, and this fact was often overlooked when phase-to-phase burdens were corrected to u.p.f. but the effect of unbalanced loading on the phase-to-neutral burdens and power factors was forgotten. Fortunately, none of these early capacitor v.t.s were used for metering and the accuracy obtained, even with incorrect loading, was sufficiently good for the forms of protection being operated by such v.t.s.

4.7 Voltage transformers for protection

4.7.1 Electromagnetic type categories, residual voltages

For the operation of meters and instruments, the accuracy of a v.t. is usually only important at or about the normal system voltage, so that with a given burden the errors are practically constant. For protection, however, although the accuracy requirements may not be very exacting, the errors are required to be within certain limits over the wide range of voltage possible under system fault conditions. This range may be from 5 to 150 or 190% of rated primary voltage for v.t.s. connected between line and ground. This requires a corresponding range of core flux density and thus appreciable change in the value of the exciting impedance Z_c (Fig. 4.1.2A) over this range. This results in a change in the no-load errors which may increase considerably at the extremes of the voltage range unless due attention is given to this problem in the design stage.

In BS 3941 : 1975 all voltage transformers for protection are required to comply with the requirements of one of the accuracy classes 0·1, 0·2, 0·5, 1·0 or 3·0 which specify limits of voltage and phase errors over a range of voltages from 0·8 to 1·2 times the rated primary voltage. In addition, protective v.t.s must meet the requirements of either class 3P or 6P, which specify limits of voltage and phase errors over two additional voltage ranges; one range from 0·05 to 0·8 times the rated primary voltage, and the other range from 1·2 to V_F times the rated primary voltage, where V_F is the appropriate voltage factor (see below).

For convenience, these error limits are given below:

Table 4.7.1A *Limits of voltage error and phase displacement for measuring voltage transformers*

Accuracy class	Percentage voltage (ratio) error	Phase displacement	
		minutes	centiradians
0·1	± 0·1	± 5	± 0·15
0·2	± 0·2	± 10	± 0·3
0·5	± 0·5	± 20	± 0·6
1·0	± 1·0	± 40	± 1·2
3·0	± 3·0	not specified	not specified

Table 4.7.1.B *Limits of voltage error and phase displacement for protective voltage transformers*

Accuracy class	Percentage voltage (ratio) error	Phase displacement	
		minutes	centiradians
3P	± 3·0	± 120	± 3·5
6P	± 6·0	± 240	± 7·0

Table 4.7.1C

Voltage factor V_F	Duration	Earthing conditions	
		V.T. primary windings	System
1·2	Not limited	Non-Earthed	Effectively or non-effectively earthed
1·5	30 s	Earthed	Effectively earthed
1·9	30 s or 8 h	Earthed	Non-effectively earthed

Voltage factors: The voltage factor V_F is determined by the maximum operating voltage, which in turn is dependent on the system and voltage transformer earthing conditions. The factors appropriate to the different earthing conditions, together with the permissible duration of the maximum operating voltage, are given in Table 4.7.1C.

Residual voltages: For applications such as directional earth-fault protection residual voltages are required and are usually provided by windings connected in broken-delta as shown in Fig. 4.7.1A.

Under normal conditions, the three phase-to-earth voltages are of equal magnitude and 120 degrees apart and residual voltage (of system frequency) is zero, but under earth-fault conditions the voltage to earth of one phase collapses, either totally or partially depending on the location of the fault, the voltage applied to the other two phase-to-earth windings is increased and changed in phase, by amounts dependent on the method of earthing the system neutral, and a residual voltage V_R appears as shown vectorially in Fig. 4.7.1B.

It should be noted that third harmonic voltages add up in a broken-delta connected winding, and if present in the applied voltages will appear at the terminals of that winding.

Because a residual voltage is the result of an out-of-balance of the fluxes linking the residual voltage windings, a low reluctance path for this residual flux must be provided in three-phase transformers. the usual method being to employ a five-limb core. (See Fig. 4.7.1C). Residual voltages may also be obtained from three single-phase units connected line to earth.

Residual voltages can be obtained from auxiliary v.t.s star/broken-delta connected, but the main v.t. must be capable of reproducing an out-of-balance in the three phase-to-earth voltages, that is it must have a path for residual flux, or be comprised of three single-phase units, while it is, of course, essential for the primary and secondary star points to be available.

4.7.2 Capacitor type

As for electromagnetic v.t.s, for certain types of protection capacitor v.t.s must have magnitude and phase errors within certain prescribed limits over a wide range

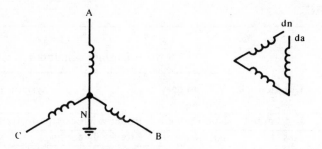

Fig. 4.7.1A   *Three-phase windings connected star/broken delta*

of primary voltage such as from 5 to 150 or 190% of rated voltages. Because the core of the intermediate transformer is usually operated at a low flux density at normal voltage, little difficulty is experienced in maintaining the required accuracy at voltages above the nominal value. At very low system voltages, however, the core flux density falls to a level at which the permeability of the core material is relatively low and thus the exciting impedance Z_e (Fig. 4.6.2B) is reduced. Because the series reactance in the intermediate voltage circuit, through which the exciting current I_e must flow, is usually capacitive (a part of the inductance being in the transformer T and in the secondary circuit) any increase in I_e relative to V_i results in a positive magnitude error (output voltage high) and a positive phase error (output voltage leading). These increases in errors at 5% of rated voltage may be as great as +5% in amplitude and +5 degrees in phase in capacitor v.t.s of relatively poor basic accuracy, but in the transformers now being supplied in this country, which permit variation of the burden from 25% to the rated value without adjustment (full range transformers), the increase in errors, due to the smaller series reactance, may be no more than +1·5% and +60 minutes.

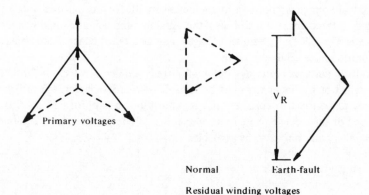

Primary voltages

Normal   Earth-fault

Residual winding voltages

Fig. 4.7.1B   *Residual voltages under normal and earth-fault conditions*

Fig. 4.7.1C *Three-phase voltage transformer with five-limb core capable of producing residual voltages (GEC High Voltage Switchgear Ltd.)*

Transient response: It is also necessary in certain protective gear applications that the v.t. should reproduce sudden changes in the primary voltage. This seldom presents any difficulty with an electromagnetic v.t. but capacitor v.t.s in which the series capacitive and inductive reactances are high in relation to the burden impedance (referred to the intermediate voltage), particularly when power-factor correcting capacitors are employed to tune inductive burdens, as in stepped range v.t.s, are prone to exhibit oscillations in the secondary voltage when the primary voltage changes rapidly. Thus when the primary voltage collapses the secondary voltage may persist for some milliseconds in the form of a damped oscillation. Because of the combination of series and parallel resonant circuits presented by the transformer and the tuned burden, such oscillations are usually a combination of two frequencies, one above and one below the system frequency. A typical oscillogram of a stepped-range capacitor v.t operating at maximum output with burden power-factor correction is shown in Fig. 4.7.2A.

In full range transformers of good accuracy, however, the relatively low values of the series reactances and the absence of burden power-factor correction capacitance

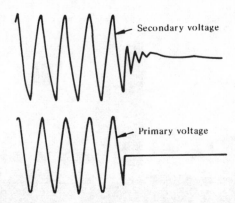

Fig. 4.7.2A   *Transient response of a stepped-range capacitor voltage transformer operating at maximum output with burden power factor correction*

ensures rapid dissipation of the stored energy with the result that the secondary voltage is for all practical purposes a true reproduction of the primary voltage as shown in Fig. 4.7.2B. It will be apparent from the foregoing that the transient response of a given capacitor v.t. will generally be best at low outputs, that is when the burden impedance is high.

Ferro-resonance effects: Owing to the non-linear characteristics of the exciting impedance Z_e (Fig. 4.6.2B), it is possible for oscillations to be initiated by transients in the supply voltage or in the output current which, once established, are sustained by the system frequency supply. The most common frequency for such oscillations is one-third that of the supply, although sustained oscillations at other sub-harmonics and at the supply frequency are possible.

The most easily measured effect of such an oscillation is a rise in output voltage, the r.m.s. value usually being some 25 to 50% above the normal value, while an oscilloscope connected across the secondary terminals would probably show a voltage wave similar to that of Fig. 4.7.2C.

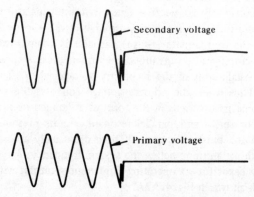

Fig. 4.7.2B   *Transient response to a full range capacitor voltage transformer of good basic accuracy*

Such oscillations are less liable to occur when the losses in the circuit are high, for example when the burden is resistive and corresponds to the rated output. If the phenomenon is encountered it can usually be dealt with by increasing the resistive load on the v.t.

A study of this phenomenon has shown that the avoidance of certain combinations of circuit parameters will prevent sustained oscillations of this nature in a capacitor v.t. supplying a resistive burden. It is possible, however, for the non-linear impedances of such burdens as auxiliary v.t.s and other iron-cored devices to modify the inductive parameters in a manner which increases the tendency for the circuit to oscillate. Auxiliary v.t.s for use with capacitor v.t.s should be designed with low flux density—B_{max} about 0·4 tesla in silicon-steel cores, which prevents high exciting currents during circuit transients. When necessary specially designed damping circuits are employed to prevent sustained oscillations of the kind in question.

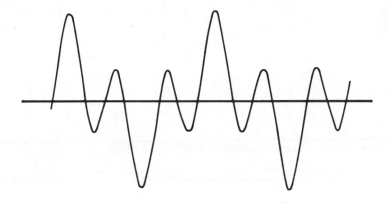

Fig. 4.7.2C *Typical oscillogram of secondary voltage with an oscillation at 163 Hz*

Carrier-current coupling: To provide for carrier-current coupling, two basic requirements must be met. The lowest terminal of the capacitor divider, normally earthed for capacitor v.t. operation, must present a high impedance to earth at the carrier-current frequencies. In British designs, this terminal is normally earthed via a link which can be removed when the connection to the carrier-current equipment is made, the connection to earth for power frequencies then being via the carrier-current coupling transformer. In some countries it is the practice to connect the bottom end of the capacitor divider to earth through an inductance which presents an impedance sufficiently high at carrier frequencies but low enough at power system frequency not to impair the accuracy of the v.t. Secondly, the intermediate voltage circuit, because it is connected between a tapping of the carrier-coupling capacitor and earth, must present a high impedance at carrier frequencies. This can be ensured by inserting an inductor of suitable value in the connection to the intermediate transformer primary winding. These blocking inductors are shown in Fig. 4.7.2D.

When it is necessary to tune the series capacitive reactance at carrier frequencies the tuning inductor can be inserted in the carrier current connection, but this raises the carrier frequency voltage between capacitor C_2 and earth and thus increases the loss of carrier current at this point. In British practice, the stack tuning coil, as it is termed, is inserted in the position shown in Fig. 4.7.2E, which also indicates the earth connection via the centre-tapping of the carrier-current coupling transformer winding. In this arrangement the capacitor divider tapping point to the intermediate tranformer is at a low carrier frequency voltage to earth and a blocking inductor is usually unnecessary. The stack tuning coil, however, is at a

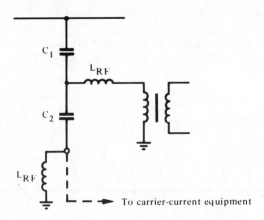

Fig. 4.7.2D   *Position of carrier-current locking inductors (marked L_{RF})*

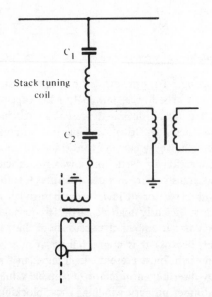

Fig. 4.7.2E   *Position of series tuning coil and method of earthing*

high power frequency voltage to earth which necessitates special provision for it on the capacitor v.t.

4.8 Construction of voltage transformers

4.8.1 Electromagnetic type

The form of construction is to a large extent dictated by the rated primary voltage. For the lower voltages, say not exceeding 3·3 kV, dry type transformers with varnish impregnated and taped windings are quite satisfactory in reasonably dry situations. For higher voltages it has been the practice for many years to immerse

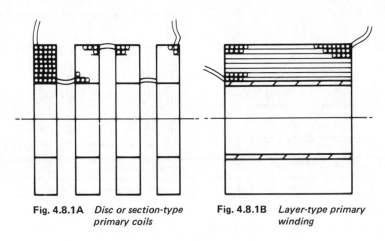

Fig. 4.8.1A   *Disc or section-type primary coils*

Fig. 4.8.1B   *Layer-type primary winding*

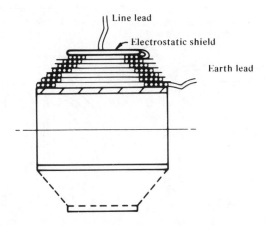

Line lead

Electrostatic shield

Earth lead

Fig. 4.8.1C   *H.V. layer winding for connection line to earth* the core and windings in oil, which makes the problem of providing reliable insulation throughout the primary winding very much easier. In recent years, however, the development of windings impregnated and encapsulated in synthetic resins has made possible the use of dry type transformers at much higher voltages than hitherto. In this country such cast resin insulated transformers are in production for 12 kV and 36 kV service and experimental transformers have been made for higher voltages. On the Continent, where the development of cast resin insulation is more advanced, a combination of resin and oil is used up to 100 kV.

The recent development of metalclad switchgear for transmission voltages has led to the introduction of SF$_6$ gas insulated voltage transformers.

Primary windings are generally of one of two basic forms, that is either divided into a number of series-connected coils (multi-coil) as in Fig. 4.8.1A or of the single-coil layer-type as in Fig. 4.8.1B. In the former the few turns per layer permit

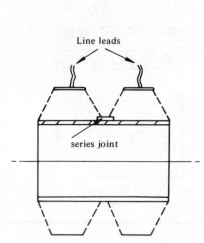

Fig. 4.8.1D   *H.V. layer winding for connection line to line*

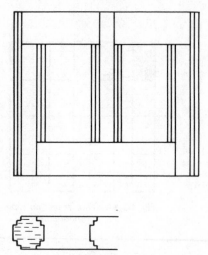

Fig. 4.8.1E   *Three-phase interleaved core with stepped or cruciform section*

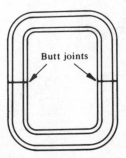

Fig. 4.8.1F   *Cut C-core*

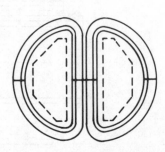

Fig. 4.8.1G   *Cut D-core (winding shape shown dotted)*

Fig. 4.8.1H *Typical three-phase 12kV oil-immersed voltage transformers (GEC High Voltage Switchgear Ltd.)*

Fig. 4.8.1J *33 kV three-phase 'plug-in' cast resin-insulated voltage transformer (A Reyrolle & Co. Ltd.)*

thin inter-layer insulation in the individual coils, but substantial insulation is required between coils. In the single-coil layer-type winding the voltage between layers is relatively high and necessitates correspondingly thick inter-layer insulation. This type of winding is, however, fundamentally better capable of withstanding impulse voltages than the multi-coil type, and forms of windings usually employed in high voltage transformers are shown in Figs. 4.8.1C and 4.8.1D.

Fig. 4.8.1K   *24 kV single-phase cast resin-insulated voltage transformer (A Reyrolle & Co Ltd.)*

Fig. 4.8.1L   *36 kV three-phase outdoor voltage transformer (GEC High Voltage Switchgear Ltd.)*

For the highest voltages, oil-immersed designs are generally preferred. The paper and pressboard insulation employed in such v.t.s when dried and impregnated with oil, often under vacuum, is capable of withstanding high stresses and provides an extremely reliable insulation at low cost.

For small low-voltage single-phase transformers shell-type cores of the type shown in Fig. 4.4.2C and D are commonly used. For higher voltages and generally for three-phase v.t.s the stepped section core is usually employed as shown in Fig. 4.8.1E. This permits the best use of cylindrical coils. Cut cores of cold-rolled grain oriented steel as in Fig. 4.8.1F and G are also employed, these forms of core being more suitable than interleaved joint cores for operating at high flux densities.

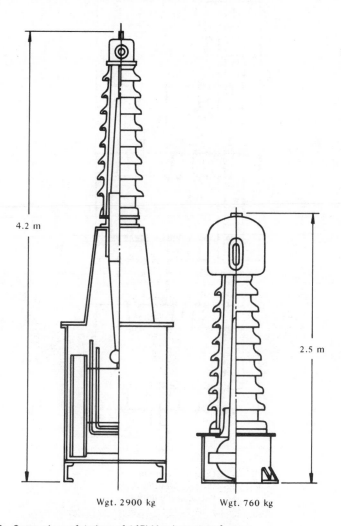

4.2 m

2.5 m

Wgt. 2900 kg   Wgt. 760 kg

Fig. 4.8.1M *Comparison of designs of 145kV voltage transformers*

Typical forms of enclosures and terminal arrangements commonly employed are shown in Fig. 4.8.1H, J, K and L. In v.t.s for the highest voltages, a conventional tank and h.v. bushing arrangement involves a bushing which is very large and expensive compared with the transformer core and windings. Fig. 4.8.1M shows the reduction in dimensions resulting from the adoption of a compact design of layer type winding, and from the elimination of the conventional demountable h.v. bushing, a substantial reduction in cost being also achieved.

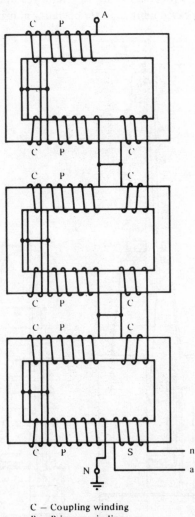

C – Coupling winding
P – Primary winding
S – Secondary winding

Fig. 4.8.2A   *Diagram for a 6-stage cascade voltage transformer*

Fig. 4.8.2B   *420 kV cascade-connected voltage transformer (GEC High Voltage Switchgear Ltd.)*

4.8.2 Cascade type

The conventional type of voltage transformer having a single primary winding becomes relatively bulky and expensive for system voltages exceeding 145 kV.

The cascade type of voltage transformer breaks away from the single primary principle by having the primary winding in several sections connected in series stepping down the voltage in stages.

From Fig. 4.8.2A it will be seen that the primary winding arrangement P is equally divided between several magnetic cores each core having windings on two opposite limbs. The secondary winding S consists of a single winding on the last stage only. The coupling windings C connected in pairs between stages provide low

Fig. 4.8.3A *Electromagnetic unit for use with a tapped capacitance bushing (GEC High Voltage Switchgear Ltd.)*

impedance circuits for the flow of the primary and secondary currents and ensures the accurate distribution of the power frequency voltage between stages. When the secondary winding is loaded, current flows in the coupling windings providing the balance of ampere turns to each stage, thus reducing to a minimum the leakage reactance between the primary and secondary windings. The potential of the cores

Fig. 4.8.3B *362 kV hairpin primary current transformer with capacitance tapping and voltage transformer unit (GEC High Voltage Switchgear Ltd.)*

and coupling windings are fixed at definite values by connecting them to selected points on the primary winding.

Because the primary winding is in several stages the insulation level of each stage need only be a fraction of the normal insulation level and is equal to

$$\frac{\text{line voltage}}{2 \times \text{number of cores in series}}$$

Thus, for a 400 kV transformer the insulation required per stage is approximately 66 kV only.

The resulting design is such that the cores and windings can be contained within a suitable porcelain housing as illustrated on Fig. 4.8.2B, thus eliminating the necessity for the large tanks associated with the conventional designs. The cascade voltage transformer is therefore smaller, has a lower oil content and is more economical than conventional units.

4.8.3 Capacitor type

The construction of a capacitor v.t. depends principally on the form of the capacitor voltage divider. Where this takes the form of a tapped bushing, the electromagnetic unit may be coupled to the capacitor tapping via a coaxial cable or by open terminals, as shown in Fig. 4.8.3A and 4.8.3B. The form of construction usually employed in this country is shown in Fig. 4.8.3C. The h.v. capacitors are contained in the porcelain housings and the large box on the side of the tank is designed to house the stack tuning coil for carrier current purposes as discussed in Section 4.7.2.

4.8.4 Capacitor divider voltage sensor

Fig. 4.8.3C *362 kV capacitor voltage transformer with provision for carrier current coupling (GEC High Voltage Switchgear Ltd.)*

A capacitor voltage divider is again used connected between line and earth, a low voltage analogue of the line voltage being developed across the capacitor which is nearest to earth potential.

A pre-amplifier situated close to the divider converts this analogue into a low impedance signal suitable for transmitting via screened cable to the relay room. At the relay room, the signal is amplified to provide a power supply for the needs of protection and measurement equipment.

The arrangement is immune from ferro-resonance and has a better transient response than a capacitor v.t. It is, therefore, the more suitable for use with high speed forms of protection.

4.8.5   Voltage transformers for SF$_6$ metalclad switchgear

Electromagnetic voltage transformers employ a conventional layer winding construction for the high voltage winding connected between line and earth. They operate at a gas pressure of several bars and consequently are housed in a suitable pressure chamber (See Fig. 4.8.5A). Capacitor divider voltage sensors are also used as an alternative to the electromagnetic v.t, the capacitor divider being constructed as an integral part of the pressurised metalclad switchgear.

Fig. 4.8.5A   *420 kV single-phase SF$_6$ gas-insulated voltage transformer for use with metalclad switchgear (A Reyrolle & Co. Ltd.)*

4.9   Fusing and protection of voltage transformers

Protection of an electromagnetic v.t. from accidental overloads and short circuits across its secondary terminals is simple. The normal secondary current is not more than 5A and the short circuit current in the region of 100 A so that simple fuses can be employed. The current normally taken by the primary winding depends on the primary voltage but is usually no more than a few milliamperes, so that fuses which would interrupt a small overload current are impracticable and the minimum fusing current of primary fuses is usually about 2 or 3A. This means that they would not fuse until quite a serious fault had developed in the v.t. windings, and all that can be expected from such an arrangement is that a defective v.t. would be disconnected from the supply before the damage spread to neighbouring equipment.

At voltages exceeding 72·5 primary fuses are impracticable and it has become common practice abroad to connect h.v. transformers directly to the line conductor without any form of internal fault protection or detection whatever. Such was the practice at 145 kV in this country for many years, but as a result of one or two v.t.s exploding due to h.v winding faults all 145 kV v.t.s on the British Grid are now fitted with Buchholz protection, that is with gas operated relays fitted into the oil pipe between the v.t. tank and the oil conservator tank. These relays are usually connected to operate an alarm on the collection of gas in the relay and thus give early warning of a winding fault. Gas-operated relays are also incorporated in some cascade v.t.s.

Capacitor v.t.s are invariably solidly connected to the system so that there is no primary protection.

The rating of secondary fuses for capacitor v.t.s may present problems. The secondary current with the terminals short circuited is limited either by the flash-over voltage of the spark gap across capacitor C_2 (see Section 4.6.2) which limits the input voltage to the intermediate circuit or, in the more accurate designs, by saturation of the tuning inductor L (Figs. 4.6.2A and 4.6.2B). In stepped-range transformers of poor inherent voltage regulation the short-circuit secondary current may be limited to two or three times the rated current, but in the more accurate full-range types it will usually reach 10 to 20 times the rated value.

4.10   Testing of voltage transformers

4.10.1   Error measurements

Some form of comparison with a standard of known errors is invariably employed for measurement of v.t. errors. The standard may be another voltage transformer of high accuracy or a potential divider circuit of some kind. The errors are usually measured with two burdens, one of which is the rated burden, and from these two sets of errors those for any other burden may be derived.

The errors of measuring v.t.s are normally measured at rated voltage only, but protective v.t.s may have to be measured at voltages both above and below the rated value, while if residual windings are involved measurements of residual voltage errors may have to be made (see BS 3941).

Capacitor v.t.s will usually require the determination of their errors at frequencies other than the rated value while if they are of the stepped-range type the correct adjustments for each output step have to be checked.

4.10.2 Core losses

Although not usually a contract requirement, the measurement of core loss and exciting current is usually made as a routine check on the quality of the material and construction of the core, and also as a means of detecting short-circuited turns in the windings. These measurements are made by means of ammeters and a wattmeter with rated secondary voltage supplied.

4.10.3 Insulation tests

Routine insulation tests are of two kinds, applied and induced overvoltage tests. Primary windings which are non-earthed, that is are insulated at all points to earth for the full test voltage, are short circuited and tested to earth for one minute at the specified test voltage, the secondary and any other windings being short circuited and earthed.

Induced overvoltage tests are made on all v.t.s to test the inter-turn and inter-layer insulation of the windings. The supply is usually applied to the secondary winding and at a frequency of two to four times the rated value to prevent core saturation and excessive exciting current. On earthed v.t.s, that is for connection between line and earth, and with graded insulation, the induced test is the only possible high voltage test and may have to be made at almost four times the rated voltage to induce the speciifed test voltage at the h.v. primary terminal.

An insulation voltage test between secondary winding and earth at 2 kV a.c. is normally made on the secondary windings.

Type tests to prove that the v.t. is capable of withstanding impulse voltages may also be required, and if it is for outdoor service an overvoltage power frequency test under artificial rain may be specified in addition.

4.10.4 Polarity

Various methods are used at manufacturers' works to prove that the terminal markings are correct. When a site test is necessary to prove the polarity it can be carried out in a similar manner to that described for a current transformer in Section 4.5.5.

4.11 Bibliography

Books

Instrument transformers by B Hague (Pitman, 1936)
Protective current transformers and circuits by P Matthews (Chapman & Hall, 1955)
Protective relays application guide (GEC Measurements, 1975)
Introduction to instrument transformers by B D Jenkins (George Newnes, 1967)
Current transformers - their transient and steady-state performance by A Wright
   (Chapman & Hall, 1968)

Articles

'Capacitive voltage transformers and their operation in conjunction with system
   protection relays' by G A Gertsch (CIGRE Report 318, 1960)
'High accuracy with amplifier-type voltage transformers' by J Lisser (*Electr. Rev.*,
   1976, **198**)
'Current transformer excitation under transient conditions' by D E Marshall and
   P O Langguth (*Trans. Am. IEE*, 1929, **48**)
'The effect of current transformer residual magnetism on balanced-current or
   differential relays' by H T Seeley (*Trans. Am. IEE*, 1943, **62**)
'The design of a capacitor voltage transformer' by E Billig (*Proc. IEE*, 1949, **96**)
'Capacitor voltage transformers' by J G Wellings, J R Mortlock and P Matthews
   (*J. IEE*, 1936, **79**)
'Calculation of errors in three-winding voltage transformers' by T Waterhouse
   (*J. IEE*, 1948, **95**)
'New developments in current transformer design' by G Camilli (*Trans. Am. IEE*,
   1940, **59**)
'New developments in potential-transformer design' by G Camilli (*Trans. Am. IEE*,
   1943, **62**)
'The effects of impulse voltages on transformer windings' by T E Allibone, D B
   McKenzie and F R Perry (*J. IEE*, 1937, **80**)
'Instrument transformers' by A Hobson (*J. IEE*, 1944, **91**)
'Design, construction and testing of voltage transformers' by J H Buchanan (*J.
   IEE*, 1936, **78**)
'Instrument transformers' by J G Wellings and C G Mayo (*J. IEE*, 1930, **68**)
'Current transformers and relays for high-speed differential protection with
   particular reference to offset transient currents' by W K Sonnemann and E C
   Wentz (*Trans. Am. IEE*, 1940, **59**)
'Voltage transformers and current transformers associated with switchgear' by
   W. Gray and A. Wright (*Proc. IEE*, 1953, **100**)

Chapter 5

Fuses

by H.W.Turner and C.Turner

5.1   Introduction

5.1.1   Definition of a fuse

A fuse is a device that, by the fusion of one or more of its specially designed and proportioned components, opens the circuit in which it is inserted and breaks the current when this exceeds a given value for a sufficient time. The fuse comprises all the parts that form the complete device (BS 88).

We see in the definition that the fuse is the complete device, consisting of a fuse-holder (which comprises a fuse base and fuse carrier) and a fuselink.

A fuselink is defined as follows:

5.1.2   Definition of a fuselink

A fuselink is a device comprising a fuse element or several fuse elements connected in parallel enclosed in a cartridge, usually filled with an arc-extinguishing medium and connected to terminations, the fuselink is the part of a fuse which requires replacing after the fuse has operated. (BS 88)

We see from this definition that the 'fuselink' is the part of the fuse popularly but incorrectly referred to as 'a fuse', and that the internal part which melts is called the 'element'.

Other definitions relating to fuses can be found in the British Standards referred to in the bibliography.

5.1.3   Categories of fuse

The powder-filled fuse is the most advanced type of fuselink, with great advantages in limitation of short circuit currents and very high breaking capacity (defined below). 'Miniature fuses' are used in electronic and similar apparatus, and 'semi-enclosed fuses' are the rewirable type still extensively used in consumer units and

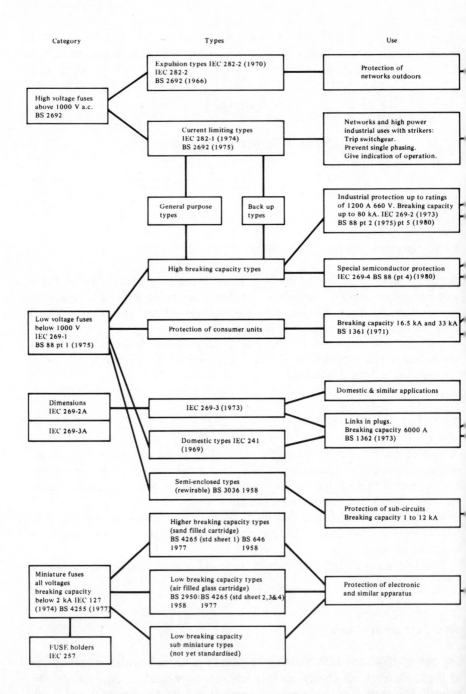

Fig. 5.1.3A   *Summary of main types of fuses available, and their national and international standards*

Advantages and disadvantages

Cheap element replaceable but emits flame and needs good clearance. Not current limiting. Class 1 more sophisticated than class 2.

Limits short circuit energy. Cheaper than circuit breakers. Special types can be oil immersed. Takes time to replace fuses when restoring supply, but exact restoration of characteristics ensured, whereas circuit breakers may need maintenance. Isolating switch required.

Ratings interchangeable for convenience.

Comparatively inexpensive limitation of short circuits. Accurate time current characteristics of different types to suit applications. Quick and easy replacement with cartridge of correct type, but longer than reclosing circuit breakers.

Very fast acting on short circuit. Pt and overvoltage very carefully controlled.

Ratings non-interchangeable for safety reasons when replaceable by a domestic consumer. Special types for supply authority replacement ensure discrimination, giving negligible chance of blowing the company's fuse.

Isolates faulty appliance only. Ratings interchangeable.

High breaking capacity for small size. Cheap, easy to replace. Remains stable when carrying current for long periods. Isolate only the faulty component, ensuring continuity of supply elsewhere. Ratings interchangeable. 13 A for "power", 3 A for "light" type of application, other ratings for special use.

Economical where frequent short circuits occur. High fusing factor, low breaking capacity. Less efficient limitation of short circuits. Variability of characteristics after rewiring. Deterioration in use. Rewiring time consuming and open to abuse.

Cheap. Large range of characteristics from very quick-acting to super time lag. Interchangeable. Assist rapid maintenance by isolating parts of circuits. Avoid: use on high prospective current circuits: replacement by incorrect type.

other applications where only limited breaking capacity is required.

A useful summary of the main types of fuse available and their National and International Standards is given in Fig. 5.13A.

Other types of fuse, such as the liquid-quenched and the expulsion fuse, which employ some mechanical feature to assist the circuit-breaking process, are available. These are used mainly for high voltage overhead-line networks and are described later.

A fuse is a weak link in a circuit, and, as such, possesses one important advantage over mechanical interrupting devices such as circuit-breakers. Because the element in the fuse is of much smaller cross-sectional area than the cable it protects (assuming, of course, that they are of the same material) the element will reach its melting point before the cable. The larger the current the quicker the element melts. If deterioration of the element should occur it operates even faster; a fuse is therefore a device that 'fails safe'.

A comparison of the modern fuse with mechanical interrupters shows that the fuse has one outstanding property not possessed by the latter, namely the ability to interrupt very large currents in a much shorter time – so short in fact that the current will be 'cut off' before it reaches its peak value, which in a 50 Hz system implies operation in less than 5 ms. Serious overheating and electromagnetic forces in the system will thus be avoided. It is not unusual for a fuse to be used as 'back-up' protection for a circuit-breaker that might, by itself, have inadequate breaking capacity. In addition, the sealed cartridge fuse is silent in operation and does not emit flame. Being sealed, it is tamper-proof and with fuse elements of, say, silver, it is non-deteriorating and gives a consistent and reliable performance.

The fuse has two disadvantages. The first is the inconvenience of replacement, because it takes longer to replace a fuse than to reclose a circuit-breaker. This drawback is often exaggerated, especially with modern cartridge fuses, some of which can be replaced quite quickly. It may, in practice, take longer to trace a blown fuse, if it is not fitted with an indicating device, than to replace it; usually far more time is consumed in checking the faulty circuit.

The other disadvantage, which has now lost much of its former significance, is the hitherto poor protection against small overcurrents. A circuit-breaker can be set to trip on as little as 5% overcurrent whilst the semi-enclosed fuse has a fusing factor (that is the ratio of the minimum fusing current to the rated current) of about 1·75. Modern cartridge fuses can, however, be obtained with fusing factors as low as 1·25; they can be supplied with even lower fusing factors, but experience indicates that values lower than 1·25 are not to be recommended if unwanted blowing due to momentary system abnormalities is to be avoided.

The earlier criticism that the fuse could not give the kind of performance obtained from a circuit-breaker fitted with a time-lag relay has lost much of its force because reliable time-lag or 'surge resisting' cartridge fuses of high breaking capacity are now readily obtainable, at least for domestic and industrial use.

As regards capital cost, fuses are cheaper than circuit-breakers of similar rating and breaking capacity, especially for use at high voltages (over 1kV) where the saving in cost is considerable.

In addition, the cost of maintenance is much less in the case of the fuse. Against these savings, however, must be set the cost of replacement fuses after operation on fault.

5.2 Fuse design

Fuses differ considerably in design, dependent upon the voltage, a.c. or d.c., at which they are to operate, and the breaking capacity required (see below). For this reason it is always very important to ensure that a blown fuselink is replaced by the correct type, as otherwise damage to the installation or personal injury may result. The following are the principal types:

5.2.1 Powder-filled cartridge fuse

This is illustrated diagrammatically in Fig. 5.2.1A.

The filler used is almost invariably high purity sand or powdered quartz (both forms of silicon oxide (SiO_2)). The sand must be very pure (some impurities like iron compounds or organic matter are particularly troublesome) as otherwise the fuse is liable to failure.

The arc produced when the fuse 'blows' creates a tube of melted sand around it, which withdraws energy from the arc and extinguishes it. The spray of metal from the arc roots is also entrained in the filler.

Excessive pressures can be reached if the filler is very fine or very coarse; an intermediate grain size provides the optimum cooling.

It is desirable to reduce the volume of metal in an element as far as possible, since this reduces the pressure in the cartridge. When using a filler the heat is conducted away from the element more rapidly than in air and thus a smaller element can melt at a larger minimum fusing current. Thus a thinner wire can be used for a given current rating. If the wire is flattened into a tape, its heat dissipation is even faster, and if it has increased width at sectors along its length, the heat dissipation from the constrictions is faster still.

By such means, the cross-sectional area of the constrictions can be considerably reduced at a given rated current, which makes the fuse operate very much faster on large overcurrents than a uniform element.

The reason for this will be discussed later in this chapter, where it is proved that the pre-arcing I^2t of a fuse element is proportional to the square of its smallest cross-sectional area.

The dissipation of heat is also improved by using a number of thinner elements in parallel instead of one thicker element. This has also two further advantageous effects: first, it has the effect of distributing the arcing more effectively in the filler and reducing the total let-through I^2t; and secondly, it improves the performance on small overcurrent, because, under those conditions, the parallel elements do not usually all clear simultaneously.

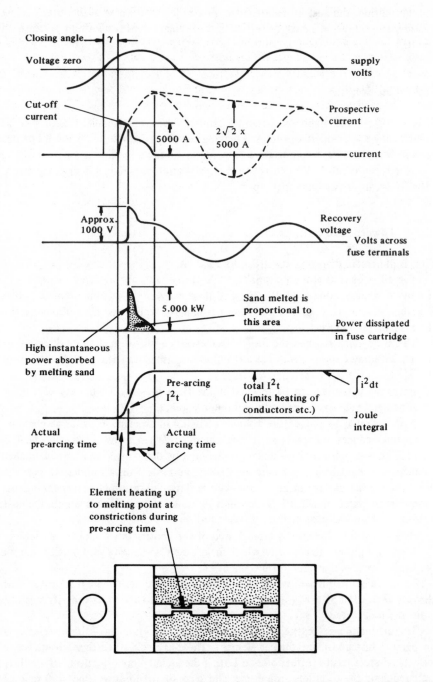

Fig. 5.2.1A   *Diagrammatic representation of a sand-filled cartridge fuse with typical oscillo-grams for the operation on short circuit (approximately 100A rating)*

The melting time of a fuse element may be further adjusted by means of special techniques of time delay. One of these is the M-effect, which consists of an addition of low melting-point alloy to the surface of the element, where it will dissolve the element material when it melts. This has the effect of opening the element at the point where the dissolution takes place at a chosen point along the length of the element. Since this process takes a longer time to complete than the melting of the unmodified element of smaller cross-section (but the same minimum fusing current) the use of the M-effect can produce a time delay in the small to medium over-current region, and thus prevent nuisance blowing of fuses by surges of current occurring in normal service.

A more extended time delay may be obtained by employing a large insert of fusible metal in the element. This acts as a 'heat sink' because of its large thermal capacity. The larger the volume of the insert, the longer the time taken to melt it and consequently the longer the time delay.

A further advantage of both the M-effect and the fusible insert methods is that they reduce the temperature at which the element opens the circuit, and thus indirectly reduce the temperature of the 'blown' cartridge immediately after clearing a fault at small overcurrent.

On high overcurrents, the fuse will melt at the most constricted points and, by designing these carefully and manufacturing them to high precision, the pre-arcing $I^2 t$ can be accurately controlled.

Note that it is possible to obtain a fuse with a slow blowing action at small overload conditions which can absorb normal surges of current but which operates extremely fast on high current short circuits. This is because the fuse element blows in a different place depending on the magnitude of the current.

Examples of fuse elements having these features are shown in diagrammatic form in Fig. 5.2.1B.

By calculated adjustment of all these parameters, the fuse designer is enabled to use his skill to shape the time/current characteristic of the fuse to suit its application, and to design as economic a fuse link as possible within the limits of breaking capacity required. The possibilities of alternative constructions also enable him to keep the cold resistance of the fuselink to a minimum and thus to minimise the power loss of the fuselink when running at rated current. This reduces waste of energy and prevents overheating of equipment.

5.2.1.1 High-voltage powder-filled fuses: The high-voltage (above 1 kV rating) fuselink uses the same basic principles of construction as the low voltage (below 1 kV), but in a manner refined to produce the special characteristics and additional features needed in high voltage applications.

Since the length of the fuse element, and the number of constrictions in it must increase roughly proportionally to its voltage rating, many designs of high-voltage fuselink would become unmanageably long if the elements were connected straight down the barrel, as in low-voltage fuselinks. For this reason they are fre-

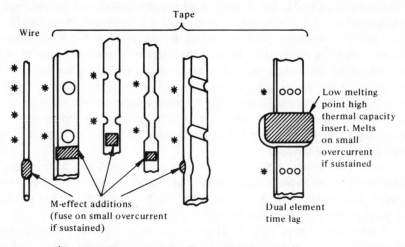

Fig. 5.2.1B   *Techniques of time delay on a selection of types of fuse element*

quently wound in the form of a helix on a star core in the barrel, which requires great care and precision in manufacture, and careful design to ensure that the arc from one turn of a helically wound element does not merge with arcs from the next turn on the helix of the same element or of another nearby, which could lead to destruction of the cartridge by sustained arcing between its end-caps. Manufacturers of high-voltage fuselinks consequently employ many more methods of non-destructive testing of their products during production, and this makes the high-voltage cartridge fuselink a particularly safe and reliable product, when used within its limits of rating and breaking capacity.

5.2.2 Miniature fuselink

This is the small cartridge fuselink, usually 5mm diameter and 20mm long (or 6·3mm x 32mm) used in apparatus, electronic equipment, radio and t.v. sets, etc. They come in two main categories: filled and unfilled.

The powder-filled types are of higher breaking capacity, and are really miniature versions of the powder-filled cartridge fuse described in Section 5.2.1.

The unfilled types, however, are usually glass cartridges with the element supported in the air inside the cartridge. These are consequently of very low breaking capacity (only 35 A in some cases) and should thus only be placed in locations where the prospective short-circuit current cannot exceed 35 A. Of course, no fuse should be placed in a position where the fault conditions can exceed its breaking capacity, but with these very small fuses, especial care must be taken.

However, within these limits, the miniature fuses present a remarkably wide range of protective characteristics. Within the glass cartridge it is possible to enclose a huge variety of element shapes, time delay springs, thermal sinks, etc. A time-lag (surge proof) type with the same rated current (I_n) would typically take 10 times longer to blow at $4I_n$ than a quick acting type. (For further detail see BS 4265). This is very useful in avoiding nuisance blowing by inrush currents, whilst still retaining the same small overcurrent protection.

5.2.3   Semi-enclosed fuse

The semi-enclosed or rewirable fuse (see Fig. 5.2.3A) consists of a base, a carrier, the fuse element and some form of protection, such as an arc resistant tube, to limit the emission of flame. The element is usually of an easily procurable material such as tinned copper. The melting point of copper is 1083°C but it cannot be run for any length of time at temperatures approaching the melting point, and rapid oxidation occurs at temperatures above 250°C, even if the wire is tinned. Hence the semi-enclosed fuse requires a relatively large overcurrent to blow it. The fusing factor is about 1·75. The performance depends to some extent on how the fuse is wired (the wire may or may not touch the sides of the tube) and on the state of the tube.

Care should be taken to ensure that the wire is not kinked or otherwise damaged in rewiring and that the correct size of fusewire is used.

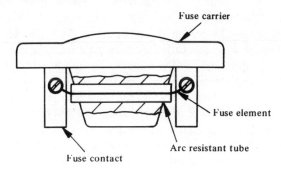

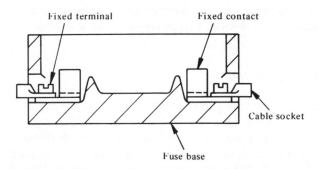

Fig. 5.2.3A   *Semi-enclosed fuse*

(The $I^2 t$ let-through is proportional to the fourth power of the diameter of the fusewire).

5.2.4 Expulsion fuse

The expulsion fuse consists (see Fig. 5.1.4A) of a tube of insulating material into which the fuse element is inserted, in some cases one end of the tube being closed whereas in others both ends are open. When the element melts and arcing takes place, the resultant gas pressure causes the arc to be blown out of the ends of the tube and thus be extinguished. In certain designs this process is assisted by lining the interior of the tube with a material such as boric acid which produces gas when heated by the arc. In order to accelerate the process of arc extinction, the element is held under spring tension and when the element melts the spring rapidly separates the two sections.

Criticism has been made of the poor performance of the expulsion fuse when clearing low overcurrents. This is due to the small pressure generated under such circumstances but this has been overcome by using a small inner tube, usually of fibre, to enclose the element within the main tube.

The operation of the expulsion fuse is violent, especially with large fault currents, and it is usually pole mounted out-of-doors, increased phase spacing being employed to avoid flashovers due to the nature of its operation. The walls of the tube may be contaminated by carbon and other arc products after blowing, and in order to prevent leakage along this path the tube is arranged to be isolated from the circuit contacts after operation. This is achieved by utilising the spring normally holding the element under tension effectively to shorten the length of the fuse carrier when released. This allows the carrier tube to disengage from the upper contact and to fall, under the influence of gravity, about the lower hinged contact.

The expulsion fuse is not manufactured for the lower voltages such as 415 V but is essentially a high-voltage fuse for use on systems up to 32 kV. It is used almost exclusively for the protection of overhead-line networks and for this purpose both fast and slow blowing elements are available. A number of ingenious automatic reclosing units have been designed using expulsion fuses, so arranged that if one blows it is automatically replaced after an interval of a few seconds.

5.2.5 Other fuse developments

Modern fuselinks are available in greater range than ever before. Special fuses for semiconductor protection have very fast operation, and carefully controlled overvoltages. Motor circuit protection fuses have characteristics specially designed for short circuit protection without spurious operation on sustained starting currents, in compact dimensions and with special characteristics designed for discrimination with motor starters.

Special back-up fuses are also available (see Section 5.6.2). Some older developments are still in use, for example, the liquid-quenched fuse. This is a high-voltage fuse, and like the expulsion fuse, utilises spring tension to assist arc extinction and provide an adequate physical break in the circuit to withstand the service voltage after operation. It has a toughened glass tube with metal end caps. To the upper cap is secured the short silver fusewire. This silver element has a high tensile strain

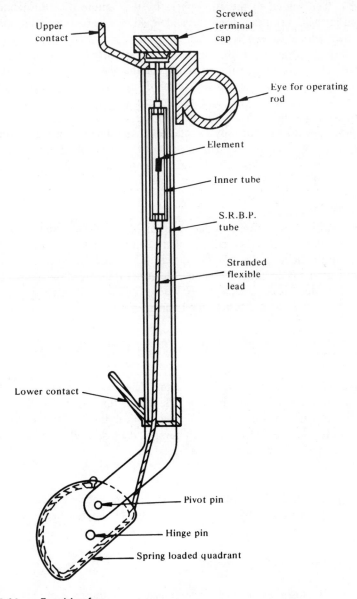

Fig. 5.2.4A   *Expulsion fuse*

wire in parallel, to withstand the tension of the powerful spring securing the bottom contact of the element to the lower end cap.

The body of the fuse is filled with a non-inflammable insulating liquid, such as carbon tetrachloride, to a level just below the element. When the element melts, the bottom contact is retracted downwards by the spring and a liquid director forces a stream of liquid into the arc path. The vapour pressure deionises the arc path and is then vented to the atmosphere by the rupture of a thin aluminium diaphragm in the top end cap. The wires and liquid may be replaced after operation and the fuse returned to service.

The breaking capacity of the liquid fuse is restricted and trouble is often experienced in service due to the shattering of the glass tube on operation. It is therefore being gradually replaced on overhead line networks, particularly in the pull down fuse isolator version and as a means of protection of outdoor type voltage transformers up to 66 kV, by fuses of better breaking capacity.

New developments yet not fully introduced at the time of writing are the dual-mode expulsion fuse and the permanent power fuse. The dual mode expulsion fuse has been designed by the Electricity Council Research Centre and employs a saturating transformer to produce a shape of time/current characteristic which gives closer discrimination (see Section 5.3.2.) with an i.d.m.t. relay, permitting lower settings in Area Board use.

The permanent power fuse is a Japanese self-healing device using a column of sodium as a fuse element. This is contained in a ceramic capillary attached to an arc chamber, and the liquid sodium is forced to flow back into this space when the arc extinguishes after the circuit has cleared. The device is intended to back-up circuit-breakers of limited breaking capacity. New ideas still to be developed include the vacuum fuse and the oil-filled fuse (not oil immersed).

5.3   Mechanism of fuse operation

All fuses operate in the same way. A conductor of limited cross-section is heated by current passing through it until it melts. This takes time, represented in a time/current characteristic for the fuse. On melting, a break is caused in the element, at which an electric arc is established, which burns in the fuse until the current returns to zero. Thus there are two stages in fuse operation:

(*a*)   the pre-arcing time
(*b*)   the arcing time.

Theory of pre-arcing is dealt with under 'time/current characteristics' in Section 5.5. The arcing behaviour is different for small, large and intermediate overcurrents, as explained below.

5.3.1   Operation on small overcurrents

When a fuse is blown by a current not much larger than the minimum fusing current so that the melting time is measured in minutes, the temperature distribution along the element is not uniform, the hottest point being near the centre. It is at this point that melting first occurs, giving rise to a short arc, and because the arcing voltage is then about 20 V, the effect in reducing the current is inappreciable in circuits at 240 V or more. An arc has a negative volt-ampere characteristic, which, balanced against the positive voltampere characteristic of the circuit resistance tends to produce stable sustained arcs at small overcurrent level. These will continue to burn until the arc has lengthened sufficiently, and developed sufficient pressure within the lumen of molten sand in order to raise the arc voltage enough to give sufficient back e.m.f. to exceed the circuit voltage and cause extinction. Fuses of higher voltage rating thus need longer elements or more constrictions than fuses of lower voltage rating.

It is unwise to connect fuses in series to obtain a higher voltage rating except perhaps for back-up protection where they will be subjected only to large fault currents. If they are subjected to a small sustained overcurrent only one may melt because it is unlikely that they will be exactly matched. The fuse that operates will do so at the full circuit voltage and may fail. Fuses may, however, be connected in parallel, provided that each takes its proper share of the load (otherwise premature blowing will take place).

5.3.2   Operation on large overcurrents

When a fuse is subjected to a very large overcurrent, the element is heated so rapidly that there is no time for heat loss to the surroundings; there is then a uniform temperature along those parts of the element of uniform cross-section, which all reach their melting temperature simultaneously. A wire thus becomes a liquid cylinder.

Now it is a well-known physical phenomenon that a column of liquid is unstable and breaks up into a series of droplets. Thus in the case of the cartridge fuse the element having been replaced by a line of globules, the current is constrained to pass through them because the surrounding filler prevents their being by-passed. In consequence the voltage drop at the beginning of arcing is considerable and causes rapid suppression of the current. The number of globules per inch is about 30, and as the voltage drop in a short arc is about 20 V the voltage across the element is about 600 V per inch. It is not unusual for a 2 inch-long fuse link to develop a voltage drop of 1200 V at the start of arcing, provided of course, that there is sufficient inductance in the circuit, which is usually the case. The maximum voltage rise across a fuse depends on the length and design of the element, and does not increase significantly if considerable extra inductance is introduced into the circuit.

Because of the initial rapid rise of voltage, a shorter element is necessary to interrupt a large overcurrent than would be required to interrupt a small one. It is, in fact, sometimes found, that a fuse operates satisfactorily with a very large prospective current, but fails to interrupt a very small one. Such a fuse is called a 'back-up fuse' and is used in conjunction with an overcurrent circuit breaker or overcurrent trip, which takes over all small overcurrent isolation.

This term was once used for any fuse used to 'back-up' a switching device, i.e. to open the circuit at prospective currents above the breaking capacity of that device. The term 'back-up fuse' is now reserved specifically for fuses which perform this function only and which may be incapable of satisfactorily isolating small overcurrents below their minimum operating current. If allowed to blow below its minimum operating current at full rated voltage, such a fuse may fail disastrously, generating persistent arcing, piercing its end caps or bursting its cartridge. A backup fuse should therefore never be used in a circuit where such an overcurrent trip is not fitted or where it can become inoperative. In such cases, use a general purpose fuse (one which is capable of breaking all currents from its minimum fusing current up to its breaking capacity).

5.3.3   Operation on intermediate overcurrents

There is another important range of current values, intermediate between the very small and very large values but large enough for globules and consequently multiple arcs to form, to which special attention is paid by testing authorities. This condition, which can be more onerous than that occurring with much larger overcurrents, arises because it is usual to test fuses at a prescribed value of time constant or power factor, since this corresponds closely with practical conditions. Before considering why this should be, it is necessary to understand two expressions much used in fuse terminology, namely 'prospective current' and 'cut-off current'.

All practical circuits contain resistance and inductance. Hence, even in a d.c. circuit, the current cannot rise instantly to its E/R value, but rises exponentially according to the well-known expression $i = E(1 - e^{-Rt/L})/R$. The current-time relation for a d.c. and for an a.c. circuit is shown in Fig. 5.3.3A. Under fault conditions the peak value of the current may be very large — perhaps tens of kiloamperes — and if the continuous rating of the fuse is a few amperes, or tens of amperes, such a large current will cause fusion in the order of one millisecond. The fuse will operate before the current reaches its theoretical maximum and the fuse is then said to 'cut off' the current. The current i_c in Fig. 5.3.3A is termed the cut-off current. The value to which the current would rise if the fuse were replaced by a link of zero impedance, is termed the 'prospective current'. It is a function only of the circuit, and in the case of a.c. circuits is conveniently expressed in r.m.s. amperes. It is used in designating the *breaking capacity* of a fuse.

Note carefully that prospective current is stated as an r.m.s symmetrical value, whereas cut-off current is quoted as an instantaneous peak value of current.

The cut-off current i_c is important because it corresponds to an amount of inductive energy equal to $\frac{1}{2}Li_c^2$, most of which is liberated in the fuse and usually represents the bulk of the arc energy. If the circuit inductance were constant the inductive energy would increase with the cut-off current (and hence with the

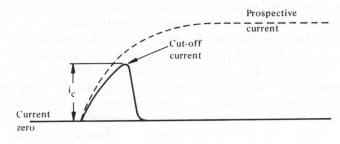

D.C. circuit

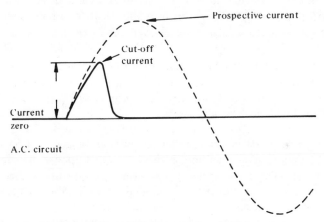

A.C. circuit

Fig. 5.3.3A   *Current-time relationships for a.c. and d.c. circuits*

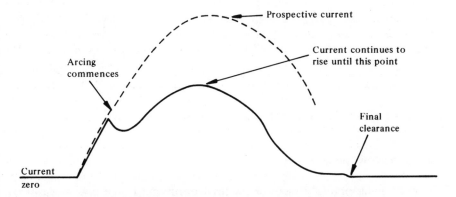

Fig. 5.3.3B   *Current-time relationship at voltages close to or above voltage rating*

prospective current), but because it is usual to test fuses in a circuit of fixed time constant (or power factor in an a.c. circuit) the circuit inductance is progressively reduced as the current is increased. The cut-off current, however, does not increase at the same rate as the prospective current. Hence the inductive energy at first increases with the prospective current until cut-off occurs and then, later, decreases. The peak energy value can represent a more onerous condition for the fuse than a test at a much larger prospective current with its lower arc energy value – a fact that was proved experimentally when a fuse that interrupted satisfactorily a prospective current of 33 000A shattered when the current was reduced to 3000 A.

The above reasoning applies only to fuses well within their voltage rating, where the current falls rapidly as soon an arcing commences. These are called current-limiting fuses.

In the case of a fuse close to or above its voltage rating (particularly if it contains a fuse element with very short necks), the current may continue to rise after arcing has commenced, as in Fig. 5.3.3B. This may also occur for a non-current-limiting fuse. In the case of such a fuse, a higher value of current may represent a more severe condition. This is one reason why Test No. 1, e.g. of BS 88 or BS 2692 (at maximum prospective current), is always necessary.

5.3.4   Operation on pulsed loading

Fuses which are very fast in clearing short circuits may appear to operate prematurely under pulsed loading conditions such as those met, for example, in thyristor controlled circuits. The r.m.s. value of the current may be below the minimum fusing current of the fuse, but if the I^2t content of each pulse is large enough, a single pulse may be sufficient to blow the fuse in the short time it is on.

This is particularly true of a fuse for protection of semiconductor devices or any other fuse with very short necks in the element, since the time/current characteristic is extremely steep in the short-time region with these types.

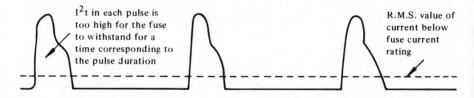

I^2t in each pulse is too high for the fuse to withstand for a time corresponding to the pulse duration

R.M.S. value of current below fuse current rating

Fig. 5.3.4A   *Example of the need to use a higher current rating in certain types of repetitive pulse load*

5.3.5   Fulgurite (roping)

These are terms normally used for the residues of sand in the fuse which were melted by the arc during clearance. These residues give much evidence of the pro-

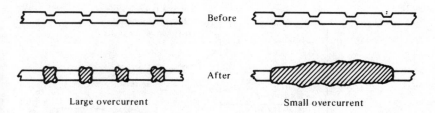

Before

After

Large overcurrent   Small overcurrent

Fig. 5.3.5A   *Fulgurite structures - fuses without M-effect (with M-effect, the fuse will operate at the M effect on small overcurrent)*

cesses which caused the fuse to blow. For example, the arc energy in the fuse may be calculated by weighing the fulgurite. If the weight of the fulgurite is w, then the arc energy was

$$E = 2100 \ w \ \text{Joules} \ (w \text{ in grams})$$

It is also possible to tell whether the fuse operated on a small or a large overcurrent by breaking open the blown fuse and studying the fulgurite. (see Fig. 5.3.5A)

5.3.6   Typical oscillograms

Typical oscillograms of operation of fuses under small overcurrent and large overcurrent conditions are shown in Fig. 5.3.6A.

5.4   Peak arc voltage

It was a characteristic of certain early types of filled cartridge fuse that the voltage rise when clearing large fault currents was considerable, most fuse specifications now prescribe a limit to this voltage which, if exceeded, constitutes a disqualification.

A simple wire fuse breaks up into globules along its length, with an arc between each globule and the next, thus producing a chain of arcs, which add up to produce a voltage proportional to the length of the element consumed and which may rise to several kilovolts.

Modern fuses employ elements with constrictions (see Fig. 5.4A for examples). This results effectually in a number of short fuse elements in series, each so short that the overvoltage is limited. Problems do not arise until the fuse is operated very close to its breaking capacity and above its rated voltage, where the excessive burn-back of the element can produce conditions leading to very high voltages, as the wider parts of the element break up into molten globules. This is seen to be a further reason why fuses should never be used in a circuit above their rated voltage.

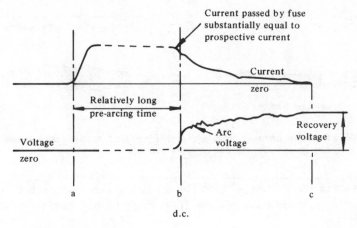

a — Initiation of current
b — Initiation of arcing
c — Final clearance

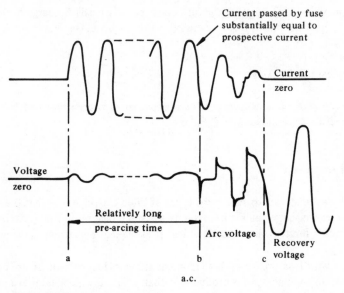

(a) Small overcurrent

Fig. 5.3.6A(a)   *Typical oscillograms of fuse operation*

Peak arc voltage is dependent upon the number of constrictions in an element, because of the arcs in series. This gives a minimum value of peak arc voltage irrespective of the applied voltage up to a certain point. When this point is exceeded, the extra applied voltage can force the arcing to persist and produce burn-back and

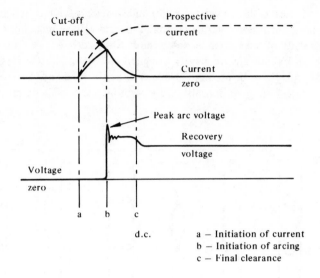

d.c.

a — Initiation of current
b — Initiation of arcing
c — Final clearance

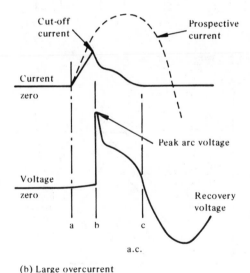

(b) Large overcurrent

Fig. 5.3.6A(b) *Typical oscillograms of fuse operation*

other effects which may increase with each incremental voltage, thus causing a larger peak arc voltage.

This is illustrated in Fig. 5.4B

It is therefore clear that a fuse of higher voltage rating should not be used to replace a blown fuse of lower voltage rating unless due cognisance is taken of the fact that its peak arc voltage will be greater. Peak arc voltage must not exceed the dielectric withstand of the system in which the fuse is placed.

Fuses for 11 kV use are frequently designed to produce low arc voltages, in order that they may also be used on 6·6 kV systems. It should not be assumed that this is the case without first consulting the manufacturer or his literature on this point.

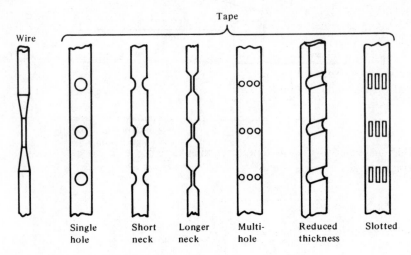

Fig. 5.4A   *Typical fuse elements with constrictions*

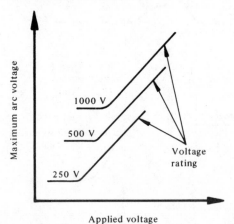

Fig. 5.4B   *Arc voltage characteristic*

5.5   Time/current characteristic and factors affecting it

When a conductor of resistance R Ω is being heated by the passage of current i through it for a time dt, the quantity of heat liberated in the conductor is $i^2 R dt$. In other words, $i^2 dt$ Joules are liberated for every ohm of conductor. If the current is varying over a period then $\int i^2 dt$ Joules will be liberated in the conductor for every ohm of resistance.

This integral is called the 'Joule integral' and is usually abbreviated to $I^2 t$. It is a most convenient way of estimating the heating effect on a protected circuit due to a very short pulse of heavy current.

If a fuselink is blown on a very high prospective current, there is no time for the heat to be lost into the surroundings, and it is all used in heating the element to its melting point at its narrowest constriction. In this short time region, therefore, the $I^2 t$ required to melt the element is constant and independent of current. This is called the pre-arcing $I^2 t$.

Consider the section of a fuse element shown in Fig. 5.5.A, of length l and cross-sectional area A, carrying a current i.

The heat produced in time dt is

$$i^2 R dt = \frac{i^2 \rho_0 (1 + \alpha\theta)l}{A} dt$$

This quantity of heat will raise the temperature by $\delta\theta$ if no heat is lost to the surroundings.

$$\frac{i^2 \rho_0 (1 + \alpha\theta)l}{A} dt = m\sigma\delta\theta$$

but $m = DAl$ (where D = density)

$$\therefore i^2 dt = A^2 \frac{D\sigma}{\rho_0 \alpha} \frac{d\theta}{(\theta + {}^1/\alpha)}$$

integrating both sides gives:

$$i^2 dt = A^2 \frac{D\sigma}{\rho_0 \alpha} \cdot \ln \left[\frac{(\theta_2 + {}^1/\alpha)}{(\theta_1 + {}^1/\alpha)} \right] \tag{5.5a}$$

This means that if θ_2 = melting point of the metal of the element and $\theta_1 = 20°C$, then, if the fuse begins its arcing time immediately the element first melts: pre-arcing $\int i^2 dt = K A^2$ (where K is a constant for the metal, directly calculable from known values.)
i.e. pre-arcing $I^2 t$ is proportional to the square of the cross-sectional area of the section melted.

Examples are given in the following table for typical metals used as fuse elements.

Metal	Pre-arcing $I^2 t$	
Silver	6.6×10^4 A^2 amp^2 sec	A = cross-sectional area of conductor at narrowest
Copper	9×10^4 A^2 amp^2 sec	point (in mm^2)

Silver is a very much used metal as a fuse element material, due to its non-deteriorating low oxidation properties. It also gives a very good M-effect with tin and its alloys (see Section 5.5.2).

At the very short-time end of the characteristic and pre-arcing time of the fuse-link is inversely proportional to the square of the prospective current, that is, if the time is plotted as 'virtual time'.

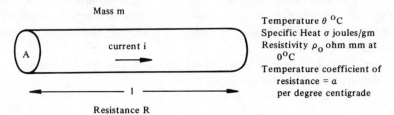

Fig. 5.5A   *Section of fuse element heated by current i*

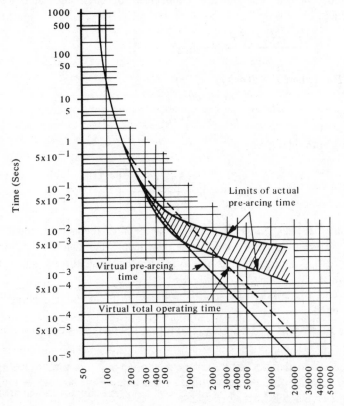

Fig. 5.5B   *Virtual time curves*

In preparing current-time characteristics it is necessary to choose a convenient basis of comparison so that the curves will show at a glance if discrimination is likely to be achieved. In this respect a curve in which prospective current is plotted against time is not of much assistance especially at times which are very short because, the prospective current is a function of the circuit, and it is always a smaller current that flows through the fuse. Fuses of the same design and different ratings tend to have the same melting time in a circuit of infinite prospective current. If the impedance of the circuit is negligible the current through the fuse will be E/R where R is the resistance of the fuse. If the rating of the fuse be increased by using two elements in parallel the resistance will be reduced to $R/2$ and the total current will be increased to $2E/R$. In both instances the fuses would melt in the same time; yet clearly if the two were in series the smaller would melt before the larger. The corresponding melting, or arcing, time is also relatively meaningless because the shape of the current wave is not always the same. In a d.c. circuit the rise of current depends on the time constant. In an a.c. circuit the current may start as a major, a minor, or a symmetrical loop; and in both d.c. and a.c. circuits the current wave during arcing follows no regular pattern. Because of these sources of variation the concept of 'virtual time' was introduced.

It has been shown above that when a fuse element melts rapidly so that there is no heat loss to the surroundings, the pre-arcing integral $\int i^2 dt$ (termed $I^2 t$) is sensibly constant. This integral is easy to determine for a given fuse because it can be readily computed from a single oscillogram. The value is independent of the shape of the current wave and it is convenient to assume a rectangular wave form, such as would be achieved in an inductance-free d.c. circuit. Since $I^2 t$ is constant it then follows that t is inversely proportional to I^2. This is the basis of 'virtual time' which can be defined as 'the time for which a steady current equal to the prospective current would have to flow in a fuse to produce the same quantity of energy as would be produced if the actual current during the period of operation considered flowed in the fuse for the actual period'.

Virtual time t_v is thus

$$\int \frac{i^2 dt}{I^2_p}$$

where I_p is the prospective current that is it is the '$I^2 t$' divided by the square of the prospective current. The usefulness of virtual time is shown in Fig. 5.5B which represents a typical fuse. It will be seen that with times less than about 5×10^{-2} s there is a spread in the normal current-time curve (shown shaded) and with the larger currents there is considerable variation in the time, the ratio of the largest to the smallest being about 5. There is, however, no spread in the curves of virtual time, and discrimination will be achieved between any two fuses provided that the curve of virtual total operating time of the minor fuse lies below the curve of virtual pre-arcing time of the major fuse.

For checking discrimination between fuses at the short-time end of the characteristic, it is convenient to use $I^2 t$ characteristics (see Section 5.6.1).

These are much more convenient in use at high prospective currents and avoid the confusion sometimes caused by the artificial conception of 'virtual time'. They also have the virtue of being able to be directly related to the short-circuit withstand of the cables or equipment being protected.

$I^2 t$ characteristics are therefore extremely useful to the protection engineer who requires a rapid assessment of the degree of protection against short circuits in a fuse protected network.

The total operating time is greater than the time shown on the pre-arcing time/ current characteristic, because the fuse element continues to arc between the melted ends until the current is reduced to zero. Hence:

total operating time = pre-arcing time + arcing time.

The *pre-arcing time* is the time between the commencement of a current large enough to cause melting of the fuse element and the instant when arcing is initiated. Total operating times cannot be shown with accuracy since the arcing time varies with the power factor and transient characteristics of the circuit, the supply voltage, the electrical angle at which arcing commences and a large number of other variables. When operated within the voltage limits prescribed by the manufacturer, the arcing time is only significant for large overcurrents, where there are short operating times.

The current usually plotted on the time-current characteristics is the *prospective current*, i.e. the current which would flow in the test circuit if the fuse were replaced by a link of negligible impedance. The time for short-circuit operation is usually the *virtual time*, because of the variation of actual time with the point on the voltage wave and other variables. On small overcurrents, however, where the pre-arcing time is long and the arcing time negligible by comparison, the times shown can be taken as the total operating times at the currents shown.

5.5.1 Definitions related to the operation of fuses at the small overcurrent region of the time/ current characteristic and the assignment of current rating

The *minimum fusing current* is the minimum current at which a fuse element will melt, that is the asymptotic value of the current shown by the time-current characteristic.

For the classification of a fuse, a *conventional current rating* is assigned to it, measured under reproducible standard conditions. In applications, the fuselink may be enclosed and subjected to unusual duty, in which case a *service rating* must be used with the advice of the manufacturer.

Current rating: A current, less than the minimum fusing current, stated by the manufacturer as the current that the fuselink will carry continuously without deterioration.

The rating is therefore lower than the minimum fusing current by a factor called the *fusing factor*:

$$\text{fusing factor} = \frac{\text{minimum fusing current}}{\text{rating}}$$

5.6   Discrimination

5.6.1   Discrimination between fuselinks

In domestic, and in many industrial, installations, it is usual for the supply authority to provide the main fuses, and consumers' branch circuits are protected by fuses of smaller rating. In the event of a fault in a branch circuit the branch-circuit fuse should blow but not the supply authority's fuse, that is to say there should be discrimination. It is usual to call the fuses the major fuse and the minor fuse, respectively. If there were no arcing, and the fuses were of the same design, the minor fuse could be 90% of the rating of the major fuse and there would still be perfect discrimination. In practice, however, it is possible for a fuse to pass more $I^2 t$ during arcing than is passed during melting (termed more correctly, the pre-arcing period), especially with large overcurrents in inductive circuits. If the major fuse is to remain intact its pre-arcing $I^2 t$ must not be exceeded: hence to achieve discrimination the pre-arcing plus the arcing $I^2 t$ of the minor fuse must not exceed, and preferably should be less than, the pre-arcing $I^2 t$ of the major fuse. This usually means that the rating of the major should be not less than twice that of the minor fuse.

For convenience in ensuring discrimination between fuses, manufacturers publish $I^2 t$ characteristics similar to those shown in Fig. 5.6.1A. In these curves the minimum pre-arcing $I^2 t$ is measured for every fuselink at high prospective current, and the maximum total let-through $I^2 t$, pre-arcing and arcing, will often occur at the condition of maximum arc energy. (This is the intermediate level of current mentioned in Section 5.3.3 at which the arcing conditions are most severe, and corresponds to test No. 2, described in Section 5.7.1.1).

To select a minor fuselink which will discriminate with a major fuselink under all conditions, we can use these curves as shown in the following example:

Let a 160A fuselink be the major fuselink in a system. It can be seen from the curves (Fig. 5.6.1A) that the minimum pre-arcing $I^2 t$ of this fuselink is 8×10^4 $A^2 s$. In the example, this is seen to be equal to the let-through $I^2 t$ of a 100 A fuselink at 415 V. Theoretically this would be just too large a current rating for the minor fuse, because the element of the major fuse would *just* melt with the maximum let-through of the minor fuse. In practice, discrimination would probably not be lost, because the condition of maximum arc energy is very unlikely. To be sure that no deterioration of the major fuse can take place, the 2:1 ratio is to be pre-

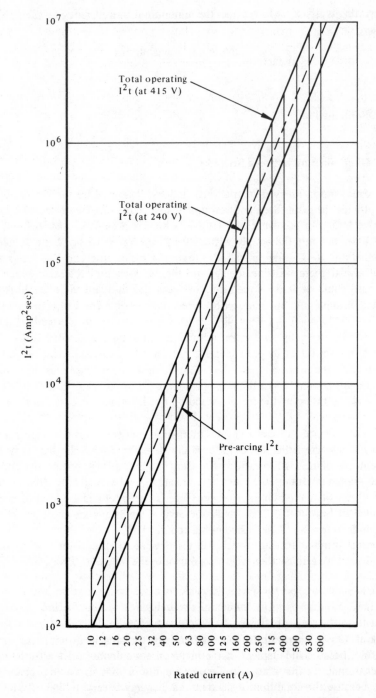

Fig. 5.6.1A   *Typical I²t characteristics*

ferred. We see that for the 80 A fuselink the I^2t let-through is only 4.5×10^4 A^{2}s, giving such a wide margin that the major fuse cannot suffer any permanent effect.

It is evident from the foregoing that, if the rating of the major fuse is not too close to that of the minor, discrimination will be assured, provided that the fuses are of the same design. If the supply authority fits cartridge fuses at the incoming feeder and the user installs semi-enclosed fuses in the branch circuits, a larger ratio than 2 may be necessary to ensure that the major fuse will not blow in the event of a fault in the branch circuit.

Circumstances can occur in which the major fuse is at approximately its working temperature when a fault occurs in a sub-circuit containing an unloaded minor fuse. Obviously the pre-arcing I^2t of a hot fuse is less than that of a cold one, but if the minimum ratio of 2 is maintained the major fuse would not normally be more than 50% loaded and the corresponding reduction in I^2t would be insignificant. Tests have shown that even if a cartridge fuse is preheated for a considerable time by a current not sufficient to melt the element, the reduction in I^2t is usually small, in the context of discrimination.

The reduction in I^2t is due to the fact that the constriction in the fuselink is no longer at about 20°C but heated to a higher temperature θ_1. Research has proved that the reduced value of I^2t can be calculated from eqn. 5.5a by inserting the higher value of θ_1.

5.6.2 Discrimination between h.v. and l.v. fuses and circuit-breaking devices

The use of standardised time/current characteristic paper facilitates comparison of operation curves of the different devices in a system to check discrimination and coordination of protection.

This is illustrated in Fig. 5.6.2A, where the possibilities of discrimination of the l.v. side of a transformer with the h.v. side is compared for all fuse protection, and an alternative circuit-breaker protection using an i.d.m.t. set at a plug setting of 75% and time multiple of 0.1.

It is seen that the use of the logarithmic paper not only makes it possible to compare the discrimination of fuses and circuit breakers, characteristics plotted at one voltage, but also, by shifting the abscissa to the right or to the left by an appropriate amount, a direct comparison can be made of characteristics available at different voltages on the network, or characteristics plotted on an MVA base, or as a multiple of rated current (as for the i.d.m.t. characteristic).

Time current characteristic axes printed on transparent paper are particularly useful for this type of comparison, and there are British Standard dimensions for this paper (see BS 88). More discussion of discrimination on rural overhead line circuits appears in Chapter 15.

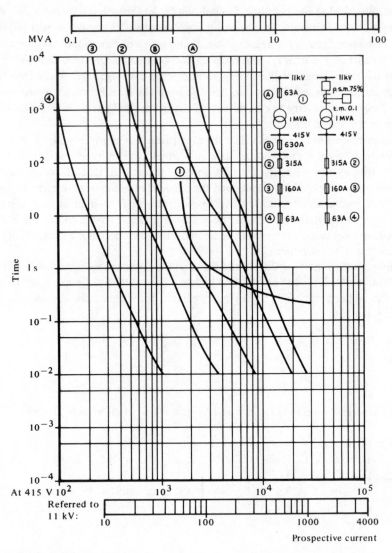

Fig. 5.6.2A *Discrimination between H.V. and L.V. in two alternative circuits*

5.7   Testing of fuses

5.7.1   Fuse testing on a.c.

5.7.1.1 Breaking capacity: In Section 5.3 it was explained that the performance of a fuse was of a different nature at large, intermediate or small prospective currents.

It is therefore insufficient to test a fuse for breaking capacity simply at the highest current it may have to break. Fuse standards therefore require that the fuse be tested for breaking capacity at at least 3 levels of current. (See BS. 2692 : 1975 and BS. 88 : 1975.)

Test 1 is at the maximum prospective current. Current-limiting fuses are capable of breaking extremely high prospective currents because by their current limiting action they prevent the current from reaching the peak of the prospective current. In fact, the cut-off current only increases proportionally to the cube root of the prospective current.

The point on the voltage wave is very important in testing fuses. For example, (in BS. 2692 Pt. 1, 1975 and BS. 88, Pt. 1, 1975) the conditions of the breaking capacity test are specified not only in terms of the current, voltage and power factor at which the test must be made, but also the instant of initiation of arcing within the fuse after the element has melted after voltage zero as follows:

> For one test arcing must commence between 40° and 65° (this is the condition represented in Fig. 5.7.1.1A by the curve a_1, b_1, c_1). This condition is considered to correspond to the maximum *thermal* stress on the fuselink.

> For two further tests, arcing must commence between 65° and 90° (this is the condition represented in Fig. 5.7.1.1A by the curve a_2, b_2, c_2). This condition is considered to correspond to the maximum *electromagnetic* stress on the fuselink.

If the fuse is capable of breaking its maximum prospective current under these conditions, it should be capable of breaking it under any other breaking angle.

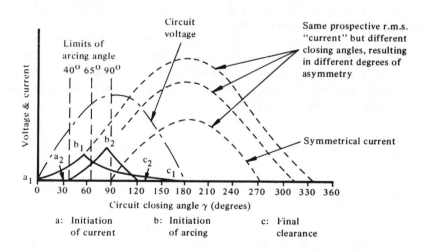

Fig. 5.7.1.1A *Fuses blowing on high current, low power factor within prescribed limits for Breaking Capacity Test No. 1 at maximum breaking capacity*

Test 2 is at the maximum arc energy condition for a current-limiting fuselink. It is made at a current, chosen such that it produces a cut-off current approximately equal to the r.m.s. value of the prospective current, when the circuit is closed at an angle of between 0° and 20° after voltage zero. The condition of maximum arc energy usually corresponds to an inductive current equal to 3 to 4 times the current corresponding to a pre-arcing time of 0·01 s.

Tests 3, 4 and 5 are made in order to verify that the fuselinks will not fail when breaking a small overcurrent. It has been explained in Section 5.3, that fuses have special difficulties in this region, and may be unable to extinguish a low current arc, resulting in overheating, burning through the end caps, or even explosion. Tests 3, 4 and 5 ensure that this does not happen, under the specified conditions.

In all tests, 1-5, it is essential that, after the fuse has interrupted the circuit, it can withstand the recovery voltage which appears at its terminals, and should not restrike or produce dangerous leakage currents.

For this reason the recovery voltage is left on for a specified period after tests (as long as 5 min if the fuselink contains any organic materials), and the insulation is tested within 3 min of completion of the test to ensure that it is better than a specified level.

5.7.1.2   Other parameters tested: Apart from the breaking capacity tests, fuses are tested at independent testing stations for the following parameters:

(*a*)   dielectric properties
(*b*)   temperature rise and power loss
(*c*)   accuracy of time/current characteristic
(*d*)   oil tightness (if intended to be used under oil)
(*e*)   weather proofness and thermal shock (if intended to be used outdoors)
(*f*)   effectiveness of strikers (if fitted)
(*g*)   accuracy of cut-off characteristics and I^2t characteristics (when required)

All these factors are recorded in the type test reports, in which the data are assembled to prove compliance with a standard. This is intended to ensure that every fuse made of identical manufacture to the fuse tested will be safe and suitable for the application corresponding to the tests.

5.8   Bibliography

British and international standards

Where the IEC Publication covers a similar field to that of the British Standard its number is given below in brackets. When different in scope, the full title is given.

BS.2692 Part 1 (1975) 'Fuses for voltages exceeding 1000V a.c.' Part 1: Current limiting fuses (IEC Publ. 282-1)

BS.2692 : 1956, 'Fuses for alternating current circuits above 660V', (This covers expulsion fuses)

IEC Publ. 282-2 (1970) 'High voltage fuses', Part 2: Expulsion and similar fuses

IEC Publ. 282-3 (1976) 'High voltage fuses', Part 3 Determination of short circuit power factor for testing current limiting fuses and expulsion and similar fuses

BS.88 'Cartridge fuses for voltages up to and including 1000V a.c. and 1500V d.c.', Part 1 (1975) 'General requirements' (IEC Publ. 269-1).

Part 2(1975) 'Supplementary requirements for fuses of standardised dimensions and performance for industrial purposes' (IEC Publ. 269-2)

Part 4 (1976) 'Supplementary requirements for fuselinks for the protection of semiconductor devices' (IEC Publ. 269-4)

Part 5 (1980) 'Supplementary requirements for fuselinks of standardised dimensions and performance for use in a.c. electricity supply networks'

IEC Publ. 269-3 'Supplementary requirements for fuses for domestic and similar applications'

BS.1361 : 1971, 'Cartridge fuses for a.c. circuits in domestic and similar premises'

BS.1362 : 1973, 'General purpose fuselinks for domestic and similar purposes' (primarily for use in plugs)

BS.4265 : 1977, 'Cartridge fuselinks for miniature fuses', (IEC Publ. 127 : 1974)

BS.3036 : 1958, 'Semi-enclosed electric fuses'

IEC Publ. 291 (and supplement) 'Fuse definitions'

Books

Electric fuses by H W Baxter (Edward Arnold, London, 1950). Based on a series of experimental investigations by the Electrical Research Association.

Electric fuses by H Lapple (Butterworth, London, 1952). A critical review of published information covering 267 references. Later references in ERA Report No. 5228 'Advances in electric fuses 1950-1965' by H W Turner and C Turner; Kept up to date by the same authors in: 'Digests of information on protective devices'. (A current-awareness service provided by ERA Technology Ltd.)

High rupturing capacity fuses by E Jacks (Spon, London 1975) A collection of important papers and articles on fuses by the author from 1951 to 1971.

Power distribution in industrial installations by T B Rolls, (Peter Peregrinus, London, 1972) IEE Monograph Series 10 (for general reading)

Articles

'Electric fuses', Engineering OUtline No. 125 by H W Turner & C Turner (*Engineering,* 17th May, 1968)

'Fuse operation on overcurrent' by H W Turner and C Turner (*Electr. Times,* 1966, **150,** pp. 135-138)

'Calculation of the effect of preheating on the pre-arcing time of cartridge fuses' by H W Turner, C Turner & J S Yap (ERA Report 5021, 1963)

'Cartridge fuse developments' by H W Turner & C Turner (*Electr. Rev.* 1971)

'The influence of preheating on the arc energy of cartridge fuses' by H W Turner, C Turner, & D Marks (ERA Report G/T329, 1963)

'The protection of electric circuits' by H W Turner & C Turner (Proc. ERA Distribution Conference, Edinburgh, 1967 pp. 486-498)

'Fuse performance data for modern applications' by E Jacks (Proc. ERA Distribution Conference, Edinburgh, 1967, pp. 439-463)

'Problems of co-ordination of protection in factory and domestic distribution systems' by H W Turner & C Turner, IEE Conf. Publ. 73, IEE/ERA Distribution Conference Oct. 1970, pp. 121-126

'Phenomena occuring during the extinction of arcs in fuses' by H W & C Turner (Second International Symposium on switching arc phenomena, Lodz, 1973, pp. 253-256

'International conference on electric fuses and their applications' (Liverpool Polytechnic, 1976) 38 papers on fuses and their applications.

'Comparing fuses by temperature rise' by H W Turner and C Turner (*Electr. Rev.* 1970)

'10 ways *not* to design a fuse circuit' (*Engineering*, 1975)

'Calculation of the burn back rate of a fuse element and its relation to contact erosion' by H W Turner & C Turner. (Proc. 3rd International Symposium on switching arc phenomena, Lodz, 1977)

'Discrimination between h.r.c. fuses' by E Jacks (*J. IEE*, 1959, **196**, pp. 299-306)

'Recent developments in medium-voltage h.r.c. fuse links' by R H Dean (*J. IEE*, **105**, 1958, **108**, pp. 263-270)

'Excess-current protection by h.r.c. fuses on medium-voltage circuits' by R T Lythall (*J. IEE*, 1945, **92**)

'A high-voltage high rupturing-capacity cartridge fuse and its effect on production technique' by K Dannenberg and Prof. W J John (*J. IEE*, 1942, **89**, pp. 565-576)

'The high-rupturing-capacity cartridge fuse with special reference to short-circuit performance' by J W Gibson (*J. IEE*, 1941, **88**, pp. 2-24)

'The boric-acid fuse' by A P Strom and H L Rawlings (*Trans. AIEE,* 1932, **51**, p. **1020**)

'The expulsion fuse' by J Slepian and CL Dennault (*Trans. AIEE*, 1932, **51**, p. 157)

Chapter 6

Relays

by J.W.Hodgkiss

6.1 Introduction

The word 'relay' is used in many different situations, such as a relay race, which is run by a team, each member completing a part of the course.In each such meaning there is the sense of handing on, and the original telegraph relay was truly in line with this idea, as described in Chapter 2. Relays are now of many diverse patterns, but they may be covered by the following definition.

A *relay* is a device which makes a measurement or receives a controlling signal in consequence of which it makes sudden pre-determined changes in one or more electrical circuits.

A *protective relay* is a relay which responds to abnormal conditions in an electrical power system, to control a circuit-breaker so as to isolate the faulty section of the system, with the minimum interruption to service. Relays may be segregated into two classes in line with the definition: those which measure and those which merely repeat a controlling signal. The latter are distinguished in the British Standard for Electrical Protective Relays, BS 142 : 1966, as 'all-or-nothing' relays, this rather inelegant expression being used to imply that these devices are intended to be energised with a power input which is substantially above their minimum operating condition. In general, such relays are not calibrated but are tested to operate with a specified minimum input.

These relays may have a simple contactor type function, but in some cases may also make a measurement. For example, a time-delay relay may be energised as an all-or-nothing device but may then measure a precise period of time before closing an output contact.

Measuring relays in general receive and measure fundamental system quantities. All measurement involves comparison, either of one input quantity with a standard, or with another input. Neither of the two quantities need necessarily be the measured quantity in terms of which the relay is calibrated. Moreover, the second quantity need not be electrical, as in the case of an overcurrent relay in which the torque produced by the current is compared with the restraint of a spring.

An impedance relay, on the other hand, compares the system current and voltage in amplitude, whereas the relay calibration is in terms of the ratio of these two, that is, in impedance.

A mho relay, however, also takes the phase angle between the two quantities into account producing a more complex response characteristic. The relay will be calibrated in terms of impedance at a specified angle but the whole response curve is related to the calibration.

It is this concept of comparison that has led to the modern description of relays as amplitude or phase-angle comparators. The full mathematical treatment of comparators is outside the scope of this chapter, but a sufficient introduction is given to enable the derivation of typical relay characteristics to be understood.

The nominal minimum value of the measured quantity at which a relay operates is called the 'setting'. Strictly, the term 'setting' should be confined to that quantity which is set either during calibration or selected in application. In many cases, this value is synonymous with the minimum operating quantity, but this is not always so. For example, a high impedance relay used in a circulating current differential system for busbar protection may be calibrated in terms of voltage. The relay will operate, however, when a certain value of in-zone fault current flows through the current-transformers, the minimum value of which is often referred to as the system setting. In some circumstances this usage can be very confusing.

The term setting should be confined to the calibrated quantity, in this case the voltage which will cause operation when applied to the relay. The current input to the relay at voltage setting is the 'relay operating current'. Similarly, the test-current which would have to be injected into the secondary circuit to produce operation is the 'effective secondary operating current', and the primary counterpart of this is the 'primary operating current'

In operating the relay may either pick-up or drop-off. (These terms, derived from early solenoid devices, are now used even when the motion is not one of lifting). The relay setting, therefore, may be either of these. In some cases both pick-up and drop-off values may be specified; in others, particularly when the relay initiates the tripping of the associated circuit-breaker, the reset value may be unimportant.

The rated current and rated voltage of a relay are the values of current and voltage upon which its performance is based. They are marked on the relay and generally correspond to the secondary rating of the current and voltage transformers or nominal battery voltage with which it is intended to work. In the case of direct-connected relays for medium voltage circuits the rating will be the circuit-rated voltage, but current windings will still usually be energised by current-transformers.

Protective relays remain inoperative, although energised for very long periods while the power-system is healthy, and yet must operate decisively when required to do so. The incidence of a fault requiring operation may not be as frequent as once in twenty years. Reliability is therefore of paramount importance. This is not synonymous with robustness, a factor to which an initiate must become accustomed. There is a natural reluctance to trust the security of a large machine or high power circuit to a delicate relay movement or small component, but in fact when used correctly these items may well be more reliable than a heavy mechanism. This is a highly specialised subject requiring attention in design, and to quality in manufacture, control of materials in formulation, characteristics or purity and cleanliness at all times, during manufacture and subsequently during commissioning or routine testing work.

6.2 Principal types of relays

Relays are generally specified according to the duty they are required to perform, for example, overcurrent relays or impedance relays. For a detailed study of properties as distinct from scheme applications they can be classified according to their constructional types.

The same basic construction may be used in different schemes and applications. The fewer basic design elements used the better; this simplifies stocking spare components and reduces the range of fundamental response characteristics with which the maintenance staff must be familiar. The following types of relays have been constructed: attracted armature, moving coil, induction, motor operated, magnetic amplifier, thermionic, semiconductor, mechanical, photoelectric.

Many variations of most types of element have been applied in protective relays. Their generalised characteristics are described below, followed by the application of typical elements to specific protective relay schemes.

6.2.1 Attracted-armature relays

Armature relays are the simplest class and the most extensively used. They operate by the movement of a piece of iron into the field produced by a coil. Typical practical arrangements are shown diagramatically in Figs. 6.2.1 A, D and E-K. Fig. 6.2.1A represents in simple form the hinged armature relay which is used in very large numbers both for measurement and auxiliary functions.

The magnetic circuit comprises an iron core which carries the energising coil, and which is mounted on an iron frame, the latter being shaped to provide the return path for the flux. An armature is pivoted so that it can move in line with the magnetic field. Journal bearings may be used but very often the armature pivots on a knife edge formed on the end of the frame.

The armature may carry moving contacts but in many cases operates contacts by push-rods or strips of insulating material. The force on the armature is given by

$$F = \frac{K \, (N \, I)^2}{\left(\dfrac{g}{A} + c\right)^2 \, A},$$

where F = force, N = turns on the operating coil, I = coil current, g = armature air gap, A = Effective area of pole-face, and c = reluctance of the iron circuit.

Before pick-up, 'c' is relatively small and the expression can be reduced to

$$\frac{K(NI)^2 A}{g^2}$$

As the armature gap closes the magnetic pull increases, usually at a rate which exceeds the increasing restraint exerted by the contact springs. In order to permit the relay to reset the energising current must be reduced. The ratio of resetting to operating current values is called the 'returning ratio' (formerly known as the differential).

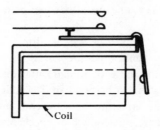

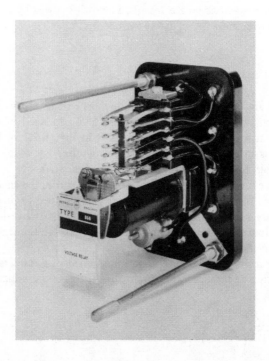

Fig. 6.2.1.A   *Typical hinged armature relay (A Reyrolle & Co. Ltd.)*

The effect of a low resetting current is to produce a snap action which gives good contact operation. A low resetting value may not be appropriate to a given application. The effect can be reduced by preventing the armature gap closing completely, usually by a non-magnetic stud or screw in the armature face.

Further, by arranging for the spring restraint to increase rapidly as the armature closes the relay may be made to reset wth only a small reduction of current as illustrated in Fig. 6.2.1B. Curve 'A' represents the magnetic pull on the armature. The spring restoring force is shown by the straight line B. The unbalanced operating force in the closed position is the portion of the ordinate AB. In order to allow the

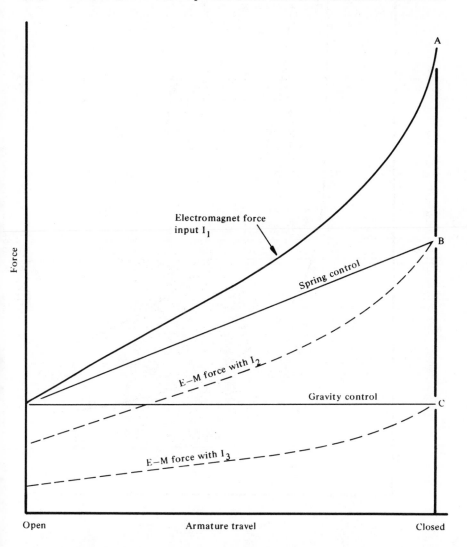

Fig. 6.2.1B   *Effect of spring restraint on returning ratio*

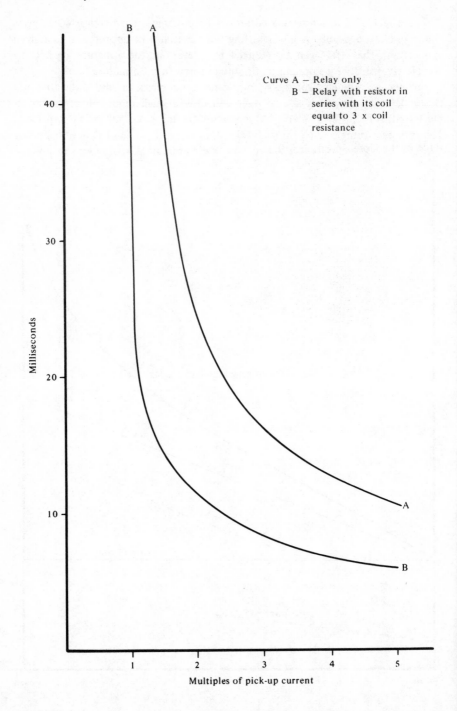

Curve A — Relay only
       B — Relay with resistor in
           series with its coil
           equal to 3 x coil
           resistance

Fig. 6.2.1C *Time/current characteristics of typical attracted armature relay*

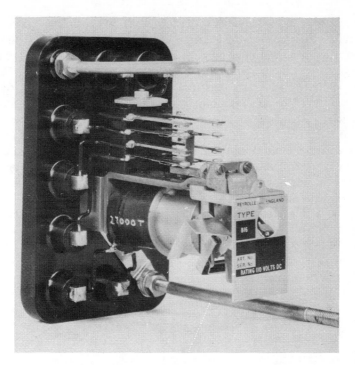

Fig. 6.2.1D   *Attracted-armature relay (delayed pick-up) (A. Reyrolle & Co. Ltd.)*

relay to reset, the current must be reduced below a value I_2 equivalent to point B, whereas had a constant restraining force been applied corresponding to point C, the reset current would be the lower value I_3 giving a pull curve C. As the spring rate is increased, the returning ratio will be raised but any such improvement is at the expense of contact performance.

A typical relay could have a resetting current as low as 25% of pick-up but by special design this might be raised to 90% or even more. In some cases instead of applying additional spring control a relay contact is arranged to insert additional resistance into the coil circuit thereby weakening the holding force so that a small reduction of applied voltage will cause the relay to reset.

Relays of this type are normally classed as 'instantaneous', this term indicating that no intentional delay has been introduced into the operation. No action, in fact, takes place in zero time, and it is possible and in fact often important to consider the operating time of a so-called instantaneous relay. Fig. 6.2.1C shows a typical time/current curve for an attracted armature relay.

The operating time is attributable partly to the time to establish the current in the inductive coil and partly to the mechanical inertia of the armature. For a given maximum current value, the build-up time of the current can be changed by altering the time-constant of the circuit by including additional resistance.

Hence the results obtained in any particular test will depend upon the test circuit and manner of control of the current. A relay used to respond to 'current' will normally be connected in series with a load which will completely predominate over the relay characteristic. Any inductive lag will not be attributable to the relay; a test for such a relay will show only the mechanical delay. On the other hand, a relay designed to measure voltage, or an auxiliary relay energised from a battery, may not require any additional resistance in series with its coil. Such a relay will therefore be slower. The effect is shown by the two curves in Fig. 6.2.1C.

If the relay is required to be slower than the typical element, the response time can be increased by fitting a solid copper cylinder over a portion of the core, occupying a portion of the normal coil space, Fig. 6.2.1D. Flux changes are delayed by the eddy currents induced in this cylinder (or slug), causing delays in operating and resetting ranging from a few milliseconds up to one or two seconds according to design and adjustment.

In general, a slug placed close to the pole tip and armature will delay both pick-up and drop-off; a slug behind the coil will have a larger effect on drop-off than pick-up. Delays in resetting can also be obtained by shunting the coil by a resistor or by a diode.

Remanent flux in the relay core is important in connection with the drop-off setting and may in fact prevent the relay from releasing. To control this effect the armature may be prevented by a non-magnetic stop from closing the magnetic circuit completely. A gap of 0·05mm is usually sufficient to largely eliminate remanent flux. Alternatively, the relay core can be made from a material having a low remanent effect.

Remanence can be used to make a bistable (or electrically reset) relay. The core is made of a high-carbon steel having a larger coercive force than has the ordinary relay core. The armature closes on to the armature pole without any residual gap, so that when operated, the relay holds-in and requires a demagnetising pulse to release. Resetting, therefore, is performed by energising the coil (or a second coil) in reverse. The reversed input must not reoperate the relay but the input value is not too critical since the relay can drop-off during the build-up time of the de-magnetising current as the flux passes through zero.

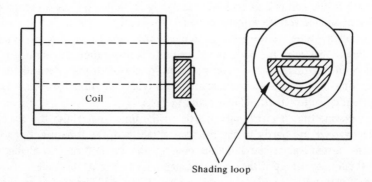

Shading loop

Fig. 6.2.1E   *A.C. relay with armature removed showing shading loop fitted to the pole*

A.C. relays: Simple armature relays will operate with alternating current but since the flux must pass through zero every half cycle, the armature will begin to reset and release slightly from the magnet pole. The relay will therefore be noisy and may vibrate severely at certain levels of energisation. To eliminate this effect it is usual to split the magnetic pole and to surround one part with a low resistance copper shading loop. Fig. 6.2.1E. The eddy currents induced in this loop cause a phase lag in the flux passing through the loop as compared with that in the other part of the pole. Hence the flux does not come to zero on the whole of the pole face at any instant with the result that some hold-on force is maintained. When a shading loop is not fitted, vibration can be prevented by rectifying the supply. With a full wave rectifier, the coil inductance will maintain the current during the idle portion of the a.c. cycle.

Burdens: The design of such elements varies over a wide range; typically a small d.c. relay will operate with between 0·05 and 0·2 W of coil energy, and will pick-up in between 0·01 and 0·04 s at five times setting current. Continuous dissipation capacity of the coil will usually be between 2 and 4W. A.C. relays require 0·5-3VA at pick-up.

The above performance values apply to small relays used for many protection functions, both for direct measurement and as auxiliaries. Operating values widely different from the above occur with relays having a large number of contacts or extra strong restraint to give mechanical stability. For example a multicontact trip relay having high mechanical stability and ability to operate over a wide voltage range may require 100 W at nominal voltage. The continuous rating of the coil may not be as high as this, so that automatic cut-off of the current may be essential.

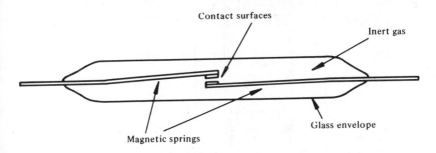

Contact surfaces

Inert gas

Magnetic springs

Glass envelope

Fig. 6.2.1F   *Reed relay*

High-speed elements – Reed relays: By reducing the armature mass and the total contact travel it is possible to make a relay which is very much faster than is quoted above. Reed relays are typical modern examples which are capable of operating in one millisecond at a moderate multiple of minimum pick-up value.

Fig. 6.2.1F shows the general arrangement. Two flexible springs of magnetic material are sealed into opposite ends of a glass tube so that their ends overlap and are separated by a small gap. The ends are covered with a suitable contact metal.

The application of an axial magnetic field causes the two springs to be attracted together and close their contact-making surfaces. The field can be supplied by a solenoid surrounding the tube or by an adjacent magnet. Hence the device can be used as a relay or a proximity switch. Several tubes can be inserted into one coil to provide a multicontact relay.

Solenoid relays: In this arrangement a steel plunger is attracted into a relatively long coil. It is usual for the magnetic circuit to be completed outside the coil by steel plates so that the principle is similar generally to that of an armature relay, but the design is more adapted to providing a long stroke. Fig. 6.2.1G. The principle has been widely used in applications ranging from simple overload devices to the operation of mechanisms which are required to do a considerable amount of work.

Magnetically polarised armature relays: The relays described above are not sensitive to the polarity of flux in the core. By including a permanent magnet in part of the core, the relay can be polarised. Such relays are constructed in various forms to be monostable that is self-resetting, or bistable in which case the relay has to be driven in either direction by applying the appropriate polarity of current.

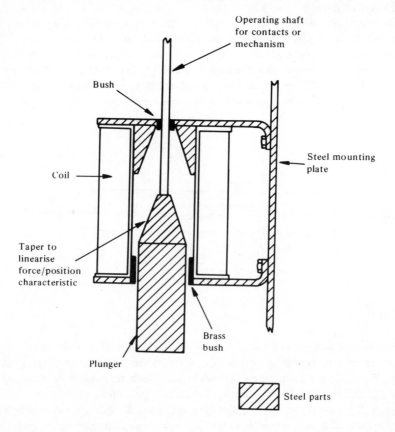

Fig. 6.2.1G *Solenoid-operated relay*

Such relays have been designed, on the one hand, to provide normal fast operation with the ability to operate a considerable number of contacts, to, on the other hand, super high speed relays capable of operating consistently in a time of less than one millisecond.

The Carpenter relay is of this type. Fig. 6.2.1H. With a symmetrical adjustment, the relay is bistable; the armature, displaced to either side of the central axis provides a low reluctance path for one of the permanent magnets, the flux passing down the armature to one of the auxiliary poles, then through the coil core back to the magnet. Energising the coil to oppose this flux, reduces flux in this path and increases flux from the other magnet, causing the armature to move over to the alternative position, where it is held even though the coil is de-energised. Return of the armature is achieved by reverse energisation of the coil. The relay can be made monostable by advancing one of the contacts past the magnetic centre.

The relay can operate with less than one milliwatt. Operating time can be less than one millisecond. The contact gap is normally small, of the order of 0·001 to 0·004 inches, which naturally is only suitable for a low rating. Fig. 6.2.1I shows a relay operating on a similar principle to the Carpenter relay but designed for protection applications. Sensitivity ranges from 3·5 to 20 mW whereas the contact performance is equivalent to that of many primary measuring relays.

The high sensitivity of polarised relays is mainly due to a large part of the working flux being provided by the permanent magnet.

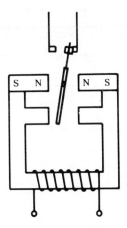

Fig. 6.2.1H *Carpenter relay*

Vane relays: A variation of the simple armature relay is shown in Fig. 6.2.1J. A thin iron vane is pivoted to permit sideways motion into the field of an electromagnet.

Balanced beam relays: A separate complete electromagnet system can be fitted to operate on either end of a centrally pivoted beam to compare two electrical quantities. Both solenoids and armature type electromagnets have been used.

An example of the former type formed a sensitive and precise comparator of two inputs. It was equally suitable for d.c. and a.c. (needing no rectifiers and giving true r.m.s. measurement). It was, however, slow in operation and was therefore more suitable for control than for protection. Beam relays of the armature type have been extensively used in 'impedance' protection schemes and to a lesser degree

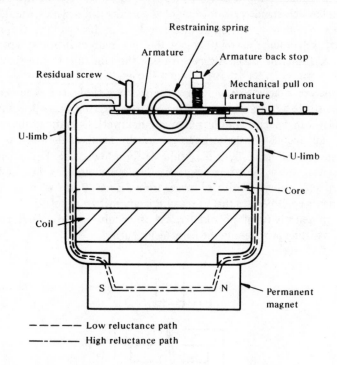

Fig. 6.2.1I   *Polarised balanced armature movement*

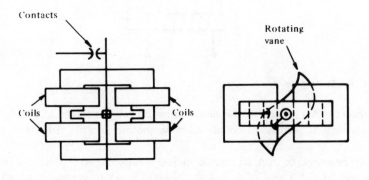

Fig. 6.2.1J   *Rotating-vane type*

in differential current protection systems. Fig 6.2.1K. These elements were fast and accurate under steady test conditions, but were affected by the phase angle between the operating quantities and were subject to spurious operation by input transients. The supply to one of the coils was often rectified to remove phase angle error and compensation circuits were added to attempt to avoid operation with offset transient current but with indifferent success. This type of relay is now largely obsolete.

6.2.2   Moving-coil relays

The 'motor' action of a current carrying conductor in a magnetic field produces a moving system which is the basis of moving coil instruments and relays. The moving-coil instrument, attributed to d'Arsonval, is a rotary movement comprising a short coil, suspended or pivoted on an axis in its plane so that it is free to rotate between the poles of a permanent magnet (Fig. 6.2.2A).

The coil is usually of rectangular form. The magnet poles are shaped and a central cylindrical iron core is mounted concentric with the coil (but not in contact with it) so that the magnet gap is uniform and the gap flux is radial. The coil is

Fig. 6.2.1K   *Typical modern beam-element relay (A Reyrolle & Co. Ltd.)*

restrained by two flat spiral springs which also serve as current carrying connections to the coil.

The torque produced in the coil is

$$T = Blwni \text{ Newton-metres}$$

where T = torque, B = flux density, l = coil length, w = coil width, n = coil turns, and i = coil current (all expressed in MKS units).

The device can be made into a relay by replacing the pointer or other means of indication with a moving contact for which it will be necessary to add an additional ligament.

Relays of this type, based on conventional instrument movements, are available but it must be realised that these can only produce sufficient operating torque to permit a low contact rating. Other issues such as the size of wire used for the coil

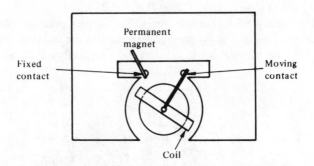

Fig. 6.2.2A   *Rotating moving-coil relay*

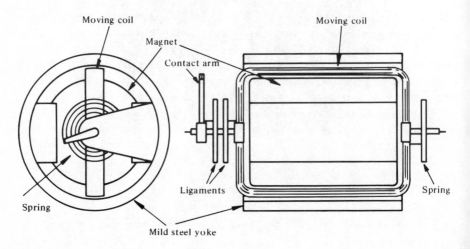

Fig. 6.2.2B   *Moving-coil relay for protection schemes*

Fig. 6.2.2.C   *Moving-coil relay (GEC Measurements Ltd.)*

and the physical clearances between the coil and magnet need to be considered before a small movement is used for a protection function.

A rotary moving coil relay designed for use in protection schemes is shown in Figs. 6.2.2B and C. In this design the core inside the coil is the permanent magnet of modern high coercive-force material. The magnetic circuit is completed by a concentric mild steel tube, leaving an annular gap in which swings the moving coil.

The coil is wound on an aluminium former, which has the important function of damping the movement by virtue of the eddy currents which are induced in it when the coil moves through the magnet field. The standard former is sufficient to make the movement dead-beat; more damping can be obtained if required by using a copper former while less is obtained by splitting the former. These variations, are, however, rarely required. The special features of the relay, as compared with an instrument, are:

(*a*)   The relatively large size and high power of the permanent magnet; this enables an adequate torque to be developed with a low input of energy and without winding the coil with excessively fine wire. Full travel (80°) operation is obtainable with 0·3 mW with normal spring restraint; super-sensitive relays can operate with 50 μW.

(*b*)   The radial air-gap in which the coil moves is ample to provide good clearances to the surrounding magnet structure; this is important, to make the relay safe from stiction due to small particles of dust etc. which may enter any time that the relay case is opened.

The relay may be arranged to have a wide angle of movement, e.g. 80°, corresponding to a contact gap of about 5 cm. Contacts can be provided to close at either end of the arc of motion, both fixed contacts being adjustable over the total arc of movement. Adjustment of these contacts (which are associated with coil stops) and of the position of the spring anchor, give a very wide scope for setting the relay to a desired performance.

The torque developed is proportional to current, there being no saturation effect within practical limits. The velocity of motion is controlled by the damping action, to be proportional to the torque. The relay has, therefore, a substantially inverse time/current characteristic (Fig. 6.2.2D).

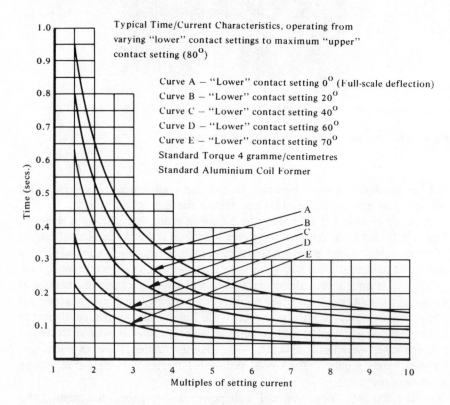

Fig. 6.2.2D   *Time/current characteristic of moving-coil relay*

The torque, for a given value of current is independent of the position in the arc of travel. In this way, the relay contrasts sharply with an armature relay. In particular, the relay has no run-in effect and has a nominally unity drop-off/pick-up ratio. The latter statement is usually modified to allow for the small effects of friction and contact adhesion, a drop-off/pick-up ratio of 0·97 being assumed.

Fig. 6.2.2E shows a smaller moving coil relay. Although no larger than some instrument movements, this relay is designed with the requirements of a protective relay in mind.

The rotary action enables the movement to be supported simply by pivots but is not otherwise fundamental. Fig. 6.2.2F shows an arrangement which produces axial motion of the moving coil. The cylindrical magnetic system, shown in section, comprises a short strong permanent magnet as a central core in a mild steel cup, completed with mild steel poles which are separated by an annular gap.

A cylindrical coil, wound on an aluminium former, is supported in the magnet gap by leaf springs which permit motion of the coil along its axis only. Current

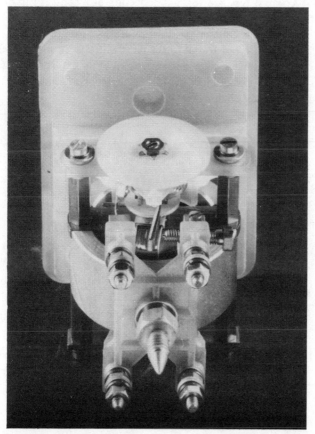

Fig. 6.2.2E   *Small moving-coil relay for protection applications (GEC Measurements Ltd.)*

flowing in the coil produces an axial force given by:

$$F = \pi B \, dni \text{ Newtons}$$

where B = flux density, d = coil diameter, n = effective turns within the pole width, and i = current (all expressed in MKS units).

It is essential, for the method of suspension, for the coil axis to be horizontal. This, however is not as exacting a requirement as might be thought. An error in vertical mounting of the relay case, sufficient to seriously disturb the relay, is obvious and unacceptable for general appearance. The usual design is adapted for only a small movement and is therefore suitable for instantaneous or definite-time delayed schemes. Damping is provided by the metal former as in the case of the rotary movement, while the absence of pivots eliminates this source of friction and risk of damage.

Operation can be obtained with an input of 0·1 to 0·4 mW. In comparison with the rotary movement it is important to compare like with like. The sensitivities given for the d'Arsonval type are for 80° deflection or a contact gap of 48mm, as compared with 1·5mm for the axial motion relay. If the travel of the rotary relay is reduced to give the same contact gap, the power input for operation is reduced as the square of the reduction of travel; in the limit with a weak spring a relay can be designed to operate with less than one microwatt. For similar contact gaps and energy inputs the two types of movement have comparable speeds. Operating times as low as 10 ms are readily obtainable.

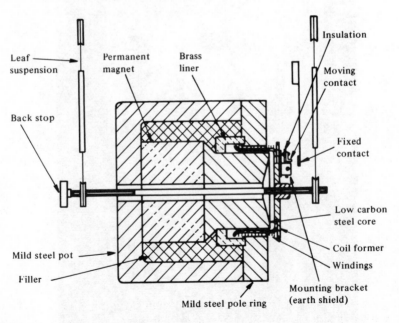

Fig. 6.2.2F   *Axial moving-coil relay (AEI Ltd.)*

Permanent magnet moving-coil relays are inherently d.c. movements. They can be applied to a.c. circuits with the aid of rectifiers. In assessing the total performance of the relay it is necessary to take into account the characteristics of the rectifier, and other components such as auxiliary c.t.s which are used to convert the current into a suitable input quantity. Moreover, the highest speeds may not be obtainable because of the pulsations of the supply. High speed is only likely to be required with a relay scheme which includes a differential or comparison function such as distance or unit differential protections. In such cases if the two quantities which are being compared are not in phase, an alternating force will be generated in the relay even though both of the inputs are full-wave rectified. It is then necessary to limit the inputs and therefore the a.c. component to a value which will not set up significant vibratory movement of the coil; alternatively the rectified inputs may be smoothed. In either case the speed will be limited so that operating times of less than one or two cycles of the supply may not be obtainable with realistic conditions.

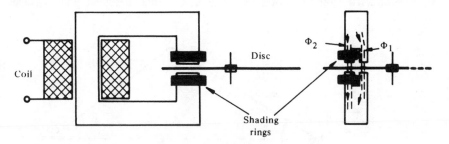

Fig. 6.2.3A   *Shaded-pole induction-disc relay*

6.2.3   Induction relays

Induction relays are based on the shifting field effect first observed by Ferraris and later used by Shallenberger in the design of the first induction meter. Induction relays have evolved from the meter by the replacement of the register with a control spring and contact arrangement. Attention to specific requirements has by now made considerable detail difference, so that only the principle remains.

The relay comprises an electromagnet system which operates on a movable conductor usually in the form of a metal disc or cup. Torque is produced by the interaction of two alternating magnetic fields which are mutually displaced both in space and phase. The response is given by

$$T = K \, \Phi_1 \, \Phi_2 \sin \theta$$

where T = torque, Φ_1 Φ_2 are the two interacting fluxes and θ = phase angle between Φ_1 and Φ_2. It will be noted from the above that the torque is maximum when the fluxes are mutually displaced in phase by 90°, and zero when in-phase. Such a device used to measure power, as in the meter, needs to have an accurate phase relation of fluxes; for other purposes an intermediate angle may be satisfactory.

A simple means of obtaining the two co-operating fluxes when only a single energising quantity is involved, as in the case of an overcurrent relay, is to divide the flux into two components as shown in Fig. 6.2.3A. The core of the C-shaped electromagnet is divided at the poles to form two pairs of opposed poles, one pair of which are each fitted with a short-circuited winding or a solid copper loop, known as a shading loop. Current induced in this loop produces a phase delay in the flux passing through the shaded pole as shown in Fig. 6.2.3B. OA represents the total flux produced by the electromagnet, a portion OB would pass through the shaded pole if the shading winding were opened.

The e.m.f. induced in this winding is OE and on closing the winding a current OI flows. The flux (BC) generated by this current when subtracted from OB, gives the flux actually passing through this pole (OC = Φ_1). The reaction of the shading winding on the main flux of the electromagnet is small and can be ignored so that if Φ_1 is subtracted from the total flux, the flux in the unshaded pole becomes OD = Φ_2.

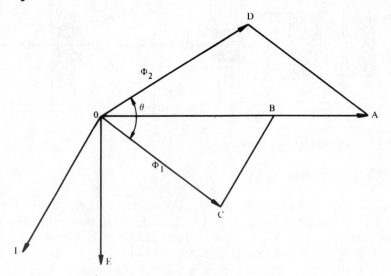

OA	=	Total flux in electromagnet.
OB	=	Portion of total flux in shaded pole with shading winding open.
OE	=	EMF in shading winding.
OI	=	Current in shading winding when closed.
BC	=	Flux in shaded pole produced by OI.
OC	=	Resultant flux in shaded pole $- \Phi_1$.
OD	=	Resultant flux in unshaded pole $- \Phi_2$.
θ	=	Angle between Φ_1 and Φ_2.
Torque		$\Phi_1 \Phi_2 \sin \theta$

Fig. 6.2.3B *Phasor diagram for shaded pole relay*

Φ_1 and Φ_2 are therefore the two fluxes, displaced by an angle, which operate on the disc producing Ferraris torque. Fig. 6.2.3C shows a relay of the above type which is very extensively used.

An alternative arrangement is shown in Fig. 6.2.3D. The upper and lower electromagnets can be energised by separate quantities and produce corresponding fluxes which satisfy the spatial displacement requirements and produce torque on the disc in line with the above equation. In this form the device is suitable for power measurement and for use as a directional relay.

When required as a single function relay, e.g. an overcurrent relay, it is usual to energise only a winding on the upper electromagnet. A secondary winding on this magnet receives an induced emf and energises a winding on the lower electromagnet. The action is shown by the phasor diagram Fig. 6.2.3E. The input current I_u produces flux Φ_u in the upper electromagnet and induces an e.m.f. E_s in the secondary winding. By virtue of the air gap this magnet acts as a quadrature c.t. (or transactor). The lower electromagnet which is of moderate X/R ratio draws a current I_L and produces a corresponding flux Φ_L. The fluxes Φ_u and Φ_L are therefore displaced in phase by a sufficient angle to develop torque in the relay disc.

Fig. 6.2.3C   *Inverse time overcurrent relay (GEC Measurements Ltd.)*

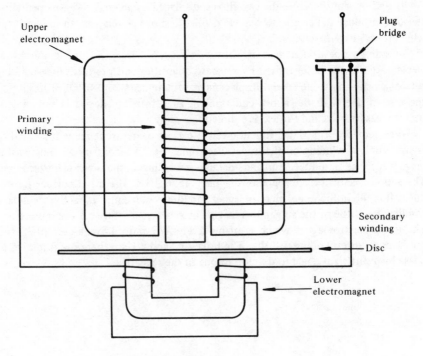

Upper
electromagnet

Plug
bridge

Primary
winding

Secondary
winding

Disc

Lower
electromagnet

Winding arrangement

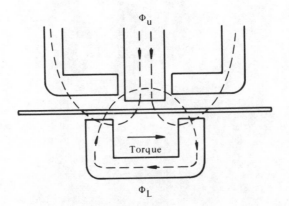

Φ_u

Torque

Φ_L

Operating fluxes showing crossing of component
fields

Fig. 6.2.3D *Alternative induction relay (shown as overcurrent relay)*

A third design of induction element is shown in Figs. 6.2.3F and G. The electro-magnet is a symmetrical four pole structure, superficially resembling a small motor. The poles are shaped to form a cylindrical tunnel within which is a fixed core. The rotor is a light aluminium cylindrical cup which is located in the gap between the main electromagnet and inner core. The cup relay has advantage over disc designs in the better utilisation of the electromagnet fluxes and in the lower inertia of the rotor due to confining the active surface to a smaller radius.

An eight-pole version is used to provide a compact polyphase relay. Many variants of these types of relay have been made; no attempt is made here to depict alternative designs, the functioning of which will be clear as one of the above types. Certain features, are however common to most relays and are briefly discussed before considering specific types.

Setting control: Relays which have a definite calibration require a mechanical restraint to control the setting. Even a sensitive directional relay is required to return to a standard initial position when de-energised. For this purpose a flat spiral phosphor bronze spring is usually fitted. The spring may be intended to be adjustable during calibration only or may be attached to a means of adjustment with a setting scale to give a range of setting in service.

Current setting can also be controlled by tapping the operating coil. In principle a relay will operate with a given ampere-turn input to the coil. To provide a range of settings, it is only necessary to be able to select a number of turns which is in

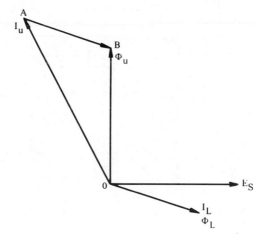

OA   =   Input current to upper electromagnet I_u (or amp turns).
I_L =   Current in lower electromagnet.
AB   =   Amp-turns in secondary winding of upper magnet due to current I_L.
OB   =   Resultant amp-turns and flux Φ_u upper magnet.
E_S =   Secondary E.M.F.
Φ_L =   Lower magnet flux due to I_L.

Fig. 6.2.3E   *Phasor diagram for overcurrent relay shown in Fig. 6.2.3D*

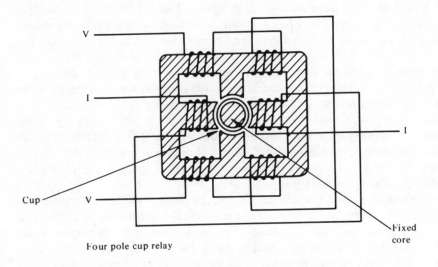

Four pole cup relay

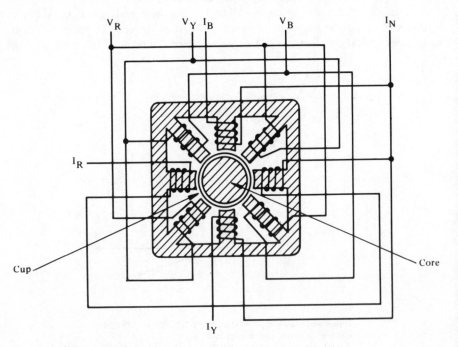

Eight pole cup relay

Fig. 6.2.3F *Induction cup relay*

Fig. 6.2.3G   *Exploded view of 4-pole induction cup relay (GEC Measurements Ltd.)*

inverse ratio to each of the current values. It is conventional, although not invariable, practice to provide seven setting values covering possibly a 4:1 current range. The taps are usually brought to a selection device known as a plug-bridge, whereby any tap can be selected by inserting a single pin plug into one of seven positions (Fig. 6.2.3H). The bridge is spring-loaded, so that the highest setting is selected when the plug is withdrawn, thereby avoiding either open-circuiting the energising current-transformer or causing unintended operation of the relay if the setting is changed while the power circuit is carrying load.

This simple approach lacks the precision which might be expected. A wide tapping range, e.g. 4:1, means that when using the smallest number of turns, only a small part of the total coil volume is energised. The pattern of flux leakage across the coil changes as the distribution of the energised portion of the winding changes. In consequence, the active flux through the magnet poles varies for the same number of ampere-turns generated by differing portions of the winding. Moreover, the variation of flux in the iron due to changes in leakage pattern changes the degree of saturation in the iron. Hence the operating time/current characteristic will change in shape so that where this is important, the performance cannot be restored by a slight correction to the turns at each tap. Overcurrent relays having an inverse time/current characteristic which is accurately specified are extensively used and the variations described above constitute an error which is additional to those for the calibrated setting, usually one near the centre of the setting range.

A special winding technique has been developed to eliminate this error. The coil is wound with a composite conductor comprising twelve separately insulated strands, thus forming twelve similar fully interleaved winding sections each of which follows a similar path distributed throughout the coil volume. The sections are connected in series outside the coil giving a winding utilising all the turns i.e. 12 times the number of turns of the composite conductor. Each junction provides a possible tapping point, of which seven are chosen to give the desired setting range. Whichever tap is used, the energised turns are uniformly distributed throughout the coil volume and in consequence the flux leakage patterns and resultant performance curve shapes are identical for all taps.

Taps can be made at intervals of integral multiples of the turns in one section. Current settings are therefore possible which are in inverse ratio to the numbers

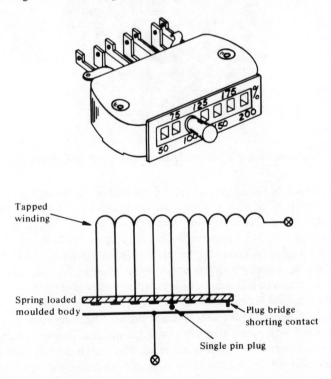

Fig. 6.2.3H *Plug bridge for tapping selection*

1-12. Of the twelve possible settings, seven are chosen. A traditional practice is to use equally spaced taps, typically for an overcurrent relay settings of 50-75-100-125-150-175-200% of nominal current. The settings 50, 75, 100, 150 and 200% are obtained naturally from the 12-strand coil. The remaining settings of 125 and 175% necessitate the addition of extra small sections which disturb the uniform distribution of the winding and hence cause some small disparity of the characteristic curve shapes on these taps.

Equal tap-setting intervals are not ideal, the increments expressed as a percentage of the lower tap setting of any pair are too coarse (50%) at the lower end of the range, and unnecessarily fine (14%) at the upper end. A geometrical progression of setting would be ideal but would involve irregular values. Settings can be selected from the possible values given by the twelve section winding which are a near approximation to a geometrical progression whilst still retaining round numbers. Using this range of setting values virtually eliminates tap error.

Disc-speed control: When an inverse time/current characteristic is required, the disc speed must be controlled by a braking system which will produce a retarding torque which is proportional to the disc speed. Since, at constant speed, the braking torque must equal the nett driving torque, it follows that the disc speed will be proportional to the excess of the electrical torque over the spring restraint.

Permanent-magnet eddy-current braking is the most convenient and accurate form, being a completely linear and frictionless system, and is now universally used. The disc is arranged to pass between the poles of a permanent magnet. Motion of the disc causes eddy currents to be induced, which produce the proportional

Fig. 6.2.31   *Induction disc relay with adjustable brake magnet poles (A Reyrolle & Co. Ltd)*

braking force. The magnet is mounted in a manner which permits adjustment of position as a means of calibration.

Fig. 6.2.3I shows an induction disc movement with brake magnet with adjustable poles in the foreground. The electromagnet is normally fitted on the remote side of the disc. The time-control adjustment and scale appears at the top. It is important that the magnet, once adjusted is securely fixed, that the mounting means are not subject to any distortion wth time or other cause and that the magnet itself is stable.

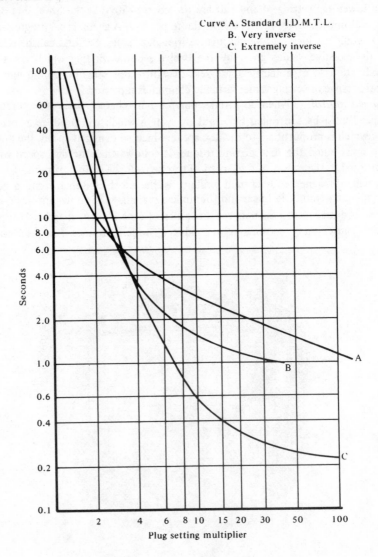

Curve A. Standard I.D.M.T.L.
B. Very inverse
C. Extremely inverse

Fig. 6.2.3J *Typical time/current curve shapes for IDMTL relays*

In cup relays the active surface of the rotor is fully utilised by the driving electromagnet. Eddy-current braking would involve extending the axial length of the cup, thereby increasing the mass of the rotor and removing the gains of the cup construction. Eddy-current braking is, therefore, not normally applied to the cup relay, which is reserved for instantaneous type applications for which the low inertia of the cup is of most value.

Inverse time/current relays: Induction relays of the disc type having inverse time/ current characteristics are widely used to provide discriminative time-graded over-current protection. The induction electromagnet is wound to suit the supply from a current transformer, the winding being tapped as described above to give a range of overcurrent settings, usually 50 to 200% or earth-fault settings of 10-40% or 20-80% of nominal c.t. rating. The driving torque is opposed by a resetting spring and by permanent-magnet eddy-current braking. This leads to a generally inverse operating characteristic, the natural current-squared law of the electromagnet being modified by the spring control and by saturation of the magnet iron circuit.

The control spring is adjusted to give the desired setting and is not thereafter varied in service. The operating time is varied by control of the angle of motion permitted to the disc, to which end an adjustable back-stop is used to determine the reset position of the disc. A scale is provided which shows the effect of this adjust-ment the scale being calibrated in multiplying factors, ranging from 0 to 1·0, for the ordinates of the time/current curve (Fig. 6.2.3J). This technique is necessary to avoid having a characteristic curve for each scale point, but in order to achieve this desirable arrangement it is necessary that the disc moves with constant speed throughout its operating range for any given value.

With a current not greatly above setting value, the spring torque balances a large part of the driving torque; moreover the spring torque is variable over the angle of travel so that the effective driving torque decreases. Compensation is provided by making the disc not circular but shaped so that the area under and round the active pole increases as the spring winds up. Careful shaping can make the disc speed con-stant throughout the motion; on the other hand, a slight departure from idealism may be made to make the driving torque increase rather more rapidly at the end of the travel than is required for perfect compensation, in order to provide a slight 'run-in' effect to assist good contact making.

Notwithstanding the above compensation, the time multiplying factors are not absolutely true over the whole range of current values, e.g. from 1·5 to 20 times setting current. This is because at high multiples of setting current and conse-quently relatively fast operation, the period of acceleration of the disc is more significant than for slower operation. Consequently, for the highest accuracy, it is customary to present the time/current characteristics for a range of time multi-pliers from 0·1 to 1·0.

The characteristic curves are usually prepared with abscissa scaled in multiples of setting current, in order to avoid a multiplicity of curves being required for different current settings.

Curve shapes: A true inverse law gives a characteristic curve which is asymptotic to the setting value; the operating time would then be infinite at the current setting. This ideal condition is not realisable, the relay being unable to operate infinitely slowly or even in a very long time on account of the pivot friction, which becomes dominant when the effective driving torque minus spring restraint is near to zero. It is, therefore, recognised that if, at the setting, the electricle torque just balances the spring control, the current will have to be increased above this value by a finite amount before the relay will actually operate. This fact has been made more positive by the British Standard for relays (BS142) which lays down that 'the relay shall not operate at the setting value'.

The relay characteristic which is most frequently used has been standardised in BS142 by the specification of the following curve points:

Multiple of setting	Operating time
1·0	Must not operate
1·3	Must operate - no time specified
2	10 s
5	4·3 s
10	3·0 s
20	2·2 s

This logical approach is not always followed in certain countries, a similar curve being used but the relay operating at the setting value. The relative uncertainty in determining the minimum operating value is then covered by the tolerance band.

Definite minimum feature: An inverse curve plotted with linear co-ordinates appears to flatten out at its extremities as it asymptotes to the axes. The flattening of the curve at high current values, attributed to saturation, was regarded as a virtue, in that the relay did not become extremely fast at high multiples of setting, and so permitted the grading of a number of relays with sufficient intervals to allow for circuit-breaker clearance time. The relay characteristic was said to have a 'definite minimum time' feature.

Actually, this concept is largely a fallacy; testing with current values between 20 and 100 times setting shows that the operating time continues to decrease notwithstanding the extreme saturation of the electromagnet. The explanation of this fact is to be found in the changing flux wave shape. The absence of a true definite minimum time is little detriment since these very high current values do not usually apply to more than a short distance from the power source.

Alternative characteristics: Relays are available having steeper characteristics than the 'BS curve'. These are known as 'very inverse' and 'extremely inverse' characteristics; they are helpful in dealing with certain problems in grading and are shown in Fig. 6.2.3J. Such characteristics are in general obtained by operating the electromagnet at lower flux densities which leads to a lower level of operating torque. It is preferable, therefore, to confine the use of these relays to those applications where the special characteristic gives substantial benefit.

Discriminative margin - overshoot: When two relays are required to discriminate, their difference in operating times has to cover the following items:

(*a*)   circuit breaker opening time to arc extinction
(*b*)   relay overshoot
(*c*)   relay and c.t. errors
(*d*)   final contact gap.

Item (a):   is a function of system design in selecting suitable switchgear.

Item (b):   When the fault current is interrupted due to the operation of one relay, the discs of other relays that have carried the current are in motion and will not stop until their kinetic energy has been absorbed by the eddy-current braking.

   The extra distance that the disc travels forward after the current has ceased can be interpreted as equivalent to extra running time at the speed at which the disc was moving while current was flowing. This equivalent extra time is known as the overshoot time. Clearly this is one of the important features of a well designed relay. Modern relays have overshoot times of 0·05 s or less.

Items (c)   It is obviously necessary to allow for the deviations between relaying
and (d):   equipments within the accepted tolerance band. It is diffcult to convert the various errors to an equivalent time by a coherent formula but it is usual to allow about 0·2 s extra margin. Adding all the items, a discriminative margin of 0·4 s will usually suffice.

Directional and power relays: The two co-operating fluxes may be derived from different sources; for example using the electromagnet system shown in Fig. 6.2.3D the upper and lower coils may be energised by different quantities. If the upper magnet is energised by the system voltage and the lower by the line current the relay will respond to the product of these two. By making the upper electromagnet highly inductive, so that the current which it draws from the voltage supply is lagging, the sine term in the torque equation is converted into a cosine so that

$$T = KVI \cos \phi$$

where ϕ is the power factor angle of the system. The relay therefore measures power, just as in the induction meter.

   The voltage electromagnet cannot be of zero power factor, i.e. current lagging by 90°. For true power measurement it is, therefore, necessary to provide a phase angle or 'quadrature' adjustment which may comprise for example a short-circuited loop or winding surrounding the voltage pole tip. True power relays are used for a variety of functions mainly associated with plant protection or for control purposes; they are made with a wide range of power settings and may be instantaneous or have an inverse time characteristic.

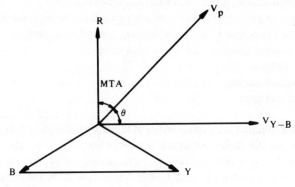

θ = Phase advance in polarising voltage

Phasor Diagram for R phase.

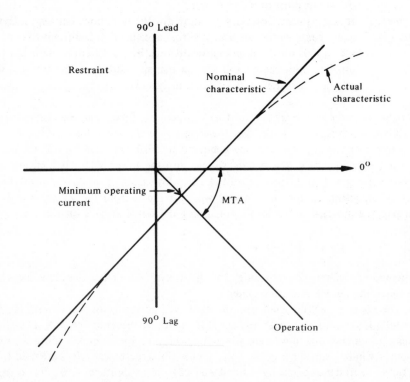

Fig. 6.2.3K *Phasor and polar diagrams for R-phase directional relay*

Many relays are used to determine fault direction in mesh systems. When used in conjunction with overcurrent relays, they control the latter, only permitting operation when the fault current is flowing in the chosen direction. For this purpose the shading loop in relays as shown in Fig. 6.2.3A is replaced by a multiturn winding into the circuit of which is inserted the contact of the directional relay. Only when this contact is closed can the overcurrent relay develop torque.

A similar control is effected on relays of the type of Fig. 6.2.3D; in this case the secondary winding on the upper electromagnet is controlled. Directional relays are required to give a positive indication of the direction of a fault regardless of current and voltage magnitude. Since power measurement is not needed they are arranged to be most sensitive at the probable fault power-factor. This is achieved either by selecting an appropriate voltage for each phase element from the three-phase system or by using phase shifting circuits.

A directional relay should have a zone of operation of approximately 180° symmetrically disposed about the maximum torque angle (m.t.a). A polar diagram for a typical directional relay is shown in Fig. 6.2.3K. Normally, phase-fault relays are energised by the quadrature voltage (*R* phase is energised by *Y-B* voltage) and a resistance is connected in series with the voltage coils to advance the phase of the coil voltage by 45°. This gives an effective m.t.a. of 45° (current lagging voltage) which suits most requirements. Sometimes an m.t.a. of 60° is preferred. Phase voltages to neutral are not used for this purpose.*

Earth fault-relays are energised by residual current and residual voltage. For resistance-earthed power systems no angle compensation is necessary. In the case of solidly earthed systems the angle between residual quantities may be high and it becomes preferable to apply angle compensation. The m.t.a. need not be accurately adjusted to the system fault power-factor. It is only essential that the relay shall operate in the correct direction with good sensitivity and speed. Thus if the fault angle is displaced from the m.t.a. by 30° the loss of torque is less than 14% since cos 30° is 0·866.

Both disc and cup elements are used for directional relays. The cup relay in particular is ideally suited to the application being capable of high sensitivity and high speed. Ability to operate correctly when the system voltage is severely reduced by the fault is of importance; relays are designed to retain their directional properties when the system voltage is reduced to 1-2% of rated value.

Induction type differential relays: Two induction electromagnets, each of the type described above, can be arranged to exert a torque in opposed directions on the same disc. Such a relay is an amplitude comparator and can be used when it is desired to control operation by the ratio of the two quantities. A typical example is the percentage differential relay Fig. 6.2.3L used for the protection of plant on the circulating current principle. The torque of the operating electromagnet A which receives the differential current is opposed by the torque of electromagnet B which carries the total circulating current. Operation of the relay occurs when the operating torque exceeds the restraining or biasing torque, this condition being satisfied

* 'A study of directional element connection for phase relays' (Sonnemann: AIEE Trans., 1950)

when the differential current exceeds a certain percentage of the summated c.t. secondary currents, according to the relative number of turns of windings A and B.

In a similar manner, such a relay can be used as an amplitude comparator for any two functions of current or voltage, the electromagnets being wound appropriately. The original mho relay made by Warrington was of this form, the two balancing inputs being $VI \cos \phi$ and V^2. Operation occurred when $K_1 VI \cos \phi > K_2 V^2$ giving a characteristic

$$\frac{K_2 V}{K_1 I} = \cos \phi$$

6.2.4 Thermal relays

Thermal relays respond to heat; they may measure temperature but very often do not, although frequently they are concerned with overload conditions which may damage plant by overheating. In such a case, the relay's operation may be associated with plant heating, although its calibration may be entirely in terms of current.

The relay may make use of any change which occurs with temperature. Effects which are used are:

(i)   the expansion of a solid or liquid
(ii) variation in resistance of a metal
(iii) variation in resistance of a specially sensitive resistor
(iv) thermoelectric e.m.f.

Fig. 6.2.3L   *Percentage differential relay (GEC Measurements Ltd.)*

The above principles may be used in thermometers which are sometimes fitted with alarm contacts, and in thermostats serving a control function. An example of the former is found in the contact-making thermometers frequently applied to power transformers or other oil-immersed apparatus.

The instrument is shown in Fig. 6.2.4A. The temperature element comprises a mercury filled steel bulb A which is connected by capillary tubing B to a Bourdon tube C, which is fixed at one end. Expansion of the mercury, with increase of temperature, alters the pressure in the tube causing the free end to deflect and rotate a plate F carrying a number of mercury switches. Compensation for change in ambient temperature is provided by a U-shaped bimetal strip in the linkage between the Bourdon tube and the plate. A pointer T indicates the temperature of the bulb and a loose pointer O shows the maximum temperature to which it has been subjected.

An instrument of this type can be used to measure oil-temperature. A second instrument is often used to measure winding temperature by the thermal image principle. In this case, the mercury filled bulb is housed in a special pocket located in the hot oil near the top of the transformer tank. The bulb is surrounded by a small heater, which is connected to a current-transformer energised by the current in the transformer winding. From test data, the additional temperature rise

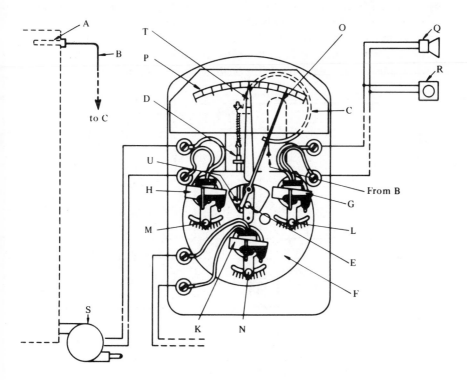

Fig. 6.2.4A *Instrument for direct measurement of temperature*

produced by the heater is designed to simulate the excess temperature of the winding above that of the hot oil.

A similar protection is obtained by using the variation in resistance with temperature of a silistor (silicon resistor), this material having a resistance change with temperature greater than that of common metals. The silistor is the 'sensing' element and is embodied at the centre of a thermal replica unit, comprising heating resistor windings encased in thermal insulation. The heaters are energised by a c.t. carrying the transformer load current, the whole unit being designed to produce a temperature rise of the silistor equal to the amount by which the winding temperature exceeds that of the oil at all times, to which end the heating time constant of the unit has been closely related to that of the transformer windings. The replica unit is mounted in the hot oil in the transformer tank. The silistor is connected to a bridge circuit which energises both an indicating instrument, scaled in temperature of the winding, and also static sensing circuits which provide outputs capable of exercising control over oil-pump and fan motors (Fig. 6.2.4B). A further output is used for tripping. The various functions can be set to occur at successive temperatures of the transformer winding.

Many thermal relays are based on the bimetallic strip which is formed by intimately welding together two layers of different metals having widely different coefficients of expansion. Such a strip bends when heated due to the different expansion of the two layers. Sometimes the strips are formed into spirals to increase their length; such spirals coil or uncoil with temperature change.

The bimetal strip may be heated directly by the current but more usually by a heater situated below or around it. The heater may be an open resistance wire or be

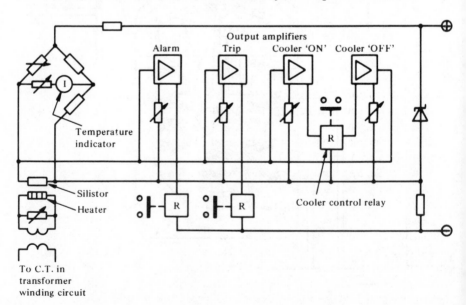

Fig. 6.2.4B *Silistor-controlled transformer-winding temperature relay*

Fig. 6.2.4C *Thermal relay (A Reyrolle & Co. Ltd.)*

encased in insulaton depending upon the response time required. Compensation for varying ambient temperature is usually provided by another similar but unheated bimetal the motion of which cancels that of the active element. The heater coils may have a thin magnetic core and an armature which will operate instantly at high values of current. A relay of this type is shown in Fig. 6.2.4C.

It is possible, by comparing the deflection of the bimetal elements in each phase, to detect unbalance in a three-phase system with a differential setting more sensitive than the overload setting. This is of advantage in the protection of motors. The principle is indicated by Fig. 6.2.4D. Three identical thermal elements, one heated by each phase current, have contacts as shown. Under normal balanced conditions, the arms carrying the individual phase contacts are deflected equally; in the event of overload current flowing YT makes contact with the fixed contact BF. If the phase currents become unbalanced the deflections of the contact arms will become unequal, leading to the YT contact closing with either RT or BT.

Thermo-electric relays: A thermocouple can form an alternative basis for a relay.

The thermocouple generates only a small emf and must therefore be used in conjunction with a sensitive moving-coil relay; the combination can constitute a perhaps surprisingly sensitive sensor.

An application of this principle is a negative sequence relay for the protection of generators (Fig. 6.2.4E). The theory of this protection, and the functioning of networks which give an output proportional to the negative sequence component, is given in Section 6.8.11 and in Chapter 12.

Detection of a relatively low value of negative sequence current and operation after a long inverse time delay is required, so that the tripping characteristic shall match the ability of the generator to withstand the condition as closely as possible. Actually, eddy-currents produce heating in the machine which is proportional to the

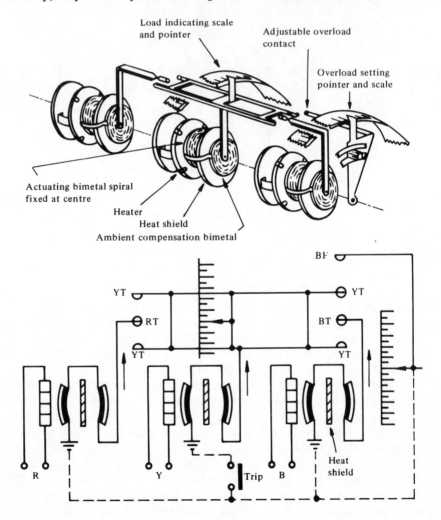

Fig. 6.2.4D *Contact system of special three-pole thermal relay*

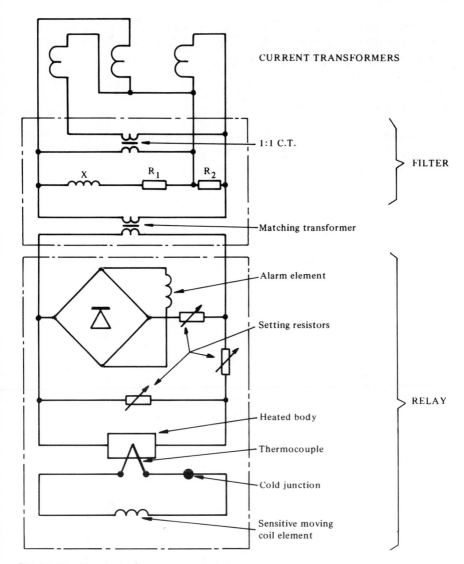

Fig. 6.2.4E *Negative phase-sequence relay (GEC Ltd.)*

square of the negative sequence current. This is correctly simulated by passing the network output through a resistor, the temperature rise of which is a thermal image of the heating due to this cause, in the generator. The image is made correct at all times if the heating-time constant is also arranged to correspond to that of the generator. The negative-sequence network near the top of the diagram delivers an output to a resistor which is embodied in a body of material having the thermal mass to give the desired time-constant. A thermocouple built into the heated body, energises a moving-coil element, the response of which keeps pace with the negative-sequence heating in the machine.

The relay also incorporates an alarm element. As the alarm is only required to have a short time lag it is energised directly from the negative sequence network output without involving the thermal image.

6.2.5 Motor-operated relays

A miniature electric motor can be used to perform various relaying functions. Setting aside the induction relays described above which are of the nature of Ferraris motor elements, motor-driven relays usually perform auxiliary or control functions. Typical is the provision of relatively long time delays, for which purpose a small motor drives through reduction gearing a contact making arrangement.

6.2.6 Gas- and oil-operated relays (Buchholz relays)

Faults inside oil-immersed electrical plant, such as transformers, give rise to the generation of gas. If the fault is severe, movement of the oil will also occur. Buchholz relays, responsive to these conditions, provide a very reliable form of protection. They will detect incipient faults at an early stage, and also others, such as core faults which are not detectable by other forms of protection.

Fig. 6.2.6A is a sectional view of one type of Buchholz relay. It is mounted in the oil pipe line between the transformer tank and conservator. The relay housing contains two pivoted aluminium buckets (one in the case of the single-element type), each counterbalanced by a weight; and each carrying a mercury switch. Under normal conditions the balance weights predominate and tilt both assemblies so that the mercury switches are open.

A small or incipient fault causes a slow generation of gas which accumulates in the top of the relay and lowers the oil level in the housing. The open top buckets remain full of oil so that they lose buoyancy as if they were solid bodies, as the external oil level falls. The top assembly therefore tilts and operates the mercury switch. This contact will usually be connected to an alarm circuit.

If no remedial action is taken, further lowering of the oil level will operate the lower assembly which will be arranged to isolate the transformer. A severe fault causes rapid generation of gas and a bulk displacement of oil which surges up the conservator pipe and through the relay housing. The oil flow is directed by a baffle plate so as to tilt the lower bucket assembly causing the corresponding mercury switch to isolate the transformer. Loss of oil due to leakage will operate the alarm and trip contacts in turn. Other designs employ floats which are either hollow sealed drums or solid plastic material. All relays are equipped with one or more pet-cocks. These are provided to enable samples of the gas to be collected for analysis, for venting the housing and for testing the operation of the relay.

The relays are made in three sizes suitable for oil-pipes of 1 inch, 2 inch and 3 inch diameter, respectively. The alarm elements operate with volumes of gas

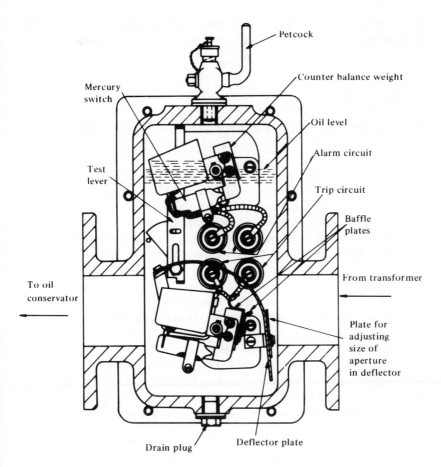

Fig. 6.2.6A   *Gas and oil operated relay (alarm circuit closed)*

collected varying from 100 to 250 cm^3, depending upon make and size. The trip elements operate with oil velocities from 70 to 160 cm/s, dependent upon make, size and pipe angle.

The pipe angle and the inclination of the relay can have a marked effect on performance. For single-float relays, the rising angle should be between 2 and 5°, and for double-float relays the limits are 3 and 7°. The inclination perpendicular to the oil flow should not exceed 1°. A machined flat surface is provided on top of the relay, parallel to the oil flow to enable these angles to be checked after installation. To avoid effects due to turbulence, the pipe should be straight for a length of at least five times its internal diameter on the tank side of the relay and three times on the conservator side.

Although the power transformer is classed as static plant, 'transformer hum' can constitute a severe vibration to equipment mounted on the tank or pipework and this has caused trouble with Buchholz relays in the past, causing excessive bearing wear and unwanted operation. Attention to design has now eliminated these troubles.

6.3   Auxiliary d.c. relays

It is usually best to fit sensitive measuring relays with only a single contact. At 'pick-up' the bulk of the force developed in the relay is expended in overcoming that of the control spring or other restraint, leaving little to produce contact pressure. If the relay has a proportional movement, with little or no run-in effect, the provision of more than a single contact is likely to lead to operational difficulties due to lack of perfect alignment; with a marginal value of operating current, the movement may be arrested when the first contact touches, so that one function may be completed without that associated with the second contact. Although a high value of relay torque, combined with careful contact setting, can minimise this trouble it is usually better to use a single main contact which energises an auxiliary relay. The latter can be an armature type having a 'snap' action and will be energised with substantially more power than corresponds to its minimum pick-up value. The auxiliary relay can therefore operate positively as many contacts as are required.

Auxiliary relays are of the 'all-or-nothing' class (see Section 6.1). They are used:

(*a*)   to provide extra contacts that cannot be carried by the measuring relay
(*b*)   to provide contacts of higher rating than those of the measuring relay
(*c*)   to assist to perform a function over long leads, the resistance of which would not permit the main operating current to be transmitted from the initiating point
(*d*)   To insert a delay in performing the function.

Auxiliary relays should operate with less than the supply nominal voltage, to cover variations in the supply and variations in the relay itself. This is particularly so when the supply is a battery as is usual in switching stations.

6.3.1   Operating-voltage limits

The common '2 volt' lead-acid cell may have a terminal voltage as low as 1·8 V when largely discharged and less if called upon to deliver a heavy current, as when closing a solenoid operated circuit-breaker. It is, however, normal to maintain the battery charge with a trickle-charger which should be adjusted to hold the voltage at about 2·3 to 2·35 V per cell. The nearest round number to this condition should be used as the normal rated voltage of the battery; for example a 55-cell battery is rated at 125 V and operating limits are expressed as a percentage of this. (110 V is sometimes used as a nominal descriptive value). To allow for some lead drop, alarm and control relays must operate at 80% of nominal or 70% of rated voltage.

Tripping relays should operate with 60% of nominal or 53% of rated voltage.

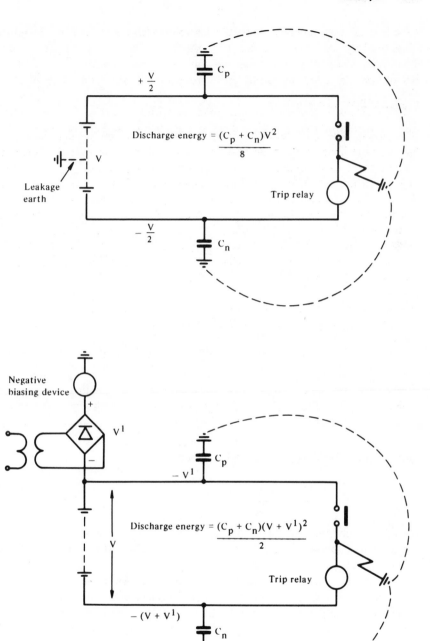

Fig. 6.3.2A *Trip-relay operation due to discharge of wiring capacitance*

If the battery is put on boost charge the cell voltage can rise to 2·7V, or 150V for a 55-cell battery. Although this condition should not be sustained for more than about 20 min, all relay operations and contact performance should be correct at this voltage, i.e. 120% of rating. Relay coils should withstand 115% of rating continuously.

In the case of batteries which are not charged while in service, the rated voltage can be reduced to 2 volts per cell and over-voltage figures need not be considered.

6.3.2   Discharge of wiring capacitance

A large switching station may contain a great amount of d.c. wiring, all of which constitutes a capacitance to earth, the total value of which may be considerable. An earth fault occurring between the protective relay contacts and the auxiliary relay coil, by effecting a change in distribution of potential, will cause a current to flow through the wiring capacitance and the relay coil. This is illustrated in Fig. 6.3.2A. If the battery is unearthed, leakage will locate zero potential at about the centre of the battery, with the d.c. supply leads at $+V/2$ and $-V/2$, respectively. With a capacitance of C_p and C_n on positive and negative poles, the energy received by the coil due to such a fault is $(C_p + C_n)V^2/8$.

If the battery is earthed on the positive pole through a resistance too high to pass a significant sustained current, the discharged energy is increased to

$$\frac{(C_p + C_n)\, V^2}{2}$$

Earthing through a negative biasing device increases the voltage at the fault point by the bias V^1. The energy discharged then becomes

$$\frac{(C_p + C_n)(V + V^1)^2}{2}$$

The danger zone, wherein the wiring fault must occur to cause this discharge of stored energy through the auxiliary relay coil, is limited as stated above, to the connection between initiating contact and coil.

When the auxiliary is a contactor contained in the same case as the initiating relay, the risk of the occurrence of a fault on this connection may be regarded as negligible, and no precautions need be taken on this account. With discretion, this exemption may be extended to an auxiliary element contained in one of a closely associated group of relays where the interconnecting lead is considered to be short enough to involve little risk and does not pass outside the cubicle on which the relays are mounted. In other cases, a tripping relay should not operate with capacitance stored energy. A practical standard of immunity has been established by requiring that tripping relays do not operate when subjected to the discharge of a 10μF capacitor charged to 150 V. (It is recognised that this test does not represent the most severe conditions which may exist). A minimum operating current limit of 100 mA is also imposed, to ensure non-operation under the above fault conditions due to the steady earth-fault current which may flow when the battery is earthed by a negative biasing device.

It is important to realise that these requirements apply not only to orthodox tripping relays, but equally to any interposing relays or contactors that may be used in tripping schemes in similar conditions.

6.3.3   Tripping relays

These are auxiliary relays provided as independent units to co-ordinate the tripping outputs of a number of protective relays. In particular, the functions of a tripping relay are:

(*a*)   To increase the number of available contacts of the protection. Where more than one circuit-breaker has to be tripped it is usually not permissible to parallel the trip coils, since different protections may trip different combinations of breakers. In the same way, control and alarm functions may need to be separated by the use of separate energising contacts.

(*b*)   To increase the rating of tripping contacts.

(*c*)   To provide a demarcation between the protection equipment and the switchgear.

Although protective relays and switchgear are technically conjoint, the physical difference between them makes it desirable that their installation and maintenance is carried out by different personnel. Also in some cases a protection controlled by one authority may need to trip switchgear belonging to a separate authority. In both the above instances, clear demarcation may be necessary.

A tripping relay must be reliable, because of its central controlling position. It should also be fast, since its operating time is additional to that of the protective relays. The operating time of the latter may be necessary to enable them to correctly achieve the measurement on which their discrimination is based, but any extra time is an unnecessary delay in tripping the circuit-breaker.

Most tripping relays are of the attracted armature type. High-speed operation is obtained by using light movements, short travel and high operating force which implies a substantial coil consumption. Usually, the coil is short-rated; the movement latches in the operated position and the operating current is interrupted by an auxiliary contact. The movement is either hand-reset or electrically reset by an auxiliary electromagnet. For some applications, a self-reset relay is required; in this case the auxiliary contact may still be provided, but will be used to introduce an 'economy resistance' whereby the coil current is reduced to a holding value, usually within the continuous rating of the coil and so reducing the breaking duty imposed on the protective relay contacts.

The main contacts of modern tripping relays will close in 10 ms or less; the auxiliary contact will usually be slower (50-60 ms) which is of advantage in the operation of series connected flags. A typical 'hand or electrically' reset tripping relay is shown in Fig. 6.3.3A. This relay has eight output contacts any of which may be normally open or normally closed. The tripping consumption is 85 W. This is a typical value which besides giving high-speed operation, enables the relay to withstand the capacitance discharge test discussed above. With some relays it is necessary to also shunt the relay with a low-inductance resistor to give the required discharge immunity.

Fig. 6.3.3A *High-speed tripping relay with eight contacts (GEC Measurements Ltd.)*

6.3.4   Time-lag relays

Time-lag relays are commonly used to provide time discrimination in graded protection schemes. They are also frequently used in control and alarm schemes to allow time for a required sequence of operation to take place, and to ensure that an unnecessary operation is not performed or an alarm given on account of a condition that is merely transient.

Time delay can be provided by many means. A short delay can be given to an armature relay by a slug as described in Section 6.2.1. A delay in pick-up of 0·05 s is readily obtained; drop-off delays can be longer, from 0·1 up to 2 or 3 s.

Drop-off time lags can also be obtained by shunting or short-circuiting the operating coil, or by connecting a diode across the coil to provide a path for inductive discharge current. Resistance-capacitance circuits can also be used.

Thermal relays can be used to provide delays of a few seconds. Although longer delays are possible, and thermal relays are designed to provide long dependent time-lag characteristics, they are not normally used to give long independent time delays.

Accurate time delays are provided by relays comprising an actuating mechanism, and a controlling system. The actuating mechanism may be a solenoid or armature type electromagnet, which, on being energised, winds a spring which then exerts a constant force, independent of the energy input, to drive a contact making arrangement, under the restraint of the controlling system. The control may be a clock-type escapement, but more usually nowadays in an eddy-current brake.

A relay of this type, illustrated in Fig. 6.3.4A, is powered by an electromagnet which winds a spiral spring via a number of interposing linkages, which serve to magnify the motion. The spring drives a main shaft which carries a calibrated time scale and two adjustable contact operating arms each fitted with rollers. The rollers effect contact operation in a smooth and frictionless manner.

The main shaft is coupled by gearing to a copper cup which rotates in the field of a totally enclosed permanent magnet. The eddy-current braking action restrains the speed of rotation of the cup and hence the rate of rotation of the main shaft and contact operating arms. The time settings are adjustable over a 5:1 range by variation of the position of the contact operating arms, while different time ranges are achieved by alternative gear ratios. Maximum time settings can be provided from 0·6 to 120 s.

The total operating time is the sum of the times taken by the actuating electromagnet and that of the timing mechanism proper. The former is made short by pro-

Fig. 6.3.4A   *Time-delay relay (GEC Measurements Ltd.)*

viding adequate operating energy and low inertia parts in the spring winding system, and is only a small part of the total time except in the case of the shortest time ranges, i.e. one second and below. Such a relay is in the 'all-or-nothing' class; it has an effective range of voltage within which it is guaranteed to operate, but has not a calibrated voltage setting.

Long time delays are usually provided by small motors which are geared down through a suitable ratio to a contact operating shaft. The motor may be an induction disc unit; alternatively it may be a miniature d.c. or a.c. motor such as are used in time switches or control devices. Any value of time delay can be provided by the use of a suitable gear ratio.

If the time delay is long (i.e. more than a few minutes at most) and therefore involving a large gear ratio, it is necessary to prevent damage due to over-running by the use of a limit switch or a slipping clutch, since the torque which might otherwise be developed on the final shaft could be excessive.

Resetting of such relays may be by reverse driving involving a comparable but not necessarily equal time delay, or instantaneously by the release of an electro-magnetically operated clutch.

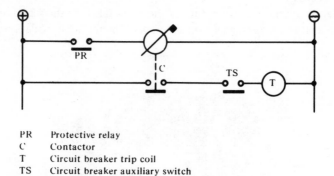

PR   Protective relay
C   Contactor
T   Circuit breaker trip coil
TS   Circuit breaker auxiliary switch

Fig. 6.3.5A   *Shunt repeat contactor*

6.3.5   Repeat contactors

Auxiliary relays were briefly introduced in Section 6.3. Repeat contactors are used to increase the contact capacity of the main protective relay, to perform a 'holding' or sealing function, or to perform logic processes which may be required in the co-ordination of the operation of the measuring relays.

Auxiliary relays are invariably of simple attracted armature type. In addition to the general requirements discussed above they may be arranged in a number of alternative circuits.

The most obvious arrangement is the shunt repeat circuit shown in Fig. 6.3.5A in which the main protective relay energises the contactor coil and the contactor operates to trip the circuit-breaker. This simple arrangement has the disadvantage

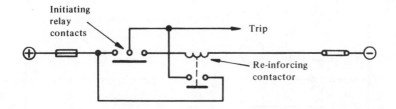

Fig. 6.3.5B   *Connections of a reinforcing contactor*

that the operating time of the contactor is added to that of the main relay. More-over, the contactor is an additional operation which is needed and must therefore reduce the overall reliability of the protection. Since the contactor necessarily has a fine wire coil the risk of failure of this item is not negligible. These difficulties are avoided in the shunt reinforcing circuit, Fig. 6.3.5B. Here the main contact makes the trip-circuit directly, but the current-carrying duty is quickly taken over by the contactor. Since more than one relay may be able to trip the circuit-breaker, in order to maintain separate flag indications it is necessary not to connect the contactor coil directly in parallel with the trip coil, but to use the three-point main trip contact as shown.

Fig. 6.3.5C shows a further development in which the main contacts are re-inforced and also the contactor is sealed in by an additional contact C2, thereby ensuring matinatenance of the trip signal until the breaker opens and breaks the trip circuit with its auxiliary switches.

As an alternative to this, the contactor may have a low resistance winding designed to carry the current of the trip coil with which it is connected in series. The contactor contact is connected in parallel with the main contact, reinforcing

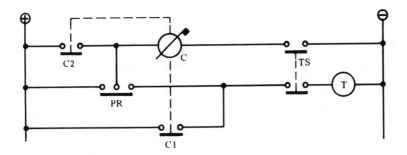

PR   Protective relay
C   Auxiliary contactor
T   Circuit breaker trip coil
TS   Circuit breaker auxiliary switches

Fig. 6.3.5C   *Shunt reinforcing contactor with sealing contact*

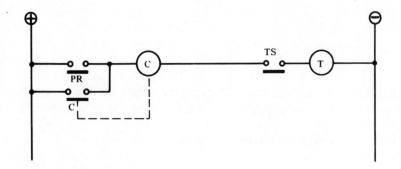

PR   Protective relay

C   Contactor

T   Circuit breaker trip coil

TS   Circuit breaker auxiliary switch

Fig. 6.3.5D *Series sealing contactor*

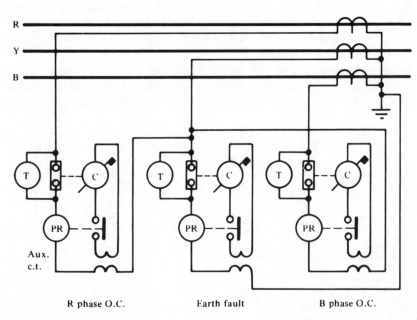

R phase O.C.   Earth fault   B phase O.C.

PR Protective relay
C   Contactor
T   Circuit breaker trip coil

Fig. 6.3.5E   *A.C. tripping from current transformers*

this latter and sealing in the trip circuit (Fig. 6.3.5D). The contactor coil is usually designed to drop only about 5% of the supply voltage when tripping the breaker. Frequently the coil is double-wound to provide a wide range of trip circuit ratings for which it would be suitable. In circumstances where more than a single relay may operate simultaneously to energise a given trip coil, the tripping current is shared by the individual series contactors. Where such a condition may exist it is necessary to allow for this division of current by choosing a suitable contactor winding while checking that the voltage drop with only one contactor energised is not excessive. The calculation should be checked at 80% of nominal supply voltage.

A.c. tripping: Where a tripping supply is not available, a scheme for energising the trip coil from the line current-transformer in series with the protective relay is sometimes used. The trip coil is normally short-circuited by a contact on the auxiliary contactor and inserted into the circuit by operation of the contactor when the main relay operates (Fig. 6.3.5E).

Naturally the contactor contact has to be of a heavy duty type for this application. The system is complete for each phase (or earth-fault) element, with separate contactors and trip coils.

6.3.6 Trip-circuit supervision

The importance of the trip circuit, which is normally not energised, leads to a desire to have a continuous check on its integrity. The simplest arrangement is the healthy

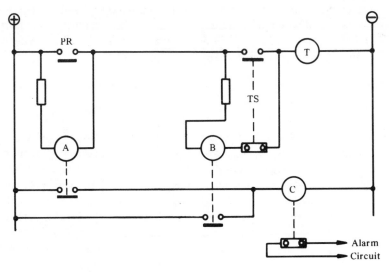

A, B, C	Auxiliary relays
PR	Protective relay
T	Circuit breaker trip coil
TS	Circuit breaker auxiliary switches

Fig. 6.3.6 *Trip-circuit supervision scheme*

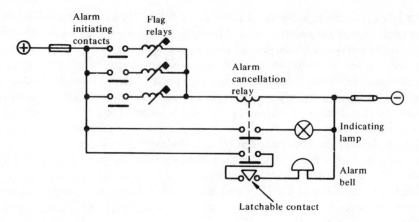

Fig. 6.3.7A   *Simple alarm scheme*

trip lamp connected across the protection tripping contacts. The lamp is lit by a small current insufficient to cause operation which is circulated through the trip coil while the circuit-breaker is closed. A resistance is included in series with the lamp to prevent accidental tripping by the initial current surge passed by the lamp, and also as a safeguard against lamp short-circuiting in the event of filament failure or on lamp replacement. This scheme does not give preclosing indication. The lamp could be replaced by a relay to give remote indication and an audible alarm.

A more comprehensive scheme is shown in Fig. 6.3.6. 'A' and 'B' relays will operate in series and both must reset to drop out 'C'. The latter has a short time lag on release to cover transit conditions. Supervision is therefore maintained continuously whether the circuit-breaker is open or closed.

6.3.7   Alarm relays

Relays to give audible and visible alarms are used to draw attention to primary relay operations. The alarm scheme may be a simple one for small stations but for more important installations, segregation of alarms for each primary circuit is desirable.

A simple alarm cancellation scheme is shown in Fig. 6.3.7A. The relay comprises an attracted armature element which carries two normally open self-reset contacts. A separate manually operated switch, normally closed, can be latched open when the relay is operated. This latching contact is connected in series with one self-reset contact in the circuit of the audible alarm device, which is therefore sounded as soon as the relay operates, but can be cancelled by latching open the normally closed switch.

The other self-reset contact energises an indicating lamp which continues to be displayed after the audible alarm has been accepted and cancelled, until the fault condition is removed. When the fault is cleared, the alarm relay resets and allows the latched switch to return to its initial closed condition. A further fault alarm can then be given. One such relay can operate in conjunction with any number of initiating relays, each with its own flag to indicate the source of the alarm.

A disadvantage of the series flag arrangement is that if the initiating contact which operated the alarm in the first place is not quickly reset a subsequent alarm coming in may be missed. Also, the combination of flags and alarm cancellation relays can occupy a lot of control panel space where a large number of separate indications is required.

An alternative to the above, which is more economic of panel space, but which is more costly, is shown in Fig. 6.3.7B. This relay can be used as an alarm cancellation relay common to a number of alarm functions, or as an individual indicating and alarm cancellation relay for each function. In the latter case it in effect combines the flag and alarm cancellation of the scheme shown in Fig. 6.3.7A. Moreover, it has the advantage that any number of alarms may operate, simultaneously or separately, and each would register.

The relay can be supplied in many different forms, according to whether it is to be energised from self-reset (fleeting) or hand-reset (non-fleeting) initiating contacts, or a combination of both. The relay itself can also be of the self-reset or hand-reset type. The self-reset type can employ an accept-push (to cancel the audible alarm) on the front of the relay bezel, or the accept-push can be mounted remotely. The hand-reset type is reset from a separate reset-push on the front bezel.

The element in this type of relay is of the instantaneous attracted-armature type, the d.c. operating coil of which is continuously rated. On being energised the operating mechanism latches. In the hand-reset version the latch is controlled by a permanent magnet. In the self-reset type the latch incorporates an electromagnet, the coil of which is energised from the alarm supply. When the relay operates, it energises a lamp which illuminates the window in the front bezel. The window is

Fig. 6.3.7B *Alarm relay (A Reyrolle & Co. Ltd.)*

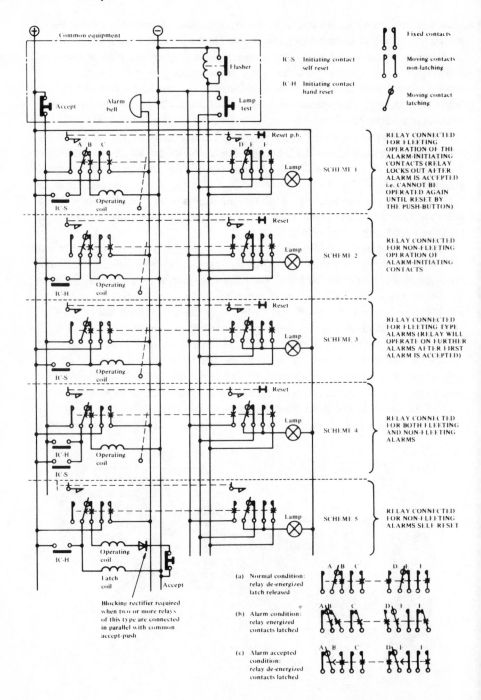

Fig. 6.3.7C *Circuit diagram for alarm relay shown in Fig. 6.3.7B (A Reyrolle & Co. Ltd.)*

inscribed to indicate the source of the alarm. A separate flasher relay may be employed to cause the lamp to flash when the alarm relay operates. Cancellation of the audible alarm by pressing the accept-push steadies the light, which remains until the relay is reset.

The schematic diagram, Fig. 6.3.7C, shows some of the applications of this relay and explains the manner in which it operates.

In generating stations, and major substations, a large number of alarm indications have to be displayed in the control room. It is desirable, therefore, that the separate indicating devices should occupy the minimum of space necessary to give the operator clear warning of the alarm condition. It was for such situations that the annunciator type of equipment was developed.

Basically, an annunciator alarm equipment consists of a facia (or window) housing a number of indicating lamps, and a separate group of alarm relays. Initiation of an alarm condition causes one of the lamps in the facia to flash and simultaneously sounds an audible alarm. The latter may be cancelled by operating a remote push button, often located on the logging desk in the Control Room, or by depressing the accept-push on the front of the facia (see Fig. 6.3.7D). Acceptance of the alarm steadies the flashing light, and enables the alarm inscription in front of it to be read. To reset the annunciator it is necessary to operate the reset-push on the front of the facia. If this is done after the initiating contact is re-opened the lamp will go out. If the reset-push is operated before the initiating contact is reset the lamp will remain alight. The reset signal, however, will be stored by the relay equipment and the lamp will be extinguished when the initiating contact is subsequently reset.

The annunciator alarm scheme is designed so that each indication is separate and any number will indicate an alarm whether they be on the same or different facias, or whether one or more alarms have already been received. The only common features are the remote alarm cancellation button, and the accept and reset which perform the same function simultaneously for each indication on the same facia.

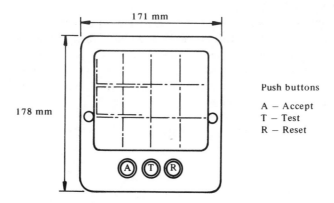

Fig. 6.3.7D *Typical 12-way alarm facia*

To achieve the maximum economy of space annunciator equipments are usually designed to operate from a 50 V d.c. supply. The relays are of the telephone type and for practical reasons they are frequently accommodated together in a free standing cubicle. This arrangement is also convenient for maintenance. Alternatively, the annunciator alarm equipment may be fully transistorised.

A lamp-test facility is provided as a check that the lamps are healthy. A separate push-button can be employed for this purpose on each facia, or a common remote lamp-test button can be installed.

Facias are designed to take 6, 9, 12, 18 or more indications according to requirements. Alarm indications are usually amber in colour, but white, red or any other colour could be employed. Spare ways on the facia should be equipped with lamps, so that there is no confusion between a spare way and a faulty lamp which is in service. The spare ways are usually marked with a star or other distinctive inscription.

6.4   General design considerations

The general requirements of protective relays are laid down in BS 142 : 1966.

6.4.1   Coil ratings

Preferred rated currents are quoted in the above standard as 1, 2 and 5 amps. A rated current of 5 A is extensively used for relays for 'distribution' systems of voltages up to 11kV. Such relays are frequently mounted on, or close to, the switchgear with which they are associated, so that lead resistances are relatively low. In the case of generator protection, on account of the high value of rated primary current, it is usually undesirable to use current-transformers having a secondary rating of less than 5 A.

Between the above two extremes, it is nearly always preferable to use a 1 A (or at most 2 A) current rating. This keeps the wasteful burden of the leads to a low value whilst not affecting the burden due to the relay itself. The total burden imposed on the c.t.s is thereby minimised, which is a very important factor in obtaining a high standard of performance for large transmission systems.

The system voltage, as presented through voltage transformers, in British practice, is invariably: 110 V phase-phase.
63·5 V phase-neutral.

6.4.2   Auxiliary supplies

Battery nominal voltages are 30, 50, 110 or 240 V. The value chosen is largely decided by the amount of d.c. power needed. For example, but not invariably:

Distribution substations	use 30 V
Communication equipments	use 50 V
Large substations and all grid stations	use 110 V
Power stations	use 110 and 240 V

See Section 6.3.1 for further discussion of batteries.

6.4.3 Relay setting adjustment

One of the most common means of setting adjustment is by tapping the coil of the relay or of an auxiliary transformer. The taps are conveniently selected by a plug bridge illustrated in Fig. 6.2.3H. The bridge is fitted with an automatic contact which closes on to the highest setting, before the plug is fully withdrawn, so avoiding opening-circuiting the current transformer. Seven settings are usually provided; when used to select taps on the relay winding, the relay burden at setting is not significantly different for each setting.

Setting may be also varied by adjustment of spring tension with or without variation of total travel. The method to be used depends upon the type of element and the effect of such adjustment on other characteristics such as, for example, operating time.

6.4.4 Contacts

Ideally, a protective relay should possess contacts which are sufficient in number and rating to perform all the functions required when the relay operates. In practice, this is not practicable except in the simplest applications. A large contact rating necessitates high pressure between contacts and/or large contact separation.

The relay element must therefore be capable of doing appreciable mechanical work, and the amount of such work is multiplied by the number of contacts. This is simple enough for a contactor, but for a measuring element the contact loading must be only a very small fraction of the effort developed in the relay movement. Hence, a large contact loading would involve a bulky relay element and a large requirement for input power, i.e. a large burden imposed on the current transformers. Economic considerations dictate that primary relay elements should be sensitive and therefore carry contacts of only moderate rating, heavier duty being performed by a repeat contactor. The desirability of fitting measuring relays with only one contact is discussed under Section 6.3.

The majority of relay contacts are made of silver which has a low resistance and does not oxidise very readily. The fine film of oxide which may form breaks down easily with heat and with mechanical pressure. In polluted atmospheres, silver

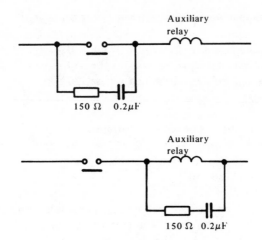

Fig. 6.4.4A   *Alternative connections for spark-quenching devices*

sulphide is formed as a blue-black tarnish. Surface films are best penetrated by high pressure, so that contact tips are often domed or formed into a wedge shape so that contact is restricted to a point or line of negligible area. Some relative movement is likely to occur when contacts make but if they can be set so that a definite transverse sliding action or 'wipe' takes place, then surface films will be more readily scraped away.

Silver is often alloyed with 5-10% of palladium to increase hardness and resistance to tarnish. Other metals such as gold, platinum, rhodium and alloys of these metals are used in special cases. Sensitive contact fingers are often fitted with supporting or 'backing' strips of stiffer material to limit the overall motion of the finger, to permit initial tension to be set in the finger, and to prevent vibration of the finger due to external shock or vibration applied to the relay. The correct setting of the contact finger and backing strips is important, to obtain correct functioning of the relay. Spark-quenching circuits are sometimes applied to a contact, particularly if the load is inductive.

A diode connected across an inductive coil energised with d.c. is an effective spark quench for the energising contact, but will delay the de-energisation of the coil, producing a slugging action on the device which it operates. The circuit shown in Fig. 6.4.4A is generally effective as a spark quench, although the values of components are typical only and need to be checked by test.

When the contact opens, the capacitor carries the coil current and charges up until the current is brought to zero. The contact gap, has therefore, initially low voltage across it and should increase to a sufficient degree to withstand the voltage built up on the capacitor. Too little capacitance will cause an excessive voltage to be developed, since the inductive energy in the coil is transferred to the capacitor; this voltage may be damaging to insulation or cause the contact gap to flash over again. A typical value of capacitance is $0 \cdot 2 \, \mu F$.

The resistor is provided to protect the contacts when closing from being burnt or welded by the discharge of the capacitor. The resistance must not be omitted.

A capacitor and metrosil unit in parallel (Fig. 6.4.4B), can be used effectively in some circumstances, but when used with relay contacts the capacitor should be smaller than the above, in general not exceeding 0·002 μF when used with induction relays and 0·005 μF with armature relays.

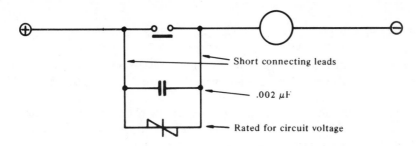

Fig. 6.4.4B   *Alternative spark quench circuit*

6.4.5   Flag indicators

Flag indicators are provided to give information of the operation of relays. Flags are, therefore, nearly always hand reset, means being provided outside the case for this purpose.

A flag may be mechanically released by the measuring element, which is simple and positive although not always feasible, or it may be electrically operated. Where a repeat contactor is used, this will also carry the flag indicator, since operation of the system is not complete until the contactor has picked up.

Flags are usually enclosed within the relay case; in special circumstances where tripping requires the operation of several relays, separate flags may be used, which may be either with or without additional contacts for remote alarm purposes. Where possible, separate flags per pole of the relay assist in identifying the faulty phases.

Operation of a mechanical flag should coincide with the trip contact operation, any error of coincidence being such as to make the flag early, so that the relay cannot trip without the flag indicating. Flags should be completely obscured when reset and be visible clearly without searching when operated. The flag should be of ample size and not liable to be confused with other parts or indications. Operational current or voltage limits for flag indicators are similar to those for repeat contactors.

6.4.6   Resetting

Most relays are intrinsically self-resetting, under the normal restraining force, whether due to gravity, spring, or other means. Some relays are designed to latch mechanically, or hold in the operated position by magnetic force. They may be reset by hand by means of a knob or push-button which releases the latch and restores the movement to the unoperated position.

Alternatively relays may be reset electrically; a separate electromagnet is fitted which releases the latch when energised, or diverts magnetic flux so that the element resets. It is usual to also fit means of hand-resetting on these relays.

6.5 Static relays

It was appreciated in the 1930s that electronic devices and techniques could be applied to protective relays and give several potential advantages, among which were:

(a)   due to the amplification of energising signals obtainable, the sources need only provide low power. Therefore the size of the associated current and voltage transformers could be reduced.

(b)   the accuracy and hence selectivity could be improved.

(c)   the fast response of the circuits could give fast tripping and clearance of faults.

(d)   the flexibility of circuitry would allow new and improved characteristics.

(e)   the relays would be unaffected by the number of operations.

Unfortunately, these advantages were outweighed by the suspect reliability caused by the fragility of thermionic valves and their heaters. Other disadvantages, particularly on small relays were the high value of the h.t. voltage and high-wattage heater supply required. Although some development work was done, these disadvantages prevented the use of thermionic equipment in protective schemes where an electromechanical equivalent existed.

The semiconductor transistor and diode, being exceptionally robust and requiring only low-voltage low-wattage supplies, overcame these objections. The lack of fragile or moving parts makes a relay resistant to shock and vibration, and should reduce the maintenance required. A considerable size reduction can also be achieved.

Development of transistorised relays has been carried out since the early 1950s, during which time semiconductors themselves have improved tremendously, modern silicon planar transistors and integrated circuits having a reliability in excess of previous conventional components. Most existing forms of protection have been produced in transistorised form, together with new types of protection and control devices for which semiconductor circuitry is particularly suitable.

Site experience with static relays has been gained since the early 1960s and the transistorised relay is now established as a practical protective device.

6.5.1 Basic circuits employed

In the same way that electromechanical schemes are in general built up from a small number of discrete elements such as induction disc, induction cup, hinged

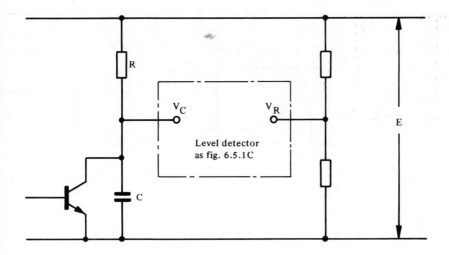

Timing is initiated by turning the input transistor off.

The level detector operates when V_C exceeds V_R.

$$t = RC \log_e \frac{E}{E - V_C}$$

$V_R = KE$ (K = ratio of potentiometer).

$\therefore$. Time for V_C to equal V_R.

$$t = RC \log_e \frac{E}{E - KE}$$

$$t = RC \log_e \left(\frac{1}{1 - K} \right)$$

Fig. 6.5.1A   *Resistance-capacity timer*

armature relays etc., a small number of basic circuits find repeated application in static relays.

These circuits have been proved in many applications and form the basis of most complex relay designs. In many static relays these circuits are built up using transistors, but tremendous strides have now been made by the semiconductor manufacturers in producing standard linear amplifiers and logic families in integrated circuit form. These are being used increasingly in relay design and the flexibility of the standard operational amplifier in particular makes it a very suitable component for standard relaying circuits.

6.5.1.1 Timers: Time-delay circuits are extensively used in relays and are generally of the resistance-capacity type. Fig. 6.5.1A shows a type where the capacitor C is

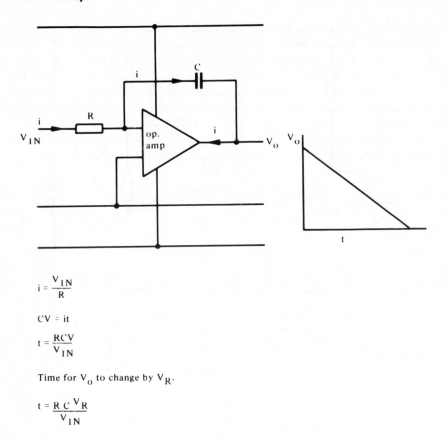

$$i = \frac{V_{IN}}{R}$$

$$CV = it$$

$$t = \frac{RCV}{V_{IN}}$$

Time for V_0 to change by V_R.

$$t = \frac{R \, C \, V_R}{V_{IN}}$$

Fig. 6.5.1B *Timing circuit using operational amplifier*

exponentially charged from a regulated voltage E through a resistor R. The time taken to reach a fixed voltage is directly proportional to R which can be varied to adjust the time delay. This timer can be started in two ways: (i) the d.c. supply can be switched on or (ii) a short circuit, shown in the form of a transistor in the circuit, can be removed from the capacitor. A transistor can effectively reset the circuit by discharging the capacitor to a negligible voltage in a few milliseconds when biassed on. Fig. 6.5.1B shows a timer of the 'Miller' type using an operational amplifier. In this circuit the voltage at the output falls linearly at a rate proportional to R and inversely proportional to the input voltage V_{IN}.

6.5.1.2 Level detectors: D.C. level detectors are used to detect when the d.c. level at the input exceeds a 'set' level. When this level is exceeded, the output is switched from the off to the on condition, usually with considerable current gain between the input and output. This allows a voltage level on a capacitor being charged at say 1 μA to be detected and a standard hinged armature relay driven by the output. Fig. 6.5.1C is a circut which has a drop-off level only fractionally below its pick-up level. This is the type least sensitive to electrical interference as it cannot be latched in by transients when the input voltage is below the set level. Figs. 6.5.1D and 6.5.1E show level detectors with a drop-off level which is a fixed proportion of the operating level. This different drop-off level is achieved by using feedback from the output to the set level which lowers its voltage level after operation.

6.5.1.3 Polarity detectors: Polarity detectors are used where an exact determination of the zero crossings on a.c. waveforms is required. The circuits in Figs. 6.5.1F

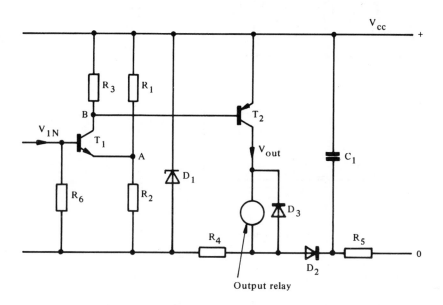

OPERATION. With $V_{in} = 0$, T_1 is switched off by reverse bias of base-emitter junction of T_1 and point B is at maximum potential; T_2 is off. When V_{in} is raised above V_A, T_1 turns ON and V_B falls, turning on T_2 to operate the output relay. There is no feed-back so that reverse action occurs with negligible differential.

Zener diode D_1 & R_4 control supply voltage to the measuring circuit.

D_2 prevents damage due to reverse connection of supply.

D_3 prevents relay coil generating excessive inductive voltage when T_2 switches off, which might damage T_2.

R_5 & C_1 suppress input transients from the D.C. supply.

Fig. 6.5.1C *Level detector with negligible differential*

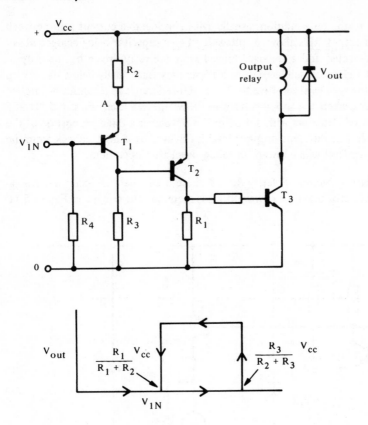

With $V_{in} = 0$, T_1 is ON, short-circuiting the emitter of T_2; T_2 and T_3 are OFF.

When $V_{in} > V_A = \dfrac{R_3}{R_2 + R_3} \cdot V_{cc}$, T_1 is turned OFF and T_2 turns ON followed

by T_3 which energises the output relay. V_A is now $\dfrac{R_1}{R_1 + R_2} \cdot V_{cc}$ which is designed

to be less than operate value ($R_1 < R_3$). V_{in} must be reduced below the latter
value to make the circuit reset.

Fig. 6.5.1D *Level detector with definite resetting differential*

and 6.5.1G can also be used as very sensitive level detectors in such applications as
transformer tap change relays where an extremely accurate comparison with a
reference voltage is required.

Fig. 6.5.1F is a transistorised version. This circuit only requires a few millivolts
input (A positive with respect to B) to saturate TR4. An even more sensitive
polarity detector is provided by an operational amplifier with no feedback (Fig.
6.5.1G). In this case, the output reverses polarity typically from +13V to −13V
when the input changes polarity.

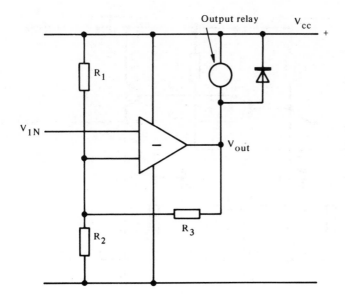

The output voltage is $+V_{cc}$ when $V_{in} = 0$. A reference voltage is provided for the operational amplifier by potentiometer R_1-R_2 and including the effect of current in R_3. Since $V_{out} = V_{cc}$, R_3 is in parallel with R_1.

$$V_{Ref} = \frac{R_2 \cdot V_{cc}}{\dfrac{R_1 R_3}{R_1 + R_3} + R_2}$$

When V_{in} exceeds V_{Ref}, V_{out} swings to zero. R_3 is now effectively in

parallel with R_2 so that V_{Ref} becomes $\dfrac{\dfrac{R_2 R_3}{R_2 + R_3} \cdot V_{cc}}{\dfrac{R_1 + \dfrac{R_2 R_3}{R_2 + R_3}}{}}$

The amplifier will not change state again until V_{in} drops below this new value of V_{Ref}.

Fig. 6.5.1E   *Alternative level detector with definite resetting differential*

6.5.1.4 Phase comparators: Phase comparators are used to detect when one a.c. input is more or less than $90°$ out of phase with a second a.c. input. They can be used to produce circular impedance and mho distance relay characteristics as shown in Fig. 6.8.7D and in directional relays.

The phase comparator used most commonly in static relays is the diode com-

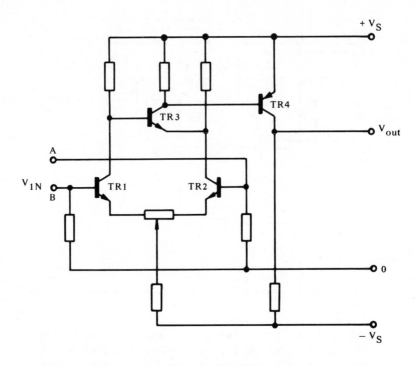

The currents through TR1 and TR2 are initially balanced by the potentiometer bridging their emitters, so that zero potential exists across TR3. An input signal which raises the potential of A relative to B causes TR2 to conduct more than TR1, which draws current through the base-emitter junction of TR3, which is turned on. TR4 turns on in consequence and produces an output signal.

When A is negative relative to B, the output is zero.

Fig. 6.5.1F *Polarity detector (using separate transistors)*

parator shown in Fig. 6.8.7A. In this comparator the output magnitude varies with that of the input quantities, its instantaneous value always being that of the smaller of the two inputs. The output consists of a.c. with a steady state d.c. component, the polarity of the d.c. component changing when the two input quantities are 90° out of phase. At 90° out of phase the time periods for which the output is positive also equals that for which it is negative.

A circuit utilising integrated-circuit logic is shown in Fig. 6.5.1H. Two exclusive OR gates are presented with square wave signals having the same zero crossing points as the input signals. The output signals from the OR gates A and C are inverted at B and D and compared in a NAND gate which gives an output when the square-wave inputs are in antiphase, and no output when they are in phase. To detect the ± 90° points it is necessary to determine when the mark/space ratio of the output, passes through unity.

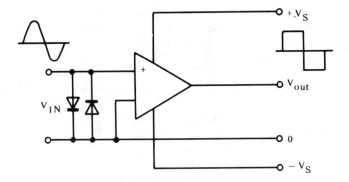

As the operational amplifier has a very high voltage gain (typically of the order of 100,000), a small positive signal on the non-inverting input gives an output voltage of $+V_S$. Similarly a small negative input voltage will give an output voltage of $-V_S$.

A sinusoidal input produces a substantially square output voltage wave between the limiting values of $+V_S$ and $-V_S$, changing from one value to the other in very short periods about the zero points of the input wave.

Fig. 6.5.1G *Polarity detector using operational amplifier*

With normal inputs, the square-wave signals produced at points X and Y in the diagram swing between the positive and negative rail voltages; with no input signal, points X and Y assume zero rail potential. A positive voltage input signal to the OR gate is represented as '1' and a negative voltage signal corresponds to '0'. A zero voltage signal is negative relative to the upper OR gate and therefore represents a '0' input but positive to the lower OR gate and so denotes a '1' input.

Truth tables showing the response of exclusive OR gates and of the NAND gate are shown in Fig. 6.5.1H below the diagram. The square-voltage waves at 'X' and 'Y' corresponding to two inputs having a relative phase displacement are also shown with the resultant output voltage at E.

The operation of the circuit to give this output is explained by the output truth table. Four zones in the cycle, in which differing combinations of polarity occur, are designated 1, 2, 3 and 4 and the responses at the various stages in the scheme are given. These will be found to agree with the basic truth-tables; it should be remembered that the two transistors following the exclusive OR gates invert signals A and C to form the outputs B and D. The duplication in the scheme would at first sight appear to be unnecessary, but is required to cover the case when either input is zero, in which case a single exclusive OR gate would produce alternate output (1 and 0) for successive half cycles and would not be readily distinguished from a low power factor condition. The final truth table shows how this condition is covered by the duplication of the first stage comparison. In this case the Y input is zero and as explained above corresponds to a '0' for the upper OR gate but is a 1 to the lower gate, producing a continuous '1' signal from the NAND gates, which represents a restraint action.

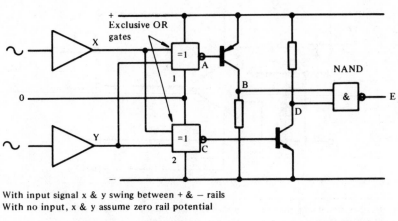

With input signal x & y swing between + & – rails
With no input, x & y assume zero rail potential

Truth tables – exclusive OR

X	Y	A or C
0	1	1
1	0	1
0	0	0
1	1	0

NAND

B	D	E
0	1	1
1	0	1
0	0	1
1	1	0

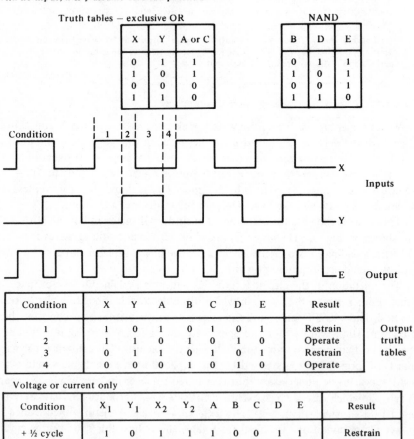

Output truth tables

Condition	X	Y	A	B	C	D	E	Result
1	1	0	1	0	1	0	1	Restrain
2	1	1	0	1	0	1	0	Operate
3	0	1	1	0	1	0	1	Restrain
4	0	0	0	1	0	1	0	Operate

Voltage or current only

Condition	X_1	Y_1	X_2	Y_2	A	B	C	D	E	Result
+ ½ cycle	1	0	1	1	1	0	0	1	1	Restrain
– ½ cycle	0	0	0	1	0	1	1	0	1	Restrain

Fig. 6.5.1H   *Phase comparator using logic units*

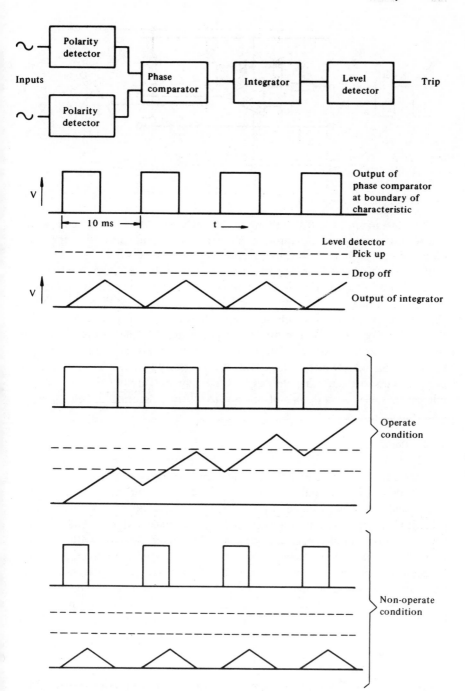

Fig. 6.5.1I *Operation of phase detector*

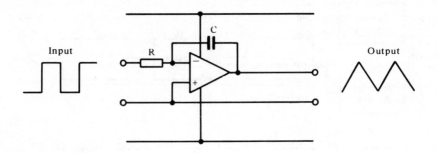

Fig. 6.5.1J   *Integrating circuit*

6.5.1.5   Integrators: Fig. 6.5.1I shows the block diagram of a complete comparator circuit. The polarity detector provides a square-wave output having differing mark/space ratios, depending on the phase relationship of the inputs.

If a waveform with a mark/space ratio of unity is fed into an integrator (Fig. 6.5.1J) having equal charge and discharge rates the output will be a triangular wave with no increasing d.c. level. If the mark/space ratio is greater than unity the triangular wave will move positively and there will be no nett movement for ratios less than unity. The nett rate of movement is proportional to the difference between the input ratio and unit. To detect this movement a level detector of the type shown in Figs. 6.5.1D or 6.5.1E is used. It is necessary to have a lower drop off to pick up ratio to ensure that the output is continuous. Careful choice of charging rate can give an operating time of half a cycle at the most sensitive point, coupled with zero overreach.

6.5.2   Components

Over the past 20 years tremendous pressure has been exerted on electronic component manufacturers by military and space development programmes to develop smaller and more reliable components. To back up this work extensive and exhaustive reliability test procedures were devised. The components which initially resulted were expensive but the manufacturing techniques used, together with increased demand have resulted in a range of high reliability components eminently suitable for protective relaying. As minimum packaging space is seldom a pressing criterion for relays, relay manufacturers can be conservative in their choice of components. Components can be used which are proved standard types of demonstrated reliability. It is generally accepted that relays should be designed for a service life in excess of 20 years with maintenance limited to operational checks. Components are therefore selected with this goal in mind.

6.5.2.1   Resistors: For general use, metal oxide resistors have proved to be reliable and stable when used within their voltage ratings. For very high stability, metal film resistors can be used. The metal oxide resistors consist of a very thin layer of tin oxide deposited on a glass or ceramic rod, and is spirally cut to achieve the correct value. They are unsuitable for use where high voltage transients are encountered, as this can cause breakdown across the spiral gap and results in burning of the resistive film.

Where voltage transients are encountered, solid carbon composition or vitreous enamelled wire wound resistors can be used. In general high value, small sized wire wound resistors are avoided because of the fine wire employed in their construction.

6.5.2.2 Capacitors: Metallised polyester and polycarbonate capacitors are used generally as these are very stable and have low leakage currents. They can also be used in the presence of voltage transients as they are 'self-healing' after voltage breakdown. This type of capacitor has largely replaced paper types and is very suitable for timing circuits, giving accurate timings with excellent repeatability.

For larger capacitance values, tantalum electrolytic capacitors can be used. These are very small and have no 'wear out' mechanism but leakage current variation renders them unsuitable for high accuracy timing applications. For high voltage, high capacitance values, aluminium electrolytics must be used. Modern high reliability types have a life in excess of 20 years if used under the correct conditions but are not used where stability of capacitance value is required.

6.5.2.3 Diodes: Silicon diodes are now used in most applications, having leakage currents down below 1 μA and voltage withstands up to 1500V. Avalanche types can also withstand voltage breakdown, dissipating pulse powers up to several kilowatts without damage. Silicon Zener diodes provide stable voltage regulation and reference levels and are used in power supply circuits and where voltage clipping is required.

Silicon transistors have generally replaced germanium types having a considerably extended working temperature range. Planar construction makes them very robust and reliable. Planar field-effect transistors are useful where a voltage operated device having a high input impedance is required. Thyristors are used for output switching devices but care has to be taken in circuit design to avoid operation due to spurious impulse voltages or 'spikes'.

6.5.2.4 Connectors: To enable relatively complex circuits to be broken down into a number of replaceable parts, components are mounted on printed circuit cards having gold plated contact fingers on one edge. These are mated with sockets having bifurcated gold plated contacts giving a modular construction to relaying schemes.

6.5.3 Transient overvoltages and interference

When working within their maximum current and voltage ratings, semiconductor devices are extremely reliable, but because of their low thermal mass can be damaged if the peak permitted voltage is exceeded even momentarily. They therefore have to be protected against any transient overvoltage. High frequency interference may also cause maloperation of circuits because of their high speed and sensitivity. For this reason particular care is taken in the design of circuits and certain standard voltage impulse and high frequency disturbance tests have been devised.

6.5.3.1 Sources of transients: Fig. 6.5.3A shows how the back e.m.f of inductive loads and wiring when d.c. current flowing through them is interrupted can cause high voltage spikes at relay terminals. Fig. 6.3.2A illustrates how an earth fault on a negatively biased tripping battery can cause sudden discharge of wiring capacitance through inductive coils setting up high-frequency resonance. Closing and opening h.v. isolators is a major source of h.f. noise, both electromagnetically

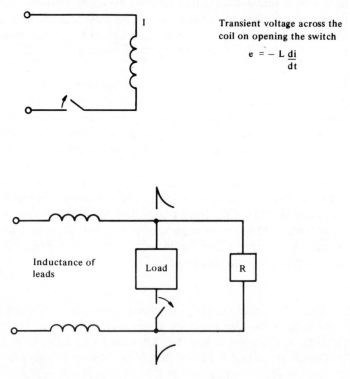

Transient voltage across the coil on opening the switch

$$e = -L\frac{di}{dt}$$

Inductance of leads

Load

R

Transient voltage across switch does not dissipate in the power source because of lead inductance and is applied to relay.

Fig. 6.5.3A *Inductive 'spike' voltage caused by switching auxiliary loads*

generated and by voltage drops across earth connections. Fig. 6.5.3B illustrates how closing the isolator can cause oscillations between the c.v.t and c.t. bushing capacitance and the loop circuit inductance. This disturbance is repeated as a short burst of high frequency for each flashover of the isolator contacts.

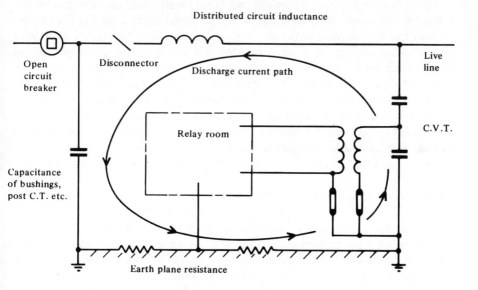

Fig. 6.5.3B *Oscillatory discharge caused by closing isolator*

6.5.3.2 Standard tests: In order to assess the ability of relays to operate correctly under these conditions, two special type-tests have been devised. One originated as BEAMA recommendation 219 and now being adopted by IEC, is a high-voltage impulse test designed to check the ability of the relay components to withstand the impulse without damage. The impulse, which has an open circuit peak value of 5 kV and a source impedance of 400 Ω is applied three times with each polarity between the terminals of each circuit, between separate circuits and between all circuits and case (earth). The second test, which is applied to the same points on the relay, but with the relay energised, is designed to check if the relay mal-operates when a series of high frequency bursts are superimposed on to its normal energising quantities. The tests consist of repetitive bursts of 1 MHz oscillations decaying to half amplitude in approximately 4 μs. The repetition rate is 400/s and the test is applied for 2 s. The peak voltage is 1 kV for tests across the terminals of the same circuit and 2·5 kV for tests between circuits.

6.5.3.3 Protection against transients: Transients generated internally by inductive components can usually be suppressed by a diode which limits the back e.m.f. Short duration 'spikes' and high frequency transients across the terminals of any circuit can be suppressed by an *RC* low-pass filter. Wirewound or carbon composition resistors are used instead of film type because of their ability to withstand high transient voltages. The capacitors must be of the 'self healing' type, metallised plastic being preferred.

High-frequency transients are difficult to suppress because currents tend to flow through intercircuit stray capacitance. For example; when a transient occurs between the d.c. terminals and earth, current tends to flow through low impedance paths in the circuitry to a point near the case and then through the circuit/case capacitance back to earth. These stray currents may cause maloperation. It is difficult to stop these currents flowing and therefore the route of the current is controlled such that it does not cause maloperation. This involves employing a low impedance route between all circuits by using screens etc. in such a way that the sensitive parts of the circuits are bypassed. Fig. 6.5.3C shows a simplified circuit with suitable high frequency current paths.

6.5.4 Power supplies for static relays

As a tripping supply in the form of a battery is usually available, simple supplies consisting of dropping resistors and shunt Zener diodes to give a regulated voltage for the transistorised circuitry can be used. Such an arrangement is shown in Fig. 6.5.4A. YY are the relay teminals and R2C1 is a low pass filter for attenuating transients in the incoming d.c. supply. D1 blocks current flow if the terminals are connected with wrong polarity, thereby protecting the relay. R3 is an appropriate value dropping resistor for Zener diode D2 which gives the regulated voltage. A transient free unregulated voltage is provided at points XX which can be used for output relays etc. R1 is an additional dropping resistor which can be accommodated externally, for higher battery voltages.

This system has the advantage of simplicity and reliability having as the source of power the tripping battery. The main disadvantage is that it takes a standing

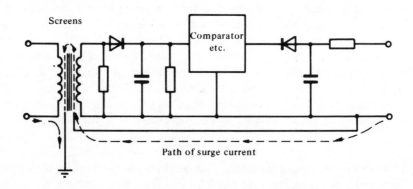

Fig. 6.5.3C   *Common mode current paths in a typical circuit with screens*

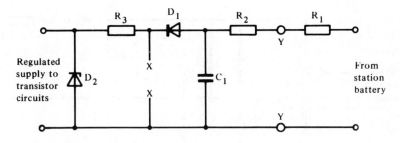

Fig. 6.5.4A   *Regulated supply from station battery*

current drain from the battery and also for more complex relays the power dissipation in the dropping resistors and the Zener diode can be high.

For current-measuring relays a power supply such as that shown in Fig. 6.5.4B can be used, which derives its power from the measured current by means of a shunt regulator. This eliminates the disadvantage of permanent drain on batteries and can be used where there is no battery supply or where the trip battery has no charger. Its main disadvantage is that the burden imposed on the c.t. can be quite high.

To avoid a standing current drain on the tripping battery and the high burden imposed on the c.t.s or v.t.s, rechargeable nickel-cadmium batteries which are trickle charged from the input a.c. supply, can be housed inside the relay. However, the maintenance required, i.e. checking the battery capacity every 2-3 years, has reduced the popularity of this type of circuit. A patented solution which overcomes both the standing current drain on the tripping batteries and high burden imposed on the c.t.s or v.t.s, without using internal batteries is shown in Figs. 6.5.4C and 6.5.4D. The low power requirements of the measuring circuits are provided by the measured quantity which when measurement is complete, switches in the station battery to provide power for the high consumption output devices. This is achieved by discharging a capacitor into a sensitive reed relay to switch in the station battery, (Fig. 6.5.4C) the d.c. power for measurement having been derived from the input current. Input burdens as low as 0·006 VA at setting current can be achieved on sensitive earth fault relays using this system.

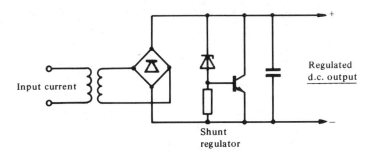

Fig. 6.5.4B   *Regulated d.c. supply from measured current*

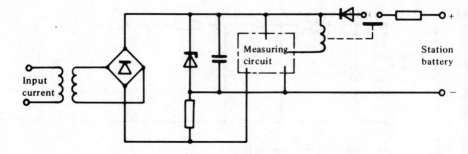

Fig. 6.5.4C *Power supply from station battery without continuous drain*

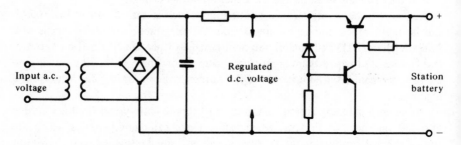

Fig. 6.5.4D *Alternative power supply from station battery without continuous drain using regulator circuit*

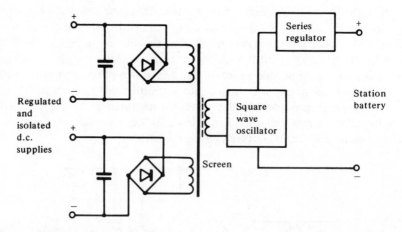

Fig. 6.5.4E *D.C./a.c./d.c. convertor*

In Fig. 6.5.4D, the measuring power is derived from the input voltage and, when this cannot supply power, a small collapse in the regulated voltage will cause a short circuit to be removed from the base supply of a series regulator causing current to be drawn from the station battery through the regulator. In larger schemes, self-powered 'starters' can be used which switch in the station battery to the main scheme when the starter setting is exceeded. In complex schemes where isolation is required between the auxiliary d.c. supply and the relay d.c. circuitry, a d.c./a.c./d.c. converter can be provided. A simplified schematic is shown in Fig. 6.5.4E. Regulation can either be on the primary or secondary side of the isolating transformer but is shown in the diagram on the primary, as it then provides common regulation to the two isolated d.c. supplies. This type of supply can be switched in by a starter or by the current as in Fig. 6.5.4C but care must be taken in its design to ensure that a regulated output is provided sufficiently rapidly after switching in, to not affect the relay operating speed and performance. This type of circuit would normally be used to isolate sensitive circuitry, such as integrated circuit logic systems, from common mode interference signals between the incoming d.c. and earth.

6.5.5 Output and indicating circuits

An output device for a high speed protective relay must fulfil three main requirements:

(*a*)   high speed operation, less than 2-3 ms
(*b*)   must be able to trip circuit-breakers directly
(*c*)   large number of operations, maintenance free.

Thyristors can fulfil these requirements but have to be surrounded by fairly complex circuitry to enable reliable operation particularly for multicircuit outputs. Different designs have been built and have been on site for some years. Two types of reed relay also fulfil the requirements; the mercury-wetted reed relay and the high power dry reed relay.

An electromagnetic rotary indicator designed specifically for static relays is shown in Fig. 6.5.5A. A cylindrical permanent magnet is magnetised diametrically

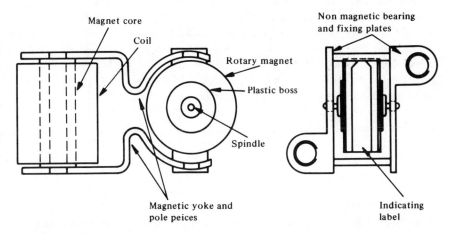

Fig. 6.5.5A   *Operation indicator*

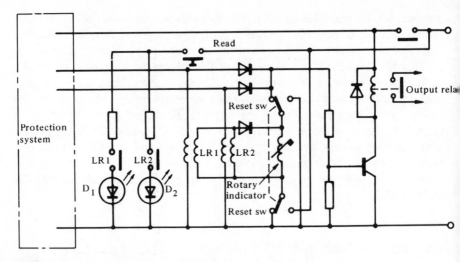

Fig. 6.5.5B *Output circuit with reed tripping and l.e.d. indication*

to produce a magnetic field, through the two pole pieces and a core carrying the operating coil. The cylindrical magnet is mounted on a spindle which locates it in the pole pieces and allows it to rotate when the coil is energised.

When energised with a current such as to produce an N pole adjacent to the N pole of the magnet, the latter rotates through 180° to the stable N/S pole position. The indicator has now reached its operated state and the portion of the magnet exposed in the window is suitably marked to indicate operation. To reset the indicator a current of reverse polarity is applied to the coil which will rotate the magnet a further 180° and return it to its original position. To make sure that there will always be a rotational couple present when the device is energised the centre of rotation of the magnet is mounted slightly eccentric in the pole pieces.

Where a scheme consists of several protective elements a system using a combination of one rotary indicator and several light emitting diodes (l.e.d.s) can be used. L.E.D.s are low-voltage light sources which do not have limited life like filament lamps. Memory for the l.e.d.s is provided by latching reed relays (LR1 and LR2) which can be pulse-operated and are bistable. The rotary indicator operates and shows that information is stored. The store can be read by operating a push button which switches the supply onto the l.e.d.s via the latching reed contacts. Both the rotary indicator and latching relays can be reset from a changeover switch. A two input circuit using these techniques is shown in Fig. 6.5.5B.

A single-channel thyristor output is shown in Fig. 6.5.5C the triggering pulse is fed via an isolating transformer and C1 prevents triggering on spurious pulses. As breaker trip coils can have a considerable time constant, TH2 is not triggered until the current through the coil has exceeded its holding current, i.e. the current above which it will remain conducting after the gate pulse is removed. The gate pulse delay is provided by low power thyristor TH1 and network R2, V_Z; Zener diode V_Z cannot conduct until the current through R2 is sufficient to produce voltage V_Z

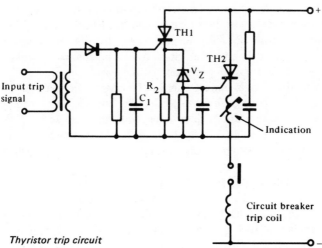

Fig. 6.5.5C *Thyristor trip circuit*

across it. Cathode-anode protection is also provided to guard against spurious triggering.

6.6. Relay cases

Most British relays can be mounted in either flush or projecting manner. The case may be designed in three basic parts, the base, sides and cover. When mounted projecting, the sides and cover can be removed leaving the element mounted on its base in situ on the panel, thus giving unrestricted access for inspection and maintenance without disturbing its connections. This cannot be done when the relay is sunk flush into the panel, so that this arrangement, although much neater, is more difficult to maintain. Alternatively relay elements may be arranged to withdraw from their case, connections being made through sliding contacts. Such an element can be withdrawn for inspection at any time without disturbing the wiring. This arrangement is now very extensively used; a typical example is shown in Fig. 6.6A.

The relay which is mounted in a metal cradle slides into supporting grooves in the case walls. Substantial sliding contacts connect the relay to the external circuitry. The stationary members of this contact system which are used to connect to current-transformers are provided with automatic short-circuiting switches which close when the relay element is withdrawn, before the sliding contacts break, so avoiding the open-circuiting of the transformers. The relay can therefore be withdrawn even though the primary circuit is carrying load. When the relay is fully inserted the cradle is latched securely into the case by rotation of the withdrawing handles into the case. To withdraw the element, the handles are first rotated outwards to make the finger grip holes accessible and this action opens a separate contact which is connected in the trip circuit, thereby removing any risk of accidentally tripping the circuit.

The facility of easy removal permits a relay to be tested away from its normal location. In fact where a standard type is used in sufficient quantities to justify a complete spare element, this may be substituted for one in service, the replaced element being returned to a service station for testing and readjustment under the best conditions, without loss of protection on the circuit.

As an alternative a multicontact plug can be inserted between the springloaded case contacts. By suitable connection of the plug contacts to test equipment, any form of injection testing can be performed with the relay *in situ*. Whatever the type, the relay case should be dustproof and should be arranged so that accumulated dust on the top of the case does not fall into the movement when the case is opened.

Relays are usually sealed to be dustproof by a gasket fitted to the cover. It is not desirable, however, that they should be entirely sealed, since slow emanation of gases from organic type insulation could accumulate and produce injurious effects. The amount of such gas is very small and the natural 'breathing' of the relay case with temperature changes is sufficient to dispel it. Certain designs of case are fitted with a 'breather' with a dust filter, to permit free interchange of air without admitting dust. The front cover of the case is usually provided with a glass window, which permits the flag to be observed and the settings checked without opening the case.

Most British relays are back connected. The connections are brought to terminal inserts into which threaded stems are screwed, either 6 mm (OBA) brass or 5 mm

Fig. 6.6A *Withdrawable-type relay showing element withdrawn (GEC Measurements Ltd.)*

Fig. 6.6B *Modular base for electronic relays (GEC Measurements Ltd.)*

(2BA) stainless steel or phosphor bronze. The smaller size is now preferred because of the saving in space.

The first static relays were housed in cases designed to accommodate electro-mechanical relays. The smaller and radically different electronic equipment has stimulated a new approach (Fig. 6.6B). The various functions of a relay are provided as modules which fit compactly together and are arranged to plug in to multicircuit connectors. The small electronic components are mounted on printed circuit boards which slide edgeways into the case in locating grooves. One or more printed boards, fitted with a front-plate which may carry facilities for setting adjustment or indications, comprise a module. The connectors at the rear of the case are interconnected by fixed wiring to complete the total scheme.

A special heavy-duty connector is provided to couple the c.t. and v.t. inputs to the electronic circuits, this arrangement also providing means for the insertion of a split testing plug. Interlocks are provided to ensure that modules are not removed until the input connector is first withdrawn.

6.7 Maintenance

Protective relays have an 'on-guard' duty. Most of the time they are inactive, although energised and possibly under some degree of stress, or subject to continuous low amplitude vibration. Instant action, however, may be required at any time. The long periods of inactivity may permit stiction effects to develop due to the deposition of traces of sticky substances evaporated from insulating materials.

Continuous vibration at power frequency can cause a fretting of surfaces in contact, such as a back stop, and this also can cause a measure of adhesion. Corrosion can cause severe problems. Although many parts may be affected, the two most vulnerable are the contacts and the coil. In bad atmospheres, silver contacts can become coated with black tarnish of silver sulphide which ultimately may cause failure. All contact failure, however, is not due to tarnish but may be due to the deposit of the same residues referred to above as a source of stiction.

A particularly severe case of this trouble may be caused by silicon oils. Such oils have great powers of spreading and if used even in minute amounts, for whatever purpose, in a relay will sooner or later contaminate the contacts. Any sparking at the contacts will then break down the oil and deposit on the contact a fine layer of insulating silica. Silicon oils must not be used in or near a relay; even the vapour is dangerous. Dust, being generally of an insulating nature, if allowed to enter the case can cause contact failure.

Coils are subject to corrosion from an electrolytic origin. If the coil is connected to a positive potential with respect to earth, leakage current will flow using as an electrolyte, traces of moisture which are nearly always present adsorbed on solid surfaces. If the coil is wound with enamelled wire, the current becomes focused on the few pinholes which are always present in the covering. Since the wire is an anode, metal is dissolved until ultimately the wire is broken. The region of the break becomes coated with a green incrustation of copper carbonate and sulphite; the effect is colloquially known as 'green spot'. Even if the insulation resistance is high (more than 100 MΩ) and the leakage current, in consequence small, a fine wire may open-circuit in a few hundred hours.

If the wire is at negative potential to earth, material is deposited, so that the wire does not corrode, nor is there much probability of the deposited material forming a short circuit between turns or to earth. For this reason coils of d.c. relays are connected to the negative pole of the supply, or negative potential biasing is applied to the supply battery. It might be thought that impregnation of the coil with a suitable varnish would be a complete solution, but in fact there is so much difficulty in making the varnish penetrate to the inner parts of a fine wire multilayer coil that it is found to be generally better not to use an impregnated winding.

The above account of potential faults may seem to be formidable but in actual fact the designer exercises his skill to circumvent these troubles. It is clear that some maintenance is desirable; this will largely consist of check testing to verify that the relay is functioning correctly and its insulating resistance is satisfactory. Rectification will be undertaken if any fault is found but this will rarely be necessary.

Too much maintenance can be as harmful as too little. It should be remembered that site conditions are not suitable for type testing, nor is portable equipment usually adapted for this purpose. An attempt to measure a relay characteristic on site over a wide range of input current is more likely to lead to damage from overheating than to give an accurate result. Relay adjustment also is a skilled operation. Recalibration may sometimes be necessary, but unnecessary adjustment to make a setting precise should be avoided; the measurements should rather be queried. The equipment must be tested on installation to prove that connections are correct and that no damage has been incurred in transport and handling. Response values need to be considered with a knowledge of the performance of the test equipment which may introduce errors.

The results, if acceptable when allowance has been made for such errors, should be recorded permanently and used as a reference for subsequent routine check tests; these should be performed at one or two selected current values which should be at low multiples of setting current. The frequency of routine testing is a subject on which diverse views are expressed. Much depends upon site conditions; a relay located adjacent to a coking plant will need much more frequent attention than a similar relay in a central control room.

It must be remembered, however, that some of the potential sources of failure, e.g. coil failure, may show no evidence in incipient stages and can not be detected until failure is complete. It follows that a failure could occur soon after a check test and if a long interval occurs before the next test, the protection may have been inoperable over this period. Frequent testing by personnel making a special visit with special test gear is a heavy burden but no assessment of probable life overcomes the above argument.

The problem can be overcome by building into the equipment a simple, one-level, injection circuit. One set only of injection equipment per suite of relay cubicles is needed; the power rating is low, requiring currents only a little above setting value and no requirements exist for accuracy. The object is simply to prove ability to operate and in fact no current measurement is made. A suitable switch to apply the test current and also to safeguard the trip circuit is fitted on each panel. With little expenditure of time and trouble, functioning can be performed by semiskilled personnel as a relatively frequent routine.

In addition to the above testing , a relay should be examined and cleaned at intervals, based on experience which may vary from 6 months to 5 years, but typically one to two years. Any dust should be brushed out, a suitable brush being a quill feather. Jewel bearings may be inspected and cleaned, care being taken to recentre the movement correctly, a small amount of end-play being left in the bearing. Contacts may be cleaned if necessary. On no account should the contacts be cleaned with even the finest abrasive material or with metal polishes. The former may leave particles of grit embedded in the contact surface and cause failure to make later, while metal polishes will leave corrosive residues.

Contacts may be washed using a pure solvent such a trichlorethylene, applied with a fine camel hair brush. The brush should not be dipped in the bottle of solvent which would soon become contaminated. A little solvent should be poured into a small container and not returned to the bottle after use. If the contacts are roughened or coated with an insulating contaminant that does not yield to the solvent, a burnishing tool consisting of a metal strip with an etched surface may be used. In the case of severe burning, the surface may be scraped or filed with a fine file, but the burnishing procedure should be used to finish the surface and remove any ridges which otherwise could promote arcing and burning. Care must be taken to check that the setting of contact fingers is satisfactory after cleaning.

It is not usual to oil bearings, gears or other working parts in a relay. Such oiling may give a slight improvement at first, but there is the danger of the oil collecting dust and ultimately causing an increase in friction. The top journal bearing of some induction relays may be filled with white vaseline to reduce 50 Hz vibration. A silicon grease must not be used.

6.8   Application and characteristics

So far, in this chapter, relays have been considered as isolated devices, without more reference than is necessary to their application. The various elements can each be used in a variety of ways to provide operational characteristics which are suitable for diverse protection functions. More detailed consideration of protection applications is given in the specialised chapters on each subject which follow; this Section is confined to the study of relay characteristics.

Protection relays measure some quantity associated with the power system and initiate appropriate action when a given condition occurs. The measurement may be of a single fundamental quantity such as current, voltage or frequency and may be a simple magnitude determination or the quantity may be integrated over a certain period of time; integration could be accurate but is more usually approximate as given by an inverse operating time characteristic.

Alternatively, the relay can be supplied with more than a single system quantity, the measurement being then of the sum, difference, product or ratio of the input quantities. The resolution may be more complex and take into account phase angle, as in power measurement, or even be of a less easily defined nature but giving the relay a special characteristic response, as is done in many distance relays.

6.8.1   Instantaneous current- and voltage-operated relays

Single-quantity measurement is used for overcurrent or undervoltage measurement. For instantaneous response, armature relays are usually satisfactory. A range of setting can be provided by tapping the coil or by providing variable spring restraint. The v.a. consumption at setting is substantially constant for all settings for the tapped coil relay. In the case of variable spring control the v.a. consumption at minimum setting will be similar to that of the tapped relay, but since the full coil is used and additional mechanical restraint is applied to produce the higher settings, the setting v.a. will increase, in principle in proportion to the square of the ratio of setting increase but modified somewhat by the effect of core saturation; a relay with a typical 4:1 range of setting may consume 0·7 VA at the lowest setting and 10 VA at the highest setting. Voltage relays very frequently are provided with a resistor in series with the coil in order to reduce the variation in impedance of the operating circuit with temperature and/or frequency, and so maintain accuracy of setting over a prescribed operative range. Such relays will have a higher burden in proportion to the amount of swamp resitance added. An operating time of 0·01 s at three times relay setting is obtainable, with typical relays.

An instantaneous overcurrent relay is sometimes used to give fast protection for faults in a feeder; the relay has to have a high setting corresponding to the maximum current that can flow to a fault near the far end of the feeder and higher than that which can be transmitted to the next section. Initial offset of the fault current waveform causes an increase in the r.m.s. current value and it is important that, with a fault in the next section, the relay does not operate with this transient effect. The relay must, therefore, be given an even higher current setting causing a severe reduction in the length of the first feeder actually protected by this element, or the relay must be designed to be unchanged in setting by the transient offset condition. Fig. 6.8.1 shows relay circuits which provide a high degree of immunity to transient effects and so permit the relay to be set to give a better protection cover to the feeder.

Time-delay overcurrent relays have been described in Section 6.2.3.

6.8.2 Double-quantity measurement

Product measurement is typically performed by induction elements which, for example, if supplied with system current and voltage can develop a response pro-

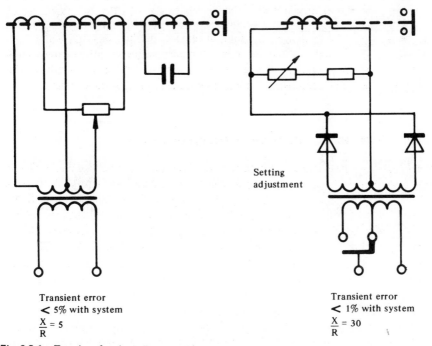

Transient error
< 5% with system
$\frac{X}{R} = 5$

Transient error
< 1% with system
$\frac{X}{R} = 30$

Fig. 6.8.1 *Transient free instantaneous relays*

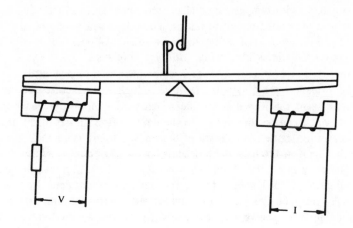

Fig. 6.8.2 *Principle of beam relay*

portional to $VI \cos \phi$, i.e. including power factor and measuring power. When supplied with current and voltage from different phases or otherwise modified, the final response may not be true power, although the element itself is not changed in principle; see Section 6.2.3 and Chapter 8.

A beam-type armature, or a moving-coil, relay, fed with opposed quantities which may, for example, have been derived from system current and voltage, will operate according to the difference of the two inputs (see Fig. 6.8.2). Forces will be developed on the movement proportional to each of the inputs, (actually to the square of the inputs in the case of the beam relay). When these are in balance:

$$K_1 V = K_2 I$$

i.e.

$$\frac{V}{I} = \frac{K_2}{K_1}$$

If the element is sensitive it will change from one position to the other when the ratio passes through the valve of the constant. Hence, although responding to a force difference, at its setting the relay measures a ratio, corresponding in this case to system impedance. In normal application as a distance relay, the element would be arranged to close its contact when the V/I ratio falls below the calibrated value; the voltage supply would restrain the element while current would be fed to the operating coil.

6.8.3 Presentation of characteristics

Responses involving no more than two variables can be plotted as a simple graph. When more than two quantities are involved it becomes necessary to choose the

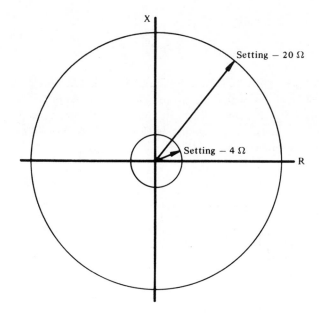

Fig. 6.8.3   *Characteristic of impedance relay*

most significant presentation. Distance relays are usually designed to maintain the voltage/current ratio constant over a wide range, but the response may still be sensitive to power factor or phase angle; in many relays the variation in impedance setting with phase angle is a design feature and not an error quantity. In such cases it is desirable to combine the voltage/current ratio as impedance and display relative to phase angle. This is effectively achieved by plotting as an Argand diagram, the real and imaginary axes becoming resistance and reactance axes, respectively, and the graph area being known as the 'complex plane'.

Fig. 6.8.3 shows the characteristic in the complex plane of the impedance relay as a circle concentric with the origin, the relay setting being independent of powerfactor. Any deviation from the concentric characteristic in a particular design corresponds to power-factor error. Relays making product or ratio measurements are termed 'comparators', the beam relay being a typical 'amplitude comparator'. The induction relay will develop torque in a given direction irrespective of the magnitudes of the two inputs provided their phase is within certain limits; the induction relay is, therefore, a 'phase comparator'.

6.8.4   Complex input comparators

The beam relay can be adapted to operate as a phase comparator. Fig. 6.8.4 shows the relay with double windings on each side and fed with mixed signals. The balance condition is given by:

$$K_1 \, V + K_2 \, I = K_1 \, V - K_2 \, I$$

As long as V and I are of the polarity indicated, the left-hand side of the equation will exceed the right-hand side, and the relay will remain unoperated. If the relative polarity of the current reverses, the right-hand side will predominate and the relay will operate. In a similar way, an induction element supplied with mixed signals can operate as an amplitude comparator.

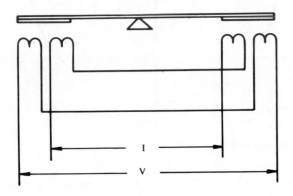

Fig. 6.8.4 *Beam relay operating as phase comparator*

The amplitude comparator with mixed inputs is analysed further below, the voltage and current component inputs being now considered to have any relative phase angle.

Generalised amplitude comparator: Mixed signals derived from current and voltage sources are fed to the two sides of a comparator which will balance when the moduli of these signals are equal, hence:

$$|K_1 I + K_2 V| = |K_3 I + K_4 V|$$

Divide by I and equate $\dfrac{V}{I} = Z = (R + j \, X)$

$$|K_1 + K_2 \, (R + j \, X)| \quad = \quad |K_3 + K_4 \, (R + j \, X)|$$

$$|(K_1 + K_2 R) + j \, K_2 \, X| = \quad |(K_3 + K_4 \, R) + j K_4 \, X|$$

$$(K_1 + K_2 R)^2 + K_2{}^2 X^2 = \quad (K_3 + K_4 R)^2 + K_4{}^2 X^2$$

$$K_1{}^2 + K_2{}^2 R^2 + 2K_1 K_2 R - K_3{}^2 - K_4{}^2 R^2 - 2K_3 K_4 R + K_2{}^2 X^2 - K_4 X^2 = 0$$

$$(K_2{}^2 - K_4{}^2) R^2 + (K_2{}^2 - K_4{}^2) X^2 + 2(K_1 K_2 - K_3 K_4)R + (K_1{}^2 - K_3{}^2) = 0$$

compare the above with the general equation for the circle

$$x^2 + y^2 + 2gx + 2hy + c^2 = 0$$

where　　$x = R, \qquad y = X$

$$g = \frac{K_1 K_2 - K_3 K_4}{(K_2{}^2 - K_4{}^2)}$$

$$h = 0$$

$$c^2 = \frac{(K_1{}^2 - K_3{}^2)}{(K_2{}^2 - K_4{}^2)}$$

Hence the characteristic is a circle on the RX plane with centre $(-g, -h)$

$$= \frac{K_3 K_4 - K_1 K_2}{K_2{}^2 - K_4{}^2} \; , 0$$

and radius

$$\sqrt{g^2 + h^2 - c^2} = \frac{K_1 K_4 - K_2 K_3}{K_2{}^2 - K_4{}^2}$$

If $K_1 = K_3$, $-g =$ radius and circle passes through origin

If $K_1 \neq K_3$ the circle is off-set

If $K_1 = K_3$ and $K_2 = -K_4$

$$-g = \frac{K_3 K_4 - K_1 K_2}{K_2{}^2 - K_4{}^2}$$

$$= \frac{K_1 (K_4 - K_2)}{(K_2 + K_4)(K_2 - K_4)}$$

$$= \frac{-K_1}{(K_2 + K_4)} = \frac{-K_1}{0} = \infty$$

Radius $\quad = \dfrac{K_1 K_4 - K_2 K_3}{K_2{}^2 - K_4{}^2}$

$$= \frac{K_1 (K_4 - K_2)}{(K_2 + K_4)(K_2 - K_4)}$$

$$= \infty$$

Hence the characteristic is a straight line passing through the origin, i.e. a directional characteristic.

6.8.5   Distance relays

The preceding Section has shown how a relay can respond to the impedance of the system. The simple impedance relay has a circular characteristic concentric with the origin (Fig. 6.8.3). The mho relay invented by Warrington consisted of an induction

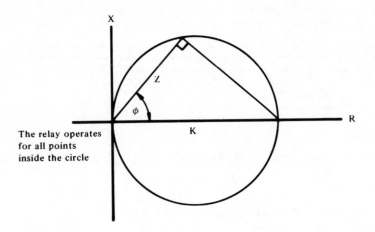

Fig. 6.8.5A   *Original mho relay characteristic*

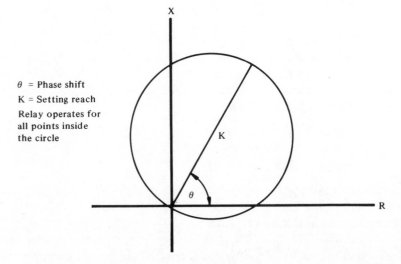

Fig. 6.8.5B   *Typical mho characteristic derived from Fig. 6.8.5A by applying phase shift equivalent to natural angle of the line*

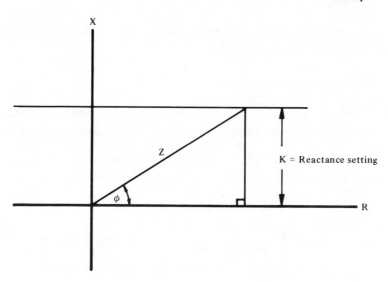

Fig. 6.8.5C *Characteristic of reactance relay*

relay with a Wattmetric operating magnet and a voltage energised restraining electromagnet; the relay therefore operated according to the equation:

$$KVI \cos \phi = V^2$$

i.e. $\cos \phi = \dfrac{V}{KI} = \dfrac{Z}{K}$

Fig. 6.8.5A shows that the locus of the extremity of vector 2 in the complex plane is a circle with diameter K on the R axis. By applying a phase shift in the voltage circuit of the operating electromagnet the diameter of the characteristic can be rotated to correspond to the impedance angle of the system (Fig. 6.8.5B).

In a similar way, an operating law

$$VI \sin \phi = KI^2$$

$$\sin \phi = \dfrac{K}{Z}$$

corresponds to a straight line parallel to the R axis but displaced by a distance K. This therefore represents a fixed reactance setting independently of any value of resistance component included in the measured impedance (Fig. 6.8.5C).

The last statement is idealistic; in practice, any relay has a finite operative range for all applied conditions and this principle applies to the amount of resistance that can be included in the measured impedance, beyond which the setting reactance will vary from the prescribed value. As before phase shift applied to the operating electromagnet can rotate the linear characteristic to any desired angle; the result is usually known as an 'ohm' relay.

6.8.6 Rectifier bridge comparators

Amplitude comparator: Two inputs can be compared by bridge networks. The rectifier bridge amplitude comparator is shown in Fig. 6.8.6. When the input currents to the two sides of the bridge are identical, the rectifier outputs will circulate, producing no voltage across the sensitive polarised output detector which is typically a permanent-magnet moving-coil relay. A preponderance of current in the left input will produce a current downwards through the relay, and a reverse output is obtained if the right-hand input is the greater. If the relay has a relatively high sensitivity compared with the input currents, it will readily detect when one input exceeds the other and so constitutes a comparator able to perform as described in Sections 6.8.2 - 6.8.4. The input transformers can be fed with mixed signals using double primary windings thereby producing mho or directional characteristics.

When an input is applied to the left-hand side, the potential tending to be developed across the d.c. connections is such as to pass current in the forward direction through the right-hand rectifier bridge; the latter might therefore be thought to constitute a short-circuit across the interconnections and relay, inhibiting operation. This is not so, because of the initial voltage (toe voltage) which is necessary to pass forward current through a rectifier. This voltage is sufficient to operate the sensitive detector; in fact little shunting of current occurs at the relay setting. With large inputs, however, the voltage applied to the relay is limited to the forward drop in the rectifier. This occurs in each direction, so that each rectifier acts as a limiter for the other; since the forward drop is much smaller than the reverse withstand voltage, the rectifiers are fully protected against voltage

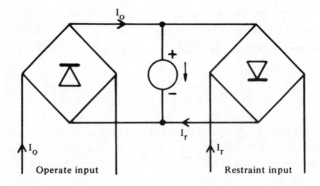

Fig. 6.8.6 *Rectifier bridge comparator*

breakdown and need never exceed a single rectifier cell per bridge arm. It is because of this fact that the accuracy performance of this device exceeds that of rectified relays with double windings.

6.8.7   Phase-comparison bridge

The circuit of a phase-comparison bridge is shown in Fig. 6.8.7A. To understand this device it is necessary to appreciate the fundamental voltage/current characteristic of a diode (Fig. 6.8.7B). The sharp change in resistance near zero current results in the normal rectifying action. If the diode is subjected to a forward current corresponding to point A on the characteristic, an additional smaller component of current in either direction can be superimposed without experiencing any rectifying effect, since the slope of the characteristic about A does not vary significantly. Alternatively, if a reverse potential is applied, bringing the diode condition to B, a small additional voltage of either polarity will be blocked since the summated voltage applied to the diode will remain in the non-conducting direction.

Referring now to Fig. 6.8.7A which shows two inputs to the bridge, $2i_1$ and i_2. The two inputs are shown in quadrature in this example.

During period (a), i_1 is greater than i_2; i_1 is negative and i_2 is positive. Current $2i_1$ divides equally through the resistors $R/2$, through diodes C and D and through the two halves of the secondary winding of transformer T2, producing no resultant ampere-turns. The nett output voltage due to current i_1 across the load resistor is zero. The voltage drop due to i_1 in diodes C and D appears across diodes A and B as a blocking potential, preventing the flow of current i_2 through them. Current i_2 is therefore routed through diode D, upwards through resistor R and diode C, producing an output voltage across R of $+i_2R$.

During period (b), i_2 is greater than i_1; i_2 is positive and i_1 is negative. Current i_2 flows through diodes A and C opening these gates and closing diodes B and D. Current $2i_1$ thus flows through the top half of resistor R giving an output voltage of $+i_1R$.

The conditions in period (c) are similar to period (b) except that i_1 is now positive and flows in the opposite direction in resistor R producing an output voltage $(-i_1R)$.

During period (d), i_1 is greater than i_2 and both are positive. i_1 opens diodes A and B, allowing i_2 to flow downwards through R giving an output of $(-i_2R)$.

The output of the comparator is shown as the shaded area on the waveform diagram in Fig. 6.8.7A. When the input waves are in quadrature as shown the nett output to an integrating sensor applied across R is zero. When the angle between the input quantities is less than 90°, the output to the sensor is as shown in Fig. 6.8.7C(a) giving an average value which is negative. For a greater angle than 90° the average output is positive, Fig. 6.8.7C(b). Hence, a sensitive sensor can very readily detect the quadrature condition.

To provide a mho characteristic, the line current is passed through an impedance Z_R adjusted to represent the fault setting impedance as seen through the measuring transformers. The inputs to the comparator are the fault voltage $V = IZ_L$ and the difference between this and the voltage drop on the replica impedance, $V-IZ_R$.

Hence $(IZ_L - IZ_R)$ is in quadrature with IZ_L at setting.

$(Z_L - Z_R)$ is in quadrature with Z_L at setting.

The vector diagram is shown in Fig. 6.8.7D in which it will be seen that the locus of the end of vector Z_L for relay setting is a circle on Z_R as diameter.

The circle characteristic represents the boundary of operation, and defines the setting 'reach' of the relay. A 'close-up' fault, i.e. one of zero impedance, corresponds to the point on the circle passing through the origin. Under this fault condition, the fault voltage is collapsed to zero so that the comparator would be energised with the single quantity $-IZ_R$, giving only an a.c. output to the integrator and resulting in no operation. In order to obtain operation under this important condition, an input from the sound phase voltage is applied to a separate primary winding of the polarising transformer, through a capacitor which brings the resulting input into phase with the fault voltage. This infeed does not affect the accuracy of measurement, since the sound phase component affects the magnitude only of the polarising quantity and does not change the position of the $V-IZ_R$ vector.

In the case of a close-up three-phase fault, crossphase polarisation is of no benefit. However, an arcing fault such as a flashover due to lightning, or a fault applied by any natural accident is very unlikely to collapse the voltage of all phases to absolute zero, so that a sufficiently sensitive scheme will still operate.

One possible source of failure lies in the omission to remove safety earthing connections, following work on the primary conductors, before re-energising. It is usual for distance protection to have three operative zones, the second and third zones extending beyond the feeder section and normally being subject to time delays which provide discriminative margins. The third zone can be provided with an offset characteristic by supplying the comparator with the quantities $(V + KIZ)$ and $(V - IZ)$. The characteristic so obtained is a circle which encloses the origin and reaches back by the fraction K of the forward reach as shown in Fig. 6.8.7E.

Such an element, provided with a long forward reach and about 10% reverse reach provides useful backup functions for both the line and busbars, and serves as a starter for the scheme as a whole. At the instant of energising the line, no discriminative problem exists, the remote circuit-breaker being of necessity open, or no power supply being connected to that end. Hence the time delay normally provided before the third zone is allowed to trip, can be omitted; by this means should a solid three-phase short-circuit exist, the condition which is well within the offset characteristic, will be tripped instantly. After a delay after energisation of approximately 200 ms; the third zone time delay is reinserted to give normal discriminative action. It is important that such a condition on another feeder being energised from the same busbar does not cause maloperation of the first zone due to collapse of the voltage. The comparator should then theoretically produce no integrated output, but small voltage drops in the bridge diodes which might be slightly unbalanced could cause an output signal. A very small amount (0·1%) offset is intro-

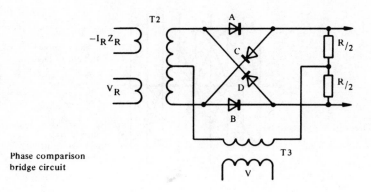

Phase comparison
bridge circuit

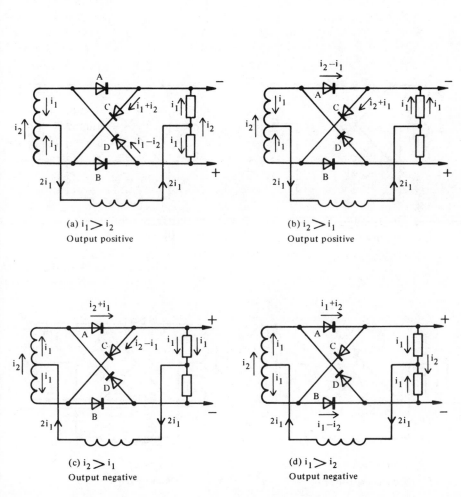

(a) $i_1 > i_2$
Output positive

(b) $i_2 > i_1$
Output positive

(c) $i_2 > i_1$
Output negative

(d) $i_1 > i_2$
Output negative

Fig. 6.8.7A   *Principal of phase-comparison bridge*

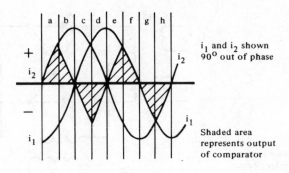

i_1 and i_2 shown 90° out of phase

Shaded area represents output of comparator

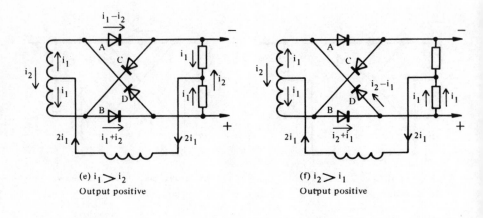

(e) $i_1 > i_2$
Output positive

(f) $i_2 > i_1$
Output positive

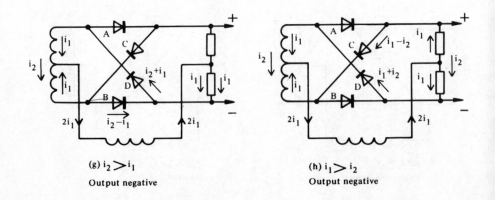

(g) $i_2 > i_1$
Output negative

(h) $i_1 > i_2$
Output negative

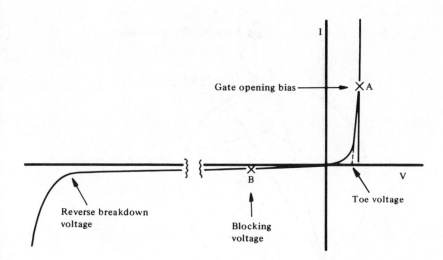

Gate opening bias ⟶ ✕ A

Reverse breakdown
voltage

Blocking
voltage

Toe voltage

Fig. 6.8.7B *Typical characteristic of rectifying diode*

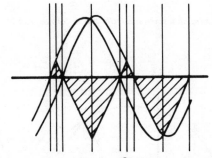

(a) Phase displacement < 90°. Integral output negative

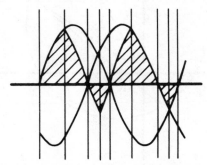

(b) Phase displacement > 90°. Integral output positive

Fig. 6.8.7C *Phase-comparison bridge outputs for phase displacement of less and greater than 90°*

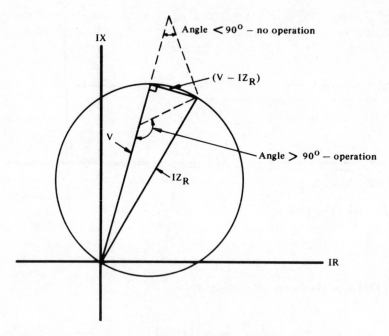

Fig. 6.8.7D   *Derivation of mho characteristic from phase-comparison bridge*

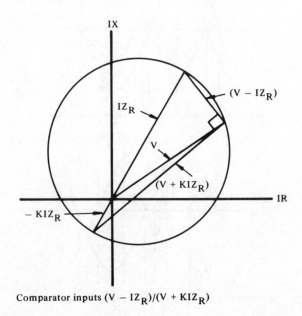

Comparator inputs $(V - IZ_R)/(V + KIZ_R)$

Fig. 6.8.7E   *Derivation of offset-mho characteristic*

duced by supplying a small amount of IZ signal to the polarising transformer. This small bias overcomes error signals whilst not interfering with functioning as above. Other characteristics can be produced by suitable inputs to the comparator.

6.8.8 Range curves

The characteristics discussed in the preceding Section may be considered as the theoretical law of the relay. It must not be thought that this law will be maintained over an unlimited range of the input quantities. For example, the applied current and voltage could be reduced to very low values and still correspond to the setting impedance, but the relay may not measure this value correctly, since the energy input may be too low to operate the movement or the voltage may be below the cut-off value of any rectifiers.

Reduced voltage occurs in protection applications due to the source impedance behind the relaying point. The source impedance Z_S and the protected line impedance Z_L constitute a potentiometer, the relay being connected to the tapping point. The relay voltage is therefore:

$$V_R = \frac{E_S Z_L}{Z_S + Z_L}$$

The term

$$\frac{Z_S + Z_L}{Z_L}$$

has been called the range factor, i.e. the factor by which the system e.m.f. is divided. At times of low plant capacity or with abnormal system conditions the factor may be fairly large.

In comparing the total performance of different relays, it becomes necessary to distinguish between the voltage range over which the relay measures with specified accuracy, and the voltage which is actually applied in a given system fault condition. Two terms have therefore been defined. The factor

$$\frac{Z_S + Z_L}{Z_L}$$

is known as the 'system impedance ratio'. Usually the factor is simplified to Z_S/Z_L, (Z_S being large compared with Z_L in all critical conditions); the term is so defined in BS 3950 - Electrical protective systems for a.c. plant. The maximum value of the 'system impedance ratio' for which a given relay can measure and operate with the prescribed accuracy is known as the 'characteristic impedance ratio'.

The performance with regard to accuracy and operating time is expressed by plotting isochronic curves with axes of system impedance ratio and fault distance as a fraction of setting distance; an example is shown as Fig. 6.8.8. Reference should be made to Chapter 9 for more specific details of design and application of distance schemes.

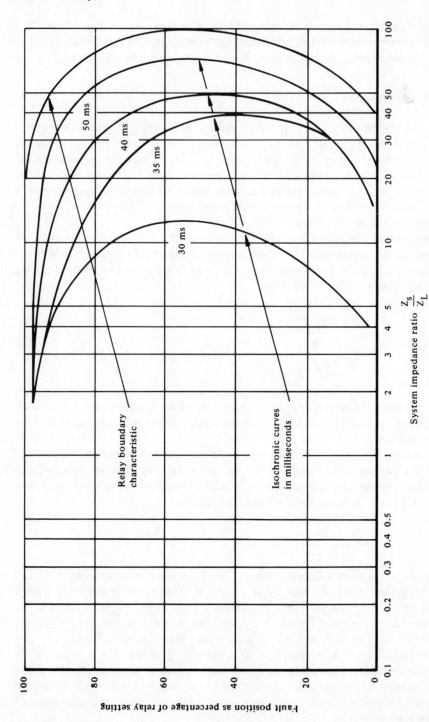

Fault position as percentage of relay setting

50 ms

40 ms

35 ms

30 ms

Relay boundary
characteristic

Isochronic curves
in milliseconds

System impedance ratio $\dfrac{Z_s}{Z_L}$

Fig. 6.8.8 *Contour curves for mho measuring relay (three-phase faults maximum offset)*

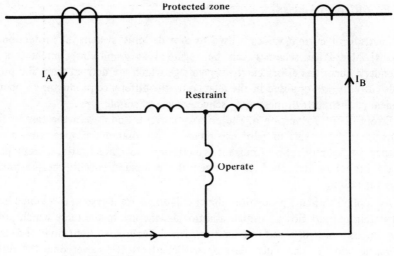

(a) Circuit diagram

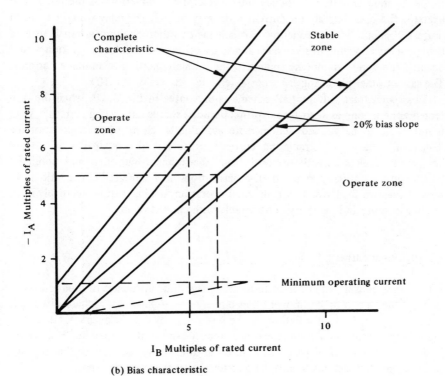

(b) Bias characteristic

Fig. 6.8.9 *Principle of percentage differential current scheme*

6.8.9   Differential relays

Comparison of current values is used to provide 'unit' systems of protection. The original Merz-Price schemes can be regarded as amplitude comparators. The secondary quantities either current or voltage which are derived from the primary fault currents, are opposed in the relay, only the difference producing an operating tendency. The relays in these early schemes were of simple type.

Errors in the conversion of the primary currents and also in the case of feeder protection, the effects of pilot capacitance, necessitated a change from a simple balance, i.e. a unity ratio of current as a criterion, to a larger ratio, thereby permitting a proportionate tolerance between the compared currents before initiating relay operation.

As applied to plant protection, the circulating current system is retained but the circulating current flows through additional windings in the relay which produce restraint or torque opposed to operation. The differential current flows through the operating winding and must develop sufficient effort to overcome the restraint before operation can be achieved. The restraint circuit will be proportioned relative to the operate circuit, to produce only a fraction of the effort of the latter. For example the operate/restraint current ratio may be 0·2. The relay would be said to possess 20% bias, in consequence of which the two through-fault terminal currents being compared would need to have a ratio exceeding 1·2:1 before operation would occur. (The above statement applies to the simple condition of in-phase currents. The case of other phase angles is considered later, in Section 6.8.10).

This 'percentage differential' scheme is illustrated in Fig. 6.8.9. When the protected zone is long as with feeder protection, the simple circulating current system is not likely to be applied; schemes are available which may be classed as of the 'balanced voltage' or 'circulating current' types but the quantities which are compared are less directly derived from the primary currents, and nonlinear components are usually involved. The bias ratio is now expressed as the ratio of inputs at the two feeder ends for marginal operation; the bias ratio is relatively high, i.e. two or more and may vary considerably with current value.

6.8.10   Polar curves

Bias ratio is considered above in terms of a magnitude difference of input currents. In fact, the operating component can equally be produced by a phase difference between inputs. Full information can be given only by a polar diagram, taking one input as reference and plotting the other input relative to it for marginal conditions. Positive direction should be taken as into the zone at any terminal, so that through fault current corresponds to antiphase conditions at the two zone ends.

In plotting a diagram for a line AB for various current levels it is useful to take I_A as reference and plot the ratio I_B/I_A i.e. I_B is plotted in per unit values of I_A (Fig. 6.8.10). For low current values, such polar curves are usually circular. Larger

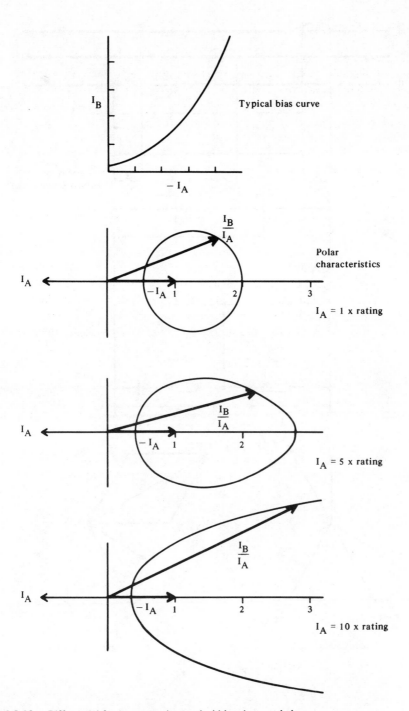

Fig. 6.8.10   *Differential feeder protection typical bias characteristics*

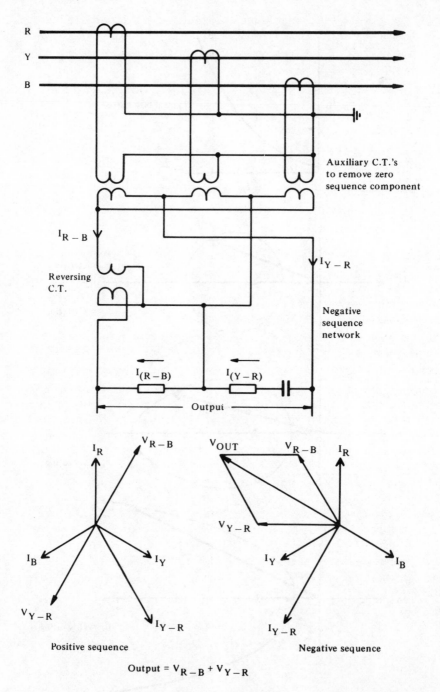

Fig. 6.8.11   *Typical negative-sequence network*

current values, because of nonlinear properties in the relay, give rise to distortion of the circular form which may ultimately become open-ended. At this stage the bias ratio may be considered to be infinite, and the relay is said to be operating in a 'phase-comparison' mode.

6.8.11 Negative-sequence protection

It has been shown in Chapter 3 that an unbalanced set of currents in a three-phase system can be represented as the sum of positive, negative and zero sequence components, these being three balanced systems. The sequence components may be compared with the harmonics of a distorted waveform; they are mathematical components, but real enough to be resolved by suitable filters.

Positive-sequence currents occur in all conditions balanced and unbalanced. Discrimination between faulty and sound conditions is therefore only made on a basis of magnitude. Negative-sequence currents occur only with unbalanced conditions; they are, therefore, a ready means of detecting most fault conditions. Sensitive protection settings are permissible, limited only by such degree of unbalance in load currents as may occur and be acceptable.

Zero-sequence currents return through the system neutral. In the case of three-phase three-wire circuits, a zero-sequence component can only occur with a fault to earth, through which it returns to an earthed neutral point. Zero-sequence current is readily detected either by measurement in the system neutral connection or by a residually connected group of c.t.s. Residual connections are, therefore, used to energise current measuring relays and any associated directional relays; residual windings are also used in more complex differential schemes to give high earth-fault sensitivity. Negative-sequence currents are also used to provide lower protection settings than could otherwise be applied, or to detect some condition of unbalance that is especially dangerous such as the unbalanced loading of a generator.

Many networks have been devised to respond only to a negative sequence component. In general, these involve applying a 60° phase shift to one-phase current, and then subtracting it from the current in another phase, the latter being selected so that the resultant is zero for positive sequence currents.

A typical sequence network is shown in Fig. 6.8.11; a study of the vector diagrams will show that positive sequence currents lead to a balancing of vectors, giving no output in the sensing relay, whereas reversing the sequence changes the angle between the two voltages which are summated. An output is thereby generated to energise the relay; the type of response will of course depend upon the measuring relay element, ranging from instantaneous operation to a very long inverse square law time characteristic, i.e.

$$t = \frac{K}{I_2^2}$$

6.9   Testing of relays and protection schemes

The high standard of performance of modern protection arises from the comprehensive testing of equipment which has led to understanding of many of the complex processes which occur when the system is disturbed. It is not always understood that testing is of several distinct categories, each having distinct functions and requirements.

6.9.1   Test at manufacturing works

(a)   *Type testing:* A new design of relay or scheme is subjected to stringent testing before it is put into production. The object is to prove the design in all respects and to determine all relevant characteristics. To this end, the relay is assembled with all ancillary components including measuring transformers, leads simulated by resistors, pilots where relevant, simulated by a network of resistors, reactors and capacitors of sufficient complexity to reproduce typical line characteristics, and any other special items that may apply to a particular case.

The equipment is connected together to form the complete scheme and is then tested by the application of current which is of magnitude to cover the range of application taking into account the current transformer ratio, and which also has transient characteristics similar to those experienced in service.

Performance is examined with respect to sensitivity, operating speed and stability (where relevant). Burdens, self-heating, contact performance durability and insulation are examined. The equipment is also tested critically with regard to such environmental conditions as the permissible ambient temperature range, the effect of frequency deviation and the resistance to mechanical shock and vibration. Part of such testing is the assessment of the range of errors and the tolerancing of components. Such testing is very expensive; it may occupy several weeks or even months and requires extensive, specialised and high power plant. It is intended to be performed only once for each scheme. The results of the tests are recorded as a permanent reference.

(b)   *Calibration:* Each relay manufactured is tested. This is a process not of design proving, but of adjustment, and is therefore to be ranked as a manufacturing process. Hence the tests applied may not have any direct relation to the normal service of the item in question; they are satisfactory provided they enable the equipment to be brought into a standard condition, the tests being chosen for their suitability and convenience in achieving this object.

6.9.2   Testing at site

(a)   *Commissioning:* Unlike a self-contained piece of apparatus which may be expected to function correctly as received, a protection system may require many interconnections with remote parts of the station or even beyond. The complete protection system may comprise the relays and ancillary equipment mounted on the relay board, current and voltage transformers, auxiliary switches in the primary switchgear, d.c. power supplies and tripping connections, with interconnections to other stations to complete a 'unit' system or for intertripping or indication purposes.

Clearly, such a complex system of equipment and connections which must be completed on site, should be proved to be correct before the equipment can be considered fit for service. It is necessary, therefore, to carry out such examination and testing as are needed to prove that:

(i) all items of equipment are undamaged by transport and handling
(ii) the correct items are connected together, e.g. the correct set of c.t.s are connected to a given set of relays
(iii) all connections, including leads and pilots to remote equipment and panel wiring are correct
(iv) the correct settings and/or other adjustments are applied according to the design of the protection scheme and the requirements of the primary system.

It will be clear from the above that any degree of type testing has no place in normal site work. Setting aside special site tests which are occasionally planned to investigate conjunctive operation with power plant on a scale which is not readily feasible in a laboratory, attempts to measure detailed relay characteristics on site are likely only to produce misleading results and may result in damage to the equipment. In general, the test equipment for site use, which essentially has to be portable, is unsuitable for detailed investigations, whilst all too often limitation of the facility of operation leads to high current values being sustained for excessive periods. It must always be remembered that relays may be continuously rated only at the maximum continuous current of the circuit and with currents of magnitude corresponding to system faults they may be very short rated.

After visual examination to check that all appears to be in order, a relay should be checked by injection testing to show that it is undamaged. For example, an i.d.m.t.l. overcurrent relay may be injected on one tap to observe:

(*a*)   no operation at setting current
(*b*)   complete operation at 1·3 times setting current
(*c*)   operation at between 2 and 4 times setting current with reasonable accuracy.
       (See BS 142 : 1966 for permitted tolerances).

The test set must have a good waveform when used with the relay at this level of current, otherwise a further tolerance may be needed for this, and also it must be borne in mind that loose test instruments which have been taken to many sites may not retain their original accuracy. If the injection is made with c.t.s still connected but the primary circuit disconnected, the c.t. will draw an exciting current which will cause a further disdcrepancy.

Several sets of current-transformers are often mounted in one circuit-breaker; they may very likely have similar ratios but may differ very considerably in output.

To establish that the correct set has been connected to a given burden it is usual to check the excitation characteristic, injecting from the relay panel terminals. Only a single point on the excitation curve need be measured, which may be the knee point or, if this is inconveniently high, as high a value as can be provided by the testing supply. The results compared with the estimated characteristics will usually suffice for identification purposes and nothing is then to be gained by measuring and plotting the entire excitation characteristic. The above two examples are given to illustrate the nature of this work. More details of commissioning procedure are given in Chapter 18. Detailed instructions for testing every scheme are impracticable in the available space, and these schemes are continually being extended or modified. In general detailed commissioning data is available from the manufacturers for all proprietary schemes; much of the procedure for these is obvious provided the working of the system is understood and is a natural extension of the principles set out in Chapter 18. Special adjustments, however, may be required to suit site parameters and for these the makers guidance should be followed.

6.10 Future trends in relay design

Although the majority of relays in service at the present are of electromagnetic construction, development work is principally directed to electronic designs. It is not yet practicable to replace the multicontact hinged armature unit by an electronic equivalent on economic grounds; in fact most electronic relays have a hinged armature unit as a final output device. There is little sign also of the i.d.m.t.l. induction relay being extensively displaced by its electronic equivalent. Elsewhere, the electronic technique offers greater flexibility in design to meet given protection functions.

In the future, solid-state relays will produce new characteristics and concepts for protection schemes. The exploitation of integrated circuits will increase as the cost of these components falls, particularly in the case of custom-built circuits.

The fundamental measurement and logic functions of a protective relay can be accommodated on a single silicon slice or 'chip' with a great reduction in size over earlier techniques. Redundancy techniques such as 'two out of three' schemes thereby become economically feasible, providing even more reliable protection.

6.11 Bibliography

Books

Automatic protection of a.c. circuits by G W Stubbings (Chapman & Hall)
Relay systems by I T Monseth and P H Robinson (McGraw Hill Book Co. Inc.)

Protective relays: their theory and practice (Vols. I and II) by A R van C
Warrington (Chapman & Hall)
Symmetrical components by C F Wagner and R D Evans (McGraw Hill)
Specification for electrical relays BS 142-1966, (British Standards Institution)

Articles

'A study of directional element connections for phase relays' by W K Sonnemann
(*Trans. AIEE*, 1950)
'The performance of distance relays' by F L Hamilton and N S Ellis (*Reyrolle Rev.*,
1956, **166**)

Chapter 7

Protection signalling

by P.C.Colbrook

7.1 Introduction

Signalling is the transfer of information between separate locations, and is usually accomplished using derived signals or messages, which represent the information to be transferred. To achieve this it is necessary to have a transmitter, a receiver and a communication medium between them. Media currently in use for signalling for protection purposes are:

(*a*) power-line-carrier circuits
(*b*) private pilot wires owned by the Supply Authority
(*c*) pilot wires or channels rented from the Post Office
(*d*) radio links.

The security standards now applicable to the high-voltage transmission systems mean that it is often necessary to employ more than one signalling facility for a given protection function; in these circumstances it is highly desirable that the individual facilities be routed over different media or, if this is not possible, then the routing should be as electrically and physically separate as possible.

Some unit systems of feeder protection, described in later chapters, are concerned with transmission over a communication channel of information that has been derived from analogue variables. The signalling systems described in this chapter are those which involve the interchange of information from one terminal to one or more other terminals to indicate the state of some device such as a relay, at the sending terminal. Normally two states only are involved, e.g. 'contacts open' or 'contacts closed'.

Faults can occur on a power system such that, although the protective systems or relays at one end of a circuit operate, those at the other end or ends either cannot operate, because there is little or no fault current, or require further information to enable them to discriminate between faults within the protected zone and those that occur in other zones. The signals required in these circumstances fall into two main groups:

(i) Command signals which result in remote circuit-breakers being directly tripped without reference to the state of the local protection at the remote end or ends. This is known as 'intertripping'. To guard against possible incorrect receiver operations, resulting from electrical noise, for example, it is essential to use signals that have a very low probability of being produced from any source other than the associated genuine transmitter.

(ii) Advisory signals which enable protective systems and relays located at different points on the power system to achieve a co-operative function, the signals either permitting or inhibiting operation. Thus, as circuit-breaker tripping is dependent upon the signal and the state of the local protection, relatively simple signals can be used compared with those required for intertripping. Facilities of this type are known as protection signalling. Protection-signalling systems may also be used to inhibit or lock out automatic switching facilities in the event that programmed switching routines are not completed, or in the event of faults occurring within predetermined boundaries.

7.2 Communication media

7.2.1 Power-line carrier

7.2.1.1 General: In power-line-carrier (p.l.c.) signalling systems, the signal propagation medium is the power circuit itself, communication between ends of the circuit being effected by means of a superimposed carrier-frequency signal carried by the power-circuit conductors. The carrier signal may exist continuously on the line or only during fault conditions (equipments operating in the latter manner are referred to as 'normally quiescent'). The band of frequencies employed in the UK for the carrier frequency signal is 70-700 kHz, but certain parts of this band are not available, in particular for continuous carrier signalling. If continuous signalling is used, the power level of the injected signal will be low, say 1 or 2 W, or if injected for a short time will be higher, usually in the range 10-20 W in the UK, but abroad higher levels are sometimes used. As it is essential to have minimum mutual interference between different carrier equipments on the system, each equipment is given a particular frequency band adequate for its function, and the allocation of the band should be such that the frequency is separated, either physically (refer to Section 7.2.1.6(e)), or by virtue of its place in the spectrum, from any existing frequencies in use.

The essential item in the coupling of the h.f. signal from the signalling equipment at ground level to the h.v. conductors is a capacitor which is designed for operation at the full power-system voltage. Additional tuning and impedance matching devices are also used to improve the coupling.

Coupling can be to a single phase conductor, i.e. phase-to-earth coupling, or it may involve two couplings, each to one of two of the primary conductors, i.e. phase-to-phase coupling, the latter being standard practice in the UK for reasons which will be given later (see Section 7.2.1.3).

Up to now, the use of power-line-carrier in the UK (with the exception of the North of Scotland Hydro-Electric Board) has been primarily on the basis of protection requirements with the main functions of control, supervision and communication, being effected through the Post Office telephony system. In many countries, the main application of power-line-carrier has been for the purposes of control, supervision and communication, with the protection requirements as an additional use. These differences affect the extent to which power-line-carrier is used and the economics involved, as some equipment such as that required for coupling and power supplies, are common to both applications, and the coupling equipment, in particular, is expensive.

However, the use of the transmission line itself as a communication medium is extremely useful for achieving the necessary diversification of signalling media which is required for high voltage transmission system protection, and the economic aspect is much improved when the carrier system provides facilities for more than one signalling function.

Power-line-carrier channels are, for obvious reasons, not normally subjected to interference by personnel outside the Supply Authority's control. However, their transmission characteristics are not as stable as either private pilot cables or rented pilot circuits, and in consequence the signalling equipment must be designed to operate over a wide range of input and output signal levels, particularly where it is required to effect signalling through a power system fault on the circuit itself.

7.2.1.2   Coupling equipment: To understand the significance of the various elements which make up the coupling equipment it is convenient to build up the coupling circuit in stages.

If an h.f. generator E is connected to the line through an h.v. capacitor then we have the first requirement of a relatively low-impedance h.f. path and a high-impedance power frequency path, as shown in Fig. 7.2.1.2A.

However, the h.f. impedance is still not low enough and therefore a small air-cored inductance is connected in series with the capacitor to resonate at the carrier frequency and thus reduce the h.f. impedance as shown in Fig. 7.2.1.2B. This is called the series tuning unit. This inductance is very small and of insignificant impedance at the power frequency.

This arrangement still allows power frequency voltages to impinge on the carrier equipment (represented by the h.f. generator) and, therefore, the next stage is to

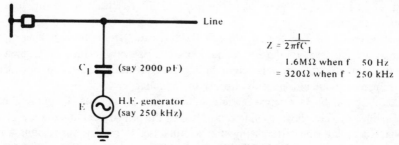

Fig. 7.2.1.2A   *H.V. capacitor provides basic p.l.c. coupling circuit*

add a parallel-tuned circuit at the earthy end, and to inject the carrier signal across this as shown in Fig. 7.2.1.2C. This is called the shunt-tuning unit and provides a high impedance at carrier frequencies across the injection point, but is also a very low impedance at the power frequency. This virtually eliminates power frequency voltages from the carrier equipment.

Looking now at the point at which the h.f. signal enters the overhead line, it will be seen that there are two possible paths, one of which is along the line to the remote end, a path which has a characteristic impedance (phase-to-earth) of some 200 to 500 Ω, depending on the line construction. An alternative path is in the opposite direction and consists effectively of the busbar impedance (normally capacitive) to ground, the impedance of this path is often too low at the carrier frequency. To prevent the carrier signal being short-circuited by the busbar impedance, the impedance of this path is increased by the introduction of another parallel-tuned circuit, the line trap, as shown in Fig. 7.2.1.2D.

The line-trap coil L_3, is difficult to design because it must have an inductance capable of being tuned to present a high impedance to carrier frequencies when tuned with capacitor C_3, at the same time it must be rated to carry the load current

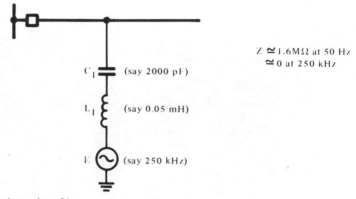

$Z \cong 1.6 M\Omega$ at 50 Hz
$\cong 0$ at 250 kHz

C_1 (say 2000 pF)

L_1 (say 0.05 mH)

E (say 250 kHz)

Fig. 7.2.1.2B   *Series tuning of h.v. coupling capacitor*

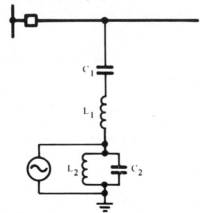

C_1

L_1

L_2 C_2

Fig. 7.2.1.2C   *Shunt tuning unit facilitates carrier injection*

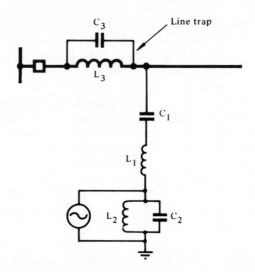

Fig. 7.2.1.2D   *Line traps help to confine carrier signals*

Fig. 7.2.1.2E   *Pair of 4000A line traps*

and fault current of the circuit, and this necessitates a relatively low impedance (for example, less than 0·1 Ω) at the power frequency. A pair of 4000 A line traps suitable for use at 400 kV are shown at ground level in Fig. 7.2.1.2E. Tuning components are contained in the box mounted below the main coil. In service, at 400 kV, line traps are either suspension mounted, as in Fig. 7.2.1.2F, or post mounted.

If there is the need for a power-frequency voltage transformer connection, then this is provided by making the h.v. coupling capacitor in two sections, C_1 and C_4, as shown in Fig. 7.2.1.2G, thus forming a tapping point at about 12 kV to earth. A reactor L_4 and an intermediate voltage transformer are added to complete this capacitor voltage-transformer circuit. A set of three single-phase 275 kV c.v.t.s is shown in Fig. 7.2.1.2H. The capacitor C_1 is integral with the h.v. bushings and the other components detailed above are contained within the metal boxes mounted below the main h.v. bushings. Fig. 7.2.1.2H also shows two of the c.v.t.s with line traps mounted on them, which is the normal practice at 275 and 132 kV.

In determining the position of the v.t. tap, care has to be taken that the carrier signal is not diverted through the v.t. tapping point, bearing in mind that this circuit is highly inductive and that at resonance the stray capacitances would represent a low impedance path at carrier frequencies. The problem is normally overcome by placing the series inductance L_1 (series tuning unit) above the v.t. tapping point as shown in Fig. 7.2.1.2G so that the impedance of the tap-off to the v.t. is in parallel with the h.f. source, the resulting loss being then negligible.

The above is standard UK practice but on the Continent the series tuning unit is sometimes placed below the v.t. tapping point so that the impedance of the v.t. tapping point is much more significant because it experiences a much higher h.f. voltage, that is, the intermediate voltage of the series resonant circuit. It is then

Fig. 7.2.1.2F   *Suspension-mounted line traps at a 400 kV indoor station*

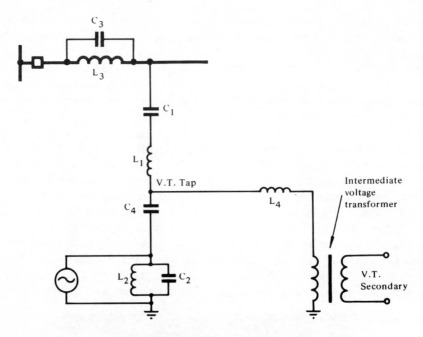

Fig. 7.2.1.2G   *P.L.C. coupling using a capacitor voltage transformer*

Fig. 7.2.1.2H   *Outdoor 275 kV station showing three single-phase capacitor v.t.s*

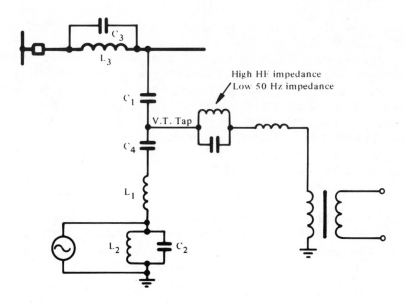

Fig. 7.2.1.2I *Alternative method of using a capacitor voltage transformer for PLC coupling*

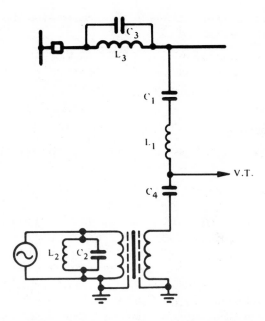

Fig. 7.2.1.2J *Interposing transformers are used for isolation and impedance matching*

necessary to introduce a parallel tuned circuit into the v.t. tapping to reduce carrier signal loss as in Fig. 7.2.1.2I.

In order to protect the carrier equipment against overvoltages or surges which can occur at the coupling equipment, it is necessary to separate the earth system of the carrier equipment from that of the coupling equipment, and this is done by the use of a screened transformer as shown in Fig. 7.2.1.2J. The capacitance C_2 and the inductance L_2 are sometimes placed on the primary side of this isolating transformer. This transformer has another important function because, by choosing an appropriate ratio, correct impedance matching of the carrier-equipment side to the coupling-equipment side can be achieved.

7.2.1.3 Design principles of coupling equipment: The basic components required for phase-to-earth injection of carrier signals have been described in Section 7.2.1.2. In fact phase-to-phase coupling is normally used in the UK as it is considered technically superior to phase-to-earth injection. The principal features of the two methods are compared in Table 7.2.1.3:

Table 7.2.1.3

Phase-to-earth	*Phase-to-phase*
Requires overhead line with earth wire for reasonable results.	Earth wire not essential.
Lower cost as only one coupling capacitor and line trap are required at each circuit end.	Higher cost as two coupling capacitors and line traps are required at each circuit end.
Higher attenuation.	Lower attenuation.
Interference levels higher.	Interference levels lower.
Appreciable coupling to other phases.	Less coupling to other phases.

Phase-to-phase coupling can be achieved using a single shunt tuning unit (non-phase-segregated coupling equipment, see Fig. 7.2.1.3A) or by using separate shunt tuning units per coupler (phase-segregated coupling equipment, see Fig. 7.2.1.3B).

This latter method is particularly suitable for the higher system voltages where greater physical separation between primary phases is required, having the advantages of keeping connections subject to high surge voltages to a minimum and, since the shunt tuning unit is mounted directly below the c.v.t., enables the c.v.t earth to be as close as possible to the c.v.t. With either method, however, the circuit can be reduced to an equivalent band-pass filter and, depending upon the component values chosen for the elements of the filter and hence the frequency to which each filter arm is tuned, different coupling characteristics can be obtained.

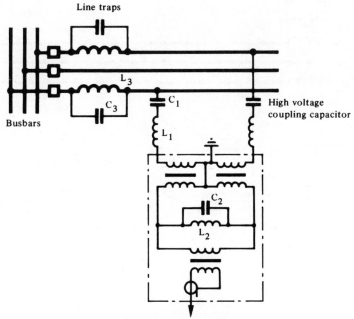

Phase to phase coupling equipment

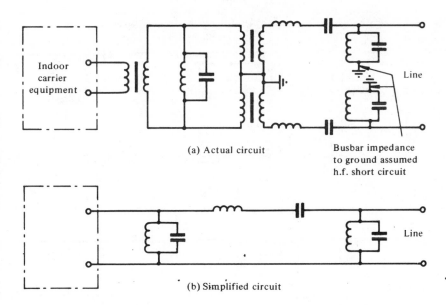

(a) Actual circuit

Busbar impedance
to ground assumed
h.f. short circuit

(b) Simplified circuit

Fig. 7.2.1.3A *Non-phase-segregated coupling equipment regarded as a band-pass filter*

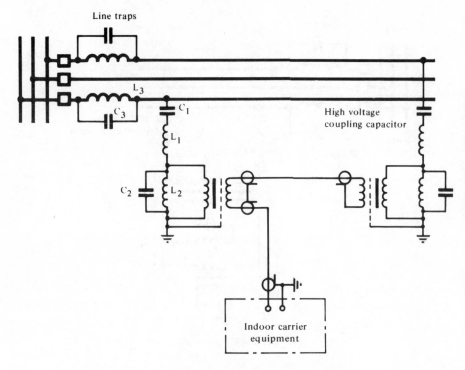

Basic phase to phase carrier coupling equipment using
separate filter units per coupler

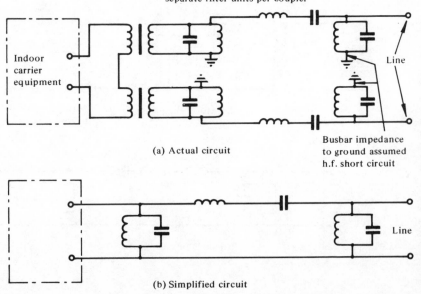

(a) Actual circuit

(b) Simplified circuit

Fig. 7.2.1.3B   *Phase-segregated coupling equipment regarded as a band-pass filter*

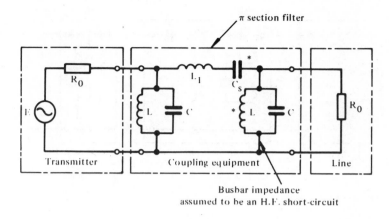

Fig. 7.2.1.3C   *Equivalent circuit of coupling equipment designed as 'π' section filter*

It should be noted that the design output impedance of the carrier equipment is 75 Ω unbalanced (some equipments incorporate facilities for matching to alternative impedances, e.g. 125 or 50 Ω), and the phase-to-phase characteristic impedances of 132, 275 and 400 kV lines are generally taken to be 700, 600 and 500 Ω, respectively. Values can vary quite widely, however, depending on such factors as the type of line construction, the line configuration and the terrain, etc.

For the original application of power-line-carrier equipment in the UK 132 kV grid system, two different design philosophies were used. One manufacturer included the line trap in the overall filter design as part of a π-section band-pass filter, and the other manufacturer designed the coupling equipment as an 'L' or half-section filter independent of the line trap.

(*a*)   *π-section filter theory:* This assumes the busbar impedance to ground (normally capacitive) to be an h.f. short-circuit and this gives the equivalent circuit shown in Fig. 7.2.1.3C where R_0 represents the line characteristic impedance, which, with correct matching, is also the transmitter impedance. The two shunt L and C circuits of the π-section filter are electrically equal and all three circuits have the same resonant frequency f_0, which is also the midband frequency. It should be noted that the components marked with an asterisk are fixed irrespective of the chosen coupling band, C_s being one half the h.v. coupling capacitor value and L being twice the line-trap inductance value. The factor of one half is due to the fact that phase-to-phase coupling is employed, C_s being the capacitance of two h.v. coupling capacitors (one per phase) in series. Similarly, the factor of two results from the effective circuit being two line traps in series. Since the line-trap inductance and the h.v. coupler capacitor are fixed, selection of a particular coupling band is effected by varying the two shunt capacitors C and the series inductance L_1, this latter inductance being twice that of the series tuning unit.

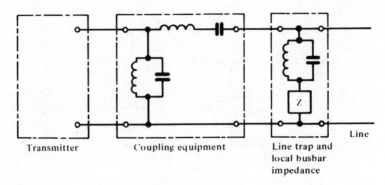

Transmitter   Coupling equipment   Line trap and
                                                 local busbar
                                                 impedance

This can be shown as:

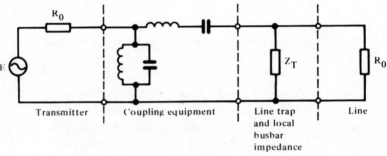

Transmitter   Coupling equipment   Line trap   Line
                                       and local
                                       busbar
                                       impedance

Note: Z_T is the combined impedance of the line trap
and busbars, the value of which depends upon the
frequency and the switching conditions

Fig. 7.2.1.3D   *Equivalent circuit of coupling equipment designed as 'L' section filter*

For correct matching we have, from filter design theory

$$R_0 = \sqrt{L_1/2C}$$

but

$$\omega_0^2 = \frac{1}{L_1 C_s} = \frac{1}{LC}$$

hence

$$R_0 = \sqrt{L/2C_s}$$

which expresses the impedance matching requirements in terms of the two
important fixed parameters, line trap inductance and h.v. coupling capacitance.

Again, from theory it can be shown that

$$\text{bandwidth } \Delta f = \frac{1}{\pi \sqrt{2L_1 C}}$$

which reduces to

$$\Delta f = 2\pi f_0^2 \sqrt{2LC_s}$$

This relates the other important parameter, namely coupling bandwidth, to the two fixed components and to the midband frequency. It should be noted that the bandwidth varies as the square of the midband frequency. Similar expressions can be derived giving the bandwidth in terms of the upper or lower cut-off frequencies, f_1 and f_2, respectively, since

$$\Delta f = f_1 - f_2$$

and

$$f_0 = \sqrt{f_1 f_2}$$

(*b*) *'L'-section filter theory:* In this approach, the design of the line trap is considered separately from the coupling circuits, and is considered as a shunt loss on the coupling equipment. Normally the shunt impedance of the busbars is in series with the line trap and this impedance may be inductive or capacitive depending upon the number of connected power transformers and instrument transformers (capacitor or electromagnetic). The arrangement can be shown as in Fig. 7.2.1.3D.

It can be seen that the coupling filter is an L-section band pass, with similar characteristics as before (but not quite as good, the available bandwidth being about 70% of that of the π case), and that the impedance Z_T will vary with frequency and the conditions of the associated busbars.

Before discussing the basis of design, it is useful to consider how the busbar capacitance (and possibly inductance) may cause high attenuation peaks in the pass band. The basic arrangement may be shown as in Fig. 7.2.1.3E which assumes that the coupling filter can be ignored since its attenuation in the pass band is low.

If the variation of resistance and reactance with frequency of a parallel LC circuit such as the line trap is plotted, they will be generally as shown in Fig. 7.2.1.3F.

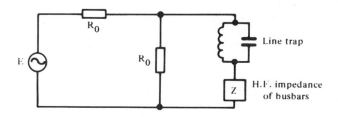

Fig. 7.2.1.3E *Simplified equivalent circuit of coupling equipment*

Therefore, in the pass-band of the equipment, the possibility exists of the reactive component of the line trap resonating with the capacitance of the busbars because this capacitance can vary over a wide range depending on particular switching conditions. Such resonance would be series and, if the circuit is of relatively low loss, that is if the resistive component is low, the resulting value of R_T across the line impedance R_0 would be low, and the loss of carrier signal to the line would be considerable. Thus, the single frequency tuned undamped design of line trap can only successfully be used when tuned accurately to the operating frequency at which it has a high real component of impedance.

(c)   *Line-trap design:* The coupling methods outlined in (*a*) and (*b*) were also used for some early UK 275 kV applications; however, with the advent in the UK of the major 275 kV and 400 kV networks it became necessary to use the power line for more than one signalling function, and for this reason, wide band coupling was adopted as it reduces the amount of retuning and resetting of the various components when signalling equipments or frequencies are

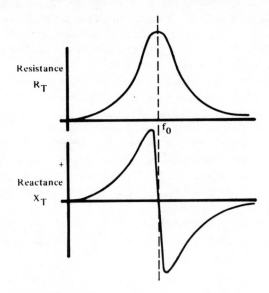

Fig. 7.2.1.3F   *Line trap characteristics*

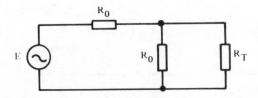

Fig. 7.2.1.3G   *Circuit to determine line trap resistance at the half-power points*

changed, and it provides a communication medium which can provide a number of separate channels for protection, protection signalling, intertripping, communication, etc. Again the coupling capacitor and series and shunt tuning units are designed as an 'L'-section filter, but deliberate damping is introduced into the line trap so that the resistive component is maintained relatively high over the whole of the pass-band. By this means we ensure that, even if series resonance takes place as described in (b) above, the resulting resistance across the line is sufficiently high to limit the loss of power to an acceptable level, for example, 50% reduction in power input to the line. In this case the line trap acts as controlled shunt loss rather than being an integral element of the overall design of the filter.

If a 50% power loss is assumed, the insertion resistance of the line trap can be expressed in terms of the line impedance, using the simple circuit of Fig. 7.2.1.3G.

Without R_T, the h.f. voltage on the line would be

$$V_1 = E/2$$

With R_T, the h.f. voltage on the line would be

$$= V_2 = [E/2] \frac{R_T}{R_T + \frac{1}{2}R_0}$$

$$\text{Ratio of powers} = \frac{1}{2} = \left\{ \frac{V_2}{V_1} \right\}^2$$

$$\frac{V_2}{V_1} = \frac{1}{\sqrt{2}}$$

$$\frac{[E/2] \dfrac{R_T}{R_T + \frac{1}{2}R_0}}{E/2} = \frac{1}{\sqrt{2}} = \frac{R_T}{R_T + R_0/2}$$

from which

$$R_T = 1 \cdot 21 \, R_0.$$

Let this particular value of R_T be designated R_{Tmin}.

Then, as shown in Fig. 7.2.1.3H, the bandwidth of such a damped line trap may be specified as that range of frequencies over which $R_T > R_{Tmin}$.

The additional damping could be introduced in the form of series resistance in the inductance or a shunt resistor across the trap. The former is impracticable because the power frequency losses would be considerably increased. Shunt damping with a resistor R_s as shown in Fig. 7.2.1.3I produces the resistance curves of Fig. 7.2.1.3J.

It can be shown for this case that the bandwidth

$$\Delta\omega = \frac{\omega_0^2 L}{R_s} \sqrt{\frac{R_s}{R_{Tmin}} - 1}$$

The maximum value of $\Delta\omega$ occurs when $R_s = 2R_{Tmin}$, that is in the case $R_s = 2.42 R_0$.

If the maximum value is made more or less than this we lose bandwidth as shown in Fig. 7.2.1.3J.

Using the optimum value of $R_s = 2R_{T\,min}$, the bandwidth obtainable is

$$\Delta\omega = \frac{\omega_0^2 L}{2R_{T\,min}}$$

It should be noted that for phase-to-phase coupling there are two line traps in series, in which case to obtain the maximum bandwidth, for each trap $R_s = R_{Tmin}$ and

$$\Delta f = \frac{2\pi f_0{}^2 L_T}{1 \cdot 21 R_0}$$

where L_T is the inductance of one line trap and R_0 the characteristic impe-

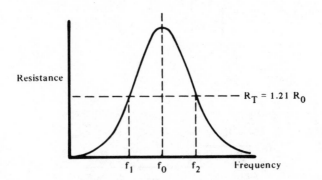

Fig. 7.2.1.3H   *Bandwidth of a damped line trap*

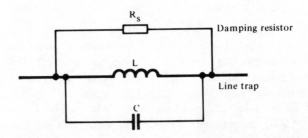

Fig. 7.2.1.3I   *Simple damped line trap*

dance of the line. Also, $\Delta f = f_1 - f_2$ and $f_0 = \sqrt{f_1 \, f_2}$ as before (see Fig. 7.2.1.3H).

As described above, there is an upper limit to the bandwidth that can be obtained by simple damping and in practice it is advantageous to add another series-resonant circuit also tuned to f_0 as well as the damping resistor, as shown in Fig. 7.2.1.3K.

With this arrangement, the resistance is more uniform over the pass band

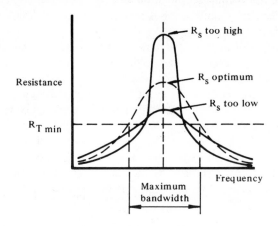

Fig. 7.2.1.3J *Resistance curves of a simple damped line trap*

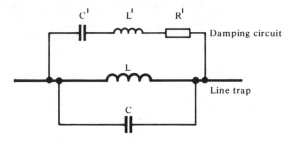

Fig. 7.2.1.3K *Double-frequency tuned (wide-band) line trap*

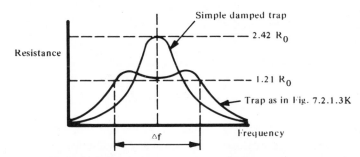

Fig. 7.2.1.3L *Comparison of resistance curves of simple damped, and double-frequency tuned, line traps*

$(R_{Tmax} = 1.33 \; R_{Tmin})$ and the bandwidth is at least twice that of the simple damped line trap, as shown in Fig. 7.2.1.3L

7.2.1.4 Coupling bands: The available carrier frequency range in the UK is 70 kHz-1 MHz, although there are a number of frequencies and frequency bands within this range which are not permitted for continuous carrier use, and no power-line-carrier equipment, quiescent or continuous, is permitted in a band designed to protect the international distress frequency.

The available frequency range is covered by a number of bands, for any given h.v. system voltage using the same line-trap inductance and h.v. coupling-capacitance values. The various bands are achieved by varying the values of the line-trap capacitance, the values of L' and C' in its shunt damping circuit, the series tuning unit of the h.v. coupling capacitor, and the capacitance values used in the shunt tuning unit of the filter.

For the 400 kV system in the UK, standard coupling bands were adopted as shown in Table 7.2.1.4. Prior to the introduction of these standard coupling bands different coupling bands were used by each manufacturer, but since about the mid-1960's, the standard bands of Table 7.2.1.4 have been used at all voltages.

Table 7.2.1.4

Band	Frequency range kHz	Midband frequency kHz
1	70 - 81	75
2	80 - 95	87
3	90 - 110	99·5
4	100 - 125	112
5	110 - 140	125
6	120 - 158	138
7	130 - 175	151
8	150 - 214	179·5
9	180 - 280	225
10	250 - 500	354
11	350 - 700	495

7.2.1.5 Protection and earthing of coupling equipment

(*a*) *Protection:* It is important that the protection and earthing of coupling equipment is adequate as there are many conditions, for example, faults, lightning strokes, switching overvoltages, etc. which impose steep-fronted current or voltage surges on the equipment. Switching overvoltages are most important as they are both frequent and prolonged, particularly when produced by slow-speed disconnectors which cause recurrent arcing at the opening contacts. The conditions producing overvoltages which stress the equipment also produce interference signals, and these are dealt with in Section 7.3.3.

It should be remembered that, when subject to very steep-fronted waves, capacitors may be momentarily charged to high voltages, and short sections of conductor may develop longitudinal voltages high enough to flash over substantial clearances in air.

Considering first the line-trap assembly, this is liable to experience high voltages to earth which are easily catered for by the normal high-voltage insulation. More important is the possibility of the line trap experiencing very steep-fronted current surges when a circuit is switched, although it would be expected that such surges could pass through the shunt capacitor and develop negligible voltage across it. The steepness of the wavefront, however, makes the inherent inductance of the capacitor and its connections significant and surge protection must be provided. This is normally a surge diverter comprising a gap and a non-linear resistor in series, the gap being fast acting and the resistor designed to limit the voltage rise to within the capacitor rating. Fig. 7.2. 1.5A shows a typical arrangement with relevant values.

Considering next the coupling capacitor-stack and its series tuning unit, a voltage surge would be developed mostly across the tuning unit and protective spark gaps are fitted both across the coil, and to earth, with appropriate settings as shown in Fig. 7.2.1.5B. The gap to earth also prevents the v.t. tapping point from rising to high voltages due to surges, or to overloading, or short-circuiting of the v.t. secondary winding. This gap setting is related to the insulation level of the v.t. circuit. Also it is essential to provide a safeguard to personnel in the form of a mechanical switch, shown in Fig. 7.2.1.5B, which connects the junction of the series tuning unit and h.v. coupling capacitor to earth if the terminal cover of the c.v.t. is removed.

The carrier injection point at the earthy end of the coupler may be subject to surge voltages and protection must again be provided. Because of the inductance of the connecting cable between the c.v.t. housings and the shunt filter cubicle, it has been found advantageous to mount this gap in the c.v.t. housing as shown in Fig. 7.2.1.5B.

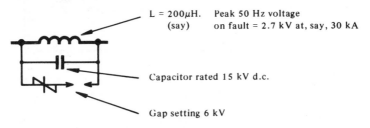

L = 200µH. Peak 50 Hz voltage
(say)   on fault = 2.7 kV at, say, 30 kA

Capacitor rated 15 kV d.c.

Gap setting 6 kV

Fig. 7.2.1.5A   *Protection of line trap*

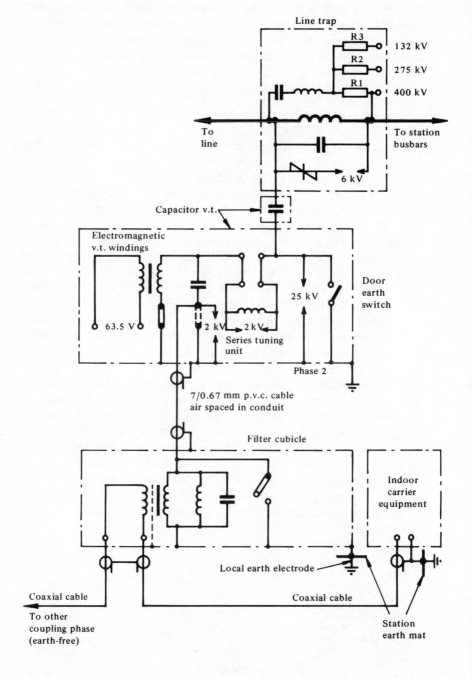

Fig. 7.2.1.5B   *Typical arrangement and earthing of one phase of phase-segregated coupling equipment*

In addition, the injection transformers are provided with earthed screens, as shown, to limit the transfer of a surge across the interwinding capacitance.

(*b*)   *Earthing:* It was mentioned above that the inductance of connections is significant in the case of surges of the type experienced. Coupling equipment is physically large and normally located adjacent to the line termination, whereas the carrier equipment may be up to 400 m away in the control or relay room. Careful attention must therefore be given to the earthing arrangements. The base of the coupling unit is connected to the station earthing system in the usual way but, in addition, is connected to earth spikes which are driven into the ground in the immediate vicinity of the coupler, in order to obtain a low surge impedance. The carrier equipment on the other hand is connected to the station earth at the relay room as is also the outer conductor of the coaxial cable, care being taken that the outer conductor is not earthed at any other point. The various earthing points and the methods of interconnection, are shown in Fig. 7.2.1.5B.

In some locations it may be found difficult to drive the necessary earthing spikes, and in this case it may be necessary to earth to a mat as an alternative. Earthing of the coupling unit solely to the general station earth is not advised because it is not certain that the surge impedance will be sufficiently low.

7.2.1.6   Attenuation

(*a*)   *General:* The overall loss in carrier signal strength incurred both at the terminal equipment and along the line is very important as it influences the application range of the protection, the required transmitted power, and the receiver sensitivities.

Attenuation (or gain) in power-line-carrier signal is defined in terms of decibels (dB). In Fig. 7.2.1.6A:

$$\frac{\text{input power}}{\text{received power}} = \frac{P_1}{P_0}$$

$$\text{attenuation} = 10 \log_{10} \frac{P_1}{P_0} \text{ dB}$$

that is, by convention, a positive quantity implying loss. For example, if

$$P_1 = 10 \text{ W}$$
$$P_0 = 10 \text{ mW}$$

$$\text{attenuation} = 10 \log_{10} \left[\frac{10}{10^{-2}} \right] = 30 \text{ dB}$$

Attenuation as expressed above is a pure ratio. If actual power levels need to be defined in a similar manner, they can be related to an attenuation or gain referred to some datum, generally 1 mW (0 dBm) so that 10 W becomes

$$= +10 \log_{10} \left[\frac{10}{0 \cdot 001} \right]$$

$$= +40 \text{ dBm}$$

and 10 mW becomes +10 dBm.

For values of power below 1 mW the expression will be negative, for example

$$10 \, \mu W = -20 \text{ dBm}$$

Provided the powers are related to a common impedance level, which is often the case, the input and output voltage ratio can be similarly expressed:

$$\frac{P_1}{P_0} = \frac{V_1^2}{Z} \cdot \frac{Z}{V_0^2} = \frac{V_1^2}{V_0^2}$$

$$\frac{P_1}{P_0} \text{ in dB} = 10 \log_{10} \frac{V_1^2}{V_0^2} = 20 \log_{10} \frac{V_1}{V_0}$$

Since the ratios obtained are in logarithmic form, the attenuation of successive stages of equipment can be simply added (taking account of sign), this being one of the main reasons for adopting this technique.

On the Continent the logarithmic base e is used, together with the voltage ratio instead of the power ratio, to define attenuation, the resulting unit being called the Neper.

Thus,

$$\text{attenuation} = \log_e \frac{V_1}{V_0} \text{ Nepers}$$

The relationship between Nepers and Decibels is 1 Neper equals 8·7 dB.

It is important to appreciate that the most significant attenuation is that which occurs on the transmitter side of any source of noise, because the receiver sensitivites will be based on the signal/noise ratio. The losses which occur after the insertion of noise into the system can be quite simply recovered by increasing the gain of the receiver without altering this value of

Fig. 7.2.1.6A   *Circuit used to define attenuation*

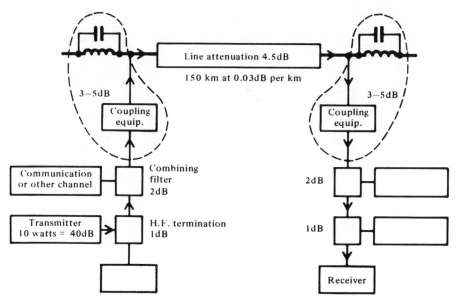

Line attenuation 4.5dB

150 km at 0.03dB per km

3–5dB

Coupling equip.

3–5dB

Coupling equip.

Communication or other channel

Combining filter 2dB

2dB

Transmitter 10 watts = 40dB

H.F. termination 1dB

1dB

Receiver

Fig. 7.2.1.6B *Typical insertion loss values*

signal/noise ratio. It will be seen that the most important losses are those occurring at the transmitting end because all significant noise on power-line-carrier is generated on the h.v. system. The source of noise may, however, be towards the receiving end of the line, so the attenuation over the line may also be considered important in this respect.

(b) *Attenuation in coupling equipment:* As explained in Section 7.2.1.3, the shunt loss of wide-band line traps is limited by the minimum resistive component of the trap which is designed to limit the losses due to both line traps at one circuit end to a maximum of 3 dB over the standard coupling bands given in Table 7.2.1.4. The bandwidth of the 'L'-section filter is approximately 1·5 times that of the line trap and thus the losses in the rest of the coupling equipment, i.e. the series and shunt units shown in Fig. 7.2.1.5B do not normally exceed 2 dB.

Where it is required to operate two or more power-line-carrier equipments into the same set of line coupling equipment some means of combining the output signals is necessary in order to maintain optimum matching and to ensure that one equipment does not have a shunting effect on the other such as might impair operation.

It is normal UK practice to use combining filters in which the pass-band attenuation does not exceed 2 dB. An alternative method is to use a hybrid transformer, which is a three-winding transformer arranged to give maximum attenuation between two separate equipments. This is a much simpler device with a theoretical minimum loss of 3 dB, but in practice the loss can be as high as 8 dB. A further loss to be considered is that incurred in interconnecting coaxial cables, and this attenuation does not usually exceed 5 dB per km.

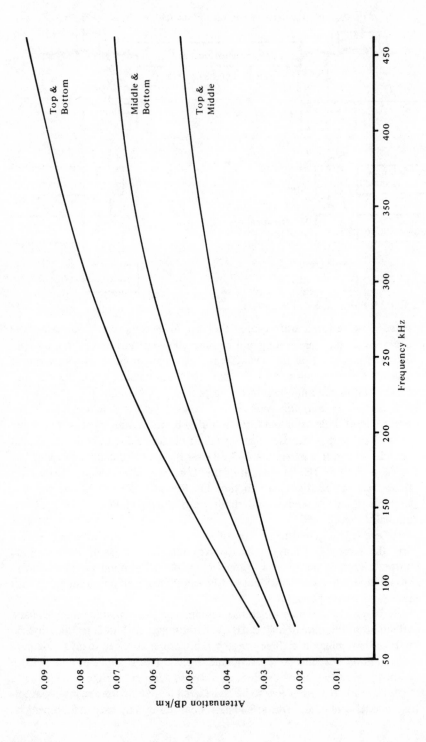

Fig. 7.2.1.6C *Line attenuation on 275 kV, 2 x 175 mm² (L3) circuit*

The attenuation of typical terminal equipment is shown in block form in Fig. 7.2.1.6B.

(c) *Line attenuation:* The transmission efficiency of an overhead line depends upon the line construction and coupling phase configuration, the operating carrier frequency, the primary system configuration, atmospheric conditions and the state of the line concerned, i.e. whether a fault exists on it or not, and thus the loss characteristics of the overhead conductors are less easy to specify than the terminal equipment. The actual loss in the conductors of a clean, healthy line is quite small, but there is a much larger loss involved at the terminals due to end effects, as a result of there not normally being line traps on the uncoupled phase(s) etc. which appears as an attenuation (insertion loss). It is customary, however, to approximate by assigning a certain attenuation for a given conductor system in terms of so many dB/km which includes all losses.

Typical attenuation values showing variation with frequency and choice of coupled phases for a healthy, standard 275 kV line are given in Fig. 7.2.1.6C, and equivalent values for a 400 kV line are given in Fig. 7.2.1.6D. The values given assume that the lines are of untransposed, double-circuit, vertical, construction, with single earth-wire earthed at each tower, and that the coupled phases are correctly terminated in the appropriate line characteristic impedance (the uncoupled phases being earthed). The ground resistivity is assumed to be 100 Ωm.

It is apparent from these curves that lower attenuation results from the use of the top and middle conductors as the coupling phases, and that the lower frequencies should be used for the longer line lengths.

Under normal dry weather conditions with a clean line, the attenuation of the carrier signal due to the transmission line itself is almost entirely the series loss due to the resistance of the conductors. If, however, the line becomes iced the dielectric losses in the ice result in an increase in the effective shunt conductance of the line and the shunt loss due to the transmission line itself can rise to a value comparable with, or even greater than, the series-loss component. With the ice thicknesses which are normally encountered in this country, however, line icing has not proved to be a serious application restriction. Other atmospheric conditions which effectively vary the dielectric between the conductors, such as fog and mist (without ice coating), can also result in increased signal attenuation.

(d) *Attenuation due to line faults:* A point of particular importance in using power-line-carrier links for protection signalling is that faults on the power line are also faults on the signalling circuit, and give rise to mismatch losses in the form of reflections and loss of power to uncoupled phases. The effect of such power-line faults on the signal attenuation may therefore be of vital importance, particularly where signalling must take place in the presence of the fault (e.g. when used in an acceleration function). The increase in attenuation due to the fault depends on the distance of the fault from the line

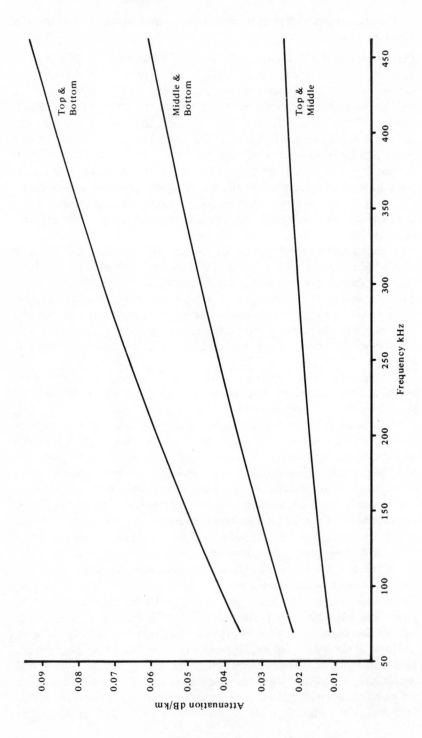

Fig. 7.2.1.6D *Line attenuation on 400 kV, 4 × 400 mm² (L6) circuit*

terminals, and again the phase-to-phase coupling method is superior in this respect. With such a system the additional attenuation, at least for asymmetrical faults is relatively low for faults on the line, except when these occur at critical distances from the terminations, when there is a possibility of standing waves, resulting in high attenuation. Fig. 7.2.1.6E shows this effect. The attenuation produced by faults is lower than might at first be expected because all primary conductors, including those on the other circuit of a double-circuit line, take part in the propagation of the carrier signal.

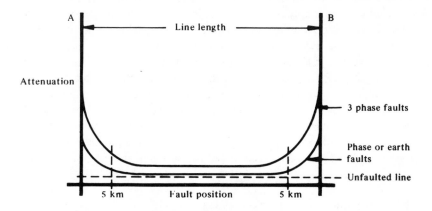

Fig. 7.2.1.6E   *Graph of line attenuation against fault position*

Double-circuit lines, therefore, give rather better performance due to the additional transmission path provided by the second circuit. Three-phase faults produce the worst attenuation, but even then, unless the fault is solid and in the region near the end of the line, the attenuation may not be excessive. However, it is normal practice to allow a larger received signal to receiver operating level margin (say 25 dB) for equipments which are required to signal successfully through line faults, compared with systems, for example, in distance protection blocking applications, or phase comparison protection, (say 10 dB safety margin) where successful signalling is only essential under external fault conditions where the conductors used for signalling are healthy.

(e)   *Attenuation through busbar nodes:* It is common practice to allow two line-lengths of physical separation between carrier equipments operating at the same frequency, i.e. three busbar nodes. However, bearing in mind that the attenuation through a busbar station node depends very much on the size of the station and the blocking effectiveness and number of line traps in series, measurements have shown that allowing two line lengths may well be pessimistic. In some specific cases the attenuation due to two large busbar nodes was found to be at least 48 dB even though circuit parallelism had a bypassing effect on at least one of the nodes.

7.2.1.7   Application to teed circuits: If it is only required to signal between two of the ends of a teed circuit then these two ends can each be properly terminated with the line characteristic impedance as for the unteed case; however, depending upon the length of the tee connection compared with the wavelength of the carrier frequency in use, the impedance at the tee point can vary over a wide range giving rise to high losses.

In these cases, line traps should be fitted to the tee connection as close as possible to the tee point. Tests, however, have indicated that the carrier frequency input impedance of some transformers is much higher than the characteristic impedance of the overhead line, implying that line traps may not always be required where a transformer is teed off the line, although line traps should still be fitted if power-line-carrier is to be used for intertripping for faults on the transformer, since the effective impedance of a faulted transformer is uncertain.

Where signalling is required between three ends of a teed circuit it is not possible to terminate the ends with a single line matching characteristic impedance such that all the transmitted power is absorbed. If, however, each end is terminated with the same line matching characteristic impedance as for the two ended case then the impedance at the tee point is $R_0/2$ and this gives rise to a theoretical minimum insertion loss of 3·5 dB and this is considered the optimum arrangement.

7.2.1.8   Application to circuits containing cable sections: The characteristic impedance of a cable differs considerably from that of an overhead line and, consequently, when cable sections are inserted in a line mismatch occurs at the line/cable junctions, resulting in reflections and very high losses. Further, the insertion loss of the cable itself is very high apart from at particular discrete frequencies which depend on the cable characteristics and, in particular, its length. There are no simple guiding rules to determine whether carrier signalling is possible on such circuits, and each case has to be separately investigated. Other possibilities include the use of impedance matching equipment, or high-frequency bypass circuits, but these are expensive. Whenever possible, coupling should be made to the overhead line with the line trap separating the line from the cable as this provides improved carrier blocking.

7.2.2   Private pilots

7.2.2.1   Underground pilot cables

(a)   *General:* For primary circuits which consist entirely or predominantly of underground cable, it is often expedient to utilise pilot cores within underground pilot cables owned by the Supply Authority for protection or protection signalling purposes. These underground pilot cables are expensive to install unless the ground is already open for the laying of the main power cables, and even for the cases where the cost of exclusive trenching can be justified, the route of the cable often approximates very closely to that of the associated primary circuit(s).

Private pilot cables are frequently assumed to be very secure since, although they are obviously vulnerable to mechanical damage by such equipment as excavators and other road-making equipment, all accessible terminations are under the control of the Supply Authority. However, the detailed protection performance statistics which have been available in recent years do not confirm the assumed reliability of private pilot cables. The relative unreliability arises from the fact that it has not been customary continuously to supervise private pilots and thus, a pilot circuit fault having occurred, it could remain undetected until the next primary system fault occurs, when the signalling channels would be found to be ineffective. In order to obtain the full security potential of private pilots, continuous monitoring facilities should be employed, even if they consist of supervising one pair of cores in each pilot cable.

(b) *Pilot-cable design:* When a pilot cable is laid in parallel with, and in close proximity to, a high-voltage primary circuit it can be subject, during fault conditions on the primary system, to high levels of longitudinal (common mode) and resulting transverse (differential or series mode) induced voltages.

The magnitudes of the induced voltages appearing in a pilot cable are determined by factors such as the separation between the pilot cable and the h.v. circuit, the pilot cable's characteristics, the length of parallelism, soil resistivity, source frequency, the screening present and the magnitude of the earth fault current. The actual value of the longitudinal induced voltage can exceed 15 kV, but this may be reduced by, for example, screening, e.g. a continuous, solid, metallic, outer sheath, earthed at both ends of the section parallel to the primary circuit. The lower the d.c. resistance of the sheath, the greater is the reduction in induced voltage. In severe cases, where the induced longitudinal voltage cannot be restricted by inherent means (e.g. screening) to less than 15 kV, it may be necessary to install control devices, e.g. pilot isolating transformers, neutralising transformers, etc. at selected points. The choice of control device will depend upon their compatibility with the type of signal being transmitted. Where equipment and pilots are subjected to high induced voltages adequate warning labels must be provided.

As a result of the longitudinal induced voltages, transverse induced voltages appear between cores due to unbalanced core-to-sheath capacitances, and these may have an adverse effect on the performance of protection and protection signalling equipment connected between these cores.

To reduce the transverse voltage to a minimum, for protection and protection signalling applications, it is essential to select the best pairs of cores. The ideal choice being a twisted pair or a pair of cores which approximate to twisted pairs. These will have a relatively high value of core-to-core capacitance and low value unbalance capacitances.

In the recent past, underground pilot cables used by UK Supply Authorities have usually consisted of 7/0·029″ (7/0·67 mm) or 3/0·029″ (3/0·67 mm) wormed cores within p.v.c. insulation. These wormed cores are by no means as effective as twisted pair cores, and recent experience with wormed cores at the higher system voltages now precludes the use of such pilots at these voltages except where careful selection of pairs of cores is employed, and where proper attention has been paid to monitoring core dispositions throughout the length of the cable, including all joints and terminations. To minimise the transverse voltages, two adjacent cores from the same innermost layer within the multicore should be selected as a core pair. Further, to reduce mutual interference effects between one core pair and another core pair used for different signalling functions, each core pair for each function should be separated from all other core pairs in the same layer used for other functions by a spare single core or pair of cores.

Expressed as a percentage of longitudinal induced voltage, the highest level of 50 Hz transverse (core-to-core) voltage induced in a pilot loop is considered to be 0·01% for twisted pairs and 0·1% for adjacent outer cores of a multicore cable. Hence, if 15 kV is taken as the limiting longitudinal voltage (see below) then 15 V (i.e. 0·1% of 15 kV) is the highest transverse induced voltage to be considered in practice as arising from unbalance in the cable characteristics. (Any transverse voltages arising from unbalances in the terminal equipment would have to be added to that arising from the cable itself).

Multicore, as distinct from multipair, cables are normally either p.v.c. or impregnated paper insulated. They are normally designed for a withstand voltage between conductors and between conductors and sheath of up to 5 kV r.m.s., and thus are only suitable for installations where the induced longitudinal voltages do not exceed 5 kV. Also the capacitance of p.v.c. insulated cables is considerably higher than either impregnated paper or equivalent polythene insulated cables, and this can often be the limiting factor for protection (power-frequency signalling) applications.

Present practice, for all pilot cables for protection or protection signalling purposes associated with UK 275 or 400 kV transmission systems, is to specify multipair (twisted pair) type cable with 1/0·9 mm conductor and insulated with polythene to 15 kV, irrespective of length. The core pairs selected for protection or protection signalling must maintain their relative position to all other core pairs throughout the cable length. For all installations where the maximum induced longitudinal voltage does not exceed 15 kV, steel wire armoured cables are used. Where the maximum induced voltage could otherwise exceed 15 kV, aluminium wire armoured cables are installed with armouring of sufficient cross-section to limit the actual induced voltage to not greater than 15 kV. In some cases a solid aluminium sheath may be necessary. The armour is electrically continuous from one end to the other and earthed at both ends of the pilot cable. The allocation of core pairs in a multipair cable should be made on the same basis as for paired cores in a multicore cable.

(c) *Parameters of pilot cables:* The transmission characteristics of private pilot cables are predictable and stable and typical design characteristics are given in Table 7.2.2.1A. There will not normally be any amplification, loading, or equalisation associated with private pilot cables and the extent of their application is largely dependent on their length. The limiting factors in determining the length of a circuit to which pilot wire protection may be applied and to pilot cables for other signalling functions are:

(i) the pilot cable inherent capacitances
(ii) the resistance of the cores
(iii) the core insulation.

From the point of view of interference resulting from longitudinal or transverse induced voltages, the most important design parameters affecting the magnitude of the interference which can appear in pilot cables are the core-to-core capacitance, the core-to-earth capacitance, the core-pair-to-earth unbalanced capacitance, and the core-pair-to-core-pair unbalanced capacitance.

Typical values of capacitances for multilayer type pilot cable are given in Table 7.2.2.1A.

Table 7.2.2.1A   *Capacitance values*

Type of pilot cable	Dielectric strength kV to earth	Type of insulation	Capacitance pF/m							
			Inner layer				Outer layer			
			(C_c) core-to-core	(C_e) core-to-earth	Unbalance		(C_c) core-to-core	(C_e) core-to-earth	Unbalance	
					(C_{up}) core-pair-to-earth	(C_{upp}) core-pair-to-pair			(C_{up}) core-pair-to-earth	(C_{upp}) core-pair-to-pair
12 core 7/0·67 mm	5	p.v.c.	58·5	261	12	—	58·5	256	12	—
19 pair 1/0·9 mm	5	polythene	17·70	56·54	0·115	0·030	19·93	60·38	0·173	0·026
61 pair 1/0·9 mm	15	polythene	13·66	50·92	0·110	—	16·23	52·62	0·140	—
61 pair 1/0·9 mm	15 +	polythene	13·66	50·92	0·110	—	16·23	52·62	0·140	—

Cables can be manufactured with good uniformity of core resistance, and provided the joints are good, resistance unbalance produces little interference. However, a limiting factor is the total conductor resistance.

The maximum conductor resistance of plain annealed copper wires per 1 000 m of conductor length is given in Table 7.2.2.1B.

Table 7.2.2.1B

Type of pilot cable	Resistance at 20°C Ω	Resistance at 70°C Ω
7/0·67 mm	7·41	8·86
1/0·9 mm	58·2	69·6

The ability of the insulation of the pilot cable and its terminations to withstand the values of the voltages induced in the pilot cores by virtue of their proximity to the h.v circuit, and the rise in local earth potential under fault conditions are also important factors.

7.2.2.2 Overhead pilots: For protection or protection signalling applications associated with overhead lines where buried pilots would have had to bear the whole laying costs, overhead pilots strung either on separate poles or on the overhead-line towers have sometimes been used. In the latter case, they may be combined with the earth wire for the circuit to form a composite cable known as an overhead-pilot earth wire. In the case of overhead pilots, and especially those strung on the same towers or poles as the primary circuit, particular care is necessary as high longitudinal voltages may be induced in the pilots because of mutual inductance between the primary conductors and the pilot. This condition is severe in the case of earth faults because of the high zero sequence coupling. A wormed arrangement for the protective cores is necessary to avoid unbalance of these induced voltages causing a voltage around the pilot loop. A high degree of insulation is required, and for overhead pilot earth wires special types have been manufactured with both magnetic and electrostatic screening in order to reduce the induced voltage. The induced voltage depends upon the length and construction of the line and the value of earth-fault current, so that it is usually expressed in V/A/mile for earth-fault conditions. A value of 0·3 is generally used for pilots without special screening. Even with this special screening the induced voltages may be relatively high (e.g. 0·1), for example a 10 mile length line with an earth-fault current of 5 kA would give an induced longitudinal voltage of 5 kV. The value would be 15 kV for the unscreened type. Equipment connected to such pilots will thus require either isolating transformer coupling or an adequate level of insulation. As in the case of underground pilot cables where equipment and pilots are subject to high induced voltages, adequate warning labels must be fitted.

7.2.3   Rented pilot circuits

7.2.3.1   General: In many countries, pilot circuits can often be rented from the Post Office Authorities. In the UK circuits suitable for protection, protection signalling and intertripping have commonly been provided by the Post Office between any required points. The cost of such rented circuits is usually assessed by capitalising the annual rental over a period of (say) ten years, and on this basis the cost is generally much lower than that of using any of the alternative media unless they already exist. Rented pilot circuits are also particularly attractive when a power system is subject to frequent rearrangement, since they are normally available for hire and release at short notice. (In the UK, when a pilot circuit is no longer required, the agreement for hire can normally be terminated at one week's notice and, while it is usual for planning purposes to give the Post Office one year's notice of a requirement for such circuits, they have, on occasions, provided circuits at a few day's notice where an urgent requirement for signalling facilities has arisen).

The main disadvantage of using rented pilot circuits is that they are not directly controlled by the Supply Authority and may be out of service or subjected to interference, both electrical and human, when required for use, and this imposes particular requirements on the signalling equipment design, in order that overall satisfactory performance can be obtained in terms of security and reliability from the signalling facility. Further equipment design constraints may also arise due to limits being imposed by the communication authorities on the signal level and bandwidths in order to avoid interference with other signalling systems.

Post Office networks are, of course, primarily provided and designed for the transmission of speech at commercial standards, the design being based on a particular expected failure rate as a result of plant and equipment faults and human errors, and the standards adopted may well vary considerably between countries.

However, in the UK, by agreement with the Post Office, it has been possible to minimise the failure rates of rented pilot circuits by precautions such as segregation of circuits and facilities, the distinctive marking of plant and equipment, and avoiding the use of mains-dependent equipment which means that the circuit should not fail as a result of interruption of local mains supplies to a Post Office repeater station.

7.2.3.2   Types of Post Office rented pilot circuit: In the UK four types of pilot circuit have been provided by the Post Office as follows:
(*a*)   Two-wire circuits unamplified, provided wholly on metallic core pairs. These circuits may be used over short distances (say up to 30 km) for the transmission of voice frequency signals (300 - 3 000 Hz), speech and d.c. signals or for signalling at power-system frequency.
(*b*)   Four-wire circuits, unamplified, provided wholly on metallic core pairs. These circuits may be used for the purposes described in (*a*) above, with the additional facility of bothway simultaneous v.f. and d.c. signalling.

(c)   Two-wire or four-wire amplified circuits provided wholly on metallic core pairs. These circuits may be used for the transmission of voice frequency signals and speech. They cannot be used to transmit a.c. signals below 300 Hz. A d.c. signalling path using a phantom circuit connection (see Fig. 7.2.3.2) is normally available for circuits up to 11 km between stations, and possibly in the range 11-40 km depending upon plant availability.

(d)   Two-wire or four-wire circuits provided partially on metallic pairs and partially on Post Office high-frequency carrier system channels. These circuits may be used for the transmission of voice frequency signals and speech. No d.c. signalling path is available, and the circuits cannot be used to transmit a.c. signals below 300 Hz.

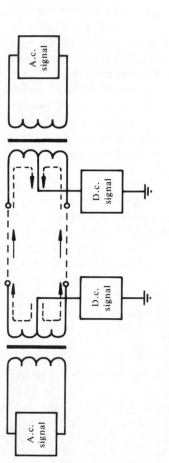

(a) Earth return phantom circuit

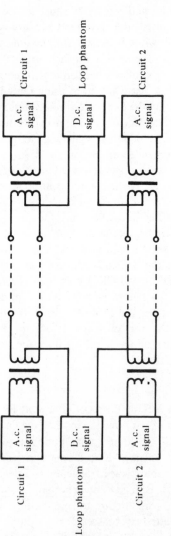

(b) Loop phantom circuit

Fig. 7.2.3.2   *Phantom circuits*

The pilot circuits described in (*a*) above have been extensively used in the past in association with unit protection systems operating at 50 Hz.

However, the UK Supply Authorities have been given notice that wholly metallic pilot circuits, as described above in (*a*), (*b*) and (*c*) and which have a route length in excess of 11 km, are likely to be phased out in the near future. Since the Post Office have also indicated that where metallic circuits are available, i.e. a route length less than 11 km, no guarantee of total circuit resistance will be given, this effectively precludes the use in the future of rented pilot circuits for the inter-connection of unit protection systems signalling at power system frequency without some form of modulation.

7.2.3.3 Pilot-circuit characteristics: The cost of renting a pilot circuit from the Post Office varies considerably according to the type of circuit required and the radial distance between the two terminals. Most future protection, protection signalling and intertripping applications will utilise a four-wire presented circuit such that the initial overall loss at 800 Hz will be 0 dB when measured between 600 Ω terminations. The frequency/loss characteristic will not normally deviate by more than +2 dB and − 6 dB, relative to the loss at 800 Hz, over the frequency range 300 Hz to 3 kHz, and the variation of loss with time at 800 Hz will not normally exceed ±3 dB relative to the setting up level. The Post Office reserve the right to provide a circuit between the specified terminations by whatever route, and using whatever line plant that they choose, bearing in mind the type of circuit that has been specified.

It is to be expected, therefore, that a pilot circuit may be made up of various types of transmission media, e.g. audio links, carrier links, coaxial links, radio links and, in the future, possibly optical fibre links. In terms of the loss characteristics this is of no significance but, by virtue of the fact that the circuit may contain links which involve multiplexing, the Post Office imposes limits on the signal levels that may be applied to the line. This is necessary to ensure that signals are not applied at levels that could overload line components and so cause intermodulation difficulties that may affect other circuits that are routed over the common links. The maximum one minute transmitted mean power level permitted on such a pilot circuit is − 13 dBm for frequencies in the band 200-3200 Hz. Thus, if signalling equipments share a rented circuit, the maximum output per equipment is a function of the number of sharing equipments.

The transmission characteristics of Post Office lines are not as stable as private pilot circuits and signalling equipments must be designed to operate over a fairly wide range of signal levels. Also, insulation barriers (isolating transformers) are required between rented pilots and the signalling equipment to prevent damage to rented equipment and hazard to personnel as a result of rise of earth potential that can occur between transmission stations when power system faults occur.

7.2.4   Radio links

7.2.4.1   General: Radio links may be used for all types of protection, protection signalling and intertripping equipments which are designed for operation over power-line-carrier or rented pilot circuits which incorporate h.f. links. Such application is, of course, subject to technical and economic considerations and to the particular limiting characteristics of a radio link.

The available frequency bands are in the region of 460-470 MHz (v.h.f.), 1500 MHz and 7500 MHz (s.h.f.). These bands are usually allocated by the Post Office Authorities and can vary from country to country. In the UK, however, it is the Home Office that is the licensing authority and they do not normally give permission for the use of radio between fixed locations, even where this has economic advantages, unless it can be shown that the Post Office is unable to provide line-signalling facilities of suitable technical quality or the necessary separation or segregation of such facilities where this is a particular requirement. There is also increasing opposition from public authorities, in particular, town and country planning organisations, which further complicates the establishment of suitable transmitting and receiving sites. Point-to-point radio paths have to be very carefully selected, particularly in the case of microwave transmission and, even when properly established, may prove difficult to maintain free from obstruction, especially in urban areas. Again, in the particular case of microwave transmission, the effective range of a single stage, typically some 50-60 km as shown in Fig. 7.2.4.1A, is inadequate, and repeaters or reflectors, or both, are required in order to achieve larger distances as shown in Fig. 7.2.4.1B. The design of such repeater

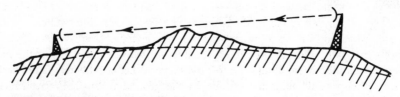

Fig. 7.2.4.1A   *Single-stage microwave link*

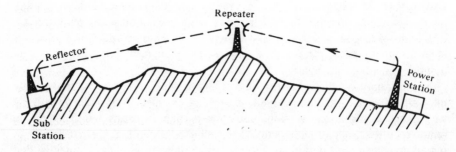

Fig. 7.2.4.1B   *Two-stage microwave link*

stations is often difficult and expensive, particularly as the preferred location for these is often in some inaccessible position, for example, on top of a mountain.

Like power-line-carrier, an advantage of a radio link for protection signalling purposes is that the transmission medium cannot be physically interfered with easily and, in addition, the wide signalling bandwidth available makes possible faster signalling than can usually be achieved with other transmission media. Alternatively, the extra bandwidth can be used to transmit a large number of separate signals, provided that the security requirements associated with the signals permit the sharing of a common medium. There are normally no restrictions with regard to continuous transmission, and relatively high audio signalling power levels can be used to modulate the radio carrier compared with those which are permitted on rented pilot circuits.

Radio links have so far been very limited in application in the UK but have been widely used in America, particularly as wide-band communication, control, and protection links between generating stations. They have also been used in countries where the route of the line crosses difficult country.

7.2.4.2 **Microwave radio links**: The microwave band is that part of the frequency spectrum above 1000 MHz. The available parts of that band in the UK allocated by the Home Office are from 1450 to 1535 MHz, and from 7428 MHz to 7896 MHz. The band 1450-1535 MHz should be relatively free from man-made electrical noise, and is out of the range of normal broadcasting. The band 7428 MHz-7896 MHz should, in addition, be free from cosmic noise, but at these frequencies waveguides have to be used to interconnect the aerial and the microwave equipment.

Between a radio transmitter and its receiver there are a number of paths over which signals may be propagated. At microwave frequencies the two most important are the 'direct' or 'space' wave, which is propagated over what is in effect, the 'line-of-sight' path, and the 'ground reflected wave' which is composed of the transmitted signals that arrive at the receiver by virtue of being reflected at the earth's surface. Other possible paths are provided by the 'ground' or 'surface' wave which is propagated along the surface of the earth, and induces electric currents in the earth. At microwave frequencies, however, this path is of no significance, since the ground wave suffers very rapid attenuation. There are two further paths by which indirect signals may arrive at the receiver. The first is by reflection in the earth's atmosphere. These tropospheric reflections occur as a result of changes in the refractive index of the atmosphere with height, which in turn varies continuously with the weather. At microwave frequencies, signals which arrive by this path constitute a source of interference to the direct path signals. Further refractions and reflections of radio waves can occur at the ionosphere, which is a layer of ionised gases at the edge of the earth's outer atmosphere some 60 km above the earth's surface. Signals propagated over this path are known as the 'sky wave' but they are of virtually no significance at microwave frequencies.

It has been shown in the literature that, if an aerial is assumed to be a point

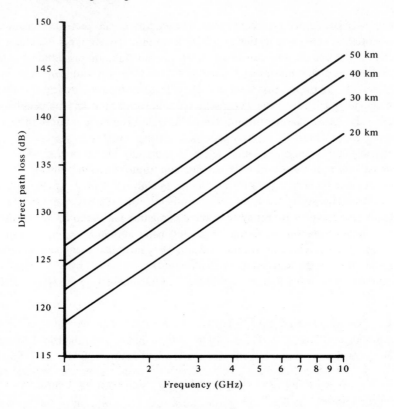

Fig. 7.2.4.2A   *Direct path loss at microwave frequencies*

source radiating power uniformly in all directions, then the attenuation in a straight line through a vacuum or ideal atmosphere with no absorption or reflection of energy by nearby objects is:

$$\text{direct path loss (dB)} = 20 \log_{10} \frac{4\pi d}{\lambda}$$

where d is the distance between the assumed point source aerial and λ is the wave length. The direct path loss for typical frequencies and line lengths is shown in Fig. 7.2.4.2A. However, ground reflected waves and tropospheric reflections are a significant problem in microwave transmission. Since their path lengths differ from the direct path length there exists the possibility that signals arriving from different paths may be in antiphase, thus tending to signal cancellation; this effect is called 'fading'.

In order to obtain optimum results from a microwave link, therefore, it is necessary to reduce interference from ground reflected waves and tropospheric reflected waves to a minimum by an appropriate choice of position, direction and shape of the transmitting and receiving aerials (together with aerials associated with intermediate repeater stations). A common shape for aerials is that of a parabolic dish. If an aerial system is made directional in this way it may be considered to introduce gain because it concentrates the total radiated power into a beam which effectively increases the total received power. However, it is not normally possible to make an aerial wholly directional and a polar plot of the radiated power usually has 'sidelobes' or secondary peaks which can be a source of interference in the link or produce 'crosstalk' in other links. Such crosstalk can be reduced by polarising the transmitted signal, usually either horizontally or vertically, but the degree of discrimination achievable by this method is limited since cross polarisation in the atmosphere can occur.

Aerial height is obviously another very important factor in reducing the likelihood of interference between direct and ground reflected waves. Sufficient clearance must be provided from the ground and other obstacles, and this can be a particular problem for power system signalling where the presence of transmission towers, aerial wires and cooling towers add to the difficulty of finding a suitable transmission path. One authoritative source recommends that to achieve an insertion loss which approximates to the calculated direct path loss, the 'line-of-sight' transmission path should clear an obstacle located at a distance of d_1 by a distance of

$$C \sqrt{\frac{\lambda d_1 (d-d_1)}{d}}$$

where C has a value of at least 0·6 and is preferably not less than unity. (λ is the wavelength, and d is the 'line-of-sight' path length between the transmitter and its associated receiver).

At the higher frequencies (> 7 GHz) absorption can introduce further attenuation. In particular, rainfall causes absorption to occur, the attenuation increasing rapidly when the radio wavelength approaches the diameter of the rain drops. However, weather conditions giving rise to serious difficulties due to this effect are rare in the UK.

It should be noted that both absorption and fading effects are frequency sensitive, and thus a considerable improvement in signalling reliability can be achieved by using two separate microwave links transmitting the same information provided that the frequency bands chosen for the links are widely separated from each other.

7.2.5 Optical-fibre links

Optical-fibre communication links which can convey information at frequencies about the wavelength of visible light, using glass fibre strands, are currently undergoing feasibility trials with UK Supply Authorities, as well as other research and industrial establishments. These links show great promise of providing reliable and economic communication links for both short- and long-distance data transmission in either analogue or digital form. Their particular ability to remain largely unaffected by severe electrical interference, and the fact that galvanic isolation exists between the transmitter and the receiver, make optical-fibre links of special interest for signalling for protection purposes.

New production techniques make it possible to have single strands of fibre with a graded profile of refractive index which results in both low per unit length loss and jointing loss. Today (1978) optical fibres are commercially available, in lengths up to 3 km, having losses of 4 to 5 dB/km in the wavelength range of 800-900 nm (330-380 THz). Typically joint losses are in the order of 0·3-0·5 dB per joint.

Optical-fibre cables can be produced which are of rugged construction suitable for use in ducts or as separately hung cables, and cables are being developed for attaching externally to conductors (the earth-wire) or for embedding within a conductor (again, this is likely to be the earth-wire). Typically, an eight strand optical-fibre cable has an overall diameter of under 10 mm, thereby providing a considerable capacity for data transmission in a very small physical size.

Although optical-fibre systems are capable of transmitting analogue information by intensity modulation of the optical sources, attention is being given mainly to the development of digital transmission techniques when the transmitting sources can be switched in a binary code to exploit the inherent wide bandwidth of the link.

Experimental installations of optical-fibre communication systems are in operation in the Post Office and British Rail, using optical-fibre cable in some cases longer than 8 km, and operating at signalling rates of 8 megabits per second, and 140 megabits per second (the unit of information, the bit, is defined in Section 7.3.1). As optical sources gallium arsenide l.e.d.s or lasers are used with typical working power levels of − 13 dBm (50 μW) and 0 dBm (1 mW), respectively.

7.3. Fundamental signalling problem

7.3.1 Effects of noise

The information that is required to be transmitted in power system protection signalling and intertripping applications is relatively simple in that it is of the 'off/on' type, the requirement being to distinguish between an 'off' and an 'on' condition. The unit of information, the bit, is defined as the amount of information required to reduce the uncertainty at the receiver by one half, and since an 'off/on' system involves only two states, 'on' and 'off', only one bit of information is required to signal the change from the 'off' (e.g. normal) condition to the 'on' (e.g. trip) condition. However, the fundamental signalling problem is that of 'interference' or 'electrical noise' in the communication medium, and more than one bit may be required in the message to represent the information being transmitted, the additional bits being used to assist in distinguishing the genuine signal from the noise.

Electrical noise in the communication channel can have three effects in protection signalling circuits. First, it can tend to simulate the transmitted signal and hence produce unwanted operation of receivers. Secondly, it can tend to interfere with a genuine transmitted signal and prevent or delay the legitimate operation of a receiver. Thirdly, if the noise is of sufficient amplitude, it can permanently damage the equipment.

The equipment design features necessary to overcome the first two effects are mutually incompatible, and it is necessary to specify particular requirements in terms of the ability of the equipment to remain stable in the presence of noise and its ability to signal through noise, depending on the demands of the signalling application (refer to Section 7.4).

Modern designs of signalling equipments often have inbuilt facilities for variation of this compromise to provide a bias towards either reliability of operation at the expense of security against maloperation, or vice-versa.

7.3.2 Characteristics of electrical noise

Apart from the inherent electrical noise which exists in the communication channel, interference can be produced from many different external sources. When high voltage switching operations using disconnectors or circuit-breakers are carried out, electric arcs are produced. Each time the circuit is re-established by the arc restriking step voltages are applied to a circuit containing reactive elements, which then 'rings' at its natural frequency and produces overvoltages. Switching operations which involve charging capacitive equipment or connections (c.t.s, c.v.t.s. etc.) from another highly capacitive source, such as a long transmission line, give rise to the highest overvoltages.

In the particular case of switching operations using disconnectors, whether motorised or manually operated, a series of bursts of electrical noise is produced, which lasts for several seconds, the burst repetition rate depending on the number of phases being switched, the power frequency and the rate of contact closure or separation. The burst repetition rate is not constant, being minimum at the beginning and end of the disconnector operation, and there is normally a period in mid-operation of some two or three seconds of continuous noise at maximum amplitude. As a result of inductive, capacitive, and direct coupling to secondary wiring circuits, peak voltages of several kV have been measured across protection equipment terminals in relay rooms. Thus all such equipment employing static circuitry is normally subjected to a 5 kV, 1/50 µs impulse test as part of the type approval testing, to ensure that the equipment can withstand this without damage. Further, a maloperation-proof test has recently been introduced into type test programmes for static equipments, and this is based on an IEC Recommendation wherein a 1 MHz chopped 400 Hz interference test signal is used.

In the particular case of power-line-carrier equipments, however, there is the additional hazard that the frequency spectrum of the generated voltage disturbances covers that which it is practical to use for equipment operating frequency, and thus represents very high level 'noise'. Further, the noise is directly coupled to the equipment through the coupling capacitors. In fact, the coupling equipment, being composed of a number of tuned circuits, can itself be shock excited by the primary steep-fronted overvoltages and thus, even though equipment operating frequencies might be outside the range of the original primary noise frequencies, 'in-band' noise can be generated by the coupling equipment itself. In addition, power-line-carrier channels are subject to continuous low level noise as a result of corona discharge, and this sets a limit on the maximum receiver sensitivity that can be used satisfactorily.

Lightning strokes to primary conductors, earth-wires, or merely in the vicinity of stations or lines, can give rise to similar interference problems as the switching phenomena described above, as can fault arcs produced by power system faults (which themselves may be the result of lightning strokes), together with the circuit-breaker operations that follow them. One of the major problems with these noise sources is that they tend to generate at the very time that secure and reliable signalling is required.

It is not just power-line-carrier and private pilot circuits which are subject to the interference sources; although every effort is made to minimise the effects, rented pilot circuits often have coupling paths. In addition rented pilot circuits are subject to man-made interference.

Although, in the UK, precautions are taken by the Post Office to identify Board's circuits, interference does occur. This can vary from increased insertion loss to complete open or short circuit of the channel. Alternatively, core pairs can be crossconnected, looped to other pairs, or connected to earth, either directly or sometimes via rectifiers. Test voltages associated with equipment used for circuit setting-up and fault-locating purposes may also be superimposed on the pilots. The standard test tone used by the Post Office is 800 Hz at a test level which can be as high as 20 dB above the maximum level permitted for protection signalling. This test tone can itself simulate part of a signal or can intermodulate with genuine signals to produce receiver operation. Normally, the output impedance of the test oscillator will be 600 Ω, which will only increase the insertion loss by 3 dB. However, there is a test set used by the Post Office when locating cables which has a very low impedance output capable of effectively short circuiting existing genuine signals and superimposing a high level 1 000 Hz signal which may be transmitted as a continuous sinewave, or, alternatively, it may be interrupted at a variable rate. This test set is known to generate a large number of intermodulation products. In addition, frequency translation can occur as a result of oscillator drift within the Post Office h.f. carrier links and this sometimes occurs during times of changeover of power supplies.

7.3.3 Equipment design principles

If a signalling equipment is to be made secure in the presence of noise, the transmitted message must be made sufficiently distinguishable from noise so that the two will not be confused. One simple way of ensuring the recognition of a genuine signal in the presence of noise is to arrange that the genuine signal level is higher than the interference but this is not always possible due to the limitations of the signalling medium or equipment, e.g. restrictions on signalling level due to possible interference problems, maximum equipment dynamic range etc. Examples of single bit messages which are used in some signalling applications are a change in d.c. level or polarity, a change from no signal to an a.c. signal, or the removal of a normally present a.c. signal. The latter, when applied to v.f. signalling, is termed 'tone-off' signalling, and has been found to give a better performance in protection signalling applications than 'tone-on' signalling.

As described earlier in this Chapter, the conditions under which signalling systems used in power system protection can be divided are those in which the signal gives a command, e.g. intertripping, and those in which the signal gives advice, e.g. acceleration or blocking of distance protection. Signals which give commands require that considerable care must be taken in both the choice of message and the design of the receiver to minimise the risk of incorrect operation in the presence of noise, and command signals, therefore, generally employ a more complex message code than is required for advisory signals. However, the general theory of information communication states that:

(*a*)   The maximum possible rate of information transmission, in bits per second, is directly proportional to the bandwidth of the signalling channel, a high signalling rate requiring a wide bandwidth and vice versa.

(*b*)   Immunity against noise, to any required degree, can be achieved by suitable signal coding, the achievement of immunity for any given bandwidth being at the expense of a reduced signalling rate or, for any given signalling rate, at the expense of an increased bandwidth requirement.

It would appear, therefore, that to obtain fast operating times with a given message code, maximum use should be made of the available bandwidth. However, the choice of a suitable bandwidth is not a simple matter, since increasing the bandwidth will in turn increase the probability of interference from unwanted signals, both increasing the risk of maloperation and making more difficult successful signalling, the choice is thus a compromise between the requirements of operating time and reliability and security in a given noise environment.

Discrimination between genuine and false signals by coding implies designing a receiver to accept a message as genuine if it conforms to a predetermined pattern, i.e. a digital code or combination of frequencies transmitted sequentially or simultaneously. However, in a limited bandwidth, the number of frequencies which can be transmitted simultaneously is also limited, and in order to obviate long and complex codes which would give rise to long operating times, other receiver design features are also used to discriminate between genuine and false messages:

(i)   Acceptance of a bit if its level lies within certain predetermined limits. Bits whose level is higher or lower than expected are rejected as false.

(ii)   Acceptance of a bit as genuine if it occurs within an expected time interval. This can normally only be applied to the second and successive bits of a message.

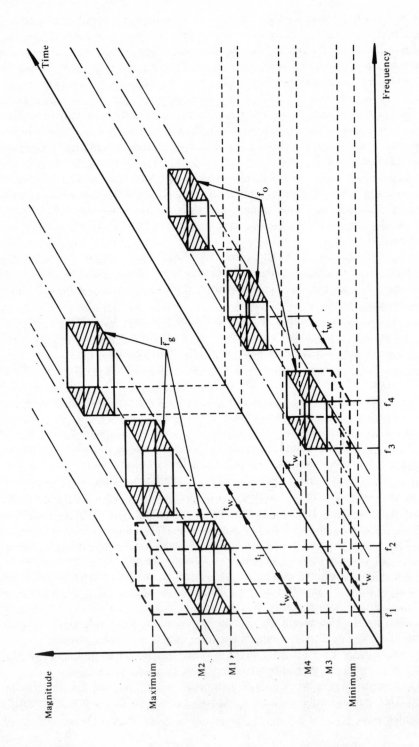

Fig. 7.3.3   *Concept of measuring 'windows'*

The use of these additional measures leads to the concept of measuring 'windows' which are illustrated in Fig. 7.3.3. Thus a coded single-frequency shift signalling system might well be designed such that a normally present signal f_g must be absent $(\overline{f_g})$ within a measuring 'window' defined by amplitude limits $M1$, $M2$, frequency limits f_1, f_2 and, coincidentally, a frequency f_0 must be recognised within a measuring 'window' defined by amplitude limits $M3$, $M4$ and frequency limits f_3, f_4. Having accepted these bits, further bits must be detected within similar 'windows' which are further constrained in time, in that the presence or absence of a signal must be detected within a time interval t_w, spaced at intervals t_i. Incorrect bits detected in t_i, t_w or $t_i + t_w$ (including the absence of f_g, and/or the presence of f_0 within t_i) may be used to restart the receiver measurement. Detection of incorrect bits, as well as correct bits, is normally necessary since it is the only way in which the presence of interfering signals likely to simulate the genuine code can be recognised, and the receiver can be prevented from incorrect operation that would result if it were permitted to select from the interference those conditions which satisfy the genuine code, and disregard those that do not. It is important that, if the receiver is momentarily blocked by the receipt of incorrect bits, any partly accepted decoded code should be completely reset, otherwise the equipment security is reduced by being in a part operated state, and further interference may cause the decoder to continue through to complete operation. The limiting amplitude levels $M1$, $M2$ and $M3$, $M4$ of Fig. 7.3.3 may not be fixed, but may depend upon the output of a noise or signal to noise detector. Normally, however, the measuring 'window' level limits are only allowed to vary between fixed maximum or minimum cut-off levels, the minimum level representing maximum receiver sensitivity, and the receiver being blocked if signals are detected above the maximum since, if the equipment was originally set up properly for the anticipated maximum/minimum signal levels depending upon the expected channel attenuation and its variation, signals detected above the maximum will have been derived from a noise source.

If the constraints of the signalling channel are such that low level continuous guard or monitor signals are permitted then, in order to improve the signal to noise ratio, 'boosting' to a higher level may be employed during a signalling condition. The degree of boost must be consistent with the maximum permitted signalling levels on the channel concerned, and again, although first considerations might lead one to suppose that a choice of maximum permitted boost would be appropriate, it must be remembered that the maximum genuine signal level increases the required dynamic range of the receiver, thereby increasing the limits that can be set for maximum and minimum receiver cut-off levels and effectively opens wider the measuring window, and may, thereby, increase the risk of unwanted operation so, once again, the choice of the degree of boost is not a simple matter. As discussed in Section 7.3.2, however, the high level noise which occurs on a signalling channel at the time of a power system fault, is impulsive in character and, at the expense of operating time, provided the signalling application permits, it is possible to arrange for the signal code to be repeated continuously such that successful signalling takes place in the gaps in the high-level noise. Thus at the receiver, recognition of the first complete message code is accepted as genuine, even though it is not necessarily the first one transmitted. The amount of delay introduced over and above the normal signalling time of the equipment will once again depend upon the complexity of the signal, and its level compared with that of the noise.

From the foregoing considerations, it will be appreciated that there are definite theoretical and practical limits to the signalling performance which can be achieved over a medium of given bandwidth, with given signal to noise ratio, and given noise characteristics.

7.4   Performance requirements of signalling facilities and equipment

7.4.1   Operating times

7.4.1.1   General: The total protection signalling or intertripping facility operating time is dependent on the operating time of the signalling equipment, inclusive of any interface, together with the signal propagation time, which varies with the type and length of the signalling channel.

The signal propagation time is dependent upon the mode of signalling, and will vary with the physical and electrical properties of particular signalling media. In general the signal propagation time over pilot wires is assumed to be 1 ms per 10 km (6 miles) of pilot route length for voice frequency signalling, and 1 ms per 6·5 km (4 miles) of pilot route length for d.c. signalling. For power-line-carrier channels the signal propagation time is negligible.

Two distinct and separate operating times are therefore normally met with in practice. These are:

(a) Facility operating time, which is that overall period of time which elapses between the initiation of signalling, and the receipt at the remote circuit end of an identical condition to that which initiated the signalling, e.g. if the signalling is initiated by closure of a contact, then the total signalling facility operating time is the period of time that elapses before closure of a normally open contact at the receive end signalling interface.

(b) Equipment operating time, which is the operating time for a particular signalling equipment, and will be less than the facility operating time by a value equal to the signal propagation time over the signal path between the interfaces at the terminal equipments. (Note that for power-line-carrier signalling, the facility and equipment operating times will be sensibly the same).

The inclusion of the interface operating time within the overall operating time of the equipment is of considerable significance for whilst reed relays used to provide the interface for v.h.s. signalling equipments may only have a combined send and receive operating time of 5 ms or less, the corresponding figures for attracted armature send and receive interposing relays is 20-60 ms.

7.4.1.2 Equipment operating time classification: In the past, in the UK, protection signalling equipment has been classified on an equipment operating speed basis, the classifications falling into two groups designated low speed and high speed as follows:

Group classification for protection signalling
(i) Low speed : an operating time not greater than 0·200 s
(ii) High speed: an operating time of not greater than 0·070 s

Because of the need for greater security in intertripping applications (refer to Section 7.4.3), intertripping equipment has had a separate group classification designated low speed, medium speed and high speed as follows:

Group classification for intertripping
(i) Low speed: an operating time of approximately 0·8-1·0 s
(ii) Medium speed: an operating time of approximately 0·3-0·4 s
(iii) High speed - an operating time of approximately 0·1-0·2 s

With the advent of signalling equipments which are suitable for protection signalling and intertripping applications, having operating times of 50 ms or less, it has become necessary to extend the above group classifications and to introduce a more precise classification based on the equipment operating time, measured in milliseconds.

The new group classification, common to all protection signalling and intertripping equipments having an operating time of 50 ms or less, is 'very high speed'.

The precise maximum equipment operating time is expressed in the form of a time class index, comprising the operating time in milliseconds preceded by the letter 'T'. (It should be noted that signalling facility operating times can also be expressed similarly). The time class index within the appropriate speed classification is specified for all approved protection signalling and intertripping equipments. When used in conjunction with the group classification it is shown in brackets following that classification. For example, an intertripping equipment having an operating time of 30 ms is designated 'very high speed (Class T30)'.

Although the group classification allows an operating time of not greater than 50 ms, the upper limit for v.h.s. protection signalling equipment will normally be 15 ms, i.e. Class T15. Again, for v.h.s. intertripping equipment the upper limit will normally be 40 ms, i.e. Class T40.

For the purposes of classifying equipments into the operating speed groups the equipment operating times used are those obtained when the equipment operates under ideal conditions which, in particular, means that both the equipment and the associated signalling channel are completely free from noise.

7.4.2 Reliability of operation: When testing a signalling equipment for its ability to signal satisfactorily through noise, it is normal practice to plot a graph of the percentage of a given number of transmitted signals which are received successfully within a specified time against signal to noise ratio. Although the absolute noise level for a given signalling application is very unlikely to be known, such graphs are extremely useful for comparison of different equipment designs, and satisfactory operational experience in a large number of applications, of equipments of known performance, has enabled Supply Authorities to specify their requirements for reliability of operation in the presence of noise as illustrated in Table 7.4.2. The example given is for an intertripping application with an operating time classification of 30 ms (v.h.s. T30), using a power-line-carrier transmission medium. For other signalling applications and basic noise free operating times, other signal to noise levels, noisy environment operating times and success percentages would be specified.

Table 7.4.2

Maximum level of random noise relative to the normal signal level at the receiving equipment connection to the h.f. coupling equipment measured over a 4 kHz band	Minimum number of transmitted protection signals received within 30 ms	Minimum number of transmitted protection signals received within 150 ms
dB	%	%
− 13	100	100
− 9	75	90
− 7	25	75

7.4.3 Security against maloperation: It is also possible, for any given equipment, to plot graphs of the number of receiver maloperations which occur in a given time with noise bursts of specified level, duration and repetition rate. However, the required performance is more difficult to specify since the performance that will be obtained will depend very much upon the particular equipment design and the features incorporated specifically to improve the security against maloperation (see Section 7.3), however, a corresponding example specification for stability in the presence of noise to Table 7.4.2, i.e. for a v.h.s. T30 intertripping equipment operating over power-line-carrier, is:

'The maloperation rate shall be plotted as a function of noise level. With white noise bursts of 500 milliseconds duration, at the most onerous noise level, the maloperation rate shall not exceed 0·01 per cent. The time between the applied bursts shall not be less than the reset time of any noise inhibition circuitry but, in any case, the repetition rate shall not exceed 1·5 per second. The number of bursts to be applied shall be agreed with the purchaser. For the purposes of this security requirement it shall be assumed that the receiver is working at maximum setting sensitivity.'

7.4.4 Pulse distortion

The permissible difference in pulse duration between the input pulse to a transmitter and the corresponding output pulse from a receiver will depend on the particular signalling/intertripping application. In the case of protection signalling applications a typical specification for pulse distortion is that the duration of the received signal passed to the protection equipment shall be within ± 4 ms of the duration of the sending pulse initiated by the protection equipment. In the case of intertripping applications, a typical specification is that the duration of the received signal passed to the protection equipment shall not be less than 100 ms, and shall not exceed the duration of the sending pulse initiated by the protection equipment by more than 100 ms.

7.4.5 Power supplies

As with all protection equipment which requires auxiliary power supplies independent of normal c.t. and v.t. supplies, it is essential, in the case of protection signalling and intertripping equipment, to derive such supplies from a reliable source such that it is not dependent on normal mains supply which may fail at the instant of fault.

All modern designs of v.f. and h.f. signalling equipment employ solid-state active devices which require an external power supply. With the advent of such devices in the early 1960s the original policy in the UK was to provide each equipment with its own independent auxiliary supply when required. These supplies had either ½-hour or 6-hour standby capabilities and, in the majority of cases this was obtained from integral sealed nickel-cadmium batteries, which were charged from the most secure a.c. supply in each station. However, experience with these sealed nickel-cadmium cells showed that they were unsuitable for such a non-cyclic application, their capacity diminishing rapidly with time such that their usable life was extremely limited.

Present-day policy is to provide 48 V (nominal) lead acid battery units to provide the auxiliary power supply requirements of protection and protection signalling equipment. One of the reasons why this method was not chosen originally is the difficulty of ensuring that equipment performance is not jeopardised by interference voltages appearing on supply leads, such interference voltages being either capacitively or inductively transferred from adjacent wiring and equipment, or being fed back on to the supply leads by other 'noisy' equipment. It is current practice to keep 48 V d.c. supplies as 'clean' as possible by including in the equipment specification requirements for the maximum level of 'noise' voltages that may be back-fed on to supply leads, and to limit the length of wiring between the battery and the equipment, thus at 400 kV, where normally there are individual relay rooms per high-voltage circuit, it is now quite common for 48 V batteries to be supplied on a per-circuit basis also. These batteries are used to provide the power supplies of some of the protection equipment on the h.v. circuit with which they are associated and are connected also to one adjacent circuit relay room to provide the power supplies for some of the protection equipment on the adjacent h.v. circuit. This is done to ensure that, in the event of failure of a single battery, not all of the protection on a circuit will be lost.

The signalling equipment specification should include the range of variation in power supply voltage over which the required signalling equipment performance is to be maintained, and also the maximum permissible burden to be imposed on the battery. It is normal to specify both the short-term operational maximum load, and the maximum permissible continuous demand.

7.4.6 Other performance requirements

The complete performance requirements for a signalling system should also include the specification of the ranges of a number of other influencing factors over which the required performance must be maintained, e.g. the range of deviation in signalling channel attenuation or variation in received signal level, the range of ambient conditions, and the permissible effects from, and upon, equipment on adjacent channels (crosstalk).

Details of the alarms, indications and test facilities, input and output interface requirements (e.g. number and rating of output relay contacts) and appropriate insulation level requirements should also be specified. A very important aspect also is the required state of the receiver output in the event of signalling channel failure.

7.5   Methods of signalling

7.5.1 D.C. intertripping

This is one of the simplest, most reliable and widely used methods of intertripping over short distances. It is generally applicable, at least in this country, to underground privately owned pilots of the 7/0·67 mm (7/0·029 in) type. It is, therefore, very widely used on cable networks when pilots and primary cables may be laid together. These systems would not generally be suitable for rented telephone pilots where the permitted maximum working signal levels are low and there are additional requirements for insulation and isolation. With rented pilots there is also a greater possibility of interference, both electrical and manual, from maintenance work being carried out on associated channels. Further, as mentioned earlier, it is becoming increasingly difficult to obtain rented telephone pilots with a continuous d.c. circuit.

In these systems operation of a protective relay causes the sending relay to apply a d.c. voltage to the pilot channel which then actuates the remote 'receive' relay. Conventional 'tripping relays' can often be used for both the send and receive func-

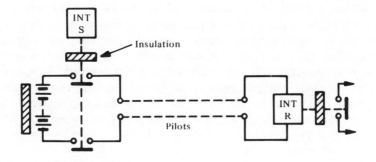

Fig. 7.5.1.1A *Simple one-way intertripping*

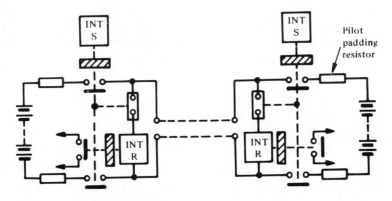

Fig. 7.5.1.1B *Simple two-way intertripping*

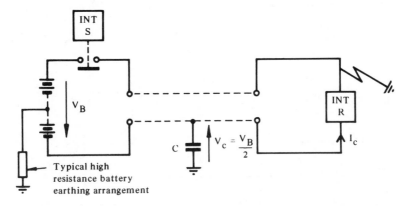

Fig. 7.5.1.1C *Mechanism of incorrect operation arising from battery earthing arrangements*

tion. A simple arrangement of one-way intertripping is shown in Fig. 7.5.1.1A. If two-way intertripping is required an arrangement such as shown in Fig. 7.5.1.1B may be used. However, although this latter system does save two pilot cores compared with using two systems similar to Fig. 7.5.1.1A, one in each direction, its application is limited to installations where simultaneous bothway signalling is not required. Note that in all cases double-pole switching is used on the send relays which isolates the tripping batteries completely from the pilots under normal conditions. This has been found necessary in order to avoid spurious operations which were experienced with single-pole switching as a result of the capacity of a pilot core becoming charged through the battery earthing arrangements, and discharging through the receive relay coil, and/or induced/impressed voltages between the two earth points, if an earth fault occurred (refer to Fig. 7.5.1.1C).

For very short pilot lengths, up to 1000 m, a simple d.c. relay may be used as the receive relay. However, care is necessary when choosing the sensitivity, that is the minimum operating power of the receive relay, in order to avoid spurious operation. Operation of such systems may be fairly fast, say 20 ms or less.

The problem with longer pilots is that of high, power frequency, induced voltages in the pilots, and for such applications special measures must be taken. These measures may take the form of complex signal coding or may entail the use of a.c. filters in conjunction with a simple d.c. signal. The a.c. filters ensure that the intertrip receive relay is insensitive to relatively high values of a.c. while remaining highly sensitive to low values of d.c. When these latter measures are employed the relay is said to be 'surge proof' and the complete system of pilot wires, batteries and relays is referred to as 'surge proof' intertripping.

There are two basic types of surge proof intertripping:
(*a*) the shunt type for use with separate intertripping pilots
(*b*) the series type for use on shared pilots and connected in series with unit type feeder protection systems.

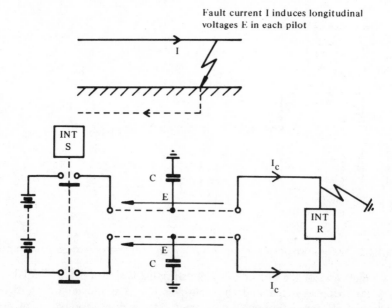

Fig. 7.5.1.1D   *Mechanism of incorrect operation arising from longitudinal induced voltages*

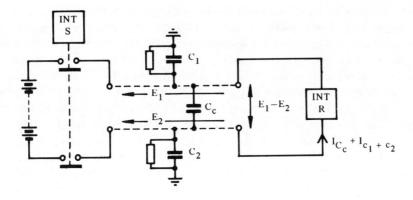

Fig. 7.5.1.1E   *Mechanism of incorrect operation arising from derived transverse induced voltage*

In the UK the series type of surge proof intertripping is normally only employed on distribution systems, and even the shunt type is rapidly becoming obsolete on the 400 and 275 kV supergrid systems because of the relatively slow operating time, compared with other signalling systems that are available, and other design constraints.

The degree of surge proofing employed must be sufficient to ensure non-operation of the relay under two particular conditions:

(i)   The development of an earth fault on one pilot core coincident with, and possibly resulting from, an induced voltage condition, which would result in the pilot capacitance current flowing through the intertrip receive relay(s). It is therefore necessary to surge proof the relay up to the highest value of pilot capacitance current likely to be encountered, following a pilot core flashing over to earth at the instant of peak induced voltage (refer to Fig. 7.5.1.1D).

From the above, it follows that the suitability of a relay, surge proofed to a given level, for application to a particular circuit will depend, to a certain extent, on the capacitance of the associated pilot circuit. One of the limiting factors in determining the length of feeder to which surge proof intertripping may be applied, therefore, is the pilot cable core-to-earth capacitance.

(ii) Under system fault conditions power frequency longitudinal e.m.f.s will be induced in the pilots by the passage of high values of fault current in the adjacent primary cable and the earth. The inherent differences which exist between the core-to-earth capacitances and leakage resistances of the pilot cores will result in a difference in the magnitudes of induced longitudinal voltages, which results in a transverse voltage between cores, which can cause a current to circulate within the circuit (refer Fig. 7.5.1.1E).

The probability of a pilot-core insulation breakdown depends to an extent on the insulation level of the pilot cores and the equipment to which it is connected; in general, the higher the insulation level the lower the risk of breakdown. If the risk of insulation breakdown can be reduced to a level such that the capacitance discharge condition can be discounted, then the surge-proofing requirements can be reduced to the level necessary only to cater for the maximum value of a.c. voltage which can be induced between intertripping pilot cores under adverse system conditions. The reduction of core-to-core unbalance voltages by the use of twisted pairs or, where twisted pairs are not available, by the selection of adjacent pairs of cores at the centre of multicore cables, will result in a further reduction of the surge-proofing requirements with a corresponding increase in system operating speed.

Precautions against maloperation of the intertrip receive relay may, therefore, take the form of either pilot-circuit insulation to the anticipated maximum induced voltage level, in conjunction with a high level of surge proofing, or, alternatively, a higher level of pilot circuit insulation with an accompanying reduction in the risk of breakdown, together with optimum pilot core selection, resulting in a reduction in the surge-proofing requirements and hence a consequent decrease in overall operating time. It is, of course, important to recognise that, as well as the pilot cores themselves, all equipment such as relays and intertripping energising supplies (e.g. batteries) require to be insulated to the appropriate level.

In the UK, the highest level of 50 Hz longitudinal (core-to-earth) voltage permitted to be induced in pilots is limited to 15 kV and special measures are taken, including, for example, the use of aluminium sheathed cables with their inherent screening properties, to contain the calculated longitudinal induced voltage within the permitted level (refer to Section 7.2.2.1). Where such containment is not achievable the pilot cores cannot be used for intertripping.

The surge-proofing performance for particular intertrip receive relays is specified on the basis of the system operating speed classification and time class index. The highest level of surge proofing that has been used in the UK is 5 kV.

Two examples of shunt-type surge-proof intertripping relays are shown in Figs. 7.5.1.1F and 7.5.1.1G. Both of these are, in effect, arrangements which accept a d.c. signal but which suppress or filter a.c. signals. In practice, this discrimination is quite difficult to achieve because the d.c. operating level of such relays would be of the order of 10 or 20 V, so that the discrimination between the peak of 5 kV a.c. voltage and d.c. operating voltage would be a rejection ratio of about 700:1. It is

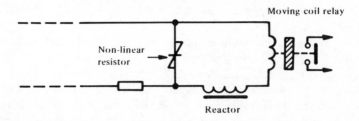

Fig. 7.5.1.1F   *Surge-proof intertripping relay*

possible to design filters or suppression circuits which can achieve such rejection on a steady state basis, but such circuits are subject to transients or shock ringing. Under these conditions the transient output can be considerably in excess of the steady state output. It must also be remembered that one of the requirements is that the relay should operate when both a.c. interference and d.c. operating signal are present. The solution of this problem is usually to limit the input to the relay from the filter by non-linear devices, but to restrict the action of these to the large transient output and not to the lower steady state output. This means that the device may temporarily limit for a short time during the transient conditions when operation by the d.c. may be prevented, but that operation is ensured after the transient has died away. With such an approach it is possible to satisfy the stability requirement on a.c. and the operation requirement with both a.c. and d.c. and achieve operating times of about 150 to 200 ms.

In the arrangement shown in Fig. 7.5.1.1F, the received signal is fed into a resistor/metrosil arrangement which is intended to limit the incoming signal, the limiting level, for practical purposes, being well in excess of the normal d.c. signalling level. The attenuated signal can still be in excess of the relay setting so that the limited output is fed to the relay via an inductance which suppresses the a.c. signal without much reduction of the d.c. signal. Finally, the relay itself is of the perma-

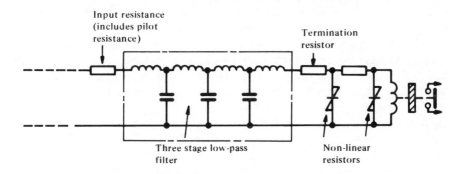

Fig. 7.5.1.1G *Surge-proof relay using low-pass filter*

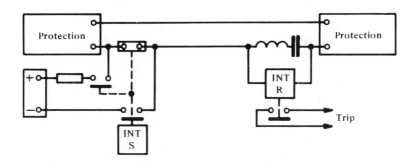

Fig. 7.5.1.1H *D.C. intertripping over protection pilots*

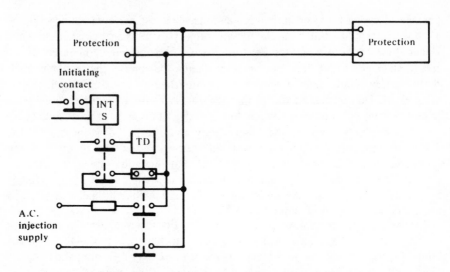

Fig. 7.5.1.1I   *Intertripping over protection pilots by a.c. injection*

nent magnet moving-coil type which, provided its response is not short compared with 1 cycle of 50 Hz, will have a further discriminating ratio between a.c. and d.c., that is its 50 Hz a.c. setting will be considerably in excess of its d.c. setting.

In the arrangement shown in Fig. 7.5.1.1G, the received signal is passed to a moving-coil relay through a three-stage low-pass filter which is properly matched in terms of input resistance and output resistance. The multistage arrangement is used because, for a given overall attenuation, the response time is reduced by using more than one stage. This filter has an attenuation sufficient to bring the steady state input to the moving-coil relay much below its setting. To deal with high transient output from the filter, a two-stage limiter is used which limits the transient input to the relay to a level which would not cause operation during the transient period. The limiting is arranged to be in excess of the combined steady state a.c. and d.c. signals so that the duration of limiting is short.

Series-type intertripping can be used to provide intertripping over protection pilots where the main protection is of the pilot-wire type. This is often done to secure fast double-end tripping on a circuit in cases where a single-ended tripping type of protection is used, where remote tripping is required on the occurrence of a busbar fault, or where autoreclosing is used. The intertripping provisions should not interfere with the correct performance of the pilot-wire protection and the intertripping relays used will naturally be subjected to power frequency effects.

Where it is possible to transmit d.c. over the pilot wire without upsetting the pilot-wire protection, a low impedance d.c. intertripping relay, somewhat similar to that already described, may be used, as shown in Fig. 7.5.1.1H. It may be necessary, however, to by-pass the intertripping relay by a power frequency acceptor circuit, as shown, in order to relieve the pilot-wire protection of the burden of the intertripping relay.

In many applications, especially in connection with busbar protection, remote tripping is effected by open-circuiting or short-circuiting differential protection pilots by relay contacts or auxiliary switches. Provided the through-fault current is above the setting of the protection, such action will 'unstabilise' the protection and cause its operation. To cover the case of low fault current or dangerous displacement of voltage, an a.c. injection feature is sometimes incorporated so that following a period of unbalanced operation of the protection, an a.c. signal is injected into the pilots to cause operation of the remote relay. A typical arrangement is shown in Fig. 7.5.1.1I.

7.5.2 Low-frequency a.c. intertripping over private pilots

Another method of achieving surge proof intertripping over pilots is shown in Fig. 7.5.2A. A source of alternating voltage energises the pilots at a frequency different from, or any multiple of, that of the power system, say 175 Hz, and this energises both receive relays which are tuned to this frequency and are thus normally energised. Operation of the send relay at either end of the circuit causes both receive relays to release and intertrip. Operation of the local receive relay can be prevented, if necessary, by a normally closed contact on the send relay as shown. The use of tuned relays ensures immunity from power-frequency effects. Isolation transformers or combined isolation and drainage transformers can protect terminal equipment from overvoltages on the pilots.

Fig. 7.5.2A   *Intertripping scheme using tuned relays*

7.5.3 Voice-frequency signalling equipment

7.5.3.1 General: Voice-frequency signals are normally regarded as covering the frequency range 0-4000 Hz, although not all of this band is available, nor necessary, for the transmission of satisfactory speech communication. As mentioned in Section 7.2.3.2, pilot circuits rented from the Post Office normally make available the range 300-3000 Hz for a.c. signals. All of this band may be divided up into discrete channels of 120 Hz or multiples thereof or, alternatively, the band 300-

1900 Hz may be used for speech communication and, with appropriate filtering, the remainder of the band, 'above-speech' (a.s.) may be divided up into 120 Hz (or multiples of 120 Hz) channels, as appropriate, for other signalling purposes.

All five communication media discussed in Section 7.2, with appropriate interfaces, and, in some cases, frequency translation equipment, can provide signalling channels for v.f. working.

7.5.3.2 V.F. protection signalling equipment: From 1960 in the UK, considerable use has been made of 'tone-off' signalling over rented pilot circuits for protection signalling, i.e. 'advisory' signals. In this system, an above speech (i.e. in the 2-3 kHz band) tone occupying a 120 Hz channel is continuously transmitted in the non-signalling state, and removal of the tone denotes the signalling condition. Electrical noise thus tends to hold the tone receiver in the operated (safe) condition and hence prevents maloperation. The disadvantage of this arrangement is that electrical noise coincident with a power system fault might delay the receipt of a genuine signal; however, this delay is normally slight and the advantage of avoiding maloperation decisively outweighs the disadvantage of a slight delay time. Continuous monitoring of line and equipment during the non-signalling period is provided by the continuously transmitted tone signal. Failure to receive the tone signal for a period of approximately two seconds denotes failure of either the signalling channel or the equipment, and results in automatic cancellation of the 'signal received' condition, together with the initiation of an audible alarm. A disadvantage of this monitoring arrangement is that loss of received tone is registered as a genuine protection signal during the two second period that must elapse before recognition as a 'channel fail' condition. This system provides signalling facility operating times normally somewhere between 45 and 70 ms depending upon pilot circuit routing. Although manufacture of this equipment has ceased in favour of v.h.s. v.f. protection signalling equipments, many such equipments remain in use where the signalling facility operating times still satisfy the protection requirements of the primary transmission system.

Recent requirements in respect of enhanced speed, signalling reliability and security for the major part of the UK transmission system, however, have led to the introduction of new designs of v.h.s. v.f. protection signalling equipment, most of which operate on a single frequency shift principle, and incorporate a continuous channel monitoring facility.

These systems occupy a bandwidth of up to 480 Hz and thus make possible faster signalling than can be achieved with a single 120 Hz channel. Faster signalling is further facilitated by extensive use of solid-state components and reed relays, the latter having replaced the attracted-armature relays used in earlier equipments.

Because the newer v.h.s. protection signalling equipments occupy greater bandwidths than were formerly used, it is not always possible to share the transmission path with a speech facility. On double-circuit power routes, it is common for the two primary circuits to share a v.f. pilot circuit by frequency multiplexing for some of the signalling requirements of each primary circuit. However, where there is a requirement for more than one v.f. signalling facility associated with a single primary circuit (e.g. one for the first main feeder protection and one for the second main feeder protection) these are not permitted to share a common pilot circuit for reasons of security.

7.5.3.3 V.F. intertripping equipment: Various v.f. intertripping equipment designs are in use and in general employ coding and other security measures typically described in Section 7.3.4. Some modern designs of equipment are illustrated in Figs. 7.5.3.3A, B and C. These intertripping equipments, wherein high security against maloperation is a prerequisite, may be utilised for protection signalling purposes, e.g. distance protection acceleration, provided that the overall operating time of such equipment is within the required facility operating time (it being noted that in practice where such a signalling equipment is available it would normally be used for direct intertripping in preference to acceleration).

Some typical codes that have been used for v.f. intertripping systems are shown in Figs. 7.5.3.3D to 7.5.3.3H. In Fig. 7.5.3.3D operation occurs when the 'guard' tone f_1 reappears while the 'operate tone' f_2 is still present.

Devices are included in the receiving equipment to ensure that the operate output is blocked if there is any appreciable departure from the genuine code. The equipment requires the use of two signalling tones per facility per direction of

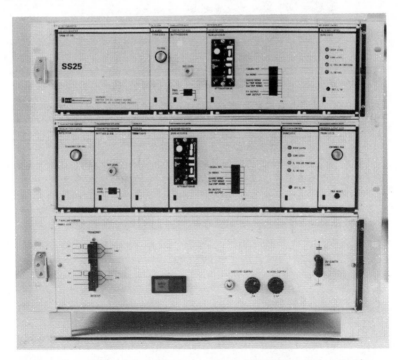

Fig. 7.5.3.3A *Type SS25 v.f.. intertripping equipment* (GEC Measurements Ltd.)

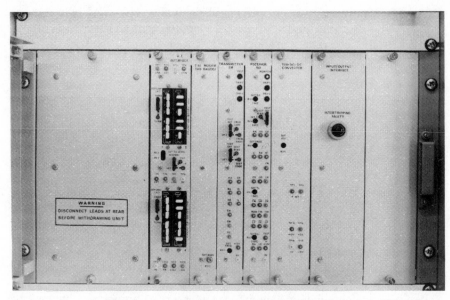

Fig. 7.5.3.3B   *Type HSDI 2 v.f. intertripping equipment* (Fisher Controls Ltd.)

Fig. 7.5.3.3C   *Type NSD32 v.f. intertripping equipment* (British Brown Boveri Co. Ltd.)

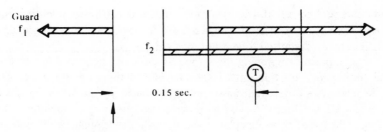

Fig. 7.5.3.3D   *V.F. intertripping high speed (1)*

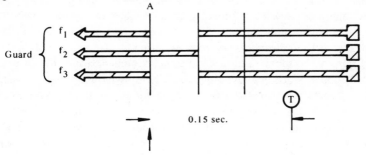

Fig. 7.5.3.3E   *V.F. intertripping high speed (2)*

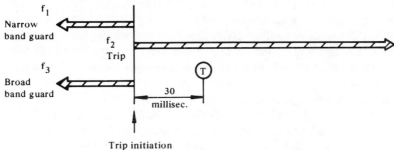

Fig. 7.5.3.3F   *V.F. intertripping very high speed (1)*

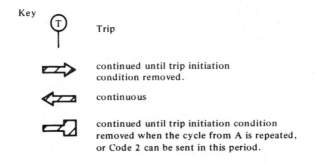

operation and thus bothway operation for two intertripping facilities requires the use of eight separate tones. Channel monitoring is effected by giving an alarm if the continuously transmitted tone is not received.

An equipment employing three tones is shown in Fig. 7.5.3.3E. In this system the three tones are transmitted continuously in the quiescent state. A two-part code having two different arrangements (frequencies f_2 and f_3 can be interchanged) is employed which can be used to provide two intertripping facilities. The system requires the use of three signalling tones for two intertripping facilities per direction of operation and thus bothway operation for two facilities would each require the use of six separate tones. The integrity of this system lies in the requirement that a complete code must be received without appreciable 'gaps' or 'overlaps' between the various parts of the code or any 'blips' of unwanted tone or 'gaps' in any wanted tone. Channel monitoring is provided by giving an alarm if any one of the continuously transmitted tones is not received for a period in excess of five seconds.

A further example which employs three frequencies is shown in Fig. 7.5.3.3F. The arrangement comprises two voice-frequency guard tones which are continuously transmitted when the intertripping equipment is in the quiescent state. When an operation is initiated, the two guard tones are disconnected from the line and a single operate tone is transmitted. The two guard tone receivers in the receiving equipment have different characteristics, one having a narrow bandwidth of approximately 80 Hz and the other having a wider bandwidth of approximately 200 Hz. An operate receiver similar to the narrow band guard tone receiver, but with a bandwidth of approximately 40 Hz, is also provided. For an incoming signal to be recognised as a genuine operate signal, no frequency within the range of the narrow band and broad band guard receivers must be present, and the operate receiver must detect the presence of a frequency within its range. Immunity against maloperation by unwanted noise is provided by the two guard channels; a frequency recognised by either guard channel will inhibit the reception of an operate signal. Because the second guard channel has a wide bandwidth, it is likely that random noise which could simulate the tone would also produce a frequency within the range of the broadband guard receiver. The system requires the use of three signalling frequencies for each intertrip facility per direction of operation. Thus bothway operation for two facilities requires twelve frequencies. Owing to the bandwidth of the broadband guard receiver, it is necessary to space the two guard tones 360 Hz apart. Continuous monitoring is provided by giving an alarm in the event of failure to receive f_1 or f_3 in the quiescent state.

A coded single-frequency shift system which has satisfied the requirements for intertripping is shown in Fig. 7.5.3.3G. The transmitter normally transmits a single frequency f_1 to provide a continuous monitor of the communication channel. Failure to receive this frequency results in the generation of an 'intertripping system fail' alarm by the receiving equipment. Transmission of an operate signal is achieved by means of a code consisting of pulses of frequency f_1 interspaced with pulses of a second frequency f_2. The lengths of the pulses are carefully controlled by the transmitting equipment, and arrangements are made so that f_1 pulses are not the same length as f_2 pulses. Security against maloperation depends upon the correct recognition of a sequence of a predetermined number. Accurate timing equipment in the receiver will reject spurious pulses of incorrect length, even if they coincide with the operating frequencies f_1 and f_2. By adjusting the number of pulses in the operate signal sequence, it is possible to vary the degree of security provided by the equipment. Since the f_1/f_2 pulse sequence is continuous, signalling in the presence of random noise in the communication channel is improved.

Intertripping equipment using standard data transmission 'modems' (modulator and demodulator) which are single-frequency shift, equal mark/space ratio, have also been designed. These systems use a 12-bit code. Frequencies f_1 and f_2 transmit a data word continuously in the quiescent condition to monitor the communication channel and a considerable proportion of the terminal equipment. This 12-bit code can be made unique to a particular intertripping equipment, thus allowing an alarm condition to be generated if two otherwise similar intertripping equipments were to be accidentally transposed. On the command to operate, the 12-bit 'quiescent' code is disconnected, 3 bits of frequency f_1 are transmitted to reset the receiving equipment followed by the continuous transmission of a 12-bit 'operate' code. The 12-bit 'operate' code is deliberately chosen to be dissimilar to the corresponding 'quiescent' code. Security against maloperation is provided by the rejection of all received codes other than the 12-bit 'operate' code assigned to the particular equipment. Continuous transmission of the 'operate' code assists in signalling in the presence of random noise in the communication channel. Failure to recognise either the 'operate' code or the 'quiescent' code by the receiving equipment causes a 'system fail' alarm to be generated.

A double-frequency-shift intertripping system is shown in Fig. 7.5.3.3H. The system normally transmits two voice-frequency signals f_1 and f_3 in the quiescent state. To produce operation f_1 is changed to f_2 and f_3 is changed to f_4 simultaneously. Security against maloperation is provided by the simultaneous frequency change, and in these systems it is arranged for the presence of a single guard frequency to block both trip channels. Another double-frequency shift system uses 'point-on-wave' signalling techniques where the precise point of frequency change is predetermined. By the use of timing devices in the intertripping equipment receiver, it is therefore possible to detect with considerable accuracy a genuine change from the 'quiescent' to the 'operate' condition. In the system shown, the operate tones f_2 and f_4 are transmitted continuously for as long as the operate condition is maintained, but in some systems, arrangements are made in the transmitting circuit for a constant repetition of the transition from 'quiescent' to 'operate' condition for as long as the command to operate is present. Failure to receive frequencies f_1 or f_3 in the quiescent state results in the generation of a 'system fail alarm' by the receiving equipment.

It is important to note that in double-frequency shift systems the frequency-shift channels are arranged to shift such that the frequencies of adjacent channels converge (as shown in Fig. 7.5.3.3H) or diverge, in the change from the guard to the operate state. This is to avoid maloperation that can occur where frequency translation in carrier telephone links takes place via a common oscillator and where, if the above precautions were not taken, oscillator drift could result in both 'guard'

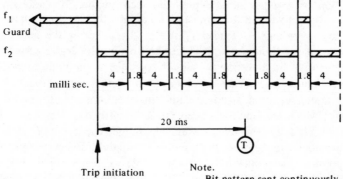

milli sec.

20 ms

T

Trip initiation

Note.
Bit pattern sent continuously
until trip initiation condition removed.
Receiver responds to 20 ms of undistorted
pattern.

Fig. 7.5.3.3G   *V.F. intertripping very high speed (2)*

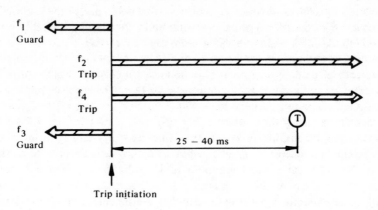

f_1
Guard

f_2
Trip

f_4
Trip

f_3
Guard

25 – 40 ms

T

Trip initiation

Key

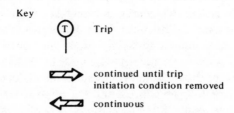

T   Trip

continued until trip
initiation condition removed

continuous

Fig. 7.5.3.3H   *V.F. intertripping very high speed (3)*

frequencies simulating their respective 'operate' frequencies coincidentally. It is
also important that in all cases receivers are arranged to be at least as sensitive to
'operate' frequencies as to 'guard' or 'monitor' frequencies in order that, in the
event of increased channel attenuation, there are no circumstances under which the
system is incapable of normal signalling, but no alarm is given.

7.5.4 Power-line-carrier signalling equipment

7.5.4.1 Keyed carrier equipment: Simple keyed carrier signalling systems consist of a normally quiescent transmitter and receiver operating at the same carrier frequency at each line end. The security against false operation obtainable with such a system is only appropriate for applications where the presence of carrier is used as a stabilising signal, which for protection signalling applications, implies use with distance protection of the blocking type, wherein the most likely effect of noise is to delay operation of the distance protection for the duration of an incorrect signal (which is unlikely to be maintained for more than a few milliseconds at a time), and not to produce an incorrect protection operation, as would occur with signalling equipment used in a permissive mode.

Since the equipment is used only in a blocking mode, i.e. successful receipt of a signal is required only when the distance protection has detected an *external* fault, essential signalling always takes place over a healthy line, additional margins for signal attenuation due to the fault itself are unnecessary and a relatively insensitive receiver setting can be used compared with permissive signalling systems (refer to Section 7.2.1.6(d)) and adequate security against incorrect blocking on noise can be achieved in this way.

Incorrect tripping as a result of failure to block on external fault is unlikely with this equipment as interference is normally impulsive, and is unlikely to obliterate the carrier signal completely for long enough for the receiver to reset. The equipment has an operating time of the order of 8-10 ms (Class T10). Keyed carrier systems of this type normally incorporate 'clock test' facilities whereby a channel test is initiated automatically at predetermined intervals normally of half an hour.

7.5.4.2 Carrier frequency-shift equipment: In the immediate past in the UK, some protection signalling requirements have been met by the use of a single-channel carrier frequency shift equipment. These equipments are also of the v.h.s. group classification (T20). The system is generally as shown in Fig. 7.5.4.2A and comprises a normally operated guard relay which is energised by a normal continuous carrier transmission at the guard frequency f_g which, of course, is outside proscribed frequency bands and is below the maximum permitted continuous transmission level of 2 W. This continuous guard-frequency transmission also acts as a monitor of the integrity of the carrier channel. An output operate signal is produced when the frequency is shifted from the guard-frequency to the operate frequency f_0, the frequency shift, for example, 500 Hz, being small in relation to the carrier frequency (70-700 kHz). The signalling power at the operate frequency is boosted to the order of 10 or 20 W. To achieve the required levels of performance in terms of security in the presence of noise for intertripping purposes in the UK, the above single channel frequency-shift system has been duplicated to form a two-channel system wherein the two transmitters are initiated in parallel and the receive relay contacts are connected in series. Crossconnection of the guard channel receivers is used to block both operate channel receivers if the presence of either guard frequency is detected above the guard receiver setting. The similarity of this system with the v.f. principle of Fig. 7.5.3.3H should be noted.

There is now available a single-channel carrier frequency-shift coded signalling equipment illustrated in Fig. 7.5.4.2B which is capable of meeting the specified

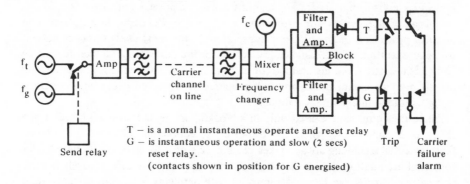

Fig. 7.5.4.2A   *Single-channel, single frequency shift PLC signalling equipment*

BBC HE 164087

Fig. 7.5.4.2B   *Type HSD30 power-line-carrier equipment*

requirements in terms of operating time, reliability and security in the presence of noise, for blocking of distance protection (Class T15), acceleration of distance protection (Class T20), and for intertripping (Class T30). The faster operating times required for blocking and acceleration are achieved by reducing the code evaluation period appropriately. The resultant corresponding reduction in security is acceptable for the applications concerned. This system can be operated with continuous carrier guard signal, or, at the expense of some 3 ms operating time, normally quiescent. In the UK, continuous carrier signalling with inherent continuous channel-monitoring is normally used for intertripping applications. In order to conserve space in the limited frequency bands available for continuous carrier signalling, normally quiescent signalling systems are used for other signalling functions where possible, and these normally incorporate 'clock test' facilities (refer to Section 7.5.4.1).

In practice, because the actual frequency shift of the equipment described is small compared with the carrier frequency, and this would require a high degree of accuracy and stability in the performance of the carrier oscillators, this problem is obviated in these particular equipment designs by using audio-frequency shift keying of an intermediate frequency oscillator rather than the carrier.

The design, in some ways, is simpler and the arrangement is generally as shown in Fig. 7.5.4.2C. Standard p.l.c. communication modules can be used to a large extent in such systems.

Thus, if a carrier frequency f_c is modulated with an intermediate frequency f_i (guard condition), then in addition to f_c there will be produced an upper sideband $f_c + f_i$ and a lower sideband $f_c - f_i$. Similarly, if the same intermediate frequency is

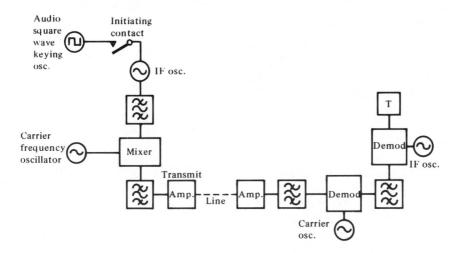

Fig. 7.5.4.2C *Single-channel, coded frequency shift PLC signalling equipment*

lowered, in the operate condition, by f_s, then in addition to f_c there will be produced an upper sideband $f_c + (f_i - f_s)$, and a lower sideband $f_c - (f_i - f_s)$. In normal single-sideband signalling, the carrier frequency and one of the sidebands are suppressed, and, in this particular case, it is the lower sideband that is sent and $f_{c0} = f_c - (f_i - f_s)$ and $f_{cg} = f_c - f_i$, i.e. $f_{cg} < f_{c0}$ at carrier frequency. Using as an example the particular design of single channel carrier frequency-shift coded signalling equipment briefly described above, in which $f_i = 16\,360$ Hz (guard), $f_s = 720$ Hz and, therefore, $f_i - f_s = 15\,640$ Hz (operate), then if we take $f_c = 100$ kHz, and send only the lower sideband, then $f_{c0} = 84 \cdot 36$ kHz and $f_{cg} = 83 \cdot 64$ kHz.

In practice, in this equipment, the intermediate frequency is keyed in the operate condition by a 400 Hz square wave beween f_{c0} and f_{cg} which results in a signalling rate of 800 baud (bits/s). The receiver has two independent detectors which each measure the duration of the received pulses of f_{c0} and f_{cg}, and both have to give an output to an 'AND' gate for operation.

7.5.4.3 Single-sideband power-line-carrier communication equipment: In particular cases, where a speech communication facility over power-line-carrier may also be required, single-sideband principles as described above may be applied to provide a combined data transmission, control or telephony/protection signalling or intertripping facility. This type of equipment has an 8 kHz bandwidth (4 kHz in each direction) and the input/output of such equipment can be arranged to present an interface similar to that normally associated with rented pilots for v.f. working. The available 4 kHz (nominal) in each direction can be utilised in any way desired, thus, as with a rented pilot circuit, 300-1900 Hz can be reserved for speech and the remaining bandwidth above speech can be used for v.f. signalling or intertripping systems.

7.6 Bibliography

Books

Carrier communication over power lines by H-K Podszeck (Springer-Verlag, Berlin/ Gottingen/Heidelberg, 1963)

Mathematical theory of communications by C E Shannon and W Weaver (University of Illinois Press, Urbana, 1959)

Mathematical theory of communications by C E Shannon (University of Illinois Press, Urbana, 1959, p. 36)

Transmission systems for communications (Bell Telephone Laboratories Inc.)

Radio engineering by F E Terman (McGraw Hill, 1951)

Papers and articles

'Guiding values for the planning of power line carrier communication systems and information on the determination of line characteristics' by E Asleben (CIGRE Paper 319, 1962)

'Some problems in power-line-carrier transmission on overhead-lines and overhead-line/cable circuits' by L M Wedepohl and R G Wasley, IEE Colloquium Digest, 1968/19, pp. 374-381

'Origine, nature et ordre de grandeur des oscillations à haute frequence produites par les manoeuvres de sectionneures sur les réseaux de transport d'energie à haute tension' by M R Jaudet (Electricité de France, Services des Transports d'Energie, 20th November 1959)

'Carrier transfer for high-speed distance protection' (*Brown-Boveri Rev.*, 1960, 5/6, pp. 345-352, Paper No. 2825E. 621.316.925.45.052.63).

'Field tests and operation experience with carrier transfer trip relaying through line faults' by D G Wohlgemuth, D A Gillies and R.E. Dietrich (CIGRE Paper 304, 1962)

'Influence of faults in power lines upon H.F. telecommunication' by H K Kuhn (CIGRE Papers 309, 1948; 316, 1950; and 312, 1952)

'Power line carrier operation during line faults' by D.E. Jones (*Ontario Hydro Research News*, 1960, **12**, (3))

'Characteristics of carrier current channels' by Y L Bykhovsky *et al.* (CIGRE Paper 312, 1962)

'Transmission of information' by R V L Hartley (*BSTJ*, 1928, **7**, pp. 535-563)

'Propagation of carrier signals in homogeneous, non-homogeneous and mixed multi-conductor systems' by L M Wedepohl and R G Wasley (IEE Paper 5433P, January, 1968)

'Information links' by L M Wedepohl (*Int. J. Electr. Eng. Educ.*, 1964, **2**, pp. 179-196)

'Tuning of carrier line traps and their employment in high-voltage networks' by K Morf (*Brown-Boveri Rev.*, 1967, **54**, 2/3)

'The performance and specification of intertripping systems' by G Fielding and N H Pendlebury (IEE Colloquium Digest 1968/19)

'Carrier transfer for the protection of tapped and two-circuit lines' by H Haug (*Brown-Boveri Rev.*, 1962, **49**, pp. 133-146)

'Power system communications using power lines or radio' by C Hahn (*Brown-Boveri Rev.*, 1959, **46**, pp. 704-716)

'Amplification by power line carrier signals at intermediate stations' by D E Jones and J R Leslie (*Ontario Hydro Research News*, Feb. 1962)

'Attenuation of carrier transmission on power lines, especially during formation of ice and rime on the conductors' by A Mikkelsen (CIGRE Paper 323, 1950)

'Field investigations into transient over-voltages in secondary wiring' by F H Birch and H J Turner (IEE Colloquium Digest 1968/19)

'Difference voltages and circulating currents in pairs of cores in auxiliary multi-core cables' by S A Wheeler (*Proc. IEE*, 1968, **115**, (8))

Index

Accuracy limit primary current, 260
  use of fuses, 304
A.C.network analyser, 220, 221
Alarm relays, 390, 415
Arcing faults
  interference, 489, 490
  result of, 8
Arc-suppression (Petersen) coil, 9, 10
Asymmetrical currents, fuse operation
  on, 335
Attenuation, 469-471
  and busbar nodes, 475
  by faults, 473
  by filters, 504
  in carrier coupling equipment,
    471-473
  microwave, 486
  on transmission lines, 473
Auxiliary d.c. relays, 380
  discharge of wiring capacitance, 382
  operating-voltage limits, 380
  repeat contactors, 386
    c.t. operated contactor (series trip
      circuit), 389
    series sealing contactor, 387
    shunt reinforcing and sealing
      contactor, 387
    shunt reinforcing contactor, 387
    shunt repeat contactor, 386
  time-lag relays, 384
  tripping relays, 383

Back-up fuses, 317, 320
Back-up protection, 16-18
  purpose, 16
  zones, 16, 17
Balanced (symmetrical) fault conditions
  calculation of, 77-125
  definition, 57, 77
Band-pass filters
  coupling, 459-466
  in surge-proof relay, 502-504

Bandwidth
  and carrier coupling, 460-466
  and rented pilots, 481-483
  of v.f. protection signalling equip-
    ment, 505, 506
  relation to signalling speed, 491
Batteries (see also power supplies)
  chargers, 42
  earth fault protection, 42
Baud, 516
Bias
  harmonic, 16
  load, 16
Bit (unit of information), 488
Boosting
  of signalling equipment, 493
British Standards
  current transformers BS 3938:, 259,
    260, 262, 275-277
  fuses and fuselinks, 307-309, 336,
    337
    high voltage BS 2692: pts 1 & 2,
      308, 309, 322, 335-337
    l.v. BS 88: pts 1-5, 307-309, 322
      333, 335-337
    l.v. BS 1361, 308, 309, 337
    l.v. BS 1362, 308, 309, 337
    miniature BS 646, 308
    miniature BS 2950, 308
    miniature BS 4265, 308, 309, 315,
      337
    semi-enclosed BS 3036, 308, 309,
      337
  power transformers BS 171, 98, 245
  voltage transformers BS 3941, 282,
    286, 305
Buchholz protection, 304
Burden (load)
  on current transformers, 253, 258
  on voltage transformers, 283, 285
Busbar
  faults, 7
  protection, 7

substations, 5, 6

Cable circuits
  equivalent-π circuit, 108, 109
  impedance, typical values, 151
Cable systems
  fault clearance, 19
Capacitance
  of pilot cables, 479
Capacitor
  coupler, 449-456
Capacitor voltage devices
  capacitor couplers, 39
  capacitor divider, 39, 302, 303
  capacitor v.t., 39
Carrier
  attenuation (see Attenuation)
  coupling equipment, 291, 450-469
    bands, 466
    filter, 459-466
    phase-to-earth, 450-456
    phase-to-phase, 456
  equipment earthing, 469
  frequency range, 449, 466
  keyed, 513
  on teed circuits, 476
  power level, 449
  single-sideband, 516
  with cable inserts, 476
Characteristic impedance, 451, 459
  of transmission lines, 451
Circuit breakers
  circuit breaker fail protection, 18
  discrimination with fuses (see Fuses)
  general, 41
  trip coils, 41
  tripping of, 12
Coaxial cable, 469, 471
Coding in protection signalling, 491
Combination, in network analysis
  of equal driving-voltages, 73
  of parallel branches, 70
  of series branches, 69, 70
Combining filter, 471
Common-base values
  choice of, 105
  common-voltage-base values, 81-87
  per-cent or per-unit values, 104-108
Common-voltage base, use in network
  analysis, 81-87
Common-voltage equivalent circuit
  ideal transformer, 81-87
  nominal-ratio transformers, 87-94
    auto transformers, 89-91
    three-winding transformers,
      91-93
    two-winding transformers, 87-89
  off-nominal ratio transformers, 94,
    95, 230-242

Communication media, 449-488
Composite error definition, 249
Co-ordination (see Discrimination)
Core
  flux density, 250, 251, 254, 291
  losses, 305
  materials, 250-252
  saturation, 250, 258, 259, 266
  types, 267, 269, 270, 289, 294
Corona-discharge noise in protection
  signalling, 490
Cross-country earth fault
  calculation, 204-206
  definition, 56
Current balance protection
  principle of operation, 26
Current limiting fuselinks, 320-322
Current transformers
  accuracy classes 5P, 10P, X, 259-261
  check on terminal markings, 277,
    305
  construction, 267-275
  core balance, 31
  equivalent circuit, 248, 249, 254
  errors
    composite, 249, 250, 260
    current, 249, 250, 260, 276
    phase, 249, 250
  for protection, 37
  high reactance definition, 275
  high voltage, 272-275
  location, 6, 7
  magnetisation characteristics, 251
  phasor diagram, 249
  requirements, 259
  steady-state theory, 248-259
  testing, 274-278
  transient-state theory, 264-267
  types
    bar primary, 267, 268
    single-turn primary, 253
    wound primary, 268, 270
Cut-off current in fuses, 310, 312,
  320-326

D.C. network analyser (fault
  calculator), 221
Decibel, 469, 470
Delta-to-star transformation, 72, 73
Digital-computer analysis, in fault
  calculations, 221, 222
Discrimination, 2, 15, 331
  between fuselinks, 329, 331-333
  between h.v. and l.v. fuses and
    circuit breakers, 333, 334
  by current magnitude, 22
  by distance measurement, 24
  by time, 22
  by time and direction, 23

Distance protection
  discrimination, 24
  with signalling channel, 28-30

Earth fault protection, 33
Earth faults
  cross-country, 56, 204-206
  currents, 8
  residual voltage, 285, 287, 289
  transformer-winding, 228-230
Earthing
  of tripping supply, 42
  types of, 7-10
Earthing of carrier equipment, 469
Eddy-current shielding in protective
  transformers, 255
Electrical noise
  characteristics, 489, 490
  damage by, 466, 467, 489
  effects of, 488, 489
  lightning, 490
Equivalent circuit
  capacitor voltage transformers, 280
Equivalent-generator circuit, 109
Equivalent network
  in fault calculations
    balanced, 108-110
    unbalanced, 120-123
Equivalent-π representation, 108,
  234-236
Errors
  in current transformers, 249, 250,
    259
  measurement, 274
Exciting current in protective transformers
  definition, 249
  measurement, 276
  percentage, 250
Expulsion fuse (see Fuses)

Fault arc resistance
  characteristic, 172, 173
  use in fault calculations, 168-172
Fault calculations, 53-246
  balanced fault conditions, 77-125
  methods, 59, 60
  open-circuit fault conditions, 173-
    177
  procedure, 182-202
  simultaneous fault conditions, 202-
    217
  unbalanced fault conditions, 126-
    202
Fault-path impedance, 168-173
Faults
  causes, 11
  current waveform, 49

  definition, 11, 12
  factors affecting severity, 58, 59
  interference with protective relays,
    49
  speed of clearance, 49
  statistics, 12-14
  types, 10, 11, 54-58
Ferro-resonance effects, 290
Fibre links, 487, 488
Filler and effect on fuse performance
  (see Fuses)
Flux leakage
  current transformers, 253-527, 267
  voltage transformers, 278
Frequency shift in protection
  signalling
  as coding method, 491-493
  carrier, 513-516
  voice frequency, 506-512
Fulgurite, 322, 323
  fault diagnosis from, 323
Fuses and fuselinks, 307-338
  a.c., performance with, 311-313,
    318-336
    compared with d.c., 312, 324,
      325
  arcing and arcing angle
    effect on performance, 334-336
    energy, 323
    in fuselink operation, 312, 324,
      325, 330
    voltage and overvoltage, 323-326
  back-up, 317, 320
  cartridge - powder filled, 311
  categories, 308, 309
  current limiting, 520-522
  definitions, 306
  element, 307, 312
    constricted, 323
    types, 313-315, 317, 323, 326
  expulsion, 317
  filler, 311
    effect on performance, 311, 314,
      323
    use to diagnose fault severity, 323
  for protection circuits, 44
  for voltage transformers, 305
  fuselinks for industrial use, 308,
    309, 337
  general purpose, 320
  high voltage, 308, 309, 313, 314,
    317, 333
  liquid filled, 317, 318
  maximum stress on
    arc energy, 336
    thermal and magnetic, 335
  miniature, 308, 314
  motor circuit protection, 316
  non-current-limiting h.v. fuses (see

Expulsion fuses)
operation, 318-336
performance on large and small
overcurrents, 318-320, 335
on intermediate overcurrent
levels, 320-322, 336
semi-enclosed, 315, 316
testing of, 334-336
time/current characteristics, 328,
329
time delay, 313
time-lag (surge-proof), 314, 315

Generators
impedance, typical values, 150
representation in fault calculations,
98, 104
Generator/transformer resistance
earthing, 10

Hybrid transformer in protection
signalling, 471

IEC standards
fuses and fuselinks, 308, 309, 336,
337
domestic IEC 241, 308, 309
high voltage, IEC 282: pts 1-3,
308, 309, 336, 337
low voltage, IEC 269: pts 1-4,
308, 309, 337
miniature IEC 127, 308, 309,
337
Impedance
effect on fault severity, 58, 59
exciting, representation of, 92
fault-path, 168-173
phase-sequence, 129-149
sub-transient, 98-104
synchronous, 98-104
transformer, representation of,
87-98
transient, 98-104
typical plant values, 152, 153
Impedance matching in protection
signalling, 456, 459
Insulation
oil immersed, 293, 295, 297
oil-impregnated paper, 272, 274
sulphur-hexafluoride (SF_6), 272,
275, 294, 303
synthetic resin, 294
testing, 277, 305
Interconnected systems, 4
Interference (see also Electrical noise)
in battery circuits, 497
in rented pilot circuits, 490
Intertripping
carrier, 513-516

d.c., 498-505
low-frequency a.c., 505
operating times, 494, 495
surge-proof, 500-503
voice-frequency, 507-512
I^2t of a fuse, 312, 331-333
calculation (pre-arcing), 327-330
effect on discrimination, 331-334
pre-arcing and total, 331, 332

Joule integral (see I^2t)
Junction law (Kirchhoff's first law), 61

Kirchhoff's laws, 61, 62
Knee-point voltage in protective
transformers
definition, 251
e.m.f., 262, 264

Line traps, 40, 451, 462-466
protective spark gap, 467
Liquid-quenched fuse, 317, 318
Loads, effect on fault calculations,
109
Local back-up protection, 16, 17

Maintenance of relays, 419
M-effect in fuses, 313, 314
Mesh-current analysis, 65, 66
Mesh law (Kirchhoff's second law),
61, 62
Mesh-type substations, 5, 6
Microwave links, 485-487
Midband frequency, 459, 461
Miniature fuse, 308, 309, 314, 315
Modems for protection signalling, 511
Motor protection fuselink, 316

Negative biasing device, 42
Negative-phase-sequence components
definition, 126, 127
relation to phase values, 127, 128
Neper, 470
Network analysers, 217-221
a.c. analysers, 220, 221
d.c. analysers, 221
fault calculation procedure, 220,
221
Network analysis
fundamental laws, 60-62
reduction formulas, 69-77
Neutral earthing
effect on fault severity, 58, 59
impedances, 137
in fault calculations, 110
methods, 7-10
of transformers, 149
reasons for, 8
Nodal-voltage analysis, 66-68

Nominal-ratio transformer circuits
  representation of, 87-94
Non-system faults, 11, 12
  causes, 12
  definition, 11
Non-unit systems
  back-up zone, 17
  definition, 15
  protected zone, 17
Norton's theorem, 75, 76

Off-nominal-ratio transformer circuits
  representation of, 94, 95, 230-242
Ohm's law
  per-cent values, 106
  per-unit values, 105
  statement of, 61
Open-circuit conditions
  causes, 55, 56
  current transformer windings, 257, 258
  single-phase, 174-176
  two-phase, 176, 177
Open-circuit faults, types, 55-57
Operating time of protection, 15, 16
Opposed-voltage protection
  principle of operation, 27
Optical fibre links, 487, 488
Overcurrent protection, 33
Overcurrent relays, 260
Overhead line circuits
  double-circuit fault, 56
  effect of circuit asymmetry, 242-245
  equivalent circuit, 108, 109
  impedance, typical values, 150

Parallel feeders, 2, 3
Per-cent values, 104-108
Permeability of core materials, 251
Per-unit values, 104-108
Phase-comparison protection
  principle of operation, 28
Phase-sequence components, 126-129
  open-circuit conditions, 173-177
  relation to phase vectors, 127, 128
  short-circuit conditions, 153-168
Phase-sequence equivalent circuits, 129-153
  cables, 138-142
  effect of off-nominal-ratio transformer,
    235
  from point of fault, 154
  neutral earthing impedance, 137
  overhead lines, 138-142
  synchronous machines, 99, 137, 138,
    224, 225
  transformers, 134, 135, 142-149
Phase-sequence mutual impedances
  definition, 243, 244
  example of use, 244, 245

Phase-sequence self-impedances
  definition, 243, 244
  example of use, 244, 245
Phase-sequence networks, 129-133
  components, 126-129
  currents and voltages, 129-130
  definitions, 131, 132
  impedances, 130
  interconnection of, 35, 168
  representation, 130-133
  simultaneous faults, 202-204
Phase-shifts in transformers
  balanced conditions, 95-98
  unbalanced conditions 178-181
  winding connections, effect of 95-98,
    142, 178-181
Phase-to-phase fault
  analysis of, 156, 157
  current and voltage formulas, 165, 167
  fault impedance, effect of 170, 171
  generator winding, 225, 226
  interconnection of phase-sequence
    networks, 168
  symmetrical-component equations, 164,
    166
Phase-to-phase plus single-phase-to-earth
  fault
  analysis of, 161-163
  current and voltage formulas, 165, 167
  fault impedance, effect of, 172
  interconnection of phase-sequence
    networks, 168
  symmetrical-component equations, 164,
    166
Phase vectors, 126-129
  relation to sequence components, 127
Pilot isolating transformer, 47
Pilot wire circuits
  types, 47
    private, 476-480
    rented pilots, 481-483
Positive-phase-sequence components
  definition, 77, 127
  relation to phase values, 127, 128
Post Office pilot wires, 481-483
Power-line-carrier (see Carrier)
Power supplies, 497
Prospective current
  in fuse operation, 320-322
  in fuse testing, 335
  relation to virtual time (see Time/current
    characteristics)
Protection
  back up, 16
  components, 37-48
  costs, 18, 19
  definition, 1
  design and application problems, 48
  duplication, 18, 20

economic considerations, 18
  failure, 14
  maintenance, 14
  maloperation, 14
  performance, 12-14
  terminology, 15
Protection signalling
  keyed carrier, 513
  operating times, 495
  voice frequency, 506, 507
Protection zones, 16, 17
Pulse distortion in protection signalling, 497

Radial feeders, 3
  discrimination, 22
Radio links, 484-487
Rated accuracy-limit factor, 260
Reactance
  sub-transient, 98-102
  synchronous, 98-102
  transformers, 152, 153
  transient 98-102
  typical values
    synchronous machines, 150
    transformers, 152, 153
Reactance earthing, 9
Relay application and characteristic, 422
  complex input comparators, 425
    generalised amplitude comparator,
      426
    mho relays, 428
    reactance and ohm relays, 429
  differential relays, 440
    polar curves for differential relays,
      440
  double quantity measurement, 423
    polar diagram for impedance relay,
      425
    presentation of characteristics, 424
  instantaneous current- and voltage-
    operated relays, 422
    instantaneous high-set overcurrent
      relay, 423
  inverse time/current relays, 367
    curve shapes for I.D.M.T.L. relay, 367
    discriminative margin, 369
    disc speed control, 365
    spring control, 361
    tapped winding, 361
  negative-phase sequence protection, 443
  range curves, 437
    characteristic impedance ratio, 437
    system impedance ratio, 437
  rectifier bridge comparators, 430
    amplitude comparator, 430
    phase comparator, 431
Relay cases, 417
  electromagnetic relays, 417
  static relays, 419

Relaying quantities
  negative-phase sequence, 32
  positive-phase sequence, 32
  zero-phase sequence, 30
Relays, 339-447
  definition and specification, 339
    all-or-nothing, 339
    measuring, 339
  design considerations, 394
    auxiliary supplies, 394
    burdens, 347, 349, 356, 384, 422
    coil ratings, 340, 394
    contacts, 395, 421
    flag indicators, 397, 415
    relay settings, 340, 361-368, 395
    relay settings, returning ratio, 342
    resetting, 383, 386, 397
  future trends in relay design, 446
  overcurrent, 259-260
  principal types of, 341
    a.c. energised armature, 347
    attracted armature, 341
    balanced beam, 349, 424
    Buchholz gas and oil operated, 378
    induction, 357
    motor operated, 378
    moving coil, 351
    polarised armature, 348
    reed, 347
    remanent, 346
    solenoid, 348
    thermal, 372
    vane, 349
  sensitivity, 16
Reliability of protection signalling, 495, 496
Remote back-up protection, 16, 17
Residual voltages, 285, 287-289
Resistance earthing, 8, 10
Rewirable fuse, 315, 316
Ring main power systems, 3, 4
  discrimination, 23, 24

Salient-pole machines, 103, 104
Saturation effects, synchronous machines,
  102, 103
Security of intertripping, 496
Semiconductor protection fuselink, 308,
  309, 316, 322, 337
Semi-enclosed fuse, 315, 316
Sensitivity of a relay, 16
Severity of fault, factors affecting, 58, 59
Short-circuit clearance by fuses, 312, 319,
  320
Short-circuit conditions, 10, 11
  standard formulas, 164-167
  types, 54, 55
Short-circuit current
  components, 98-102
  variation with time, 98-102

Short-circuited-turns fault
    definition, 57
    fault calculation, 226
Short-circuit, types, 54, 55
Shung admittance
    effect on equivalent circuits, 138, 139
Sidebands in protection signalling, 515, 516
Signalling (see Protection signalling)
Simulation in network analysis, 60
    principle, 218
Simultaneous fault conditions
    calculation, 202-217
    impedance-earthed systems, 56
    representation by sequence-network
        interconnection, 206-209
Single-phase representation, 77-81
    validity for transformers, 95-98
Single-phase-to-earth fault
    analysis of, 158, 159
    current and voltage formulas, 165, 167
    fault impedance, effect of, 171
    generator winding, 226
    interconnection of phase-sequence
        networks, 168
    symmetrical-component equations, 164,
        166
Small wiring requirements, 45
Solid earthing, 8
Stability of protection, 15
Standby protection, 18
Star-to-delta transformation, 70-72
Static relays, 398-417
    basic circuits employed, 398
        integrating circuit, 408
        level detectors, 400
        phase comparators, 403
        polarity detectors, 401
        timers, 399
    components, 408
        capacitors, 409
        connectors, 409
        diodes, 409
        resistors, 408
    output and indicating circuits, 415
    power supplies for, 412
        from d.c./a.c./d.c. converter, 415
        from internal batteries, 413
        from measured circuit and tripping
            battery, 413
        from measured circuits, 413
        from tripping battery, 412
    transient overvoltages and interference,
        409
        protection against transients, 411
        sources of transients, 410
        standard tests for transient immunity,
            411
Statistics of faults, 12-14
Summation networks

combination of phase-sequence networks,
    35
summation transformers, 34
Superposition theorem, 73, 74
Surge diverter, 467
Surge-proof intertripping, 500-503
Surge-resisting fuse, 311, 313-315
Switching stations, 4
Symmetrical components
    analysis by method of, 126-133
    equations, 153-163
    summary of formulas, 164-167
Synchronous machines
    impedances, 109
    open-circuit and short-circuit
        characteristics, 104
    reactances, typical values, 150
    representation in positive-sequence
        network, 98-104
    three-phase short-circuit, 90
    winding faults, 223-227
Synchronous reactance, 101
System faults, 11, 12
Systems
    distribution, 19
    earthing, 7
    high-voltage transmission, 19
    interconnected, 4
    layout, 3, 4

Testing (see Fuses)
Testing of protective transformers
    balance, 277
    current transformers, 274-278
    insulation, 277
    polarity, 277, 305
    turns-ratio, 276
    voltage transformers, 304
Testing of relays and protection schemes,
    444
    calibration testing, 444
    commissioning, 444
    type testing, 444
Test links, 46
Thevenin's theorem
    statement of, 74
    use of, 109, 122, 175
Three-phase fault
    analysis of, 154-156
    current and voltage formulas, 165, 167
    fault impedance, effect of, 170
    interconnection of phase-sequence
        networks, 168
    symmetrical-component equations, 164,
        168
Three-phase system
    components, 77
    single-phase representation, 77-81
Through-fault conditions, 262-267

Time constant of components of short-circuit current, 100-102
Time/current characteristic of a fuse, 311, 312, 326-331
and discrimination, 333, 334
Time-delay techniques in fuse elements, 313
Transformers
basic principles, 247
equivalent circuits, 142-153, 248
impedances, 109
interconnections, 81-87
protective, 259, 285
reactances, typical values, 152, 153
types
auto-, 89-91
earthing, 149
three-winding, 91-93
two-winding, 87-89
Transient analysis, in fault calculations, 222, 223
Transient conditions, 15
Transient response of voltage transformers, 289, 290
Trip circuit supervision, 389
Trip coils, 260
Tripping relays
use in intertripping, 498
Tripping supplies, 42
Two-phase-to-earth fault
analysis of, 159, 160
current and voltage formulas, 165, 167
fault impedance, effect of, 172
interconnection of phase-sequence networks, 168
symmetrical-component equations, 164, 166

Unbalanced (unsymmetrical) faults, 56, 57, 126-177
Unit systems of protection, 15, 17

Vector symbol references BS 171, 98
Virtual time of a fuselink, 328-330
Voltage-arcing on fuse operation, 312, 323-326
Voltage transformers, 452-456
capacitor type, 39, 279-283, 302
accuracy, 282, 283, 286
circuit, 280
errors, 281, 282
phasor diagram, 281
construction, 293-303
error diagram, 279, 282
errors, 278, 279, 286
for protection, 285, 286 ·
fusing and protection, 304
testing, 304, 305
theory, 278, 283
types, 293-303
phasor diagram, 278
voltage factors, 287
wound type, 38

Winding faults, 223-230
definitions, 57
generator, 223-227
transformer, 228-230
Windings
balancing, 255-257
cast-resin insulation 294-296
types of
current transformer, 270-272
voltage transformers, 293-300
Wound-primary transformers, 267

Zero-sequence components
definition, 126, 127
relation to phase value, 127, 128
Zero-phase-sequence systems, 30
Zones of protection, 16. 17